MW01091683

Up BY ROOTS

Healthy Soils and Trees in the Built Environment

James Urban

ISA
International Society of Arboriculture

ISBN: 1-881956-65-2

Publisher Note. This reprint of *Up By Roots: Healthy Soils and Trees in the Built Environment,* published by the International Society of Arboriculture, includes updated technical information made with the assistance of tha author.

Editorial and Production Manager: Peggy Currid
Cover Design: Marti Betz Design/Illustration
Text Composition: Jody Boles
Printed by ADR Bookprint, Wichita, KS

International Society of Arboriculture
Champaign, Illinois, U.S.
(217) 355-9411
www.isa-arbor.com

10 9 8 7 6
02-16/RF/800

ISA®
International Society of Arboriculture

Dedication

To Dr. Thomas Perry, who put a wine glass on a dinner plate and taught me about trees.

Spring Pools

These pools that, though in forest, still reflect
The total sky almost without defect,
And like the flowers beside them, chill and shiver,
Will like the flowers beside them soon be gone,
And yet not out by any brook or river,
But up by roots to bring dark foliage on.

The trees that have it in their pent-up buds
To darken nature and be summer woods—
Let them think twice before they use their powers
To blot out and drink up and sweep away
These flowery waters and these watery flowers
From snow that melted only yesterday.

—Robert Frost

New Enlarged Anthology of Robert Frost's Poems
Washington Square Press, New York, 1971

TABLE OF CONTENTS

Acknowledgments

The author wishes to thank the following individuals.
Without their help this book would not have been possible.

PEER REVIEW TEAM

Bonnie Appleton
Jim Clark
Bill Fountain
Kathy Howard
Sharon Lilly
Susan Little
Ed Macie
David Meyers
Larry Morris
Joe Murray
Bob Peters
Bill Reibold
John Royster
Peter Schaudt
Steve Shurtz
Larry West
Nicole Whiteside

CONTRIBUTORS

Miles Barnard
Nina Bassuk
Erin Cler
Larry Costello
Phil Craul
Peggy Currid
Chuck Darrah
Michael Dirr
Ed Gilman
Rob Griesbach
Anne Hays
Lonnie Hefflin
Paul Josey
Jen Lilly
Brent Marble
Steve Martino
David Nowak
Annice O'Doherty
Emily Parrino
Keith Pitchford
Michael Raupp
Paul Reis
Tom Smiley
Brandon Spun
Mike Taft
Peter Tasi
Michael Van Valkenburgh
Joe Waddell
Pat Washburn
Gary Watson
Kathleen Wolf

COVER DESIGN

Marty Betz

BOOK DESIGN & LAYOUT

Jody Boles

EDITORS

Peggy Currid
Sharon Lilly

PHOTOGRAPHS AND ILLUSTRATIONS

The majority of the photographs and illustrations are by the author.

Many other photographs are by other contributors and are acknowledged where the image is printed. The contribution of these photographers to this work is greatly appreciated.

Preface

Two things must be understood to grow successful trees: the tree from the ground up, and the roots and soil below the ground. *Up By Roots* will help improve the quality of trees in your city. It is intended to guide the design professional, the citizen tree activist, the politician who must vote for tree funding, and the developer who wants trees that will increase property value. The first chapter of this book summarizes the problems and solutions of planting trees in urban areas and is intended to guide policy decisions. The remainder of the book is a technical manual to assist in the day-to-day, tree-by-tree work of building the urban forest. Part 1 looks at the basic science of soil and trees as well as introduces the tools needed to analyze soil conditions. Part 2 presents the skills needed in the design and construction process. The needs of the shrubs, lawns, and groundcovers in urban soils are not addressed, and the book will not delve deeply into the special issues of preserving large trees during construction. However, the principles of tree biology and soils are the same for almost all plants in proposed and existing situations.

A few definitions specific to this book:

THE FUNCTIONAL TREE

Throughout the course of this book the term **tree** refers to a large-canopy tree. These trees should be large enough to provide functional environmental benefits to the landscape in which they are placed. They must be large enough to shade houses, pavement, cars, and people. Each tree should expect to live long enough with minimum maintenance so that its benefits are not outweighed by the cost of maintenance and replacement. There are many situations in which a small tree is appropriate, but small trees do not offer the environmental benefits large trees provide. This book is about increasing the quantity and quality of large trees in our communities.

Figure 1.P.1. The functional tree.

Actors in the play *Urban Trees.*

PEOPLE AND ROLES

The principal audience for this book is expected to be the people who have some responsibility in the planting of trees in our cities. They are grouped into five areas of expertise. Throughout this book these titles will be used to define professional groups.

The first group is **decision-makers**. These are the groups and individuals who make the decision to pay for or permit the planting of trees on land over which they have legal or financial control. This group includes politicians, landowners, land managers, urban foresters, and developers, whether they are planting a single tree on their property or voting on the tree-planting budget for an entire city.

The second group is **designers**. These are the people who decide exactly where a tree should go and how it will be planted. They write the specifications and normally oversee the work. This group includes landscape architects, landscape designers, urban foresters, arborists, and landscape contractors.

The third group is **associated designers**, the related professions who affect the conditions around the tree by their actions, but do not actually specify the tree. This group includes civil engineers, architects, and builders.

The fourth group is the contractors and tree planters. These people construct the environment, prepare the site including the soil, purchase the tree, and place it in the ground.

The final group is **maintenance providers**. They manage and provide for the care of the tree throughout its life and ultimate removal. This group includes landscape maintenance contractors, arborists, and urban foresters.

Homeowners and average citizens may play all five roles during the management of their own property or through public participation in tree-planting efforts.

The practical reality of how the landscape is built makes **designers** the principal coordinators of decisions that guide what is built. On their shoulders falls the primary burden to get the science right. *Up By Roots* introduces designers to sufficient knowledge of soil science, urban soils, and tree biology to make daily decisions during the course of a project. The need for this knowledge begins with the first site visit and does not end until the project has been turned over to its maintenance providers.

ARBORISTS

Often it will become necessary for the designer to engage an arborist to assist in design, construction, or maintenance of a project. An arborist may perform tasks ranging from tree evaluation and preparing a tree for construction to long-term care. Arborists can provide expert testimony in zoning cases or other legal proceedings, and can also be of assistance in preparing tree preservation specifications.

Arborists differ in their training and areas of expertise, and there are many areas of specialization. Some arborists perform tree care operations such as pruning, cabling, or removal. Others concentrate on plant health care and treatment of various disorders. A few arborists may be strictly consultants, providing arboricultural advice. Legal testimony is its own area of specialization within the consulting field.

Arborists enter the profession through a variety of paths. Some have formal college training, while others have learned through years of hands-on experience. When hiring an arborist, it is important to define the project's needs first, then look for relevant expertise. If you do not know the reputation of the individual or company, ask for references and seek information from trusted people in related fields.

On large projects, it may be beneficial to separate the arborist consulting firm from the tree care provider firm. This provides an independent assessment of the work required that is not influenced by the need to keep a company's crews busy. A consulting arborist may be useful to review the work of the arborist.

In hiring an arborist, one useful first step is to ask about certifications. The International Society of Arboriculture (ISA) has several certification programs for arborists. An ISA Certified Arborist has met education and/or experience requirements, has passed a comprehensive knowledge test, and is required to maintain continuing education. ISA certification combined with a degree in arboriculture is the normal entry level for a consulting arborist. Other ISA credentials include several specializations, including Board-Certified Master Arborist, which is the highest level.

The American Society of Consulting Arborists (ASCA) is a professional organization that sets standards for its members that indicate a high level of competency in this field. Their credential program, Registered Consulting Arborist, represents the highest degree of training in consulting available. ASCA members often specialize in expert testimony.

A few states have a licensing requirement for arborists. The requirements vary from state to state, leaving the ISA certification program as a consistent national benchmark for competency. Most states also require a pesticide applicator's license. Proof of this license should be required whenever chemicals must be applied.

Figure 1.P.2. Arborists play a critical role only if brought into the project by the designer. *(Photo courtesy ISA)*

Figure 1.P.3. Arbor Day. *(Photo courtesy Arbor Day Foundation)*

SUGGESTED READINGS

The depth of available knowledge on the subject of trees and soil goes far beyond what one book can convey. Several references will be indispensable to the reader during the course of study and should be a part of every designer's personal library. These include the following.

Brady, Nyle C., and Ray R. Weil, 2007. *The Nature and Properties of Soils.* 14th ed. Prentice-Hall, New York, NY.

Craul, Phillip J., 1992. *Urban Soil in Landscape Design.* Wiley & Sons, New York, NY.

Craul, Phillip J., 2001. *Urban Soils: Applications and Practices.* Wiley & Sons, New York, NY.

Harris, Richard W., James R. Clark, and Nelda P. Matheny, 2003. *Arboriculture: Integrated Management of Trees, Shrubs, and Vines.* 4th ed. Prentice-Hall, New York, NY.

Matheny, Nelda P., and James R. Clark, 1998. *Trees and Development: A Technical Guide to Preservation of Trees During Land Development.* International Society of Arboriculture, Champaign, IL.

Watson, Gary W., and E.B. Himelick, 1997. *Principles and Practice of Planting Trees and Shrubs.* International Society of Arboriculture, Champaign, IL.

Introduction

A large-canopy tree is not only beautiful—it also benefits its community. It provides shade and shelter, protects air quality, and reduces air temperatures, water runoff, and human stress. A street lined with such trees is a desirable place to live and work, and a community with many large trees is attractive to visitors, residents, and businesses.

Growing large-canopy trees is a worthwhile investment and a cornerstone of today's movement toward sustainable communities. Yet the designers of today's built environments continually make mistakes that doom their trees to failure. We wouldn't hesitate to condemn an engineer who designed a building without being sure the columns would support its weight. Yet we allow designers to populate our landscapes with trees that have little chance to grow to canopy height.

The success of a tree is fundamentally linked to the soil in which it grows. Seems obvious, doesn't it? Yet this simple idea has had trouble taking root (so to speak) in the public realm.

To provide benefits to the community, trees must be put into built environments in entirely new ways. This introduction offers some basic principles for successful trees. If you find it useful, I encourage you to read the rest of *Up By Roots: Healthy Soils and Trees in the Built Environment* and to share this book and its ideas with the people who plan and maintain trees in your community.

Figure 1.I.1. Great trees make great streets.

The road from the forest to Main Street.

a. Forest.
b. Suburban tree.
c. Small street tree.
d. Empty tree pit.

MAKE THE SPACE RIGHT FOR THE TREE

Ten years ago, James Patterson, then a soil scientist with the National Park Service, speculated that as many as "90 percent of all urban tree problems are soil-related." Far too often, trees are planted in poor soil, soil with poor drainage, high levels of compaction, chemical imbalances, or other forms of contamination. With such disadvantages, trees are more likely to suffer disease, insect infestation, premature decline, and even death.

Some trees decline as a result of poor nursery stock or from inadequate or inappropriate maintenance. Yet in most cases, trees in good soils can overcome these problems. Without question, starting with proper soil is the most important factor in growing healthy trees.

For years, the arboricultural profession has supported putting "the right tree in the right place." This concept directs a designer to understand the planting site conditions, including soils, drainage, and aboveground conditions, and to find a tree species that matches those conditions. As soil in urban areas becomes increasingly degraded, there are fewer and fewer tree species that will grow in it. At some point on the road from the forest to Main Street, soil becomes so poor that almost no tree is "right." The results are city streets with minimal species diversity, and inner-city areas containing limited numbers of poor-quality trees.

If the goal is to create a diverse urban forest with healthy trees, we must design soil environments with that goal in mind. After determining which trees best fit a project's aesthetic, environmental, and technical goals, we must adapt the project site to those trees' requirements. We must "make the space right for the right tree."

This approach does not assume a perfect world. Budgets, political issues, and physical restraints on soil improvements will still limit the number and quality of trees. Yet designers should no longer resign themselves to accepting difficult growing conditions. Instead, they must make a strong case to improve soil conditions

Figure 1.I.2. Trees in different soil situations.

a. Tree in 4- by 4-foot parking vs. larger parking island.
b. Tree in narrow space with the start of crown die-back.
c. Street trees prospering in interconnected soil zone below pavement.
d. A single large tree in a good soil area is more effective than small street trees.

so they can grow trees that meet the goals of the design. Budgets for soil and trees will need to be increased to provide a better balance between trees and other elements of the design. Design fewer trees, but make allowances for soil conditions to support each one as a healthy, long-lived specimen. We can thus significantly increase the number of tree species in the urban environment. Trees will live longer, require less maintenance, and provide the benefits expected when the tree was planted.

TREES NEED DIRT

The fates of trees and soil are absolutely interlinked. Trees planted in urban areas by people who ignore their soil needs are likely to fail.

If you are hiring a design firm, landscape contractor, or an employee to undertake the planning, design, or installation of trees, make sure that they have knowledge of both soils and the biology of trees. Do not assume that they know these things just because they are landscape architects or landscape contractors. Despite the name, landscape architects get little training in plants, especially the biology of trees. Coursework in the science of soils is almost nonexistent.

If you are a citizen, make sure the people purchasing landscape design and maintenance services with your tax dollars are employing consultants trained in the science of trees and soils.

If you are a landscape architect, architect, engineer or other professional who designs landscapes that affect the way trees grow, please read the rest of this book and use it as a desk reference. Attend seminars that include training in tree and soil issues, and read professional journals that discuss the science of trees and soils. Finally, adopt tree biology and soil requirements as an inspiration for your design philosophy.

Up By Roots is an approach to designing landscapes, but also an approach to thinking about the role of trees and landscapes in your community. A large, healthy tree is an investment in sustaining a healthier, more inviting world.

Figure 1.I.3. Large, healthy trees make healthy urban spaces.

Part 1
The Science of Trees and Soils

Part 1 is an in-depth look at the science of trees and soil as it influences the design and planting of trees in urban areas. This is a distillation of complex scientific data intended to guide designers to the most important principles that will influence their work.

It is often said that the planting of trees is not rocket science. Actually, rocket science might be easier. The laws of physics are well understood, and the resources available to collect information and test theory are enormous.

Planting trees in urban areas, on the other hand, is quite complex, combining biology, soil science, arboriculture, entomology, microbiology, hydrology, and structural and civil engineering. Human psychology also plays a role in predicting the interactions of people and trees, planting budgets, love and/or disdain for trees, and understanding the reactions to conflicts among people, the built environment, and trees. The resources available to collect information and to test theory are depressingly limited.

A designer must know both the correct way to design a tree-planting space and a range of alternatives to react to changes. Most particularly, the designer needs to know what is best to do when budgets are slashed and clients want trees to get an approval, but are not really interested in growing mature trees.

Part 1 provides the basic skills to make trees grow "up by roots." Part 2 will provide the tools and standards to apply this information, presented as a set of design principles.

PART ONE

1
Designing Spaces for Trees

This first chapter sums up all the components in understanding a site, developing a design, and constructing a landscape that incorporates large, healthy trees. It provides a series of principles that serve as a framework for learning the science and techniques presented in the remaining chapters. Let's start underground, in the areas too often overlooked.

UNDERSTANDING NATIVE SOIL

To design spaces for trees, a designer must first understand soil. This does not mean becoming a soil scientist, but the designer needs to have a basic understanding of the existing soil at the site and what soil improvements are needed to attain the desired results. In large or complex landscapes, the design team may want to hire a soil

Figure 1.1.1. Trees survive in difficult places, but success needs to be more certain in the densest parts of cities.

consultant, but for most projects, the designer must have enough skill to evaluate the soil and make decisions based on a reasonable level of knowledge.

A designer also needs a thorough understanding of the biology of trees. Together, these two sets of information provide a basis for determining sizes of soil areas and predicting the response of trees to available conditions.

The following five principles of soil science are vital to successfully evaluating soil resources and designing with soil.

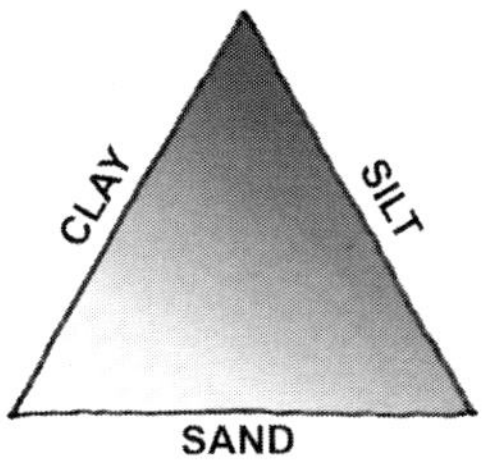

Soil Physical Properties

How did the soil get there? What is it made of? How coarse or fine is it? How are the particles arranged? Are the particles glued together to form a larger mass? Finally, how tightly are the particles compacted?

Soil Biological Properties

What is the organic content of the soil? Is there a viable, living set of organisms such as fungi, bacteria, insects, and worms? Are leaves left on the ground to provide a food source for these organisms?

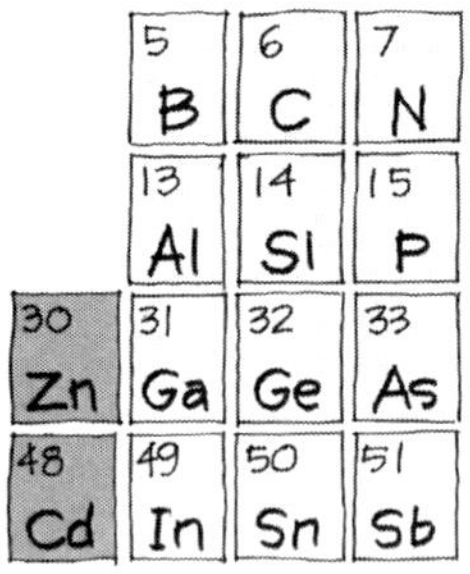

Soil Chemistry

Are there sufficient chemical elements to sustain trees and support soil biology? What is the soil's pH? Are there chemicals in the soil that are toxic to trees, soil organisms, or animals?

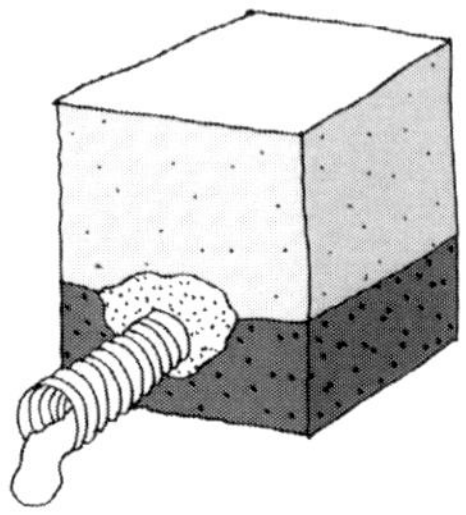

Soil Drainage

How well does the soil drain? Is this a function of its physical properties, biological properties, topography, underlying or adjacent conditions, or a combination of several factors?

These first four soil principles are interrelated. A change in one might trigger a change in the others. The designer must understand what exists and how it may change or be changed during the development process. There are many ways to correct deficiencies during the early part of the design process. However, good soils are quite fragile and can easily be degraded if not given priority in the design process and protected during construction. The simple act of moving good topsoil from one place to another can seriously degrade its quality.

Soil Volume

Soil volume is the principle that links issues of soil quality and tree growth. In urban areas, there is intense competition for space. Buildings, underground utilities, and large areas of paving for vehicles and pedestrians consume much of the urban landscape and squeeze the zones where tree roots can grow. Yet tree growth is directly related to the volume of soil available for root growth. Small soil volumes result in small trees, no matter the species.

For this reason, soil volume requirements must be factored into the many compromises that represent the urban design process. This process determines space and budgets for roads, sidewalks, utilities, grading, stormwater systems—and trees.

Designers can easily look up the minimum soil volumes required to sustain trees of different sizes in the urban landscape. Soil volume calculations must be made during the earliest phases of the design process, and must have equal standing with the determination of the sizes of pipes or the turning radius of automobiles.

UNDERSTANDING URBAN SOIL

Urban Soils Are Highly Disturbed

Human activity changes soil. Urban areas have more human activity, and thus more disturbed soil. This is not a recent problem. It began centuries ago (depending where you are) with the removal of the first trees and the start of agricultural activity. Each overlay of activity further alters the soil.

In many places, there may have been four or more soil disturbance cycles on each piece of land over the last 200 or more years. These might include a tree removal cycle, an agricultural cycle, and at least two different building cycles. Some soils, particularly coarse, sandy soils in the southeast coastal United States or the glacial outwash soils of New England, can better handle repeated soil disturbance than silt or clay loam soils often found in floodplains or uplifted ocean bottoms.

The more times and greater distance the soil has been physically moved, the more likely it will become degraded. As different soils are layered over previous disturbances, or include building material, they degrade even further. Toxic material may harm the soil's ability to support roots.

Some soil disturbance can be beneficial. Old rubble building foundations or the loose backfill over utility lines may provide good rooting opportunities. However, it is difficult to predict when they will be good places for roots to grow.

Undertake an Urban Soil Assessment

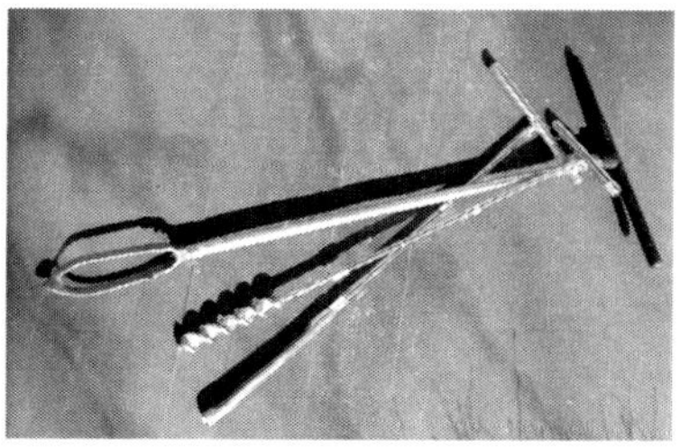

In natural spaces, analyzing the site's geologic and weather history makes it possible to reasonably predict soil conditions. Urban soil is the result of random disturbance, subject to the whims of human need, and its quality is much more difficult to predict.

An important first step in a design approach to an urban space is to determine the number of soil disturbances and when they occurred. Within the profession of landscape architecture it is well accepted, even required, to undertake a thorough analysis of soil and water conditions at a site where existing soil conditions are "natural" before the start of the design process. In urban sites with highly disturbed soils, this preliminary research is almost never done unless a significant amount of toxic material is anticipated. The analysis process at an urban site, especially a paved site, is difficult, less precise, and therefore ignored. Yet it is precisely in these tough conditions where additional information can pay the biggest dividends by reducing development cost and environmental impacts.

Assessing urban soil requires a thorough understanding of the human history of the site. Information on development history can come from old maps, planning documents, tax records, and photographs. A small amount of time at the local planning office, historical society, and library can unearth great quantities of useful data.

A thorough field assessment can yield a second layer of information. Each plant has critical growing requirements that reveal the soil conditions. Studying any plants, including weeds growing in cracks in the paving, and examining the type and condition of existing trees in the area will reveal information on soil type, drainage, and compaction level.

Finally, look at any excavations that may be open and take soil samples using a soil probe at any opportunity where the soil is accessible.

Use the Soil Information

The soil assessment will identify areas of usable and unusable soil and good or poor drainage. Wherever possible, designers should incorporate usable soil resources into their plans. It may be necessary to safeguard these areas in the same way the soil around an existing tree would be protected. In fact, it is the same thing, except in this case the rooting area is being set aside for a future tree.

As the intensity of land use increases, there may be no usable soil resources remaining after construction. However, there still may be opportunities to recycle mineral soil on the site. Using this material is more sustainable than removing it and importing new soil from another site. Often, the only actions needed to make urban soil usable are the elimination of compacted layers and the addition of organic components. Recycling can only occur if the site designer understands the composition and location of existing soil types.

UNDERSTANDING TREE BIOLOGY

Trees are living, growing organisms. This may seem obvious, but one would never know it to look at the trees in many of the urban streetscape and plaza designs built in the last half of the 20th century. Trees look like they were intended as small sculptures or decorations, and are regularly replaced as part of normal maintenance. They may never become large enough to provide shade, cool the space, retain stormwater, or otherwise improve the environment.

In the worst cases, urban trees go through a prolonged and unsightly decline and then are not replaced, leaving a bleak monument to the failure of the design and those who funded the project. In other places, trees have been able to find unintended rooting environments, often within the pavement systems. Here the tree survives, but tears apart the walking surfaces, making the landscape dangerous to traverse. Entire plazas have been closed and rebuilt as a result of designs that did not respect basic tree biology and physics. Understanding a few basic principles of tree biology and physics during the design period can make a huge improvement in the long-term success of the trees.

The following seven principles define the most important areas of tree biology to be understood when designing spaces for trees.

Figure 1.1.2. Lack of understanding of the relationship between tree biology and urban soil often results in either dead trees or dead sidewalks.

Trees Grow

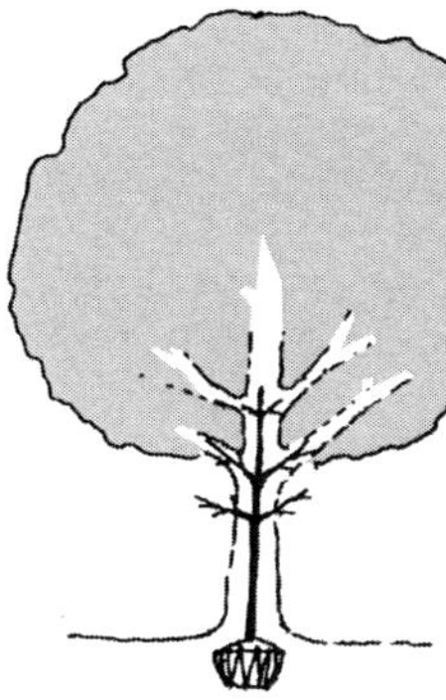

The most basic principle of tree biology is that the entire tree system must grow and become larger each year in order to survive. Branches must continually get longer, trunks thicker, trunk bases more swollen, and root systems increasingly larger and more complex. Any design that ignores this principle will fail when the tree bumps into a restraint. Anything that is placed around the tree—a string to secure burlap, a band to hold a light, a tree grate or tree guard—will, if not removed, strangle the tree or branch.

Nature regulates the ultimate size the tree can attain, but urban trees die long before they reach their natural limitations. The Japanese art of bonsai demonstrates that tree growth rates can be artificially reduced to low levels with enough maintenance and constant care. Many bonsai techniques, including root pruning, would be impossible to perform on a full-size tree, while the required frequency and continuity of maintenance is well beyond most tree management budgets. Chemical growth regulators show some promise for slowing tree growth, but the impact of long-term use in urban soils is not well understood, and finding ways to grow long lived small trees is counter to the environmental goals of planting trees.

Leaf-to-Root Balance

Trees, like all plants, must maintain a balance between the surface area of the tree that can photosynthesize (mostly the leaf area) and the surface area of the tree that can take up water and chemicals (its absorbing roots). When one part of the system gets out of balance, hormonal regulators within the tree adjust the other.

If the trees roots are cut, damaged, or have no more room to grow, branches die, twigs do not grow as long, and the tree produces smaller and/or fewer leaves. If branches are removed or die, tree roots will die or fail to grow the following year. This balancing act leaves many telltale signs, such as smaller leaves, fewer buds, and shorter branch extensions. Arborists use these indicators to help determine the health of a tree. This principle may be applied to extend the life of a tree in a confined space by constantly pruning branches and following established pleaching or pollarding practices. Europeans have been successful at this technique on a limited number of species, but the process requires a trained arborist to work continuously on a given tree population. The level of effort needed to achieve success is far beyond that provided to trees in typical American cities.

Horizontal Roots

To survive, tree roots need oxygen and water, both found in the upper layers of the soil. Tree roots often grow directly under pavement in a thin layer of soil so as to get the best balance of water and air. Tree roots can grow much faster than branches, and have been measured at up to 10 feet or more per year. The need for oxygen and the rapid growth of roots mean that a tree's root system is often horizontal in structure and will cover far more territory than its crown. The extended roots will intertwine with the roots of adjacent trees.

The depth of this horizontal system is limited by the degree of transfer of oxygen and carbon dioxide between the air and the soil. This may be as little as a few inches to many feet depending on soil type, drainage, and compaction. Deep roots can be found in cities and shallow roots are not limited to urban soils. Old building foundations and soils disturbed by the installation of utility lines can create opportunities for urban trees to find deep rooting space. A buried sheet of asphalt, a perched water table, or a buried compaction layer can confine roots to a thin upper layer of soil.

Aggressive, Opportunistic Roots

Roots tend to be aggressive and opportunistic in finding and exploiting resources. They create complex, dense mats in favorable conditions and long, less dense systems in poorer conditions. Roots also tend to grow in the most favorable environment available. One tree might grow only a few roots in a poor soil if better opportunities are available, while the same species of tree might grow many roots in the identical poor soil, if it is the best one within reach.

Tree roots can exert great force on objects. If a root grows under or beside an object and later finds an area of good growing conditions, the expansion of that root can move or break objects of great weight or strength. These root qualities cause damage to paving, curbs, and walls if not understood.

Fragile Roots and Strong Roots

When preserving existing trees or preparing sites for new trees, it is important to consider all the factors that can damage tree roots. While roots can be aggressive and opportunistic, the smallest roots, those that start the growth process and take up water and nutrients, are quite fragile and short-lived. They are easily killed by soil compaction, cutting, too much water, too little water, extremes of heat and cold, and many chemicals that are toxic to plants, including chemicals produced by other plants.

The larger roots, bigger than an inch, that connect the fine roots to the trunk are stronger. With the exception of mechanical damage that breaks the bark, they are much less susceptible to the types of impacts that damage smaller roots. Often, reduction in soil compaction is used as a justification for installing tree grates in urban areas. However, the large structural roots that grow immediately out of the trunk are not as vulnerable to soil compaction. Instead of protecting the tree, the grate often damages it as the metal collar girdles the expanding trunk.

Dynamic Structure

A tree's structure is conceptually a vertical cantilever, which resists the dynamic forces of wind and gravity in the crown. The root plate anchors the trunk, which is cantilevered from this horizontal structure. To accomplish this, the tree depends on a strong joint between the trunk and the roots. As the tree grows larger, the dynamic forces of its movement stress this joint and the tree responds by adding more wood at its base. This produces a pronounced swelling called the trunk flare. Large trees lacking this flare usually have some restriction at or below the ground, were planted too deeply or had fill placed around the trunk. Over time this buried joint may become rotten, and the tree may decline or simply fall over.

One avoidable cause of this weakness is paving directly around the base of a young tree. Designers should be required to plan for and draw a mature tree with a full trunk flare in the proposed planting hole, to demonstrate that the design will function when the tree becomes large.

The principle of dynamic structure applies to other joints in the tree. Branch unions can become weak if the tree is not pruned properly, leaving branches with tight angles. Roots that are damaged or cut can cause the tree to fall over. Trees that grow more branches on one side due to the shade of a competing tree or building may become unstable.

Light

Existing tree canopy and tall buildings often limit the natural light that trees need to grow. Only certain species can tolerate the low direct-light levels available in deep, canyon-like urban spaces. This principle also comes into play when trying to establish new tree plantings among large existing trees. In low light, use climax species of trees that can grow under existing forest canopies.

If you are familiar with tree biology, you will note that the principles listed here do not mention most of the detailed parts of a tree, such as cambium, xylem, and phloem. In this overview of tree biology, we need consider only the issues that affect the success of the tree and that can be controlled during its design, installation, and maintenance.

UP BY ROOTS—DESIGN PRINCIPLES

Once the designer understands the environment of the site and the requirements of the trees, this information can inform and inspire a suitable design approach. Trees need more space at the soil line and below the ground than is allotted in most contemporary urban design. There is fierce competition for this space, and for the budget needed to prepare this space for trees.

To ensure that each tree gets its needed share of space and budget, the designer must defend tree requirements from the beginning of design through the end of construction. Designing space for trees cannot be left to the construction document phase. Successful tree design cannot be an afterthought once the design direction is set.

The following ten principles can guide the process of building landscapes from initial concept sketches through construction and the start of maintenance cycles. The principles are organized into soil-based strategies, tree-based strategies, and management-based strategies.

Soil-Based Strategies

Soil-based strategies work with existing soil resources, protect and improve those resources, and recognize when to abandon the existing soil in favor of replacements.

Principle 1. Plant the Easy Places First

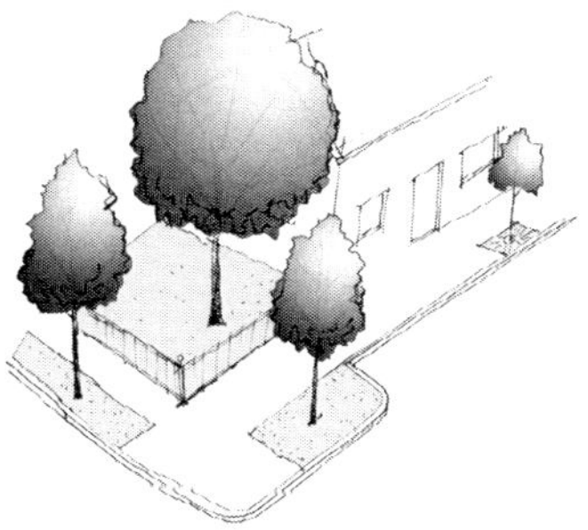

It sounds simple, doesn't it? Assign large trees to areas where you have the largest or the best soil resources.

In the urban environment, there are always easier and more difficult places to grow trees. Big differences in growth possibilities may be only a few yards apart, a result of slight variations in a design decision or changes in soil or drainage patterns. These sometimes subtle differences may be identified in the site assessment or perceived by an experienced designer who understands trees and their needs. Starting the design with the easier locations yields a greater chance of successful trees at a lower price. This may mean other goals have to be compromised, but all designs involve balance among conflicting goals.

Working with existing resources is also fundamental to the principles of environmentally sustainable design. One of the best examples of this principle is the decision to place street trees between the sidewalk and the curb, as opposed to placing them between the sidewalk and the building. The soil between the walk and the building is often more suitable to grow a healthy large tree, but it is rare for this location to be selected. Conversely, the space between the curb and the walk is usually too small and the soil too compacted for a large tree. The curbside location may be preferred for aesthetic and urban design reasons. Yet unless the project has the resources to overcome the technical problems of putting trees in very confined space, these advantages may be beside the point. There is no aesthetic value to a dead tree or an empty planting hole.

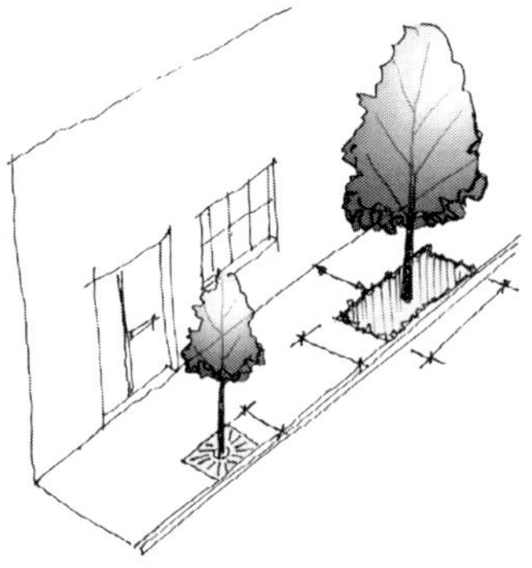

Principle 2. Make Larger Planting Spaces

Another simple way to improve the health of trees in urban areas is to reduce the areas of paving and increase the areas open for soil. Of all the principles, this is the most important and the easiest to undertake. Competition for space in the city is severe, but rarely does anyone ask, "Could the paving be reduced even slightly to improve tree growth?" This is because designers who are not interested in the health of trees often make paving decisions.

Architects, civil engineers, and many landscape architects see paving as the primary element in the design. They either do not know how their decisions affect tree health or may shrug these concerns off in the belief that trees can be replaced when they die. Paving is considered easy to maintain and is necessary for pedestrian and vehicle traffic. The size of a paved area may also be part of an aesthetic plan. Yet it is possible to ask how wide roads and sidewalks have to be, and how much paving is really needed for a plaza.

Fewer larger spaces for clustered trees are better than many smaller isolated tree plantings. Often a small change in the widths of drives, walks, and spaces between obstructions can result in enormous benefits to the amount of soil available to the tree, increasing tree longevity.

Formulas for determining the amount of soil needed to support a large tree are provided in this book. Use them to gain support for larger soil areas.

Principle 3. Preserve and Reuse Existing Soil Resources

Despite dire predictions of destroyed soils and poor growing conditions, there are often usable soils at urban sites. If these soils can be identified, incorporated into the design and protected during the construction, a small piece of the environment has been preserved. It is hard to make good soil, so anytime reasonable soil exists, reuse is the best option.

Removing and replacing soil is a very environmentally destructive act. Existing soil must be moved at great expense and use of fuel, and often ends up as fill dirt or, worse, in a landfill. The harvesting of topsoil and other materials to make replacement soil results in large areas of degraded land, silting of waterways, and again considerable use of fuel. If promoters and stakeholders wish to represent a project as sustainable, then preserving, protecting, and reusing existing soil must be a priority. Even without this concern, a simple budget calculation can make a strong case for reuse.

Soil reuse, protection, and preservation are not easy tasks in a complex construction process. They demand the same level of effort as tree preservation, and many of the principles are the same. Think of soil preservation as growing space for future trees. Reusing soil—moving it around the site and restoring it in a new location—is the second-best option, but comes with its own requirements and an acceptance of a significant level of soil degradation no matter how carefully it is handled.

Principle 4. Improve Soil and Drainage

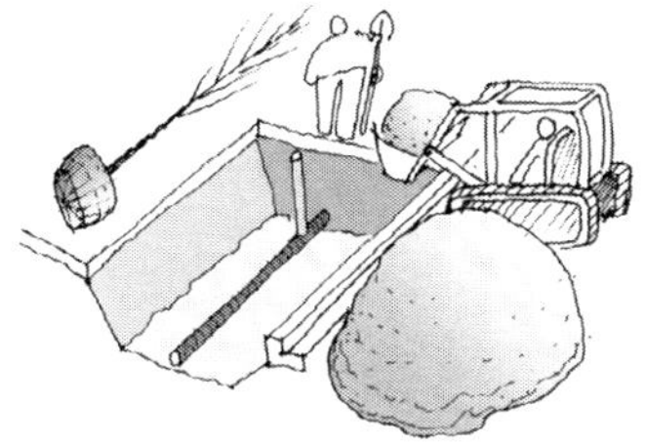

Once the design has established the limit of available soil area, make this soil "right for the tree." Sometimes simple deep tilling of compacted soil is sufficient, while in other places complete soil replacement is required. Knowledge of soils, drainage, and the requirements of the trees to be planted is necessary to make the right decisions. In some cases, a little soil amendment can actually create more problems by forming "bathtubs" that hold water. Improper soil amendments are one of the most common mistakes in working with soil, and much of this book is devoted to this subject.

Too much water creates more problems in the urban landscape than too little. Plants can adapt to dry conditions, and a little supplemental water at establishment or during a drought can make all the difference. In contrast, drainage problems can be difficult to fix, especially if not discovered until after the project is finished. Poor drainage will undo all the other principles.

Tree-Based Strategies

Tree-based strategies discuss the needs of the tree and instruct the designer on how they are accommodated into the design.

Principle 5. Respect the Base of the Tree

Do not pave within the area of the tree's future trunk flare. The mature trunk flare is the pronounced swelling at the base of the tree just before the trunk disappears underground. It is usually more than twice the diameter of the trunk at 4 feet above the ground. This area must be treated with great care and respect. The trunk will expand to dimensions dictated by the tree, not the designer. The tree will either push aside any constrictions or suffer damage from them.

Just beyond the trunk flare, the first set of large roots extends out underground and rapidly tapers away from the trunk over the next 6 to 8 feet. These are the roots that cause the most conflict with paving and curbs. Obstructions within this area are always at risk unless measures are taken to prevent root intrusion or develop conditions that allow roots to grow deeper within the soil.

Principle 6. Make Space for Roots

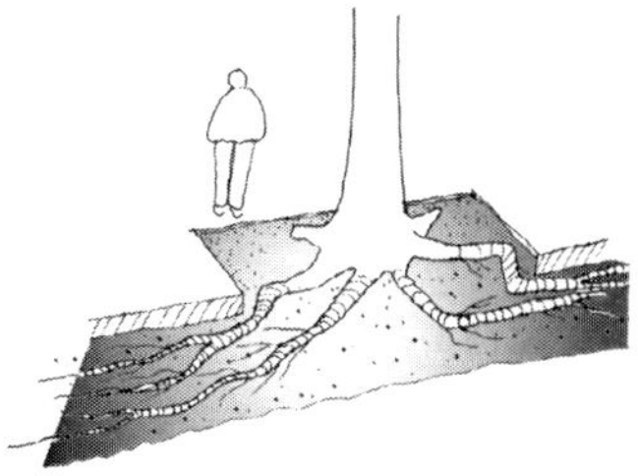

Design spaces for roots under the pavement and adopt different approaches to root space design as conditions change.

At some point in the design process, it may simply be impossible to provide sufficient soil for the tree in an area separate from the paved areas. At that point the designer must begin to anticipate roots growing under the pavement. This may limit the type of paving that can be used and may increase the cost of the project. Yet it is possible to encourage root growth under pavement in ways that do not impact the stability of the pavement.

In urban areas, when the rooting space is smaller than required by the tree, uniform design and detailing of the tree rooting space often does not result in uniform tree growth. Trees will adapt to subtle differences in the area around the prepared rooting space. Designers must consider each tree as a unique organism in a unique environment and develop solutions that reflect these differences in conditions. This book offers many approaches to solve soil and drainage problems. Use as many of them as are appropriate to optimize the budget with a goal of growing large, healthy trees.

Principle 7. Select the Right Tree

Put the right tree in the right place and make the place right for the tree.

Only after all the above principles have been followed can the design consider tree selection. Selecting the right tree assumes that one has made every effort to make the place right for the tree. This order of priority gives the designer a much wider range of available trees from which to choose. Select trees primarily for their ability to perform the desired functions and aesthetic contributions to the design. Even pines can be used as street trees, if their use would meet the goals of the project.

Selecting the right tree also assumes a high level of professional knowledge about the requirements of each tree. Designers must still take on the responsibility of learning the nuances of horticulture. This is more than a quick look at a textbook resource or the use of a digital plant selection program. Those resources are great beginning points, but are no substitute for personal experience. Local climate, maintenance, nursery availability, regional soil differences, and other variables must become part of the designer's thought process.

Once the tree is chosen, go back through the design process and make sure the site has been made right for that tree. Be prepared to change elements if a tree selection changes.

Management-Based Strategies

Management-based strategies provide tools to fund and implement the first two sets of strategies.

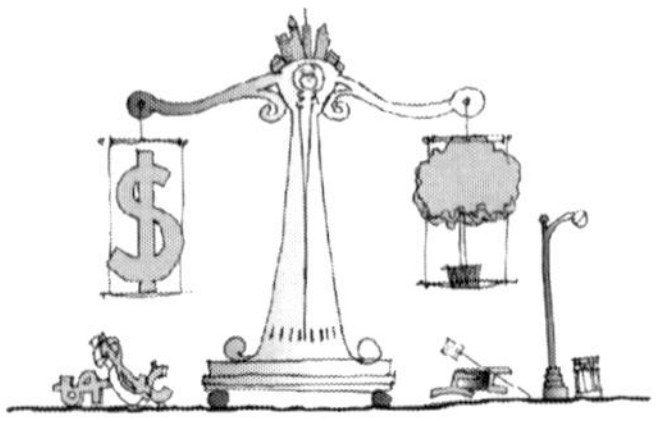

Principle 8. Establish Reasonable Tree and Soil Budgets

Balance the design quality of all elements in the landscape.

Trees are just one element in the urban fabric needed to support design goals of bringing people together in dense yet attractive spaces for economic and social interaction. Other elements, such as paving, furnishings, and lighting, are also important. It is necessary to keep the resources devoted to each element balanced within the available budget.

Growing and maintaining a large, healthy tree in urban soils requires about the same resources per unit as installing and maintaining a good-quality street light. Trees and lights offer different benefits to the community, but these benefits are reasonably similar in value. Too many landscapes are built with high-quality light fixtures, paving, and furniture placed among dead or stressed trees because the designer did not understand the need to balance project resources.

As budgets run up against limits, adjust the quality or quantity of everything a little bit. Planting fewer trees, but providing each with healthy soil, will be a better investment and produce a better landscape over the long term.

Principle 9. Create Detailed Tree and Soil Construction Documents

Once the concept design has been developed with the basic systems needed to support trees, the construction document process must continue with the same high level of care and commitment to the principles of soil science and tree biology. As in any construction system, there is a big leap from the planting concept plan to the finished product.

Make detailed drawings of the soil design. A separate soil and drainage installation plan should be a requirement. Draw the trees in sections to scale, accurately depicting the root ball size. Make sure that each tree fits in the allotted space at the time of construction and that the mature root system will fit in the space in 30 or 40 years. Draw the predicted mature root system, at least during the detail development period, to test the suitability of details.

How does water move into and out of the soil? Can the contractor actually place the soil in the locations and in the sequences of other construction? It should be an embarrassment to design professions how often they fail at these basic documentation tasks. Project documentation that relies on standard details or specifications will invariably fail when the conditions are not "typical." It is the designer's job to look at all the conditions and develop solutions for each variation from the mythical norm.

Even the best set of documents cannot succeed without cooperation and coordination between designer and contractor. It is the designer's job to ensure that the contractor follows document requirements. Soils and plants are highly variable commodities, and there is always a wide range of possible interpretations of specifications.

Inspect materials frequently, starting at their source and continuing during the construction process as needed to ensure quality. The problem of root balls with overly deep roots or circling roots must be corrected in the nursery, not at the job site. Test and review soil to ensure that it supports the plants selected and is compatible with the drainage assumptions.

Review drainage systems, subgrade conditions, soil installation, soil compaction, and root balls throughout the construction process. The same tool the designer used to assess the soil at the beginning of the project, a soil probe, is useful when reviewing landscape installations, allowing inspection of root ball, soil quality, drainage performance, and soil compaction. The designer must have the scientific knowledge to interpret what is observed.

Principle 10. Design for Maintenance

Urban environments depend on maintenance. In intensely used urban settings, the concept of low maintenance is not a practical reality. During the design process, identify the source and capability of that maintenance, and be sure that the maintenance team is informed of specialized requirements and system designs.

A properly designed landscape should be able to support trees with minimum maintenance. If the tree fails because the level of maintenance available could not provide for its minimum requirements, is the design at fault? Understanding the maintenance capabilities of the client should be a fundamental design criterion.

Many projects that receive wide acclaim for design success have small armies of maintenance staff who can overcome soil design flaws. When another designer tries to emulate these award-winning projects without the same level of maintenance, plant failure is almost ensured. Sometimes, particularly in cases of poor drainage, the design is simply not maintainable. Design choices do affect the ability to maintain the design.

Maintenance providers, like designers, must understand soil and tree biology. How soil and trees are treated during maintenance is as crucial as it was during construction.

For example, few people, including landscape maintenance contractors, know that plants look wilted from being either over- or underwatered. Lots of hard work can be undone by overwatering the soil during the first summer after the project is built. Well-developed soil biology can be severely damaged by chemical applications intended to improve plant health. Soil testing, including monitoring of soil biology, should be a regular part of the maintenance process, and soil lab reports should be consulted before deciding on any chemical application.

Pruning must be done with the long-term growth goals for the tree and to set up proper branching patterns for the creation of strong branch joints.

While the primary designers are rarely part of the ongoing maintenance team, they must set the landscape on an attainable maintenance course and make strong recommendations to influence quality maintenance practices by certified arborists and other providers.

FURTHER STUDY REQUIRED

These ten principles are not intended to provide definitive answers to the challenge of designing spaces for trees in urban spaces. They are general guidelines that require further study of the science of trees and soils. In the following chapters, we'll go into more detail about applying these guidelines.

PART ONE

2
The Physical Properties of Soil

The next three chapters are devoted to understanding natural soil. There are three properties of soil that are important when working with soil during construction: its physical makeup, its biological activity, and its plant-related chemical components. These properties are closely interrelated. A designer or planner must take all three, separately and together, into account when learning about soil, assessing soil, and modifying soil.

SOIL-BUILDING PROCESSES

Soils are primarily the result of geologic forces, weather, water, and biology breaking down rock over time. Geologic changes have been moving the earth up and down, back and forth, for billions of years. The resulting arrangement of rock fragments and weathered mineral particles that we call "soil" becomes quite complex. Understanding local geology is critical to understanding local soil conditions.

The processes that create soil include all activities that deposit or alter the mineral material found on the surface, such as the lifting and folding of the earth's crust, earthquakes, landslides, volcanoes, erosion, glaciers, floods, sedimentation, and wind. The resulting mineral material is called the soil's **parent material**.

Once the geologic process begins to stabilize, weathering of the parent material begins. This phase of soil formation changes the parent material into a more complex form, adding organic matter, reducing the size of soil particles, and moving water-soluble chemicals through the soil. In some places, this weathering process has been in progress for millions of years, starting with the bare rock of uplifting mountains. In other places, weathering is more recent, from a few tens of thousands of years following the last glacial period to last season's floodplain deposits. The process of soil formation is cyclical and constant.

Figure 1.2.1. Different geologic processes contribute to the deposition of soil parent material.
a. Talus.
b. Glacier.
c. Lava.
d. Water deposition.
e. Sedimentary rock.
f. Volcanic ash.

PHYSICAL PROPERTIES OF SOIL

The physical properties of soil are the measurable characteristics of soil and to a large degree define how soil will react to physical forces. They are important factors in decisions on the suitability of a soil for plant growth and when to allow changes such as grading or how to amend the soil. The most important physical soil factors are:

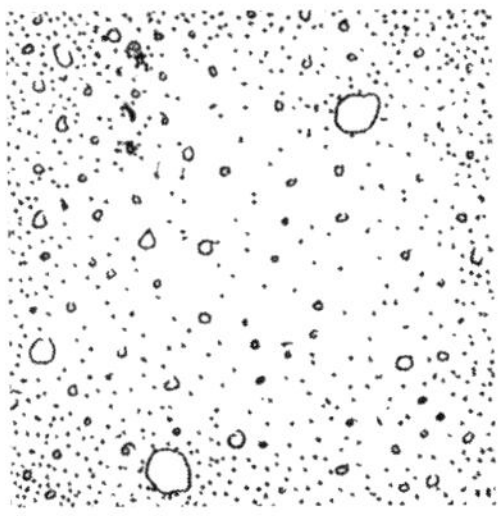

Texture

Texture is the proportion of different sizes of particles in a given sample. These particles are identified as clay, silt, sand, and gravel.

Structure

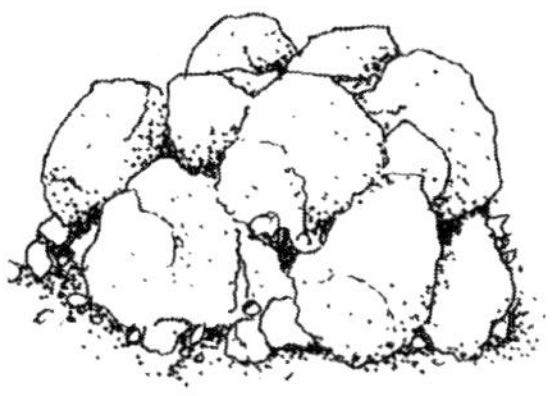

Structure is the arrangement of soil particles and how they are bonded together. Structure is created primarily by the process of weathering in the parent rock and/or by organic components in the soil. Soils, such as sandy soil, where the individual particles have loose bonds in small groups (called **peds**) are considered to have weak or poor structure, while soils where peds are more strongly bonded together, particularly soil with high clay content, have strong structure. The shape of the soil peds when they are broken apart is an expression of their structure.

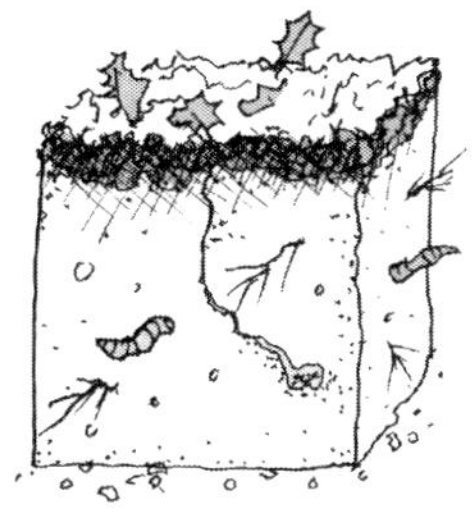

Organic Activity

Organic activity will be covered in the next chapter, but its impact on the physical properties of soil is dramatic and cannot be left out of the current discussion. Organic factors affect soil structure, consistence, profile, compaction, water movement, and nutrient-holding capacity.

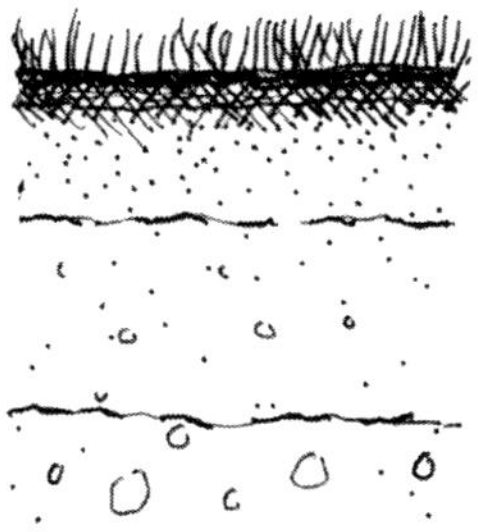

Profile

A soil profile refers to the group of layers in a vertical section of the soil from the surface to the parent material. The layers are called **horizons**. The pattern, texture, color, and other properties reflect the soil formation process.

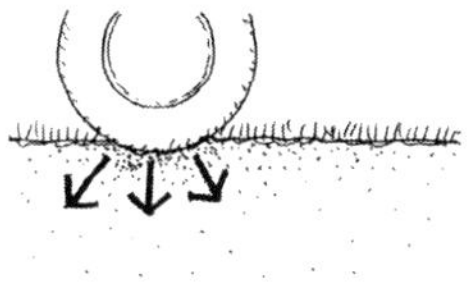

Compaction

Compaction is the degree to which soil particles are packed together. The measurement of soil compaction is called **bulk density** (weight per unit volume). A slight change in soil compaction can dramatically change how plants grow in a given soil.

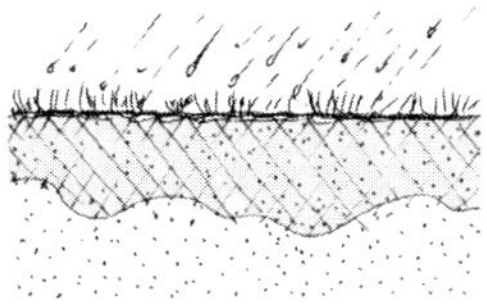

Water Movement in Soil

Water movement is defined as the speed at which water moves into and through a soil in response to gravity and capillary action. This affects the volume of water held in the soil after the water has drained and that is available to a plant.

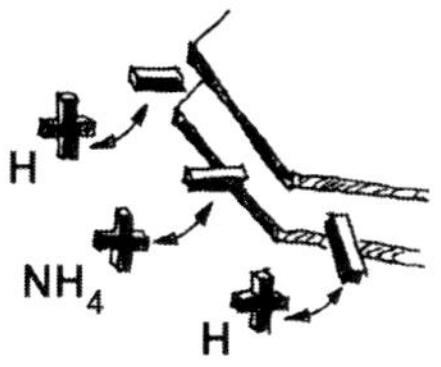

Nutrient-Holding Capacity

Nutrient-holding capacity is the ability of the soil to hold chemical elements needed by plants in a form available to those plants. While the chemistry of soils and plants is explained later in this book, the nutrient-holding capacity of the soil is also a reflection of its physical properties.

Each of these soil factors is interrelated. Changes in one may change the others. To successfully understand and work with soil, each factor must be fully understood as a component in the soil equation.

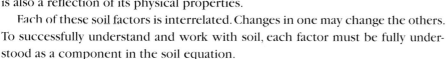

Trees Need Dirt or Soil?

Soil scientists bristle at the term "dirt." Soil is a natural body with mineral, organic compounds, and living biological elements that support plants. Dirt is something that is under your fingernails. How much abuse does it take for soil to become dirt? Can dirt ever be made back into soil? If a million people cleaned out their fingernails, could you grow a plant in the resulting dirt? Are most urban trees actually planted in dirt, not soil? Do soil scientists take the definition of soil too seriously? By the end of Part 1 of this book, you should be able to debate these questions.

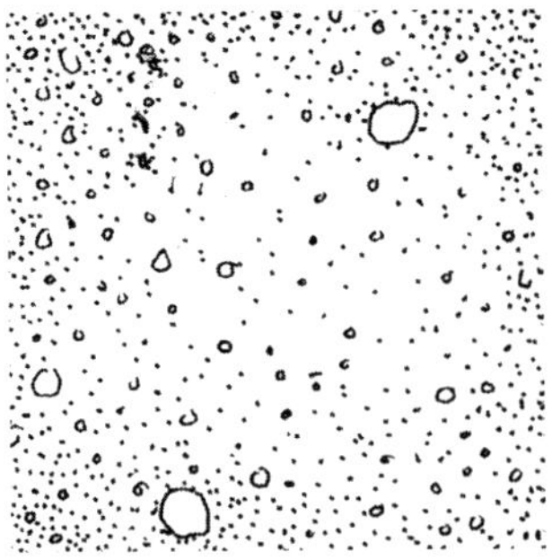

TEXTURE

Texture is the proportion of different sizes of soil particles, ranging in size from microscopic clay particles to fragments of stone called gravel. Particles are grouped by size and given the names of clay, silt, sand, and gravel. The soil's structure, consistence, profile, and compaction are all dependent on the proportion of each classification in the soil. Each of these particle types generally reacts differently to water, chemical elements, and biological activity.

Differentiation between the properties of a soil particle, such as clay, and a soil texture, such as clay soil, is important. Each particle exhibits particular properties, and each soil texture is a blend of different particles. The following sections will discuss properties of the different soil particles and how their combinations create different soil textures.

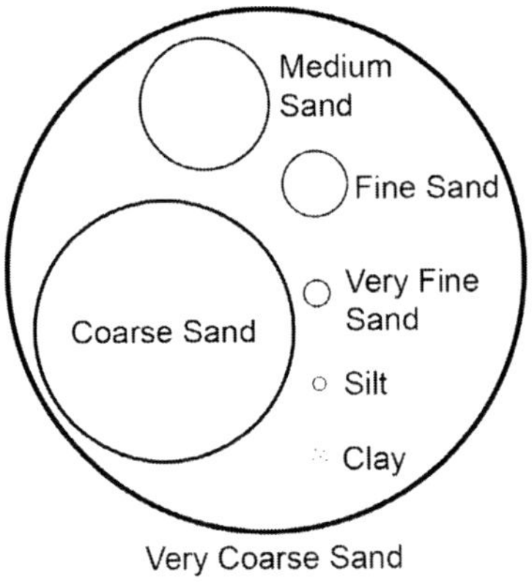

Figure 1.2.2. Relative size of different soil particles per USDA-NRCS system.

Sand in Soil

Sand is the largest particle size that is still classified as part of soil. Sand size varies, and the size affects how the sand functions in the soil. Within the USDA-NRCS classification (see Table 1.2.2), there are several sand sizes, called **sand fractions**. Understanding the difference between these fractions is important when determining the drainage capability and compaction resistance of a soil.

Figure 1.2.2 shows the relative size of the different classifications of soil particles. From this depiction, it is apparent that the sand size range is extremely broad. Soils composed primarily of fine sands may drain slowly, while soils made primarily of very coarse sand may drain too fast to support root growth. Sand particles generally do not bond together well, but clay and silt coatings on sand improve the formation of soil aggregates, or peds, that increase the soil's ability to hold water and nutrients and form soil structure.

Clay in Soil

Clay particles are microscopic, capable of forming electrostatic bonds with individual atoms, including nutrients important to plant growth. Clay can also bond to other clay, silt, and sand particles to form larger soil particles. These larger particles can improve drainage while maintaining good nutrient and water retention.

The bonds that hold together clay peds are relatively weak and easily broken if vibrated in the presence of too much water. As the bonds break, the particles are compressed, raising the bulk density of the soil. This is why farmers do not like to plow wet fields and landscape contractors should not be permitted to grade wet soils.

Clay particles are able to hold significant amounts of water, but in soil that has high clay content, the water between clay particles is not easily accessible to the plant. It is also difficult to add water to a high-clay-content soil once it dries out. Moderate amounts of clay, 10 percent to 30 percent, can improve the ability of soil to support plant growth.

Not all clay is the same. The particles have different shapes and can vary widely in their ability to hold nutrients and water. Some types of clay dramatically expand and contract as they become wet or dry.

Expanding Clay

Clay tends to expand when wet and contract when dry. Some types of clay expand more than others, which can be difficult for development projects.

There are three groups of clay types classified by their expansive tendency. The first group (which includes smectite, vermiculite, montmorillonite, bentonite, beidellite, nontronite, and saponite) is quite expansive and can cause significant damage to structures as they shrink and swell. A second group, which includes fine mica and chlorite, has less expansive qualities. The third group, which includes kaolinite, is not significantly expansive. In a bit of geological irony, the physical qualities that tend to make a particular clay type expand when moist are the same qualities that significantly increase its nutrient-holding capability. Thus the clays that are most welcoming to plants are the least friendly to buildings.

In areas of expanding clay, trees are often blamed for damaging foundations. Indeed, trees can draw water out of clay soil, causing it to shrink and subside. Yet this damage will occur whenever the soil simply dries out in prolonged drought. Irrigation can maintain proper soil moisture levels, assuming that the proper level is known at the time of construction. Root barriers can help prevent trees from growing too close to foundations.

Expansive clay is found over a wide area of the United States. Figure 1.2.4 indicates the approximate areas where a landscape designer may expect to encounter such clays. A local soil scientist should be able to identify expansive clays, and soil tests can determine the types of clay in the soil. Beware of inadvertently purchasing expansive clay soils.

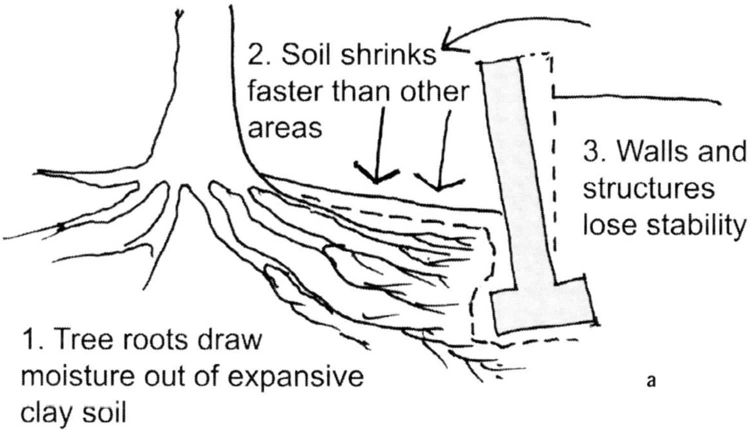
2. Soil shrinks faster than other areas
3. Walls and structures lose stability
1. Tree roots draw moisture out of expansive clay soil

a

b

Figure 1.2.3. Expansive clay damage to structures.
a. How trees in expansive clay contribute to structure damage.
b. Wall cracking due to expansive clay.

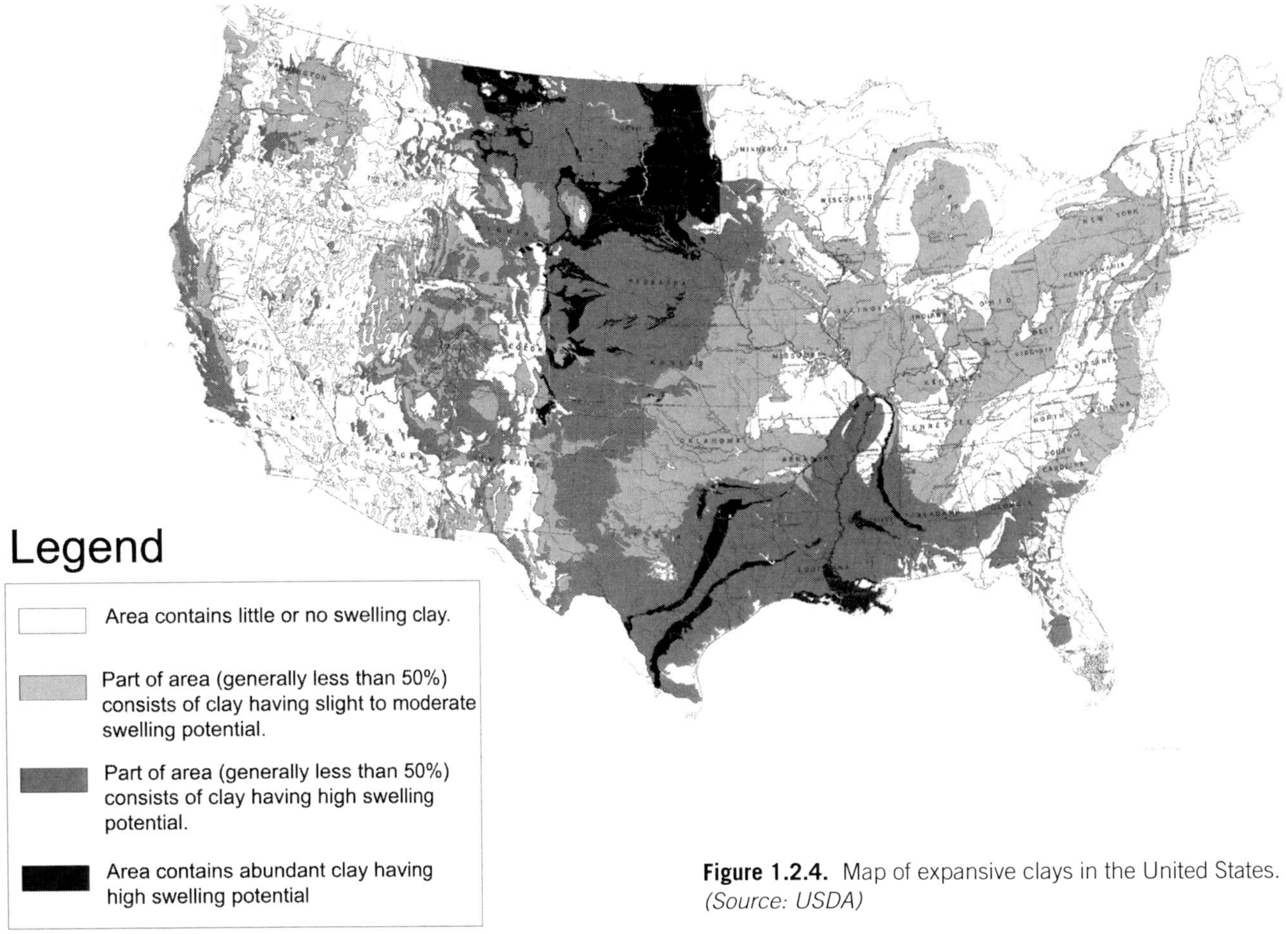
Legend
Area contains little or no swelling clay.
Part of area (generally less than 50%) consists of clay having slight to moderate swelling potential.
Part of area (generally less than 50%) consists of clay having high swelling potential.
Area contains abundant clay having high swelling potential

Figure 1.2.4. Map of expansive clays in the United States. *(Source: USDA)*

In England, expansive clay has become a national issue. While there are significant amounts of clay in the south of the country, local arborists believe trees may be directly responsible for only a small percentage of reported structural damage to buildings. However, insurance claims and lawsuits have cast a cloud of suspicion over all trees, and there is great anxiety over allowing large trees close to buildings. This is contributing to a significant reduction in tree canopy with a resulting increase in urban temperatures.

Silt in Soil

Silt particles are in between clay and sand in size. They contribute significantly to the soil's plant available water-holding capacity. The nutrient-holding capacity of silty soils is lower than clay soils, but higher than sandy soil. Silt particles do not stick together easily and do not easily bond to form larger peds.

Gravel in Soil

Gravel and larger rocks do not contribute favorably to a soil's ability to support most plant types. Until the gravel reaches a significant proportion in the soil, its only practical function is to reduce the volume of smaller particles, thus reducing nutrient- and water-holding capacity without contributing significantly to drainage. Only when the gravel pieces begin to touch each other, above approximately

50 percent of the total soil volume, is there much increase in drainage. Due to the decreased small particle volume, plants in gravelly or stony soils normally grow at slower rates. Soil textural classifications do not mention gravel unless it is at least 15 percent of soil volume; at that point the soil classification adds the prefix "gravelly" such as in "gravelly sandy loam." Gravel is normally removed before conducting agricultural soil classification tests. When labs report the amount of gravel removed, the total of all types of soil particles will be greater than 100 percent, which can skew the interpretation of soil texture.

TEXTURAL CLASSIFICATION

Soil Particle Size

There are several classification systems that set the minimum and maximum sizes that may be applied to the names clay, silt, sand, and gravel (see Table 1.2.1). The size system developed by the United States Department of Agriculture, Natural Resource Conservation Service (USDA-NRCS), is used in this book, and is the one most often used when describing agricultural soils. When reviewing soil sample descriptions or test results, always check which system of gradation was used for the report. Table 1.2.1 shows the USDA-NRCS size ranges for each of the four classifications of soil particles, plus larger stone size designations.

Two other commonly used classification systems, the Unified Soil Classification System and the AASHO (American Association of State Highway Officials), are also shown for comparison. These systems were developed by the engineering profession and are used in soil reports and soil specification. They use the same nomenclature, but have slightly different sizes for each particle designation. From an engineering perspective, clay and silt are lumped together and are given a slightly larger size limit. To the engineer, these smaller particles exhibit similar mechanical functions.

Table 1.2.1. Soil classification systems. *(Source: USDA-NRCS)*

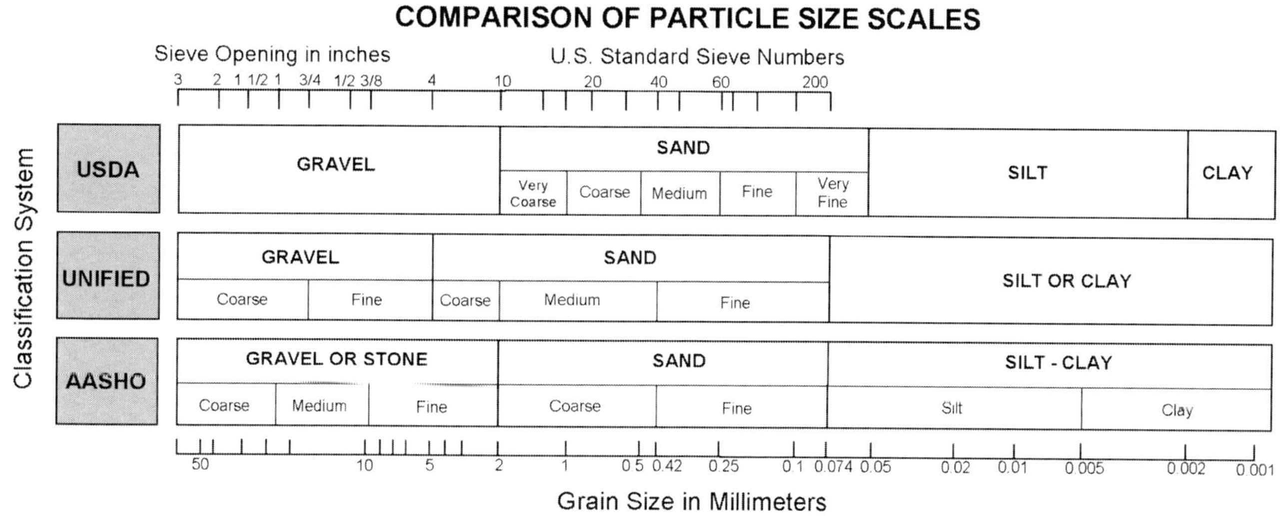

Table 1.2.2. USDA size ranges for different soil and stone particles.

Soil Material	Size (mm)	
Clay	**< 0.002**	
Silt	**0.002 - 0.05**	
Silt, fine	0.002 - 0.02	
Silt, coarse	0.02 - 0.05	
Sand	**0.05 - 2.00**	
Very fine sand	0.05 - 0.10	Sand Fractions
Fine sand	0.10 - 0.25	
Medium sand	0.25 - 0.50	
Coarse sand	0.50 - 1.00	
Very coarse sand	1.00 - 2.00	
Gravel	**2.0 - 75.0**	
Cobbles	**75.0 - 250.0**	
Stones	**250 - 600**	
Boulders	**> 600**	

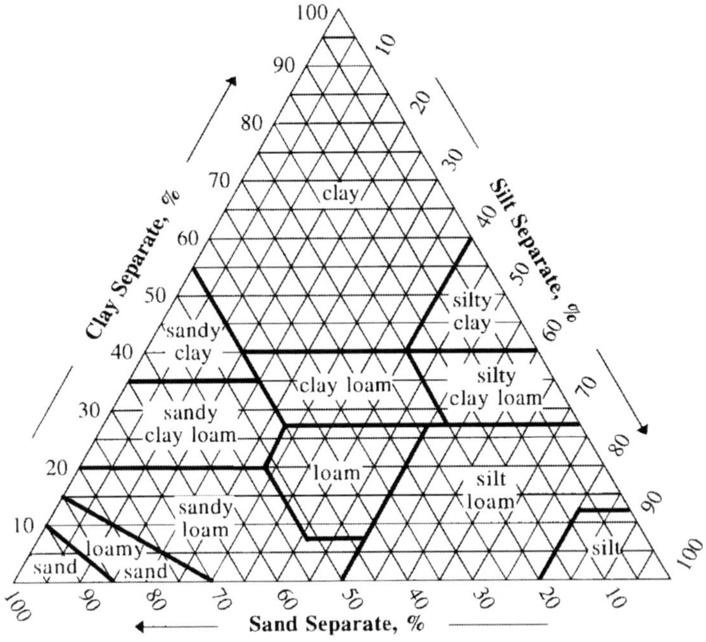

Figure 1.2.5 UDSA-NRCS soil texture classification triangle. *(Source: USDA-NRCS)*

Soil Texture Nomenclature

The USDA-NRCS classification system names different soil textures based on the ratio of clay, silt, and sand. Figure 1.2.5 is the USDA-NRCS Soil Texture Classification Triangle. Soils that contain a mixture of all three particle types are called loams. This name covers the majority of soil types within the triangle, so a classification that includes the word "loam" does not necessarily indicate a good-quality soil. Soils in the bottom central portion of the triangle are better agricultural soils. At the edges of the triangle the soils are missing one of the particle sizes and will be less suitable for good crop production.

As soil designations move into the corners of the triangle, the resulting soils take on the character of the particle size dominant in that corner. A soil that falls into these areas may be too wet or dry to support large trees even though both may be sandy loam.

Since the USDA soil classifications are so broad, it is important to know not only the classification, but also where in the classification limits it falls. The set of soil strategies that will be effective at 80 percent sand may be a different approach than if it were 50 percent sand, even though both may be sandy loam.

Note that the designation "clay" takes up a third of the triangle. This indicates that within this area of the triangle, all soil will function similar to almost pure clay even if only 40 percent clay. Clay soil that has good structure can be a great soil for growing some types of plants. On the other hand, the area of the triangle that is designated as sand is quite small, indicating that a soil must be almost pure sand in order to stop having the qualities of a loam soil.

Soil Texture by Feel

Learning to identify soil texture by feel and appearance is the first step in the process of working with soil. While a soil test can provide precise identification for the practitioner, these are time-consuming and only give information for the sample submitted. Field assessment of complex urban soils will require examining many samples to piece together the conditions at the site. This only can be accomplished when one is able to identify subtle changes in soil texture. Figure 1.2.6 presents the time-honored method of determining soil texture by feel. Practicing with soils of known texture will quickly improve identification skills.

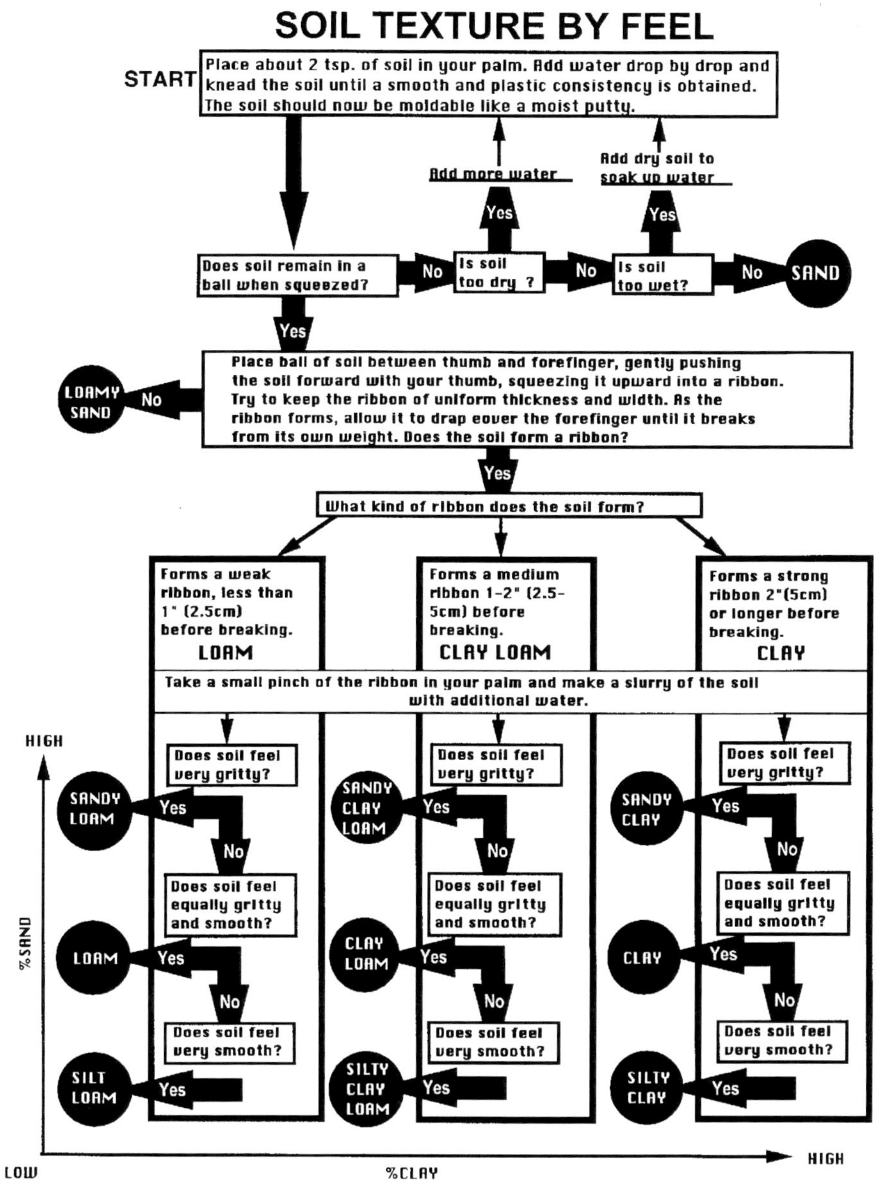

Figure 1.2.6. Texture by feel.

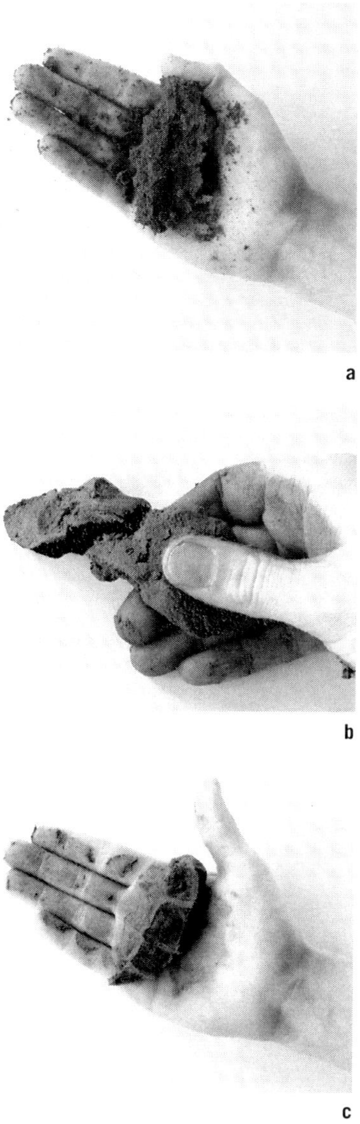

Figure 1.2.7. Examples of soil texture by feel.

a. Sandy loam.
b. Making a soil ribbon to determine clay content.
c. Sandy clay loam after it is compressed.

Soil Is Much More Than Texture

The textural ratio of sand, silt, and clay is only one part of the soil picture. Other properties of a soil's makeup must be considered when evaluating soil. The following is a list of items that are missing from a standard textural evaluation.

Gravel

Most soil testing labs do not test for gravel unless specifically requested. Gravel is often found in urban soil. It reduces the usable volume of the soil by displacing smaller soil particles that contribute to the water- and nutrient-holding capability of the soil. Always request the amount of gravel that is in the soil.

Sand Fractions

Different sand sizes affect soil performance. The difference between coarse and fine sand can be significant when predicting the performance of soil.

Clay Type

Variations in the parent material of the clay can have a significant impact on the way water and nutrients move through or are held in the soil and if a soil is an expansive type. Testing for expansive clay types is not a part of a normal soil test.

Soil Structure

The way soil particles are arranged and stuck together, known as soil structure, is a critical component of soil quality. Good soil structure greatly improves drainage, but is easily damaged or eliminated during the development process. A clay loam that has good structure may be an excellent soil, while the exact same clay loam that has been heavily graded and/or compacted, destroying soil structure, may not support plant growth.

Organic Activity

Organic activity can vary widely, with corresponding variance in soil drainage and nutrient-holding capacity. Organic activity may need to be protected or restored during the development process. The chapter on soil biology will discuss this aspect of soil.

Soil Horizons and Profile

Each soil is made up of several layers. The layers below the soil being tested may change its drainage and capacity to nurture plant growth. Each layer must be examined separately.

Compaction

This is often the most significant factor in soil health and ability to support plants, but it cannot be reported in a standard testing procedure.

Soil Water and Drainage

Soil drainage is determined not only by texture but by structure, profile conditions below the soil, and topographic conditions that may concentrate or divert water resources.

Soil Chemistry

The chemical composition and pH of the soil are significant factors in its ability to support plants, and must be tested and evaluated separately from soil texture.

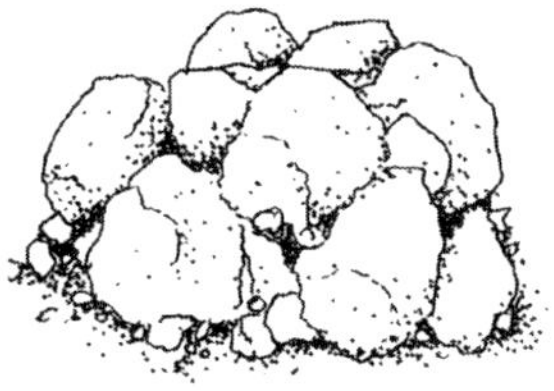

SOIL STRUCTURE

Structure is the result of the soil maturing under the forces of weather and biological activity. Smaller particles, particularly clay, begin to stick together to form clumps of soil called peds. When we break the soil apart, the ped structure is reflected in the shapes of the resulting clumps or clods. Small cracks between the peds are the passages where air and water can move rapidly into and through the soil. Peds are held together by a combination of films of clay and organic material. These films are quite sticky and become hard when dry. If you've ever washed dry clay mud off a pair of boots, you have already experienced the ability of clay to stick to a surface.

Soil expands and contracts as it moistens and dries, freezes and thaws. This movement forces soil particles together where they can be bonded by clay and organic glues created by the soil's biological activity to form large peds separated by fractures and spaces. The activity of roots, micro-organisms, and larger insects further binds the soil, completing the formation of its structure. The process of binding the particles together is also called "aggregation."

Soil peds tend to form consistent shapes. Dig into a piece of soil, especially when dry or only slightly moist, and break it up into clods. The soil will tend to break along fissures or weak points, revealing the shapes of the peds and helping the observer identify the soil structure.

Sandy soil and topsoil that has high organic content tend to have loose or granular structures. As clay and silt content increases and organic content decreases, the soil will form larger blocky units.

The structure of soil depends on the type of rock from which it has evolved. Parent rock forms soil with a structure similar to the structure of that rock; shale or other sedimentary rock creates soil with a horizontal, platelike structure; and soils evolved from igneous or metamorphic rock will have an angular structure. In drier regions, soils may form vertical columns or prism shapes as a result of extreme wetting and drying.

Many compacted urban soils form very large, horizontal, tightly bonded blocks, and this structure is called **massive**. Figure 1.2.8 indicates the different types of structures encountered in natural soils.

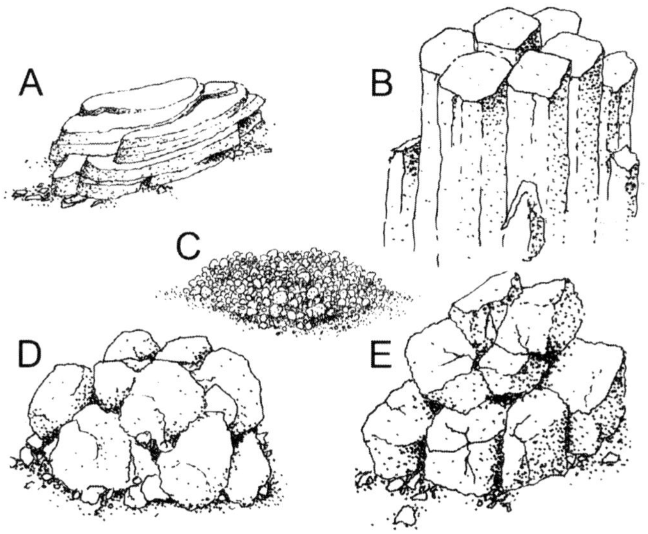

Figure 1.2.8. Soil structure types.
a. Platy.
b. Prismatic.
c. Granular.
d. Subangular blocky.
e. Angular.

Knowing a soil's structure can help us understand how well it will drain and withstand mechanical damage. It is easy to damage or eliminate soil structure. Soils that are moved or worked when they are wet will tend to lose their structure. Site analysis may tell us we have a great structure and good soil, but after it is dug up, transported, spread, graded, and compacted, it may fail to drain or support plants.

Once the structure is damaged, it is impossible to recreate it. Any mechanical disruption will degrade the structure to some degree, and will always reduce the soil's ability to drain and support plants. Clay soils often can withstand some amounts of mechanical damage if graded at the optimum moisture content. Sandy

a

b

c

Figure 1.2.9. Soil structure in natural and urban soils.
a. Subangular, blocky natural soil.
b. Soil clumps, residual soil structure in a soil mix.
c. Massive soil overly compacted by heavy machinery.

soils generally have poor structure, but their water particle sizes still may permit drainage even when the original structure is disturbed. A silty soil's structure may be the easiest soil to damage when grading and compacting.

Learning to identify the structure of a soil is as important as learning its particle distribution. Since soils easily lose their structure when disturbed, this investigation must be undertaken at the site. Soil moisture is a significant determinate in the ability to see structure. Avoid examining soil that is wet. If you must do so, carefully remove a large sample and allow it to dry to the point where it can be crumbled. Always look at the structure of the soil below the organic topsoil layer.

A good test of soil structure is to look at the strength of its aggregation. Place lightly crumbled soil peds into a bowl and soak them in water. Pour the water off and see if the ped structure is still visible. Strongly aggregated soil will look similar to the original soil, while a soil with weak aggregation will break down into soft lumps (Figure 1.2.10).

Part of assessing soil structure is the determination of the soil's **consistence**—its ability to resist crushing when pressure is applied at various moisture levels.

The term friable is used to describe soils that have sufficient clay and are at the right soil moisture that they crumble easily. The term is often misused to describe a soil type or quality. It should be used only when referring to the ability of a soil clod to be crushed easily. A particular soil may be in a friable state, but avoid describing a "friable soil," because this is not a permanent status the soil carries with it, but a particular condition resulting from its structure and water content in a certain place and time.

Figure 1.2.10. Aggregated soils. When dry, both well-aggregated (a) and poorly aggregated (b) soils may look similar. When wet, the well-aggregated soil "crumbs" hold together (c), while "crumbs" of the poorly aggregated soil do not (d). *(Photos courtesy ISA)*

ORGANIC ACTIVITY AS A PART OF THE SOIL'S PHYSICAL PROPERTY

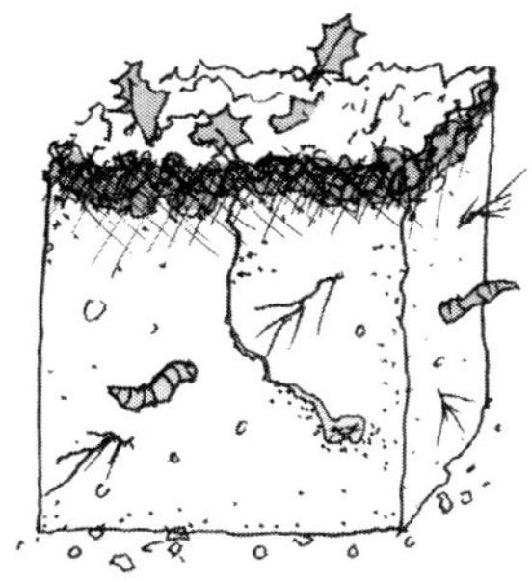

Organic activity has a significant impact on the physical functioning of soil. Organic matter and biologic activity are responsible for much of a soil's ability to drain and to hold water and nutrients. Soil biology creates much of the structure and consistence in the soil, providing the organic glue that sticks the soil particles together. Organic activity brings raw organic matter in the form of root exudates, leaves, and decaying plant matter into the soil.

A good way to envision the process and importance of the organic component in soil is to consider an abandoned parking lot. At first, nothing will grow. Over time, thermal expansion and contraction open up cracks, which accumulate small amounts of dirt and begin to support small annual grasses and other plants. These plants send out roots that further loosen the pavement. Gradually, more permanent plants arrive, die, and decay, forming a more complex organic soil within the cracks. Insects arrive and larger plants find a foothold, further breaking up the pavement and increasing the amount of soil.

The process continues until a reasonably functioning soil develops within the asphalt. Soon, only the sturdiest parts of the pavement are visible. The speed at which this soil will develop depends on the strength of the pavement construction and the climate of its location. In places with temperate, moist climates, this transformation can happen in just a few decades. Without the organic component, the same amount of time would yield just a slightly cracked piece of pavement. In a disturbed soil that is not paved, this process happens more rapidly. In the next chapter, we'll go into more detail about how this organic component works.

Figure 1.2.11. Parking lot being reclaimed by soil-forming process.

SOIL HORIZONS AND SOIL PROFILE

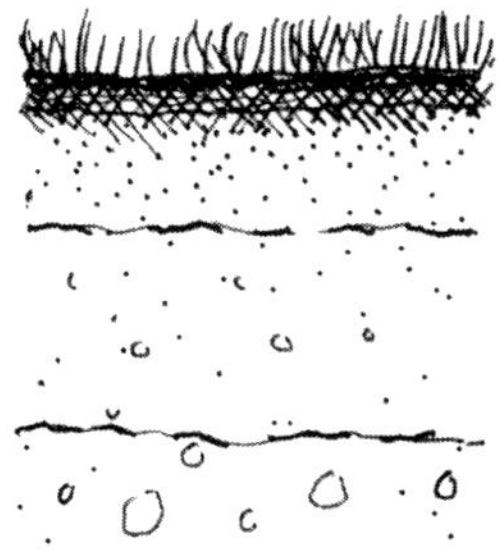

Whether soil creation takes place over the expanse of geologic time or in annual seasonal floods, it does so in layers. After each period of deposition, the weathering process modifies the layers and creates additional differentiations by adding organic material to the top and by leaching organic and mineral material through the soil. Different layer combinations drain and support plants at different rates. These layers are called **soil horizons** and help scientists identify soil types and better understand their capabilities.

The section of all layers in a soil is called the **soil profile**. In some soils, the horizons can be made up of dramatically different parent materials, while in others the mineral makeup is quite uniform from layer to layer. Soils with similar profiles are given the same name, and all the named soils that include subtle variations of that profile are called a **soil series**. There are nearly 19,000 soil series in the United States. Soil series are grouped into families of similar series and then further grouped into larger categories in a fashion similar to the classification of plants. The soil series name is roughly equivalent to a plant genus name.

The depth of most soil profile descriptions is defined by the practical depth to which a soil pit can be dug, the depth to the soil parent material, and the limit to which lower soil levels have any real impact on the growth of plants. A soil profile based on the USDA-NRCS soil classification protocol is dramatically different from a geotechnical soil profile. The latter looks at much deeper soil sections for the primary purpose of evaluating engineering limitations in the soil. Geotechnical soil reports have limited information on factors that will impact the growth of plants.

The range of soil profiles that may be encountered is as varied and complex as can be imagined after billions of years of geologic activity. NRCS soil surveys are the best source for general information on the types of natural soil that may be anticipated in any particular area of the United States.

These surveys may hold clues to what might have existed in urban areas. Unfortunately, most urban soils are mapped as "Urban Land" with very general discussion that sometimes indicates information about the base condition. (We'll go further into the assessment of soil in a later chapter.) Figure 1.2.13 shows several typical soil profiles that indicate a normal range of conditions.

Several Web sites listed in the references contain many full-color photos of soil profiles, several with explanations. They make a good introduction into the world beneath our feet.

The horizons of a typical soil profile are divided into groups based on soil formation history, the degree to which organic material has penetrated the soil, the leaching of minerals, and the location of parent material. Figure 1.2.12 indicates the nomenclature of soil horizons used to describe a soil profile. Not every soil will have all of these horizons and not necessarily in this order. The primary soil horizon designations, descending from the surface, follow.

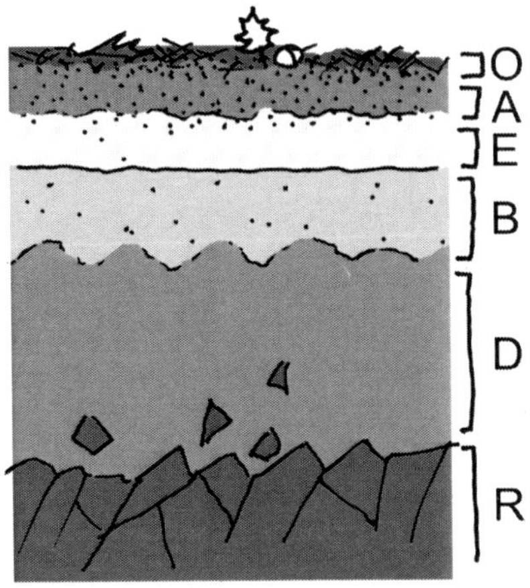

Figure 1.2.12. Soil horizon nomenclature.

O Horizon

The O horizon consists of decaying organic material, if present, that is seasonally deposited by plants. This layer only exists where a continuing source of organic matter is supplied by nature or human activity. This layer is always dark brown to black.

A Horizon

The A horizon consists of a mixture of mineral soil and organic material, usually dark brown, red-brown, or yellow-brown. This is the layer typically called **topsoil** and is the location of most plant root activity. The depth of the A horizon varies greatly with the climate and the types of plants growing on the surface. As soil temperatures increase, the rate of organic decomposition also increases. In the colder portions of the Great Plains, the A horizon is many feet thick under the grasslands, but less than a foot in nearby forested areas. The A horizon is thin in tropical rainforests due to rapid breakdown and leaching of organic matter. In desert areas, the A horizon may not be visible due to extremely slow accumulation of organic matter and high temperatures.

The A horizon is susceptible to erosion. Between erosion and land management practices that alter the organic cycle, much of the "topsoil" in the United States has disappeared or is of greatly diminished quality.

E Horizon

In some soil, organic material, clay, and other chemicals leach out of the A horizon and are carried by water down to a lower level. This creates, under the A horizon, a less fertile layer known as the E horizon, which is usually of lighter color. This layer is present in limited soil types.

B Horizon

Material that leaches out of the A and E horizons accumulates deeper in the soil, forming the B horizon. The color of the B horizon can vary greatly, and roots can extend here if drainage is adequate. The E and B horizons are the beginning of the subsoil.

Depending on the nature of the parent material and groundwater levels, hard layers (hardpan, fragipan, or caliche) that restrict root and water penetration can form in or just under the B horizon. Plow layers, which result from previous agricultural activity and which restrict root growth, may be found in the upper portions of the soil.

C Horizon

This is the parent material of the soil, at a level that is not heavily influenced by weathering or organic activity.

R Horizon

In areas where bedrock is near the surface, the rock is indicated as the R horizon.

Transition Layers

In humid areas of deep parent material, the transition between horizons is gradual. Transition layers (e.g., AB horizon or BC horizon) may also be identified in the soil survey. Some soils may only have a single readily identifiable horizon, but within that horizon, subtle differences may exist that are sufficient enough to note on a soil survey. Such sublayers are designated by number suffixes such as B1 and B2.

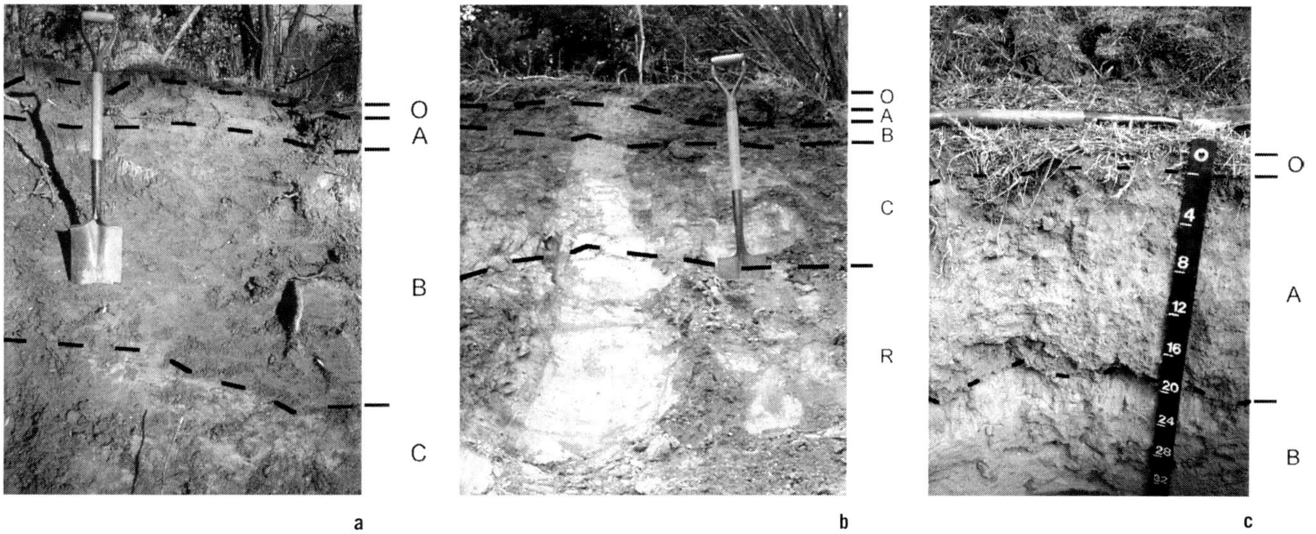

Figure 1.2.13. Soil horizons.

a. Coastal plain marine deposit soil, with little differentiation between horizons and root penetration throughout the B horizon.

b. Mountain weathered rock soil. Thin B horizon and no root penetration below the B layer. Light-colored streak at the top of the R horizon is weathered sandstone, while B horizon is a sandy clay loam, the result of millions of years breaking down the sand particles into clay.

c. Urban soil. Uniform 20 inches of topsoil placed over a sandy, compacted fill with a sharp interface between the A and B horizon.

Caliche, Claypans, Fragipans, Hardpans, and Plow Layers

Naturally and human-degraded soil may contain dense layers that make it difficult for water or roots to penetrate. These layers may result from soil forming processes such as high water levels, mechanical compaction, or a sharp change in soil type between layers. Such conditions may create soil interfaces (boundaries between horizons). The names for these soil conditions as used in the industry can overlap somewhat, and definitions can change slightly by region.

- **Caliches**, often found in the western United States, are layers that were formed as soil particles became cemented together by compounds that include calcium or magnesium.
- **Claypans** are layers that were formed by the accumulation of clay particles.
- **Fragipans** are layers that were formed by compaction.
- **Hardpans** are almost any type of hard layer in the soil. This general term is sometimes used to refer to layers formed by soil particles becoming cemented together with compounds of calcium, silica, or organic matter.
- **Plow layers** are layers that were formed by repeated compaction by the bottom of a plow pushing down by the weight of the soil.

Soil Interface

A **soil interface** (vernacular term) or **abrupt boundary** (scientific term) is a sharp or distinct joint between two different horizons and is the result of a dramatic change during soil formation. Roots and water may have difficulty crossing layers where there is a dramatic difference in porosity across the interface. Minerals and/or clay particles may collect along interfaces resulting in caliches, claypans, fragipans, or hardpan layers. If water sits on top of the interface, it is called a **perched water table**.

COMPACTION

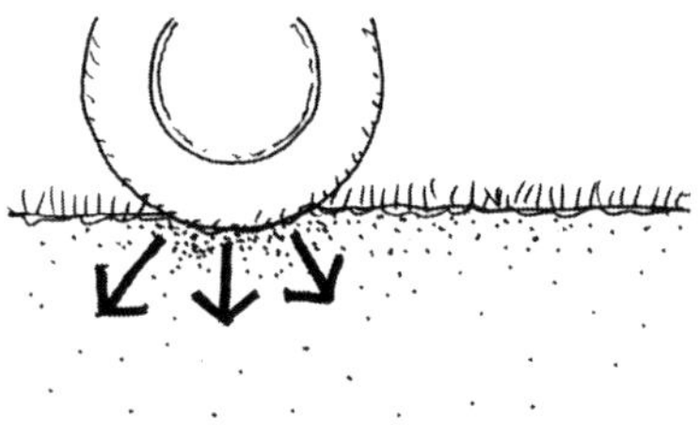

The natural soil forming process tends to create soil that is at suitable levels of **compaction** (or, to use the scientific term, **bulk density**) for ground stability and the growth of some kind of plant. Very few natural places exist where the soil bulk density is so high that plants will not grow. Human activity tends to change the compaction level in the soil, most often making it more compact, but sometimes reducing its compaction. Identifying compaction levels in the soil and when they need to be modified is a critical step in creating good growing conditions.

As soil becomes mechanically compacted, the organic bonds that were holding the soil structure are broken and soil particles are pushed together, filling the **pore space**. Think of what would happen if you stepped on a bag of popcorn. Your foot would crush the fluffy kernels together, and the spaces between them would be difficult to re-create. The same goes for soil. As pore space is eliminated, space for air and water is lost and roots must push harder to get through the soil. The plant has access to less water and grows fewer roots in the more difficult conditions.

Pore Space

In a good-quality natural soil, the minerals in the soil normally make up about 50 percent of the soil volume. An additional portion, less than 5 percent, is organic matter ranging from bacteria and insects and their excretions, to roots and pieces

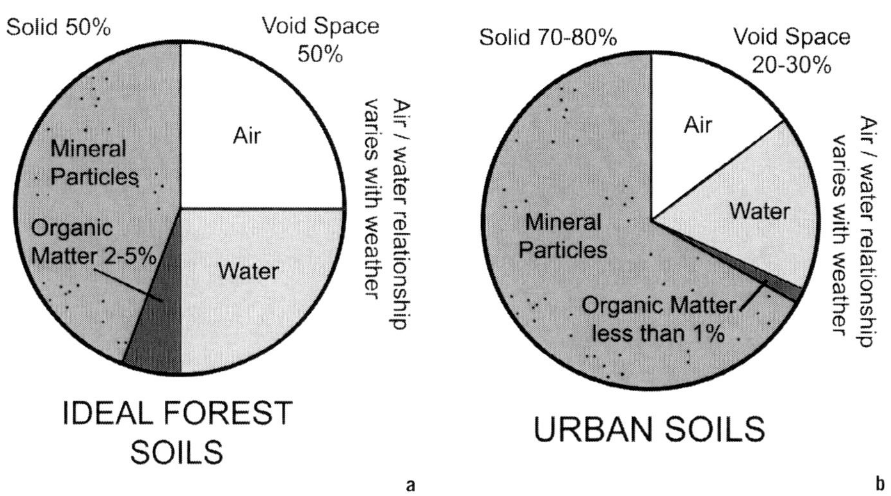

Figure 1.2.14. The relationship of mineral material, air, water, and organic matter in forest and urban soil.
a. Forest soil.
b. Urban soil.

of decaying plants. The remaining soil volume, almost half, is pore space within the soil structure. The pore space is filled with a combination of air and water, with the proportion dependent on current weather. The pore space devoted to the interchange of air and water in the soil is critical to plant growth. Figure 1.2.14 shows the relationship of the various components of natural soils and how changes in compaction in urban soil can change this balance.

Soil Types and Compaction Response

Soil texture has a significant impact on the ability of a soil to become compacted to the point where it limits water and/or root penetration. Because there are infinite variations of soil textures, it may be easier to look at soil from the perspective of a soil engineer rather than an agronomic soil scientist. In this less complicated view, soil textures can be divided into just four basic types based on their different compaction responses in constructed landscapes.

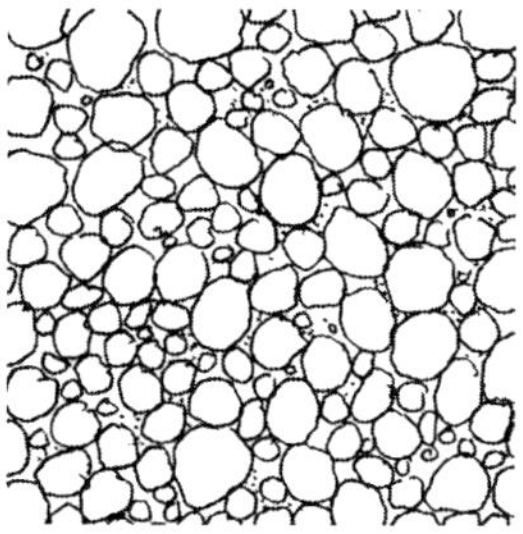

Coarse-Grained Soil

Mostly large sand particles. May retain significant pore space even when compacted.

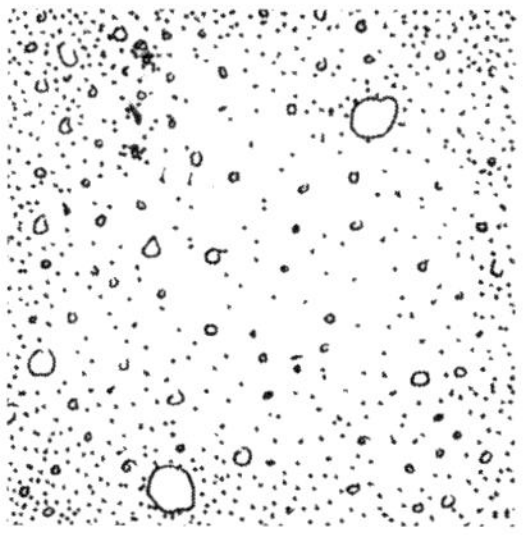

Fine-Grained Soil

Mostly clay silt and fine sands. May have very few usable pore spaces when compacted.

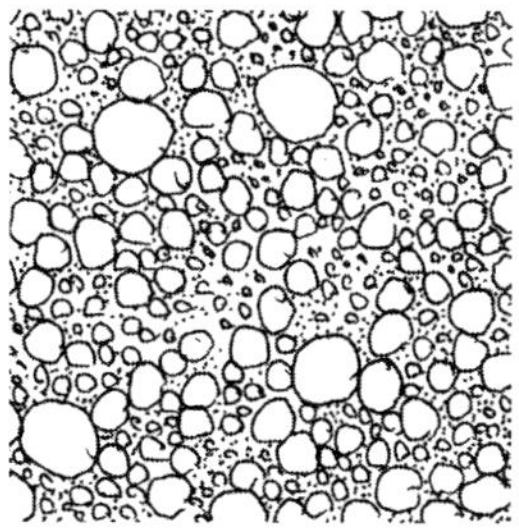

Fine-Graded or Even-Graded Soil

Even distribution of particles across most of the particle size range from coarse to fine. There is a particle size to fill every size pore. These soils may be self-compacting or at least are easily compacted. Engineers treasure fine-graded soils for their ability to be easily compacted, and often import them onto a construction site for controlled fills.

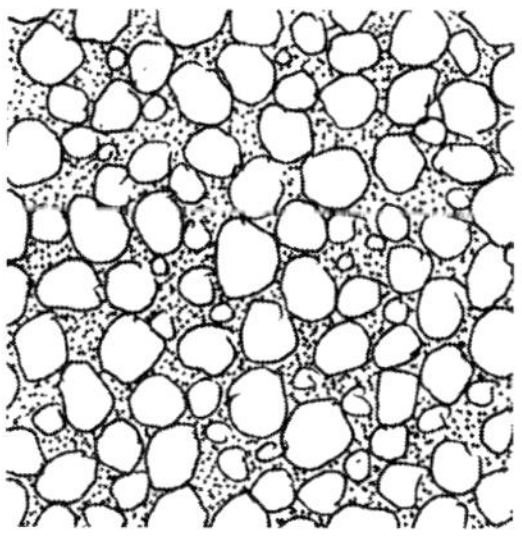

Gap-Graded or Poorly Graded Soil

Contain both fine and coarse particles but without some of the intermediate-size particles. These soils tend to be compaction-resistant, and may retain large pores. They may not become root-limiting even at fairly high compaction rates. Gap-graded soils are not prevalent in nature and usually are manufactured.

Measuring Soil Bulk Density

Soil compaction is measured as **bulk density**, which is the soil's dry weight divided by its volume. In soil science this is normally expressed in mega grams per cubic meter (Mg/m^3) and also written as grams per cubic centimeter (g/cm^3). Mg/m^3 and g/cm^3 are of equal value, and the more common g/cm^3 will be used in the rest of this book to express bulk density.

Different soils have different densities at which they will no longer allow roots to penetrate the soil. Different plants vary in their ability to penetrate dense soil or to function in soils with small amounts of pore space. As soil moisture increases, plants may be able to penetrate a soil that at lower moisture content is at a root-limiting density. This may explain why urban trees can form roots in seemingly root-limiting compaction, but only during wet seasons of the year.

Generally, coarse-grained soils may be compacted to a greater degree than fine-grained soils before they become root-limiting. This is due to the larger pores that are retained in between larger particles. Tables 1.2.3b and 1.2.4 indicate the root-limiting bulk density in different soils and, for comparison, the bulk density of other materials. Note that these bulk densities are for typical trees and large plants commonly used in landscape application. The almost limitless variations of nature provide plenty of exceptions to this rough outline.

We'll go into detail about field testing for bulk density later in this book, but here's a brief overview. Optimum soil compaction for planting soil is best specified as a bulk

Table 1.2.3. The relationships of soil types to bulk density and Proctor values.

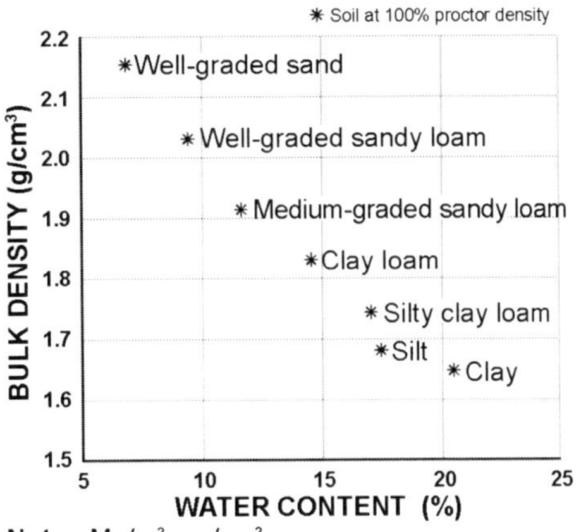

Note: $Mg/m^3 = g/cm^3$

a. Various soils compacted to 100 percent of maximum dry density (Proctor). Note that as sand content increases, less water is needed to obtain the maximum density and the soil reaches maximum dry density at a higher bulk density. *(Source: Abramson et al. 1995)*

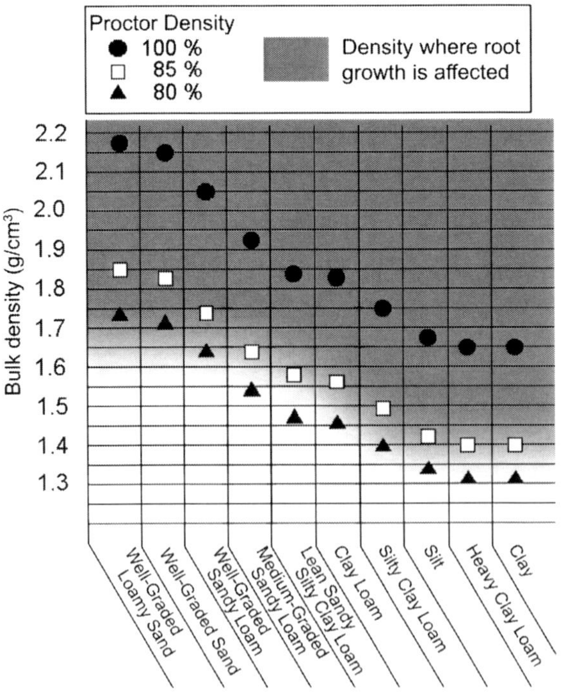

b. Bulk density and levels affecting rooting compared to several Proctor densities. Note that soils to be used for most trees and shrubs should always be compacted to less than 85 percent of maximum dry density. There is limited research comparing bulk density to Proctor value, but a reasonable specification for compacting planting soil would be between 75 and 80 percent, with some settlement expected at that range. Sandier soils can be compacted up to 85 percent, with the exception of well-graded sandy soils. *(Source: Data adapted from Daddow and Warrington 1983, Lichter and Lindsey 1994, and Brady et al. 1999)* density range. The upper limit should be at least one tenth of a gram per cubic centimeter below the root-limiting value. For example, the root-limiting bulk density of sandy loam is approximately 1.65 g/cm^3. Therefore, the maximum specified compaction should be 1.55 g/cm^3. The lower limit of compaction for installed planting soil should be around 0.15 g/cm^3 lower than the upper limit. Thus, the specified compaction for a sandy loam should be 1.40 to 1.55 g/cm^3.

Engineers often measure compaction as a percent of maximum dry density that may be obtained under optimum moisture content. This is determined by the **Proctor density test**. Table 1.2.3a also indicates the relationship of Proctor levels to bulk density levels. Table 1.2.3b shows that compaction rates specified for engineering fills, typically 90 or 95 percent of maximum dry density, are substantially higher than the bulk density that limits root penetration. Compaction rates between 80 and 85 percent dry density will begin to restrict root growth depending on the soil type. Note on the table that root-limiting bulk density levels are depicted as a soft band with an imprecise edge. There is considerable variation among plants and the same plant may respond differently to minor variations in soil texture.

If soil compaction is specified in Proctor units, the maximum compaction should be 80 percent of maximum dry density except in sandy soils. Always specify a range of acceptable compaction. The lower Proctor limit should be around 5 percent below the upper limit.

Table 1.2.4. Soil types and bulk density relationships. Note that these tables should not be used to evaluate compaction in soil mixes that include organic amendments or lightweight aggregates.

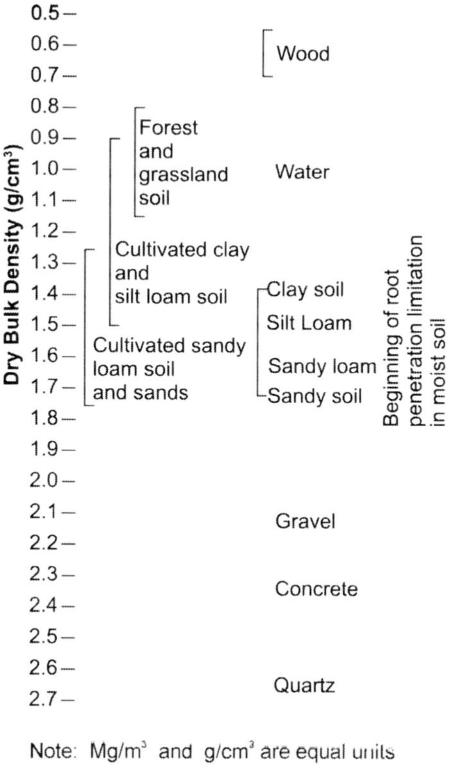

a. Ranges of soil densities. *(Source: Brady et al. 1999)*

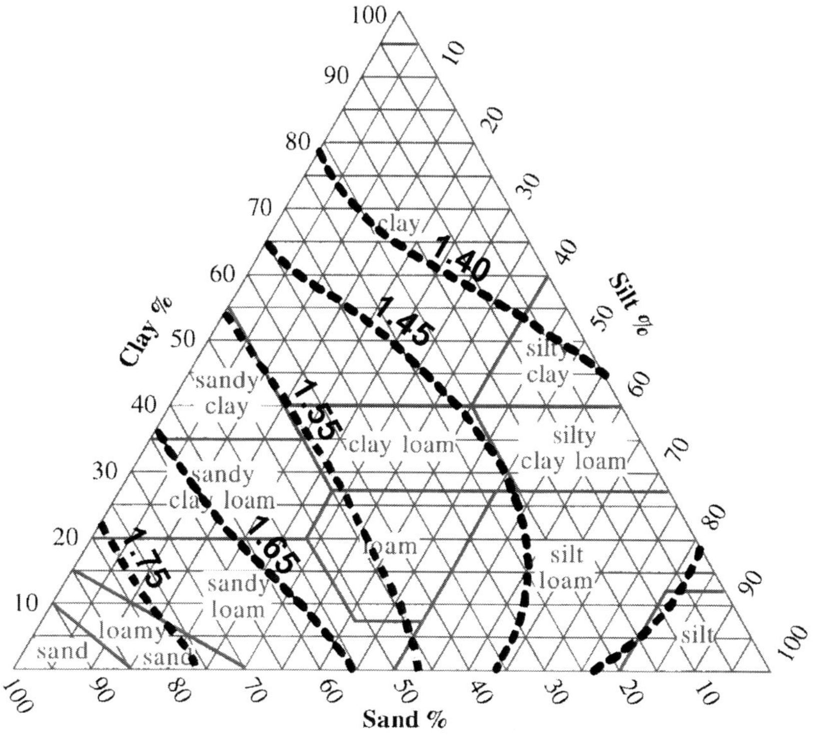

b. Root-limiting soil densities. A reasonable specification for compacting planting soil by bulk density would be between 0.1 g/cm^3 and 0.25 g/cm^3 below the value predicted as root-limiting with some settlement expected at that range. *(Source: Adapted from Daddow and Warrington 1983)*

Settlement of Mineral Soil vs. Loss of Organic Matter

Mineral soil settles as particles fill in voids. Except for high-sand-content soils, it may be impossible for the contractor to compact a planting soil to the point where it will not settle and still support root growth. Settlement of the mineral portion of the soil can usually be contained to less than 10 percent of the soil depth.

Large amounts of organic soil amendments are often added to planting soil mixes. This organic amendment will continue to decompose in the soil, significantly reducing its volume and causing a reduction in soil volume. Most of this lost volume leaves the soil as CO_2 into the atmosphere. Increasing bulk density cannot control soil settlement from loss of organic matter. Soil settlement roughly equal to 50 to 75 percent by volume of organic amendment added should be anticipated in addition to the normal mineral settlement. If 20 percent by volume of compost is added to the soil, the shrinkage will be between 10 and 15 percent of the installed soil depth. Add only small amounts of organic amendments (10 percent by volume) to planting soil mixes to reduce shrinkage. Greater amounts of organic amendments (up to 50 percent by volume) should be added to the top 6-inch layer of planting soil where soil shrinkage is not as critical.

Compacting Forces

Damage from soil compaction starts with the first person who walks on the soil. One person walking on a path once a day for 100 days adds the same amount of compaction to the path as 100 people walking on the path on the same day, assuming the water content in the soil is the same each day. Water lubricates the soil particles and makes them easier to push together. So, one person walking on a path on 100 rainy days will cause more compaction than 100 people walking on the path on a dry day.

Compaction levels from surface traffic decrease with depth. As compacting loads are transferred downward, they are spread out laterally through most soil types at an approximate angle of 45 degrees from the point of impact. This reduces the compacting force dramatically in just a short distance below the impact level. A force of 1 pound per square foot applied at the surface of the soil will equate to a force of only 0.11 pound per square foot 1 foot below the surface of the soil and 0.01 pound or less per square foot at a depth of 2 feet. To obtain a consistent compaction rate in an installed soil, engineers specify soil compaction to be performed by the contractor in thin layers called **lifts** as the soil is being placed. For example, compaction for a road bed may be specified in 6- to 8-inch lifts. For general soils, lifts may be 12 inches thick. Planting soil compaction will vary from 12- to 24-inch lifts, depending on the sensitivity of the project to tolerate settlement.

Figure 1.2.15 shows the transfer of loads in soils.

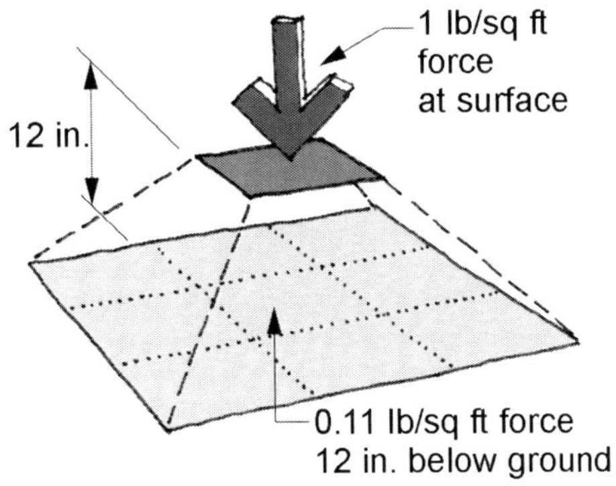

Figure 1.2.15. Load transfer in soil and its impact on compaction. Compacting force dissipates with depth.

Vibrating soil while applying the compacting force helps the particles fit more tightly together. The vibration can also break the bonds between clay soil particles, helping to increase compaction levels. As noted above, adding water to a soil helps lubricate the particles so they slide together, but too much water and the particles begin to flow, transferring the force without compacting the particles. Some of this force is transferred upward toward the surface, causing the soil next to the compacting force to bulge up. This is called **pumping**, and indicates that the soil is too wet and not being effectively compacted. The right combination of soil water level and vibration can create serious compaction in a soil, pleasing the engineer, but causing anxious moments for the designer if the soil is intended to support tree roots.

The weight of the soil also is a compacting force, and in natural soil of a consistent soil texture, bulk density normally increases with depth. Conversely, where urban soils are compacted solely by surface loading, compaction decreases with depth due to the lateral transfer of the compacting force. This decreasing compaction continues until it reaches the level that would have resulted from the weight of the soil above. At this point the compaction rate begins to increase.

Time also increases bulk density in lower soil levels. The weight of the soil continues to compress the soil below it until equilibrium is reached between the weight of the upper soil and the lower soils' ability to resist that weight. Natural soils may be quite stable, while graded soil continues to settle for periods that can last years. Engineers use this principle to prepare subgrades in sites with deep areas of soil that are insufficient to hold the structure planned for the surface. Fill soil is mounded on top of the final grade for a specified period. Both the depth of the mound and the length of time are factored into estimating the compaction rate.

The compaction force is a function of both the weight of an object and the surface area over which the weight is distributed. Track vehicles and low-inflation rubber tire vehicles have a much lower compacting force than a standard car or truck. Note that pedestrians, with their small footprint-to-mass ratio, can cause more compaction than a track-grading machine.

Table 1.2.5. Compaction force of vehicles and pedestrians.

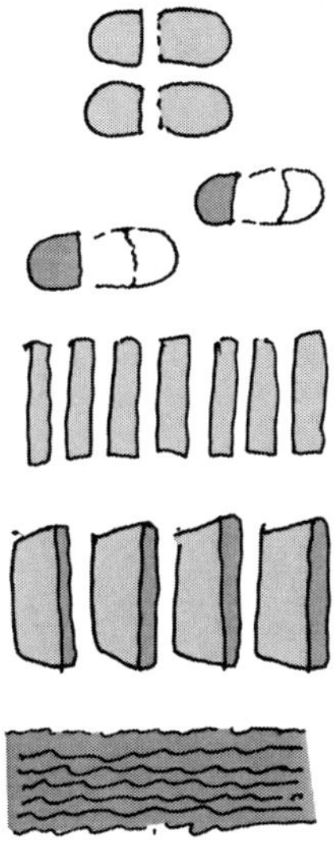

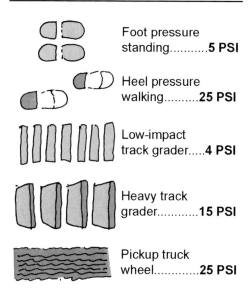

Foot pressure standing	**5 PSI**
Heel pressure walking	**25 PSI**
Low-impact track grader	**4 PSI**
Heavy track grader	**15 PSI**
Pickup truck wheel	**25 PSI**

Changes to Soil Compaction

The forces of freeze/thaw and swelling/shrinking in the soil tend to slowly reduce surface layer compaction, especially when combined with high levels of surface biological activity. This process is slightly more rapid in colder and wetter climates, but many winters are needed to allow a compacted soil to begin to recover even in the northeastern United States. Mulch layers to stimulate biological activity and retain moisture also help soils recover from compaction. Lightly compacted soil and soil where the compaction is only on the surface few inches will recover more quickly if mulch is added to the soil. In warm or dry climates, the soil may stay compacted. Once the soil reaches a point where root penetration and soil biology are severely restricted, time and the addition of mulch will have a diminishing impact on reducing compaction. Portions of the compacted tracks of the Oregon Trail through the high desert are still visible after more than 100 years of rest.

SOIL WATER AND DRAINAGE

One of the principal functions of soil is to make water available to plants. To do this, water must move quickly into the soil each time it rains, and some of this water must be held in the upper layers of the soil profile. Plant roots also need air within the soil to respire while taking up water, so draining away some of the water is also critical. Thus we need two types of water controls that operate in the soil simultaneously.

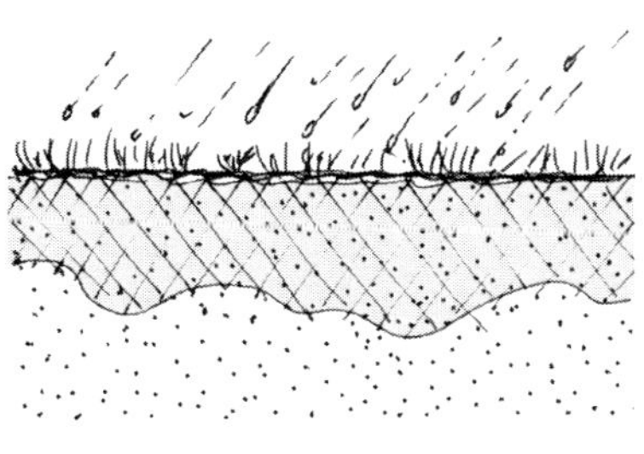

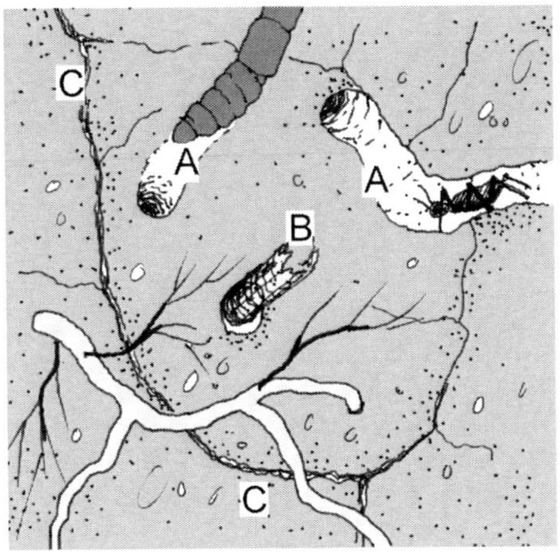

Figure 1.2.16. Macropores.
a. Insect passages.
b. Decaying roots.
c. Cracks between soil peds in dry weather.

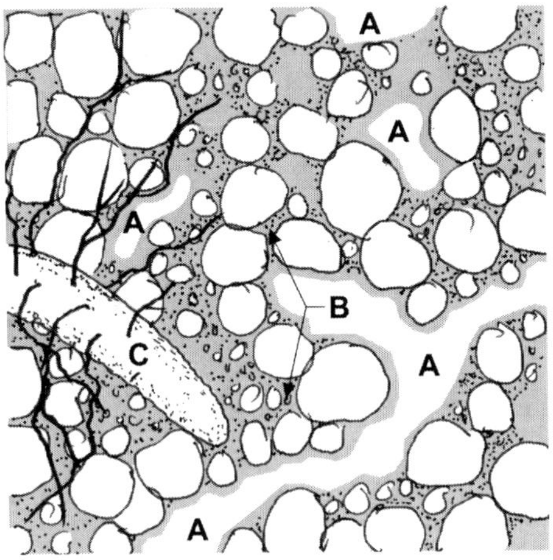

Figure 1.2.17. Macropores and micropores.
a. Macropores filled with air after soil drains to field capacity.
b. Micropores—water films between particles—held in place by surface tension.
c. Root.

Within the soil structure are two types of passageways. The first are large passages or pores that are interconnected and allow water to slowly percolate through to a lower level. These passageways are called **macropores** and are large enough for water to drain under the pull of gravity. Macropores are generally found between soil peds, and include worm and insect holes and passages created by decaying roots. As the water in the macropores drains away, a fresh supply of air enters the soil to provide oxygen for root respiration. If the water remains in the macropores, the roots of many plants will literally drown. Nature is always adapting, however, and some plant species have evolved that can tolerate high levels of soil moisture, including permanently flooded soils.

Once the water drains from the macropores, some water is left in smaller spaces called micropores. This water is held in place against the force of gravity by water surface tension and capillary action. To better understand how this works, place two pieces of glass on top of each other. Water applied to the edge will wick far into the space between the glass and stay there even if the glass is held vertically. This is the water that will be available to the plant between rainfalls. Micropores are found within the ped structure and include the spaces between small soil particles, water films that coat soil particles, and space within small soil cracks and organic matter.

There are a few more terms you may find useful in understanding how water operates in soil. During an extended period of rain, when the water fills all the micro- and macropores, the soil reaches a **saturated** state. After the rain ends, the water in the macropores slowly drains, leaving only the water held in the micropores. This is a state known as **field capacity**, or the maximum amount of water that can be held in the soil. At this point, roots begin to pull water from the micropores and some of the water begins to evaporate from the surface of the soil. The plant uses this water, with much of it being transpired into the air through the leaves.

The smaller the space between soil particles, the greater the surface tension holding the water in place. Roots are capable of pulling water out of the larger micropores, but at some point can no longer take up water from the soil. This state is known as **wilt point** or **wilting point**. After this point the plant begins to show drought stress. The water held between the states of field capacity and wilt point is called **available water** or the **water-holding capacity** of the soil. It will be important to recognize when different soils are at these critical stages, as they will direct management decisions during construction and maintenance.

Water evaporates directly out of the soil as well as being used by the plant and lost to transpiration through the plant. Both kinds of water loss into the air are grouped under the term **evapo-transpiration**. In sandy soils, direct evaporation can be a significant amount of water, especially in climates that have long periods between rains. In climates that have frequent and regular rainfall, the plant community becomes adapted to this flow. Here, just a few extra days of dry weather can begin to cause stress in the plants. Slight changes in compaction, differences in organic matter, and surface topography and soil profile conditions will impact how rapidly water moves into and out of soils of similar texture.

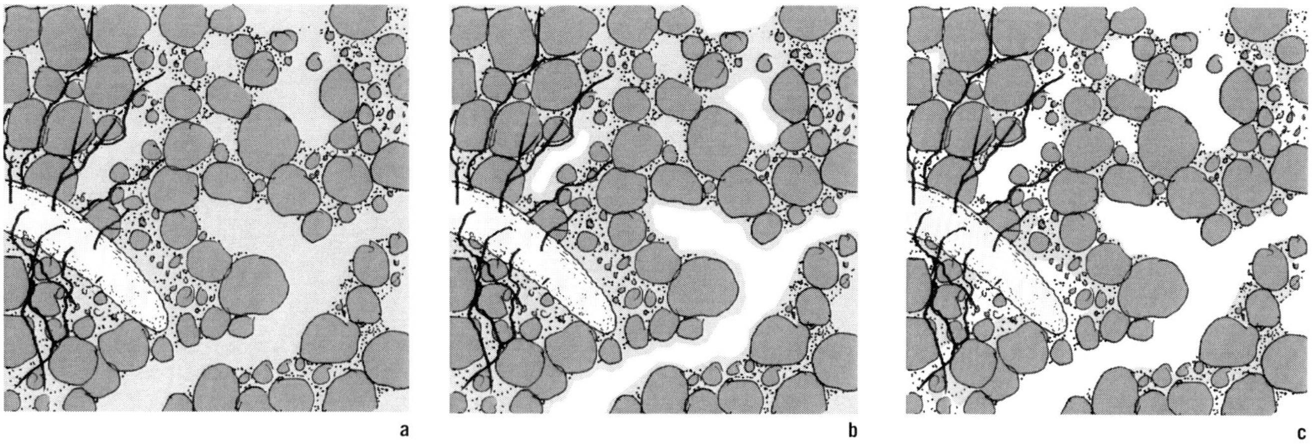

Figure 1.2.18. Soil and water at different states.

a. Saturated.

b. Field capacity.

c. Wilting point.

Different soils hold different amounts of water at wilt point and field capacity. Sandy soil has many macropores but few micropores, so the available water between field capacity and wilt point is small. Clay soil, particularly when compacted, and compacted silt soil have many micropores and few macropores. The micropores are often too small for the roots to access this water. Available water is limited and wilt point is reached quickly even though the soil may contain significant moisture. In these soils, oxygen is also limited due to the slow movement of water, and plants are forced to grow roots close to the surface. Soils with combinations of sand, silt, and clay create a variety of particle sizes and the best balance of macro- and micropores. Of course, once any of these soils becomes compacted, pore space and available water are greatly reduced.

Water moves within a particular type of soil and between layers of different soil types in predictable ways. In fine-grained soils, water moves slowly horizontally, downward, and even upward by capillary action through the micropores. It moves downward by gravity through the macropores. In sandy soils, the movement is much more rapid and mostly down by gravity due to a lack of micropores. This principle makes for dramatic differences in the rate and distribution of soil water from irrigation sources. Figure 1.2.20 shows two types of soil and movement of water from surface irrigation.

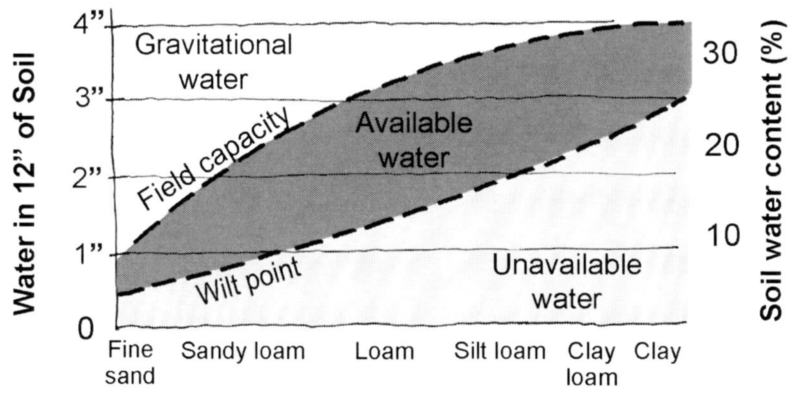

Figure 1.2.19. Schematic diagram of available water by soil type. As soils become compacted, field capacity and wilt point lines move higher on this chart and become closer together, resulting in less available water.

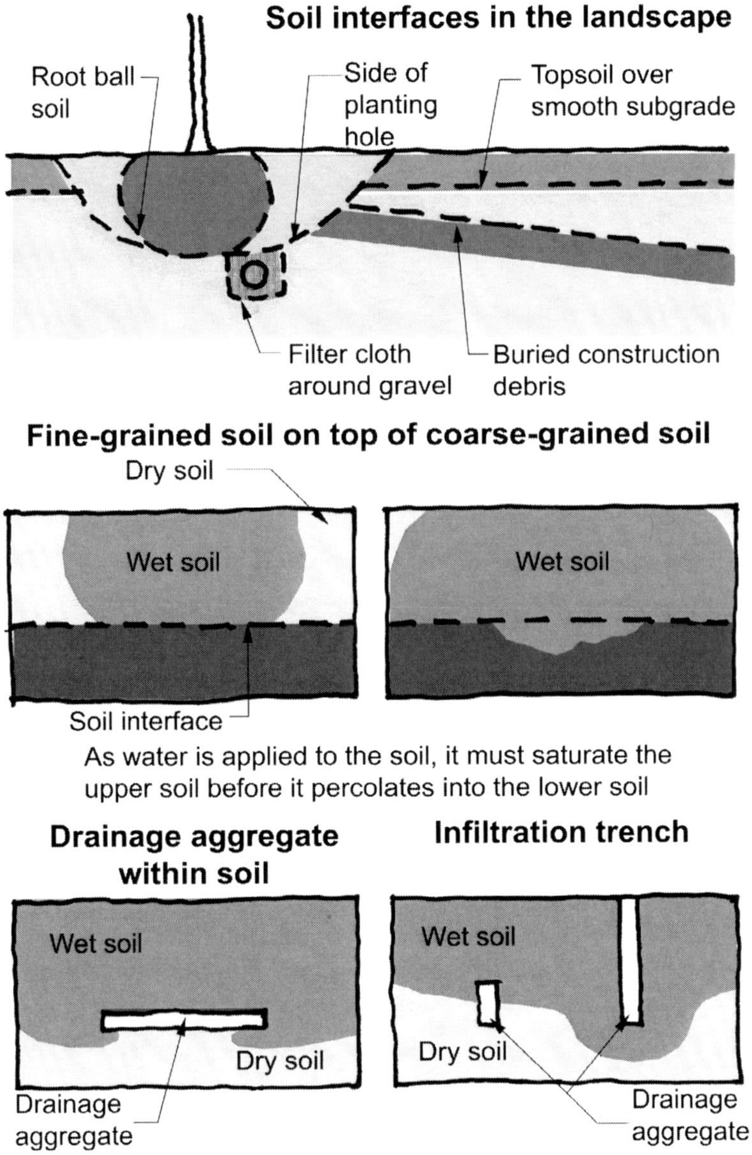

a

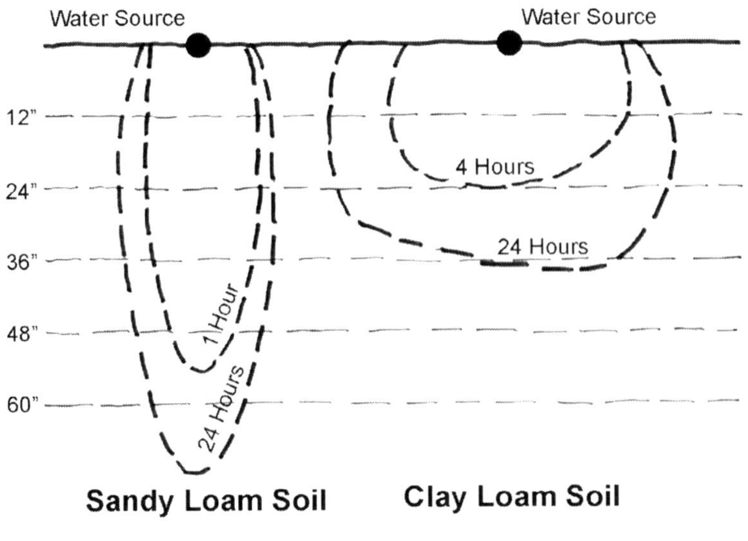

b

Figure 1.2.20. Water movement in soil.

a. Water movement at interfaces between different soil textures. *(Source: Adapted from Gardner 1979)*

b. Water movement from drip irrigation through sandy loam and clay loam soil. *(Source: Adapted from Brady et al. 1999)*

Water **infiltrates** into the surface of soil and then **percolates** through soil. The rate at which water infiltrates is a good indicator of both the soil type and level of compaction. Water infiltrates faster as sand content increases and compaction decreases. Disturbed or cultivated soil will infiltrate water much faster than adjacent undisturbed soil. The backfill soil around recently installed plantings or around a building foundation will be much wetter than the adjacent undisturbed soil.

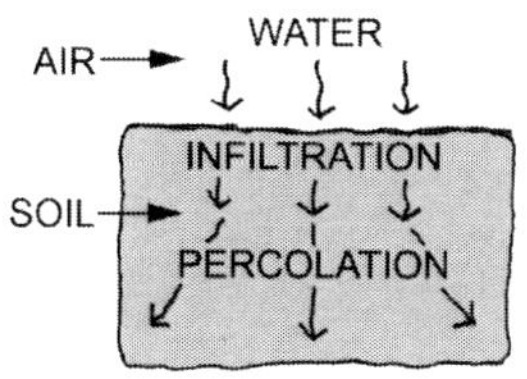

In lawn areas, fine, dense surface roots can dramatically reduce the infiltration rate of the soil, making it harder to apply water. This is why lawns are not as effective at reducing storm-water runoff as mulched shrub beds or forested areas. The infiltration rate of a golf green, which is approximately 10 to 15 inches per hour at installation, normally drops to under 5 inches per hour after the first growing season. The soil right below the lawn will still be fairly dry after a summer thunderstorm.

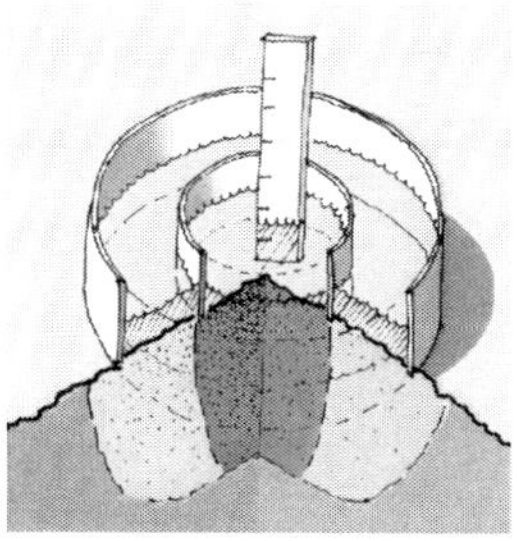

Infiltration rates can be measured in the field by a double-ring **infiltrometer**. The outer ring compensates for any horizontal movement of the water in the inner ring. The drop in water levels in the inner ring is measured at timed intervals. The infiltration rate of a soil may also be measured in a laboratory. The sample must be compacted to a known rate that represents the anticipated compaction in the soil after installation. Table 1.2.6 indicates the infiltration rates for several soils.

Table 1.2.6. Infiltration rates of several soil types. ***(Source: Adapted from Brady et al. 1999)***

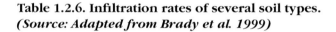

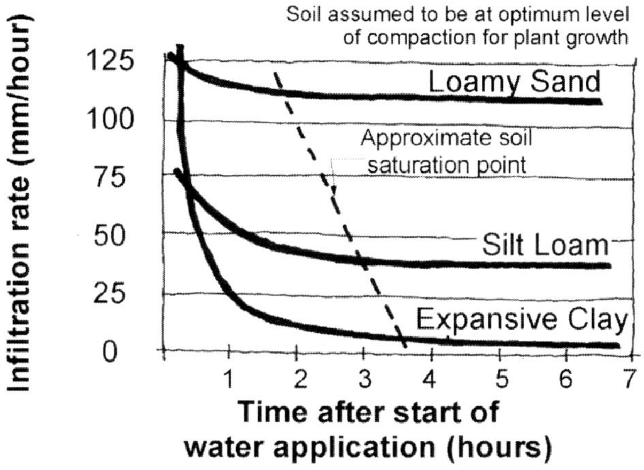

When two soils of significantly different pore sizes or compaction rates are placed on top of or adjacent to each other, they will form an interface. If the interface is distinct, meaning little to no mixing of the two soils, and the difference in pore size great enough, water applied to one will not percolate into the other until the first soil is completely saturated. This slows the movement of water in the soil and may cause water to be held in a layer of soil above the interface called a perched water table. In these extreme conditions, saturation caused by the interface can reduce plant growth or kill plants. If the two soils are mixed along the interface, percolation rates are significantly increased.

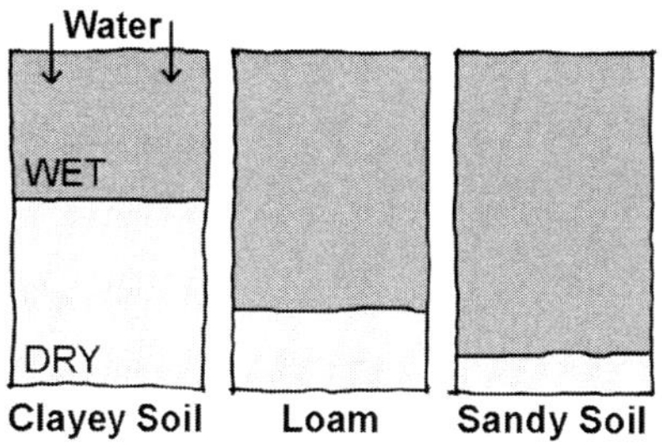

Figure 1.2.21. Soil percolation into several soil types. Water percolates through loam soils almost as fast as sandy soils, while clay soil percolates at nearly half the rate. *(Source: Adapted from Gardner 1979)*

A piece of filter cloth or the burlap around a root ball also acts as an interface and slows the flow of water into drainage layers or root balls. The creation of multiple interfaces at the face of the root ball and the edge of the planting hole, combined with the increased infiltration rates into the disturbed soil within the planting hole, may cause plants to drown. This principle will be discussed further in Chapter Six of Part 1.

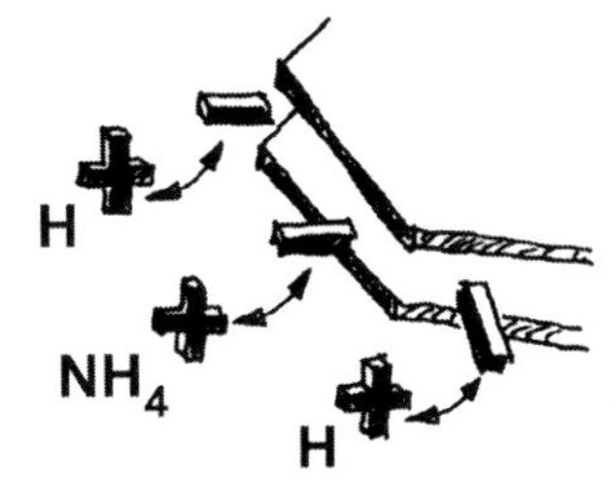

SOIL TEXTURE AND NUTRIENT HOLDING

Plants need chemical elements from the soil to grow. These elements must be held in the soil and available to the root. Many important nutrients, most notably nitrogen, are water-soluble and may wash through the soil. The relative ability of nutrients to be held in the soil is its **nutrient-holding capacity**.

Nutrient-holding capacity is a measure of soil fertility and is affected by soil texture and organic content. Clay holds onto elements better than silt or sand. Organic compounds in the soil are very efficient at holding elements. Clay soils and highly organic soils are the most fertile. Silty soils are somewhat less fertile and sandy soils are relatively infertile. Adding organic matter to a sandy soil will significantly increase its fertility. In Chapter Four of Part 1, we'll look at trees' chemical needs in greater detail.

OTHER PHYSICAL PROPERTIES OF SOIL

A number of other physical properties are important to know when trying to gain a better understanding of soil.

Soil Color

Color tells much of the story of a soil's origin and the forces that were present during its weathering processes. It is a significant factor in the identification of soil type and the understanding of conditions that affect plant growth.

Soil coloration begins with the color of the parent material. The most common minerals that form soil parent materials are quartz, which is white or gray; feldspar, which is red to pink; and limestone, which ranges from white to gray. These particles are then coated or stained by other elements in the soil and by organic compounds. Iron is a common staining element in the soil and can take on a wide range of color from bright red to yellow, dull gray or blue-gray, depending on the level of oxygen in the soil. Organic compounds are black, dark gray, or dark brown, and normally coat over any previous color, dulling or masking that color.

Soil scientists use specific color designations found in the Munsell Soil Color Charts to record soil color and to communicate soil identity. The nomenclature system identifies a color name along with numerical designations that rate the color's hue, value and chroma. For example, "dusky red—2.5YR 3/3." These notations will appear in soil descriptions in soil surveys, and the reader must consult the Munsell guide to understand the code.

The following are some general guidelines on how various colors in soil are interpreted as well as how several key soil factors affect color. As with all things in nature, there are exceptions, and an informed opinion relies on all the clues at hand.

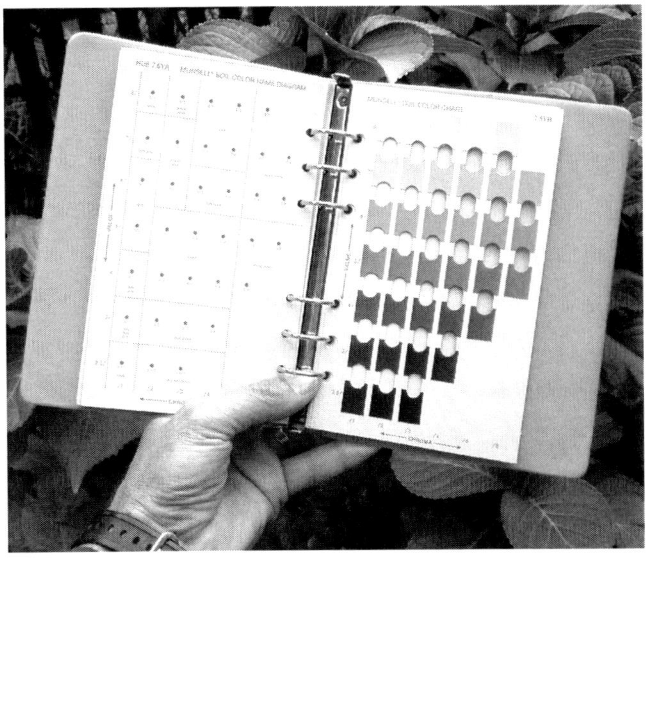

Figure 1.2.22. Munsell chart.

Black: Soil very rich in humus and other decayed organic matter.

Brown or browner tones of other colors: Soil particles coated in organic matter.

Red or orange: Iron in well-drained soil. Note that soil commonly called "red clays" in the southern United States are sometimes not actually clay soil, but can be a wide range of soil types coated with oxidized iron.

Yellow: Often iron in slower, but still adequately, draining soil.

White: Leached soil, soils without iron.

Gray: Iron in very slow draining soil or seasonally high water levels.

Blue-gray: Iron in soils that are not draining or which were formed at times when the soil was saturated or submerged.

Mottled soil: Multicolored or a change in soil color indicates fluctuating drainage or an indication of the level at which drainage rates change in the soil.

Soil Odor

Soil odor, especially when considered with color, is an important indicator of organic content and its drainage capability. The intensity of the smell of biological activity in the soil, characterized as musty-sweet, indicates the degree of organic matter and good drainage. A rotting, sour smell indicates limited to no drainage as the smell intensifies. Little to no odor indicates low organic levels, or the soil may be too cold, wet, or dry for biological organisms to be active.

Learning to identify these odors and their strength by soil type and season is an important skill in identifying soil conditions. Odor will be stronger in late spring and early summer, when soil temperatures are elevated and in soils with higher organic content and or better drainage. These soils are identified as **aerobic**. This sweet odor will be reduced in colder months and in soils with less organic content or poor but adequate drainage. The sour odor in poorly draining soil is the result of bacteria that can function in an oxygen-deficient environment and indicates soils that are saturated for long periods of time. These soils are identified as **anaerobic**. In the next chapter, we'll go into more detail about soil bacteria.

Soil odor can also be used to identify some types of human activity—in particular, the introduction of hydrocarbons into the soil. An oily smell will remain in the soil for long periods after contamination.

Soil Temperature

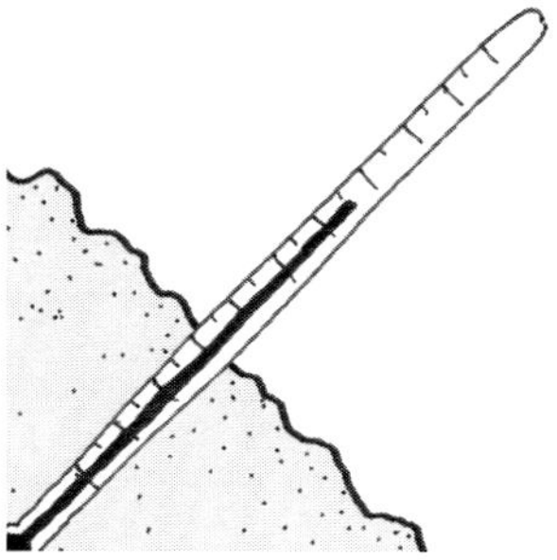

The temperature of soil affects its organic qualities and its ability to support plant growth. Soil temperatures can vary significantly with soil conditions and location. North slopes are colder as they receive less sunlight. Colder areas of the country with cooler summer soil temperatures, below 75 to 80°F, oxidize organic matter more slowly, resulting in larger accumulations of organic matter.

Biological activity in the soil generates heat, and soil high in organic matter is slightly warmer in winter. Mulch and forest leaf deposits also contribute to higher winter and lower summer soil temperatures by their insulation value. Frost depth in forests is generally closer to the surface than in nearby non-forested areas. Gardeners still line the bottoms of glassed cold frames with organic matter, which helps raise the temperature in the structure sufficiently to overwinter sensitive plants.

Table 1.2.7. The relationship between soil temperatures and plant activity. ***(Source: Adapted from Brady et al. 1999, Craul 1992, and Graves et al. 1991)***

Soil Temperature (Fahrenheit)	
120	Nitrification stops above 120°F Roots killed above 120°F
110	
100	
	95°F approximate limitation to root growth
90	
	Nitrification ideal at 65-85°F; slows above 95°F
80	
	75°F optimum for plant growth
70	
	Lower limit of nutrient uptake 60-65°F
60	
50	Root tip growth begins at 50°F
40	40°F and lower limits bacterial activity Root activity stops below 40°F
30	
	Roots killed by cold are species-specific

Roots have greater difficulty absorbing water in cold soils, so plants tend to grow more slowly. Evergreen winter burn is the direct result of slow water absorption in cold soils.

Drier soils tend to be warmer in the spring and summer and colder in the fall and winter, as they transfer heat and cold better from the air. Conversely, poorly drained soils are colder in the spring and summer, but warmer in fall and winter.

Cold or warm soils may each be limiting or advantageous to root growth, depending on the degree of temperature change, the type of plant, and local conditions. In nature, soil temperature plays a significant role in which plants are successful in different locations. In urban landscapes, when designers have not planned properly, soil temperature can be a contributing factor in the failure of plantings. Soil temperatures immediately under pavements can rise above the root-limiting range. Larger planting holes with mulch or vegetative ground cover, combined with better soils at lower levels below the pavement, can significantly reduce soil temperatures in the root zone. Table 1.2.07 shows the association of soil temperatures and plants.

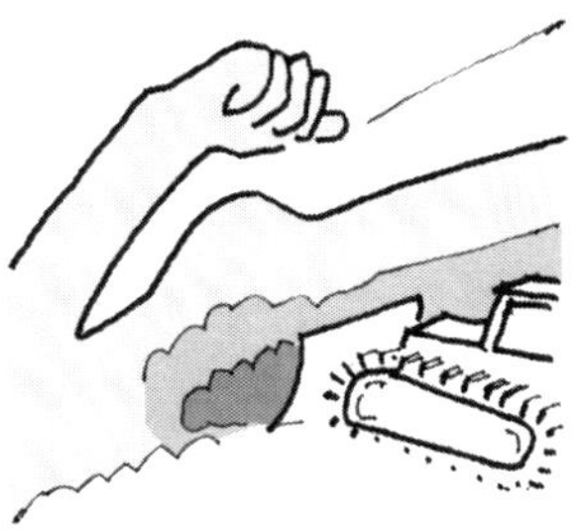

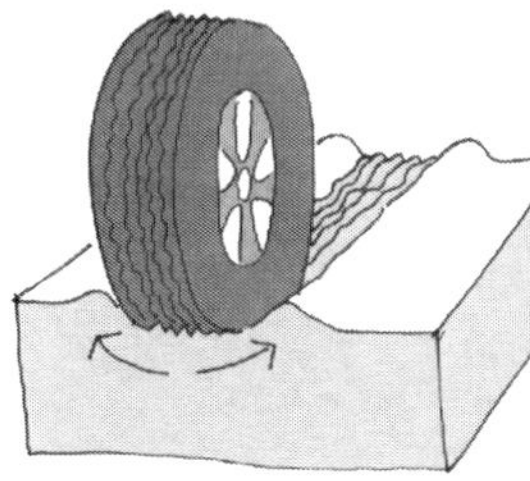

Soil Strength

Soil strength is the measure of a soil's ability to withstand stress without failing, deforming, or breaking, and is defined in several different ways. When the intended use of a soil is to serve as the foundation for a permanent structure, soil engineering properties help designers set compaction amounts and methods. Soil strength is a function of how cohesive the soil is, and how much water is in it. **Soil cohesion** is a combination of the friction between the particles and the strength of the particle bonds, the electrostatic bonds of the clay and silt particles, organic glue, and other cements.

Cohesive soils are generally considered to have a minimum of 15 percent clay. Below that amount they are non-cohesive. Cohesive soil may be graded to steeper slopes than non-cohesive soils. Dry soil is slightly stronger than when damp. As water is added to soil, the clay particles become lubricated and are forced apart, breaking particle bonds and making the soil less stable. If enough water is added, the soil becomes **plastic** or may be molded. This is the point where a soil begins to "pump" when driven over by a heavy vehicle. If even more water is added to the soil, at some point, it becomes a liquid and flows if vibrated.

Non-cohesive soils are sandy soils with less than 15 percent clay and rely on the friction between the particles for strength. Unlike cohesive soil, non-cohesive soils generally get stronger as they get wetter. The water forms temporary bonds between the sand particles that had no bonds when dry. As the soil reaches saturation, this gain is greatly reduced. Experienced sand-castle builders always have their younger siblings tote large amounts of wet sand from the shore to the castle site to ensure structural integrity of turrets and ramparts.

TESTING SOIL FOR PHYSICAL PROPERTIES

Testing and sampling of soil for physical properties will be discussed in Part 1, Chapter Seven.

REFERENCES

Key References

Brady, Nyle C., and Ray R. Weil. 1999. *The Nature and Properties of Soils*. 12th ed. Prentice-Hall, Upper Saddle River, NJ. 881 pp.

Craul, Phillip J. 1992. *Urban Soil in Landscape Design*. John Wiley & Sons, New York, NY. 396 pp.

Gershuny, Grace, and Joe Smillie. 1999. *The Soul of Soil: A Soil-Building Guide for Master Gardeners and Farmers.* 4th ed. Chelsea Green Publishing Company, White River Junction, VT. 173 pp.

Graves, W.R., J.R. Joly, and M.N. Dana. 1991. Water use and growth of honey locust and tree-of-heaven at high root-zone temperature. *Hortscience* 26:1309–1312.

Lichter, J.M., and P.A. Lindsey. 1994. Soil compaction and site construction: Assessment and case studies. In Watson, G.W., and D. Neely, eds. *The Landscape Below Ground.* International Society of Arboriculture, Champaign, IL. 222 pp.

Macbeth Division of Kollmorgen Instruments Corporation. 1994. *Munsell Soil Color Chart.* Revised ed. Kollmorgen Instruments, New Windsor, NY. http://usa.gretagmacbethstore.com.

Trowbridge, Peter J., and Nina L. Bassuk. 2004. *Trees in the Urban Landscape: Site Assessment Design and Installation*. John Wiley & Sons, Hoboken, NJ. 205 pp.

U.S. Department of Agriculture, Natural Resources Conservation Service. 2002. *National Soil Survey Handbook*. http://soils.gov/technical/handbook.

Other Information

Abramson, L. W., T.S. Lee, S. Sharma, and G.M. Boyce, *Slope Stability and Stabilization Methods*. 1995, John Wiley & Sons, Inc. New York, NY.

Daddow, R.L., and G.E. Warrington. 1983. *Growth-Limiting Soil Bulk Densities As Influenced by Soil Texture*, 1983 WDG Report. WSDG-TN-00005, USDA Forest Service.

Gardner, W.A. 1979. *Water Movement in Soil.* Publication CRSOAS 32(2). American Society of Agronomy.

Hillel, Daniel. 1980. *Fundamentals of Soil Physics*. Academic Press, San Diego, CA. 413 pp.

Neely, Dan, and Gary W. Watson, eds. 1998. *The Landscape Below Ground II.* International Society of Arboriculture, Champaign, IL. 265 pp.

Plaster, Edward J. 2003. *Soil Science & Management*. 4th ed. Delmar, Clifton Park, NY. 384 pp.

Roberts, John, Nick Jackson, and Mark Smith. 2006. *Tree Roots in the Built Environment.* Crown Copyright, The Stationary Office, Norwich, England. 488 pp.

Singer, Michael J., and Donald N. Munns. 2002. *Soils: An Introduction*. 5th ed. Pearson Education, Upper Saddle River, NJ. 429 pp.

Watson, Gary W., and Dan Neely, eds. 1994. *The Landscape Below Ground.* International Society of Arboriculture, Champaign, IL. 222 pp.

Watson, Gary W., and E.B. Himelick. 1997. *Principles and Practice of Planting Trees and Shrubs*. International Society of Arboriculture, Champaign, IL. 199 pp.

Other Resources

OpenAg.info's Soil Science Encyclopedia. 2007. http://www.openag.info/wiki/index.php/Soil_Science_Encyclopedia.

PART ONE

3
The Biological Properties of Soil

This is one of the shortest chapters in this book, but it may be the most important. Without biology, a collection of mineral particles is truly just dirt.

Healthy soils are alive with organisms. From bacteria and fungi to insects and small mammals, the **soil food web**—a complex community of organisms that depend on each other as food sources—serves as the soil's living component. One cup of forest humus scooped up from below the dry leaf litter may contain billions of organisms that play critical roles. Learning to identify the sweet, musty smell emanating from these organisms is the first step in understanding the soil food web.

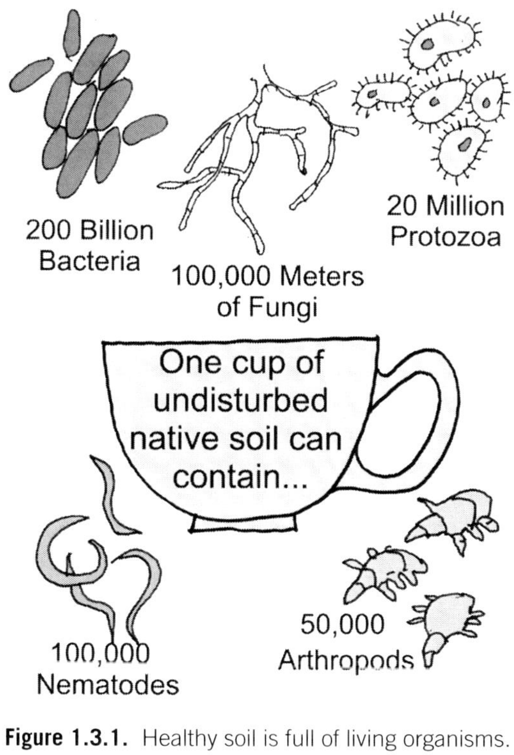

Figure 1.3.1. Healthy soil is full of living organisms.

The foundation of this web is a continuous flow of decaying organic matter supplied by the trees and plants growing in the soil. Unfortunately, humans are especially adept at interrupting this flow of organic matter. The "messy" parts of plants are moved to the landfill, which removes an important food source for the soil organisms.

Like any ecological system, the soil food web is designed to recycle material and fit closely with other parts of the overall ecology. Biological activity breaks down and reformulates chemicals, assists in the decay of dead and dying material, and binds soil particles together to help form soil structure. This improves aeration and drainage, while increasing the soil's water- and nutrient-holding capacity.

From a human perspective, the soil food web has "good guys" and "bad guys." Some parts of the web are highly beneficial to the plants used in the landscape, while other parts attack plants, causing all manner of diseases. From the food web perspective, there are no real good guys or bad guys—only a lively competition that constantly culls less-competitive organisms such as plants that are in the wrong place or that are stressed from other causes. Rarely do the bad guys in the food web successfully attack a healthy plant growing in an appropriate site with soil suited to that plant's requirements. Humans are constantly trying to control the bad guys, but often these controls also eliminate many important good guys and throw the web out of balance.

Landscape designers have learned to select plants that are less dependent on this web. Adding water and fertilizer to replace this organic function compensates for lower levels of soil biology, but doing so further throws the web out of balance. If the profession can learn to develop soils with sustainable food webs, it can reduce maintenance costs while broadening the diversity of plant types.

Reinstating the flow of organic material to the soil will require considerable rethinking of the way the urban landscape is designed and maintained. One thing is certain: The less a design covers the soil with paving, the easier this task will be.

THE SOIL FOOD WEB

The soil food web (Table 1.3.1) is a gigantic refinery and processing system as well as a construction company, an industrial giant running 24/7 with billions upon billions of tiny factories. These factories produce fertilizer, pesticides, and insecticides; the concrete and steel for soil structure; and the roads and pipelines needed to build a healthy soil. While a full explanation of these interrelationships is beyond the scope of this chapter, the important point is that biological activity is vital to maintaining a healthy soil. For further information regarding these interrelationships, see *The Compost Tea Brewing Manual* by Elaine R. Ingham (listed in Other Information at the end of this chapter).

Two of the most important boxes in Table 1.3.1 are in the lower left-hand corner, "Dead Material" and "Organic Matter." These are the recycling functions. All organisms eventually die and form the base of the food chain for other life forms. Also notice that arrows from one box to another indicate that the higher life form consumes the lower form. Eliminating a lower life form eliminates a food source for a higher life form. It is important to know when these different levels are in balance, and soil testing is now available that evaluates levels of protozoa, bacteria, nematodes, and fungi.

Table 1.3.1. The soil food web. Organic matter moves through the food chain, gradually increasing the complexity and stability of carbon compounds, and producing rich humus at the end. ***(Source: Adapted from Soil Foodweb)***

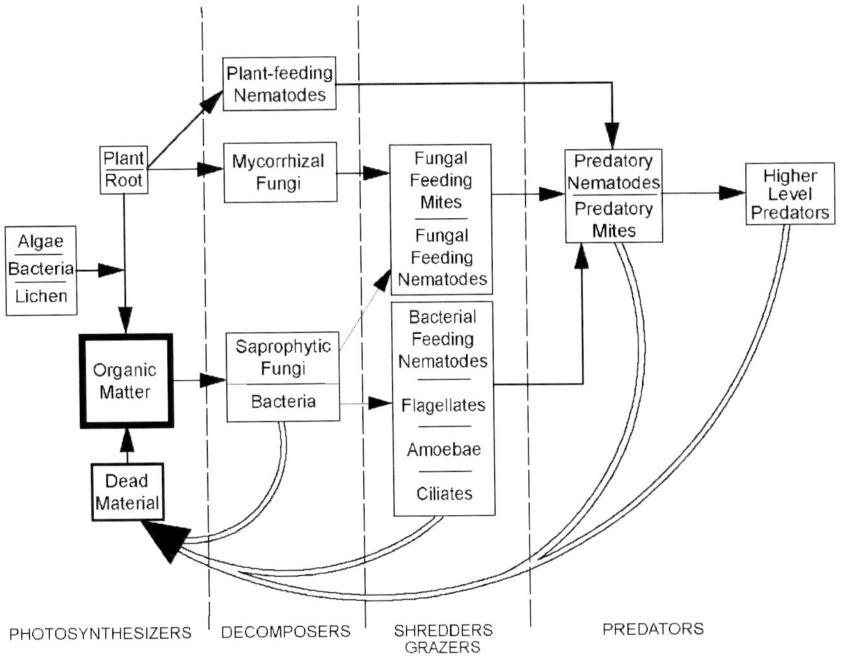

CARBON CYCLE

Carbon is the basic building block of all life forms. The carbon to support the soil food web comes from plants. Plants remove carbon from the air to build plant mass through photosynthesis. All other organisms obtain carbon by consuming carbon-based organisms. When a plant dies or leaves fall, this organic matter accumulates on the surface of the soil and decays. It is moved deeper into the soil by the various organisms of the soil food web. Plant roots also contain large amounts of carbon, which is consumed by the web when the root dies. Finally, carbon is added directly to the soil from living roots. They secrete carbohydrates known as **exudates** into the thin layer of soil around the root known as the **rhizosphere**. Soil bacteria in the rhizosphere use this carbon source. In return, they lower soil pH and process soil chemicals into forms available to the plant.

Each time carbon-based molecules are consumed and reprocessed by the various layers of the food web, they become increasingly complex in their structure and more stable to decay. Some carbon eventually ends up as a stable humic compound in the soil, but the vast majority eventually is returned to the air during respiration and decay. Large amounts of the world's supply of carbon are temporarily locked up, or sequestered, at or within the crust of the earth, in long-term states such as coal, petroleum, wood, and soil carbon or in short-term states such as the bodies of bacteria, insects, plants, and animals (including humans). Figure 1.3.3 shows the carbon cycle.

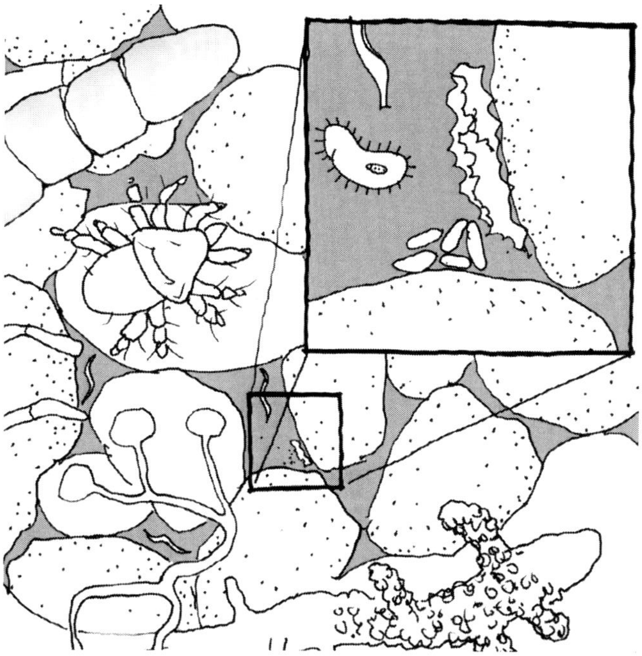

Figure 1.3.2. Soil organisms take on many forms from earthworms to bacteria. Each fills a niche in the soil food web.

Trees and Carbon Sequestration?

Human activities are releasing much of the locked-up carbon back into the atmosphere. Global CO_2 levels have already been raised and are changing the climate of the planet in the process. It has been proposed that the United States plant trees to sequester some of the released carbon as atonement for its carbon transgressions.

Unfortunately, if enough trees were to be planted each year to sequester the carbon use of every U.S. inhabitant, in just a few years, trees would have to be planted on every acre in the country that can support trees, including all usable farmland. Trees are not very efficient at sequestering carbon. Prairie grass is actually more efficient. Trees are more important for reducing carbon emissions by cooling cities.

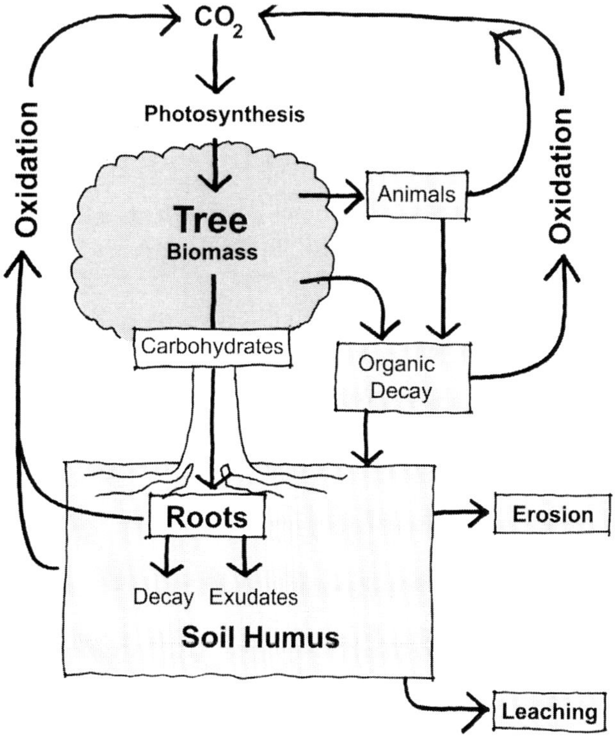

Figure 1.3.3. Carbon cycle.

Each stage of the process produces different carbon-based compounds used by different parts of the web. Wood and dried leaf sources tend to supply carbon to fungi, while decaying green leaves and microbial, insect, and animal matter tend to supply carbon to bacteria. Organic decay happens rapidly at first, then stabilizes in the form of **humus**, the form in which carbon can remain in the soil as complex chemical compounds. Humus has an enormous cation exchange capacity, or ability to hold soil nutrients, and is a major contributor to soil fertility.

Fungi break down organic matter and knit the soil particles together with strands of **hyphae**, which are rootlike extensions of the fungi. Fungal growth opens up the soil for water and nutrient infiltration and helps to create large amounts of micropores to hold water for plants.

A special class of fungi, called **mycorrhizae**, grows along with the roots of plants and helps roots absorb water. While mycorrhizae are important, they are only one small aspect of the soil food web. The landscape profession, to the extent that it focuses on soil biology at all, often sees mycorrhizae as the primary biological element in the soil. Unfortunately it is not that simple. If active mycorrhizae are deficient in the soil, much of the soil food web is also going to be deficient. The causes of this deficiency must be addressed before adding mycorrhizal spores to the soil.

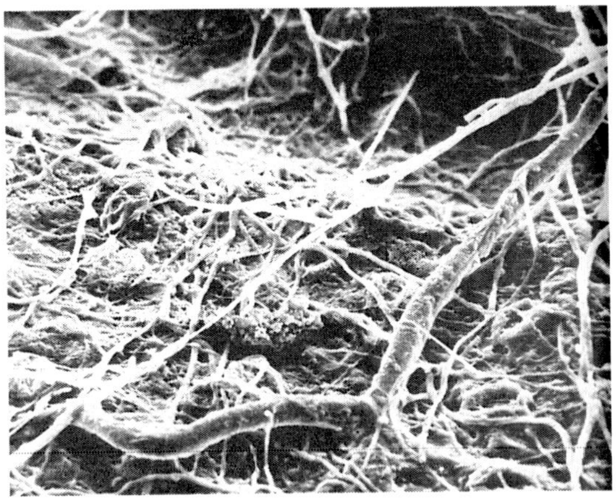

Figure 1.3.4. Hyphae of soil fungi hold soil particles together. *(Photo credit: Soil Foodweb)*

Bacteria and other microbes play an important role by digesting simple forms of carbon and other chemicals in the soil. They process needed proteins and acids, making a wide range of chemicals available to the plant. These acids break down soil particles into smaller sizes, but they also stick soil particles together, help build soil structure, and increase a soil's cation exchange capacity. The excretions from soil microbes are organic "glues."

These glues combine with other types of "glue" in the soil, including the fluid from decaying organic matter, clay films, dissolved chemicals in soil water, small roots, hyphae of soil fungi, and excrement from other living organisms ranging from bacteria and protozoa to worms and animals.

Organic glues are powerful. Try this experiment: Take two sections of newspaper and soak one in water and the other in milk. Let the paper dry. The pages that were wet with water will easily separate, while the milk-soaked pages will be stuck together. That is organic glue at work. Whole milk is stronger than reduced-fat milk; skim milk will not work as glue because most of the fats have been removed.

Organic activity affects soil chemistry. It changes pH and the concentration of important elements in the soil. The nitrogen cycle is a good example of the role of soil biology in soil chemistry. Nitrogen is plentiful in the atmosphere as N_2. However, most plants cannot utilize N_2; a complex set of mechanisms is required to convert the nitrogen into plant-usable forms.

Some plants are said to "fix" nitrogen for their use, but this function is actually performed by microorganisms that live in the root nodules of those plants. Nitrogen gas in the air can be changed to plant-usable N_3 by lightning and washed into the ground with rainwater. This is why plants seem greener immediately after a thunderstorm. Because nitrogen is water-soluble, some other process is required to hold the nitrogen in the soil. Plants take up some of the waterborne nitrogen, but much of it simply washes through the soil. Microbes process much of the nitrogen into more stable, plant-usable forms. We'll go into more detail about soil and plant chemistry in the following chapter; for now, it's important to remember that biological and chemical processes interact in ways that create healthy soils.

ORGANIC MATTER

The amount of organic matter gives an indication of the level of organic activity that may be possible in the soil and allows a soil lab to estimate the amount of nitrogen available. In most soils, the organic component is fairly shallow, restricted to a zone where oxygen, water, and organic material come together. Excluding the layer of actively decaying matter on the surface, the organic content, by weight, in good topsoil is normally around 3 percent.

Organic matter is measured by oven-drying the sample, weighing it, burning it to remove all organic material, and weighing it again. Less than 1 percent is low. Between 1 percent and 5 percent is normal for a wide range of soils. Soil with greater than 10 percent organic matter is high and may experience significant soil shrinkage when installed as a planting medium.

Adding organic amendments such as compost to a soil is not equal to adding organic matter to soil. A 10 percent (by volume) addition of well-composted organic amendment will result in only a 1 percent (by weight) gain in soil organic matter when measured by standard soil testing procedures.

Two factors, temperature and moisture, influence the amount of organic matter that can accumulate in soil and the rate at which it decays. In temperate climates, the soil's organic component is reasonably stable, with the active part of the system processing food sources at about the same rate as food sources are produced. These soils are generally structurally stable and, with the exception of the top organic layer, can support light structures like walks, walls, and even small houses while still supporting root growth. In wet or low areas, organic food sources may accumulate faster than they can be processed—and soft, spongy, unstable soil can result.

In the built environment, sometimes well-intentioned plans call for too much organic matter, greater than 15 percent by volume, to be added to the soil. Too much organic matter creates similar unstable soil conditions that cannot support even light structures. In extreme cases, overly organic soils can be too unstable to allow trees to remain upright.

Warmer soils generally increase the production of plant-based organic material, but they also increase the rate of decay of organic matter. Drier soils generally decrease the production of plant-based organic material. As illustrated in Figure 1.3.5, hot and dry areas of the United States are low in soil organic matter, while cool and moist areas have high accumulations. Microclimatic factors found on urban sites will affect this accumulation and can cause rapid decay of organic matter in hot, dry plazas or organic buildup in shaded, poorly drained sites.

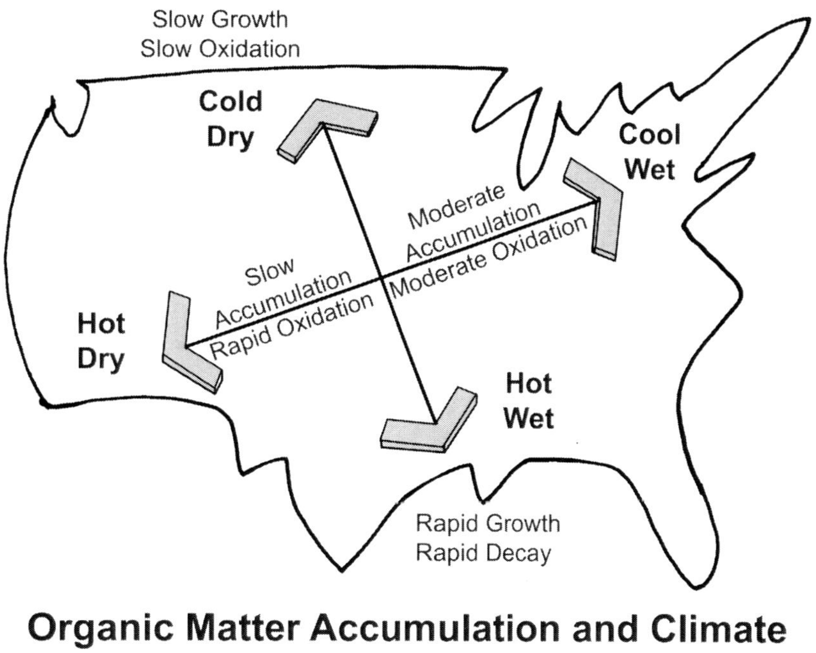

Figure 1.3.5. The relationship of climate to organic matter accumulation.

SOIL MOISTURE AND ORGANIC ACTIVITY

Moisture influences the type of soil food web that develops. Well-drained soil has sufficient air exchange for microbial activity that requires oxygen. This soil is called **aerobic**. The living matter in aerobic soil produces the sweet, musty smell associated with composting leaves. As soil drainage rates are reduced, or the organic matter becomes more stable, or the soil temperature is lowered, the odor of organic decay is gradually reduced.

Once the soil is saturated and the soil water becomes oxygen-deficient, the soil becomes **anaerobic**. The types of bacteria that live in soil without oxygen emit a sour, sulfurous odor. The longer the soil is in a saturated state, or the greater the organic content, or the warmer the temperature, the stronger the odor. Anaerobic soils are generally unable to support growth of most of the plant species used in the urban landscape.

Figure 1.3.6. Soil odor is one way to gauge the health of the soil food web and soil drainage. *(Photo credit: Bill Fountain)*

ASSESSING SOIL BIOLOGY

Simple tests can determine the health of the most important types of organisms that make up the soil's living matter. Much of the soil food web is invisible to the eye but not to the nose. A soil's odor is one of the best initial tests of soil biological activity. A second quick test is to look for larger insects and worms. These predators feed on the invisible parts of the food web. A soil lacking in large insects may not have a healthy food web.

Odor alone, though, can be an inaccurate, even misleading, indicator of soil quality. It is not quantifiable and subject to too many variables. However, as one of many simple tools in evaluating urban soils, it is useful when considered with many other observable variables such as color, state of plants growing in the soil, soil history, and soil texture in determining if a soil may be usable or not. The presence of odor is likely a good indicator of soil conditions, while the lack of odor may not have any relevance.

Seasonal temperature fluctuations and the state of organic matter in the soil also affect soil odor. The odor of soil in the cold winter will not be as strong as that in spring. As summer temperatures increase, biological activity may decrease and the soil odor will diminish. In the fall, the infusion of new organic matter with cooler temperatures will increase the strength of soil odor. Learning to know these smells is critical in learning to identify soil conditions. Soil ecology varies with soil type and region. A local soil ecologist will know what insect varieties to expect and what they may indicate. Ironically, one of the most commonly accepted indicators of good soil, the earthworm, might not always indicate a healthy ecology. Not all regions of the United States have native populations of earthworms, and when observed, they may actually be exotic invaders that have changed the equilibrium of that ecosystem. Earthworm invasions are a good way to illustrate how humans have influenced the soil food web.

The Skinny on Earthworms

(Source: USDA NRCS)

Earthworms are considered by soil scientists to be one of the most important large organisms in the soil. They till the soil, bringing organic matter deep into the upper soil horizons. Worms crawling across the ground indicate that the soil was saturated in a recent rain. In agricultural soils, earthworms normally number 50 to 200 per square yard. Earthworms in moist Southern climates, urban, and agricultural soils are a good indicator of a healthy soil. As exotic species, though, they can dramatically alter northern forest soil ecology.

After the Ice Age, forests in glaciated regions evolved in soils devoid of earthworms. The European invasion of this continent brought with it species of earthworms that are now changing the soil ecosystems of these forests. Earthworms rapidly decompose the leaf layer in the spring, making it difficult for species that need a heavier leaf layer to reproduce and may consume important fungi needed by some types of plants. These changes favor the germination of different types of trees and understory plants. Invasive exotic earthworms have also been linked to increased soil erosion and nitrogen runoff due to the rapid breakdown of organic matter. Moving plants, mulch, and soil from one area to another continues the spread of this problem.

So, if you enjoy fishing, do not contribute to the problem by discarding those leftover baitworms at your favorite fishing hole.

HUMAN INFLUENCE ON THE SOIL FOOD WEB

All human influence alters the biological balance of soil. Compaction limits the air and water that can enter the soil and the level to which organic matter can be distributed in the soil. Modifying drainage makes the soil wetter or drier, which alters the rate of decay of organic matter and changes the types of microbes found in the soil. Grading and tilling increase the amount of oxygen in the soil, increasing the rate of organic matter decay. Fungicides, herbicides, and pesticides kill off populations of microbes and insects. These chemicals cannot differentiate between beneficial parts of the web and the particular organism toward which the application is directed. Synthetic nitrogen fertilizer, unless the dose is carefully controlled, can dramatically increase levels of nitrogen in the soil, which favors certain types of microbes. Removing dead trees, limbs, leaves, and other decaying matter robs the food web of a major source of food. Even something as benign as a misplaced earthworm has an impact.

A web that is out of balance is more susceptible to disease and insect attacks on plants that might otherwise have been kept in check by other parts of a balanced web. The response to insect or disease infestations is often more chemical controls, which further throw the web out of balance. Since the web is cyclical, removing even one part of the cycle can impact large portions of the system.

The destruction of the soil food web is sometimes mitigated by replacing the natural organic cycle with imported organic material in the form of mulches and

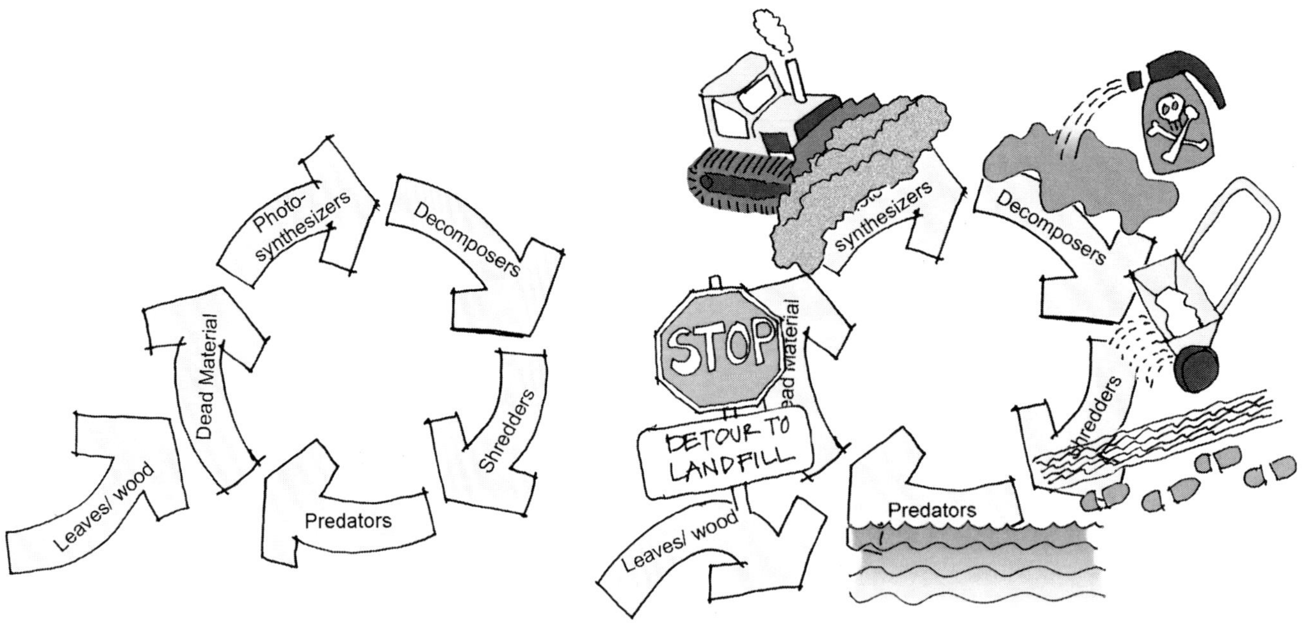

Figure 1.3.7. Human influences on the soil food web: diversion of organic matter, soil grading, chemical applications, compaction, and poor drainage.

fertilizers. This comes at great environmental cost not only to the specific project, but also to many other parts of the environment. Figure 1.3.7 shows human influences that interrupt the soil food web. Reducing the destruction of elements that support the soil food web and restoring favorable conditions is vital to creating sustainable landscapes. This process begins at the first land use decision and carries through to every detail of landscape design and maintenance.

TESTING FOR ORGANIC CONTENT AND SOIL BIOLOGY

Testing and sampling of soil for organic content and soil biology properties will be discussed in Part 1, Chapter Seven.

REFERENCES

Key References

Brady, Nyle C., and Ray R. Weil. 1999. *The Nature and Properties of Soils*. 12th ed. Prentice-Hall, Upper Saddle River, NJ. 881 pp.

Brinton, William F. 2002. *Earth Plant and Compost*. BIO-Dynamic Farming and Gardening Association, San Francisco, Calif. 73 pp.

Craul, Phillip J. 1992. *Urban Soil in Landscape Design*. John Wiley & Sons, Inc., New York, NY. 396 pp.

Gershuny, Grace, and Joe Smillie. 1999. *The Soul of Soil: A Soil-Building Guide for Master Gardeners and Farmers*. 4th ed. Chelsea Green Publishing Company, White River Junction, VT. 173 pp.

Other Information

Edwards, Clive A. 1998. *Earthworm Ecology.* CRC Press, Boca Raton, FL. 389 pp.

Ingham, Elaine R. 2003. *The Compost Tea Brewing Manual.* 4th ed. Soil Foodweb Incorporated, Corvallis, OR. 88 pp.

Plaster, Edward J. 2003. *Soil Science & Management.* 4th ed. Delmar, Clifton Park, NY. 384 pp.

Pouyat, Richard. 2002. Earthworm effects on forest soils. *Proceedings of the State of the Forest Symposium: Ecological Issues Regarding Highlands Forest Degradation and Restoration*, October 2002.

Roberts, John, Nick Jackson, and Mark Smith. 2006. *Tree Roots in the Built Environment.* Crown Copyright, The Stationary Office, Norwich, England. 488 pp.

Silvia, David M., et al. 1999. *Principles and Applications of Soil Microbiology.* Prentice-Hall, Upper Saddle River, NJ. 550 pp.

Singer, Michael J., and Donald N. Munns. 2002. *Soils: An Introduction.* 5th ed. Pearson Education, Upper Saddle River, NJ. 429 pp.

Other Resources

Soil Foodweb, Inc. 2007. http://www.soilfoodweb.com

PART ONE

4
The Chemical Properties of Soil

Modern plant management is overly focused on a few chemicals in the soil. Fertilization is often the first maintenance option selected when plants appear stressed. While plants often respond quickly with lush growth, chemical fertilizers have many unintended side effects if applied too heavily. Overfertilization has the potential to pollute water and may make the plant less healthy. That lush growth is like the rapid weight gain in athletes when they take dietary supplements. They are not necessarily healthier, just larger. Healthy soil rarely needs the amounts of fertilizer commonly applied when there has not been a soil test to determine a recommended rate. Soil biology can change soil chemistry. In many cases, the plants might be better served by adding only organic matter rather than chemical fertilizers.

Fertilizer Is Not Plant Food

People often call fertilizer "plant food" or say they are "feeding the tree." Plants actually make their own food by combining carbon, hydrogen, and oxygen during photosynthesis. Plants do need small quantities of other elements to facilitate growth functions. These elements are more comparable to vitamin supplements consumed by humans. A balanced human diet supplies all the supplemental minerals required for growth and good health. Supplements are only needed when something is out of balance. Plant scientists get upset when soil scientists call essential elements in the soil "nutrients," thinking that it reinforces the notion that these elements are food. However, in the soil science literature, the word "nutrient" is the accepted term. To be consistent with this literature, we'll use "nutrient" as a synonym for "essential element" where it serves to improve communication. But please remember, fertilizers are not plant food.

Soil chemistry is important when analyzing existing soils, making plant selections, writing specifications, and installing and maintaining soils and trees. Soil chemistry is a lot more than just fertilizer application rates. Soil and plant chemistry are intertwined with the physical and biological properties of soil.

Plants get all their carbon and some of their oxygen through the leaves. The leaves can also absorb other elements if made available by foliar application. Most of the required elements are absorbed from the soil by the roots. To be absorbed, they must be held in the soil in a form available to roots. Some elements, most notably nitrogen, are water-soluble, and may wash through the soil quickly.

CATION EXCHANGE

Soil holds onto many essential elements by a process called **cation exchange**. Atoms of positively charged elements, called cations, attach loosely to decayed organic matter, clay particles, and to a lesser degree, silt, by electrostatic bonds. Each particle is like a crowded bus with a limited number of seats. These negatively charged seats must always be filled with positively charged atoms. They are often occupied by hydrogen atoms that have weak positive charges. The cations of positively charged essential elements have a stronger charge and can bump the hydrogen molecules out of their seats, exchanging places, thus the name cation exchange. Negatively charged elements are called anions and attach to positively charged anion exchange sites in a similar way.

The number of cation exchange sites is based on the surface area of the particle. Clay particles are extremely small and have a large surface area in relationship to their volume. This larger ratio of surface area to volume means a clay soil has more places to attach elements. Organic matter has very complex shapes, giving them a greater ratio of surface area to volume. In larger particles like sand, this ratio is much lower. The more a soil can exchange cations, the greater its **cation exchange capacity** or CEC. This rate can be measured to evaluate the ability of a soil to hold nutrients. Understanding cation exchange will be key to understanding many chemical relationships in the soil.

Fertility refers to soil's ability to hold nutrients and make them available to the plant. Since clay and decayed organic matter have the highest **cation exchange capacity**, clay soils and highly organic soils are often the most fertile. Sand has poor cation exchange due to its large particle size, so sandy soil is significantly less fertile. Soil pH also significantly impacts soil fertility.

Table 1.4.1. Cation exchange capacity (CEC) rates. *(Source: Brady et al. 1999)*

Soil / material	CEC range
Humus	150–250
Compost	35–75
Clay loam soil	20–35
Silt loam	12–30
Sandy loam	8–15
Loamy sand	5 or less

Not all clays have the same cation exchange value. Expansive clays have dramatically higher CEC values than more stable clays due to a complex layered structure that absorbs water as well as offering more surface area for cations. Table 1.4.1 indicates the range of CEC rates for different soils. Note that humus, the completely decayed form of organic matter, has a much higher CEC level than compost, indicating the importance of using completely decayed organic matter.

It is not easy to add clay to sandy soil as a way of increasing its fertility. The clay tends to remain in clumps surrounded by the sand. Organic matter, on the other hand, is fairly easy to work into soil and is the most effective way to increase soil fertility. Organic matter is not permanent in soil and must be continuously replenished. Designs of planting areas must allow long-term management of the organic matter.

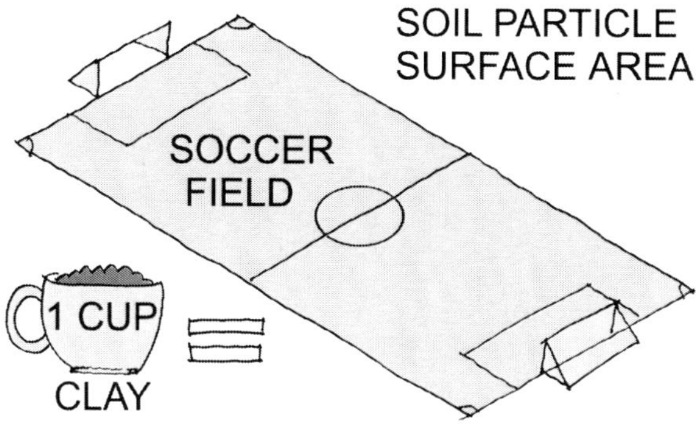

Figure 1.4.1. The surface area of the particles in one cup of clay soil is equal to the surface area of a soccer field.

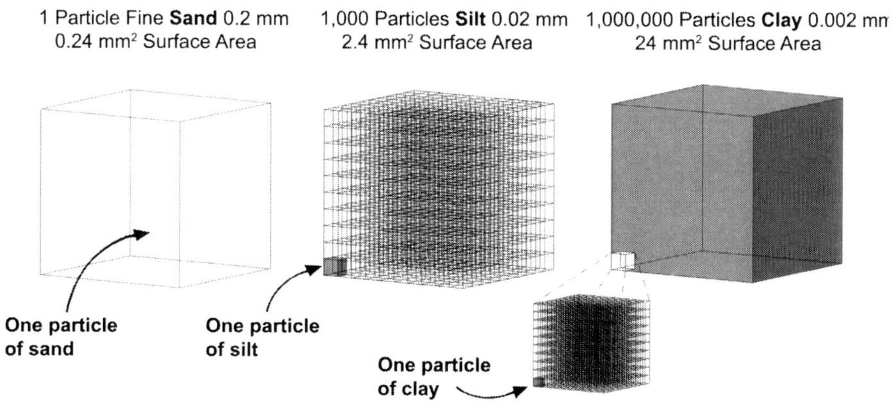

Figure 1.4.2. Comparison of the surface area of sand, silt, and clay particles.

PLANT ESSENTIAL ELEMENTS IN SOIL

More than 100 elements are found on the earth, but only about 17 of these are essential to plant growth. Essential elements can be divided into three groups. The first is the three base elements, oxygen, carbon, and hydrogen that the plant uses in large amounts to make the sugars that build all parts of plant structure. The second is a group of six elements called **macronutrients** used by the plant to facilitate many general functions.The third is a group of seven elements called **micronutrients** that the plant uses in very small quantities for specialized functions. Table 1.4.2 lists these essential elements.

Table 1.4.2. Elements required by plants.

Base elements	Macronutrients	Micronutrients
Oxygen (O)	Nitrogen (N)	Boron (B)
Hydrogen (H)	Phosphorus (P)	Chlorine (Cl)
Carbon (C)	Potassium (K)	Cobalt (Co)
	Calcium (Ca)	Copper (Cu)
	Magnesium (Mg)	Iron (Fe)
	Sulfur (S)	Manganese (Mn)
		Molybdenum (Mo)
		Zinc (Zn)

Plants extract oxygen (O), hydrogen (H), and carbon (C) as CO_2 from the air and soil, and as water (H_2O) from soil water. They convert these three elements into sugar during photosynthesis, with excess oxygen released into the air. Much of the weight of a tree is carbon atoms that are literally sucked out of the air. In the next chapter, we'll discuss photosynthesis in more detail.

The amount of each macro- and micronutrient needed in the soil is extremely small, normally expressed in parts per million. Plants are adapted to fairly small quantity ranges of each element. Too much or too little will begin to change plant appearance, color, growth rate, drought tolerance, and/or susceptibility to insects and diseases. Significant variations may result in growth deformities.

Permanent changes to soil fertility are difficult to maintain. Most soil will tend to revert to its original level if chemical fertilizer applications are stopped. A designer's first choice should always be to select plants that fit the chemical properties of the existing soil.

Adding micronutrients directly to the soil to address a deficiency is generally not recommended. These elements are needed at such low levels that there is a good chance of adding too much and creating problems in the opposite direction. Elevated micronutrient levels might be the first warning sign that a chemical pollutant or other historical activity has altered the soil, such as previous farming practices.

Plant Response to Chemicals

Plants respond to deficiencies and excesses of each element in different ways. The relationships between soil element levels and plant responses are quite complex, and require the training of a soil scientist or horticulturist to draw conclusions and make recommendations.

Some of the ways plants express chemical imbalances include yellow, purple, or red leaves; stunted growth; small, limp, or curled leaves; and deformity of the branch tip buds. These symptoms can also reflect overwatering, diseases, insects, or the presence of other toxic chemicals, particularly herbicides. In urban soils, multiple factors are often at work, complicating any diagnosis.

Evaluating plant problems and determining their causes is beyond the expertise of most designers, despite many clients' expectations in this area. Knowing when to consult a trained expert is critical. At the end of this chapter are several good references to guide the interested reader deeper into the subject of chemical/plant relationships. These references include numerous color photographs and descriptions of plant problems. Designers will find that having these resources in their libraries may be the first step in determining when to call a soil or horticultural consultant.

MACRONUTRIENTS

Nitrogen, phosphorus, and potassium are the focus of most agricultural fertilizer programs. They are easily produced, easily applied to fields, and make significant improvements to crops when applied in the correct amounts. In landscape applications, there are different constraints and goals, and these three elements need to be considered in relationship to other soil factors.

When soils are deficient in chemicals, many people turn to fertilizers. In most situations, particularly with nitrogen deficiencies, it is possible to correct the imbalance simply by adding organic matter, using soil organisms to process the needed chemicals. Organic matter offers slower but longer-lasting results while improving the soil biology and the relationships between plants and soil.

The Father of Fertilizer Recants

Justus von Liebig, 19th-century German chemist, is credited with discovering the link between nitrogen and plant growth, and along with it much of the chemistry that created modern synthetic fertilizers. Toward the end of his life, he recognized that synthetic fertilizers had created an agricultural system that robbed the soil of important recycling functions needed to keep soil healthy. He then championed the beginnings of the principles of organic farming: "After I learned the reason why my fertilizers were not effective in the proper way, I was like a person that received a new life."

(Photo source: University of Texas Library)

Nitrogen (N)

Nitrogen, the most important of the essential elements, is a key component in most fertilizer. It is found in chlorophyll, which is responsible for photosynthesis in the plant. Chlorophyll makes a leaf green.

Nitrogen is not chemically stable. It is water-soluble and can also volatize into the air directly from the soil. It is constantly changing its chemical form by combining with different numbers of oxygen and hydrogen atoms. Some of these nitrogen compounds are useful to plants and some are not.

Nitrogen is usually present in urban landscapes in sufficient quantities for trees, especially in soil that has adequate organic content. Excessive nitrogen causes too much soft growth in plants, making them more susceptible to some types of insect infestations. Too much nitrogen, like too much of any other element, can be toxic to plants. Excess nitrogen normally leaches out of the soil into waterways, where it may harm aquatic wildlife by causing algae blooms that reduce waterborne oxygen levels.

Most of the earth's nitrogen is atmospheric gas, delivered to plants through the soil either as a dissolved compound from rain or as a compound immobilized by microorganisms in the soil food web. It is estimated that the natural decay of leaves in a forest applies approximately 1 pound of nitrogen per acre per year to the soil.

Chemical fertilizers easily, but temporarily, infuse nitrogen into soil. They can be sprayed directly on foliage for rapid, short-term greening of leaves. For a longer-term boost, adding well-composted organic matter to the soil can stimulate nitrogen release through the soil food web.

Figure 1.4.3 shows the nitrogen cycle, moving between a gas state to a plant-available form and back to a gas.

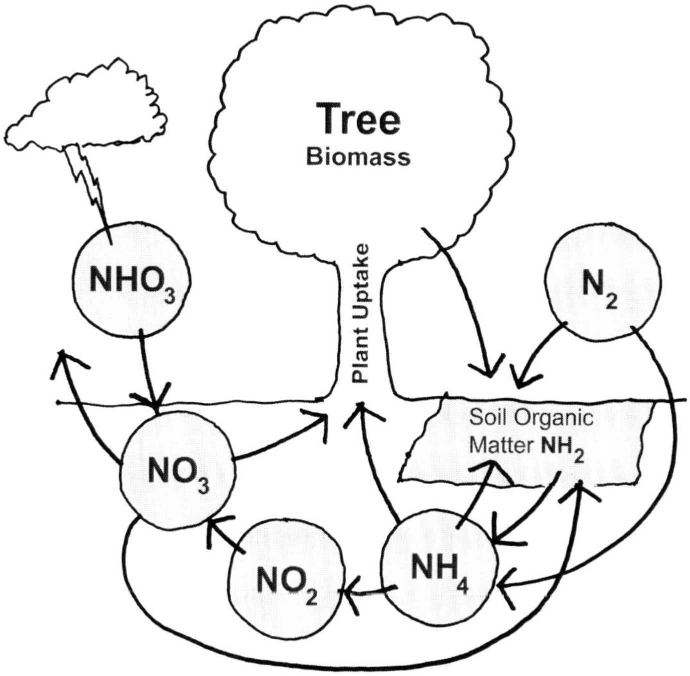

Figure 1.4.3. Nitrogen cycle.

Carbon/Nitrogen Ratio

The microorganisms that make up the soil food web need both carbon and nitrogen. Different sources of organic matter have different proportions of carbon and nitrogen, referred to as the carbon/nitrogen ratio. In nature the C/N ratio is well balanced. Decay is slow, with multiple sources of organic matter. In constructed or managed landscapes, artificially supplied organic matter can short-circuit this natural process and throw the C/N ratio in the soil out of balance.

Natural and agricultural soils have a stable C/N ratio between 10:1 and 20:1. When organic matter is added to soil with a higher C/N ratio, some of the plant-available soil nitrogen is used to digest the extra carbon. While much of this nitrogen is returned to the soil when the soil organisms die, a temporary soil nitrogen deficiency can result. Ground wood, straw, and dried leaves can have a C/N ratio of up to 100:1. Using fully composted organic matter with a C/N ratio of no more than 30:1 provides the soil with organic matter that is more useful to plants.

Because nitrogen is so unstable in the soil, it is difficult to measure and is often not usually included in standard soil tests. Since a healthy soil food web makes nitrogen and other elements available to the plant, soil testing labs often estimate nitrogen levels based on the level of organic content. In some soil types, nitrogen levels in soil can be estimated by measuring the more stable forms of this element.

Phosphorus (P)

Phosphorus is essential to many functions in the plant, particularly respiration and root growth. It is relatively insoluble in water and therefore difficult to add or leach out of the soil. Because it is so stable, phosphorus can reach very high levels in some heavily fertilized agricultural soils.

Phosphorus levels are normally low in most sandy soils. Trees rely on mycorrhizae to help absorb this element. Much of the phosphorus is made available by the soil food web and is found in the humus layer. Despite the fact that phosphorus assists in root growth, plants in low-phosphorus soils tend to have larger root systems, possibly to make them more efficient in gathering the limited resource.

Potassium (K)

Potassium helps with carbohydrate production and aids in water absorption. This element is soluble in water, but leaches less readily than nitrogen. It is a common element that weathers from several mineral materials. Most of the available potassium is held on cation exchange sites, and soils with low CEC rates are often low in available potassium. The soil food web contributes little to the available potassium, but adding organic matter will improve available potassium levels to the extent that CEC rates are improved.

Calcium (Ca)

Calcium is abundant in most natural soils. Its main function is root tip and branch tip development. Deficiencies are evidenced by dieback of the terminal bud.

Magnesium (Mg)

Magnesium is abundant in most natural soils but tends to be deficient in acidic, coarse sandy, and low-clay-content soils. It aids in the uptake of other nutrients and is essential in chlorophyll production. Deficiencies are evidenced by the yellowing of lower and older leaves, and plants may be less resistant to drought and disease.

Sulfur (S)

Sulfur is abundant in most agricultural soils due, in part, to the large amounts applied in fertilizers. Significant amounts also come from atmospheric pollution, which returns to earth in rain. As use of lower sulfur-based fertilizers increases and clean air regulations continue to improve air quality, sulfur deficiencies may become more commonplace. Sulfur-deficient soil may produce plant symptoms similar to nitrogen deficiencies.

MICRONUTRIENTS

Deficiencies of micronutrients are not prevalent because such small amounts are needed. Many of the micronutrients are metals associated with 20th-century industrial products and activities and are therefore more likely to be at elevated levels in urban areas. Plant responses to an overabundance of these nutrients are varied and likely beyond the expertise of the typical designer to recognize. For an excellent review of micronutrients, the reader is referred to *Soil Science and Management* by Edward Plaster.

Micronutrients should always be included in any soil test and the results interpreted by a soil scientist or horticulturalist.

pH

pH may be the most significant aspect of soil chemistry, and designers ignore soil pH at great peril. It affects many plant choice decisions and is difficult to permanently change. Much has been written about the pH suitability of each plant, and this information is very accessible.

pH is somewhat mysterious to the person who has no chemistry background. In simplest terms, it is a measure of the acidity or alkalinity of the soil. A soil with a pH of 7 is considered neutral. Distilled water, pure H_20, has a pH of 7 and is tasteless. Adding only a small amount of other elements will change the pH and the taste of water.

The H stands for hydrogen. pH is actually a measure of the concentration of positive hydrogen atoms in a solution. The higher this concentration, the more acidic the material. The p stands for "negative logarithm." Thus, pH is shorthand for the negative log of hydrogen. The use of a negative log means that the higher the concentration of hydrogen, the lower the pH number.

More importantly, pH must be understood for its logarithmic relationship. Each single digit change in pH represents a ten-fold change in actual acidity. Thus a pH change in the soil from 7 to 8 means that the soil is ten times as basic (or alkaline) as the neutral 7. A pH change from 7 to 9 means that the soil is now 100 times more basic than neutral. Figure 1.4.3 represents this on a graphic scale. This logarithmic effect must be considered when deciding how far away from a plant's normal pH range one dares to go when matching pH to plant requirements.

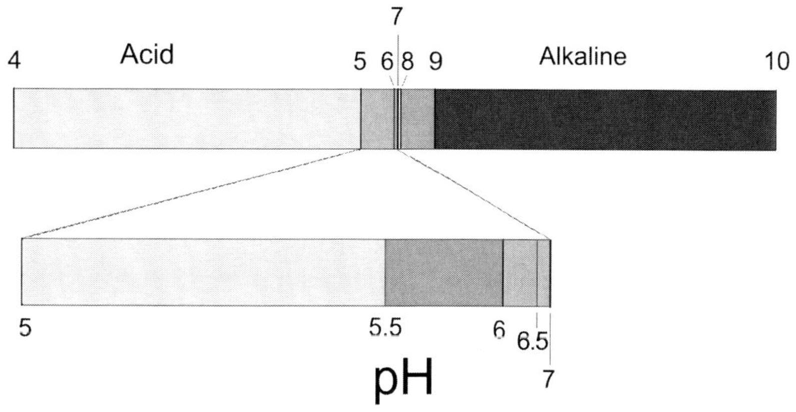

Figure 1.4.4. pH as a graphic scale.

Table 1.4.3. pH of various compounds. *(Source: Adapted from Brady and Harris)*

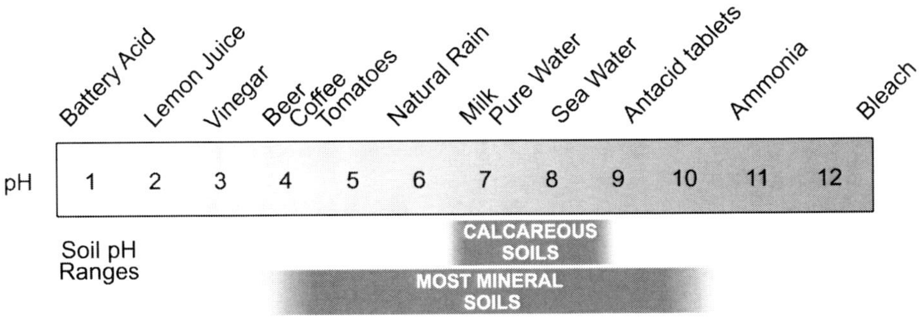

Acidic solutions below 7 will turn a litmus paper pink. Basic or alkaline solutions above 7 turn it blue. Hydrangea flowers are known to have different colors in different pH soils. In an interesting twist, they turn from pink to blue as the pH becomes more acidic, the opposite of litmus paper. Table 1.4.3 shows the pH of different compounds and familiar liquids.

pH

For coffee it's 5; for tomatoes it's 4;
While household ammonia's 11 or more.
It's 7 for water, if in a pure state.
But rainwater's 6 and sea water is 8.
It's basic at 10, quite acidic at 2
And well above 7 when litmus turns blue.
Some find it a puzzlement. Doubtless their fog
Has something to do with that negative log.

—Doris Kolb
(Used with permission)

pH Adaptability

Often, plant texts will not use specific pH numbers, using instead descriptive terms when mentioning the adaptability of particular plants. The terms "pH adaptable" or "wide range of pH" are not defined and must be interpreted. These terms are not consistent within the available texts, especially at the extremes of high and low pH levels, and it is advisable to consult multiple sources. Plants are more likely to exhibit stress symptoms in soils that have too high a pH than in soils with a pH lower than their optimum range. Factors such as moisture, soil temperature, organic content, salt, and soil texture also affect a plant's adaptability to different pH conditions. Temper your decisions with personal knowledge of the plant and soil conditions.

Table 1.4.4 depicts the USDA nomenclature for different pH ranges. However, note that authors of plant texts, including the widely used *Manual of Woody Plants* by Michael Dirr, do not always follow these official designations.

Table 1.4.4. pH levels and USDA nomenclature. *(Source: USDA)*

USDA pH Classification	pH range
Ultra acid	<3.4 (toxic to most plants)
Extremely acid	3.5–4.4 (restrictive to most plants)
Very strong acid	4.5–5.0
Strongly acid	5.1–5.5
Moderately acid	5.6–6.0
Slightly acid	6.1–6.5
Neutral	6.6–7.3
Slightly alkaline	7.4–7.8
Moderately alkaline	7.9–8.4
Strongly alkaline	8.5–9.0 (restrictive to most plants)
Very strongly alkaline	>9.1 (toxic to most plants)

Adaptable pH as Viewed by Dirr

The following is clarification on the meaning of "adaptable pH," sent to the author by Michael Dirr in 2004.

pH is the most misunderstood cultural factor in plant growth. Most plants are amazingly adaptable over a wide range. pH affects availability of essential elements and is probably most deleterious in the 7 and higher numbers because of iron, manganese, etc., tie-up. The visual symptoms like chlorosis are obvious. At the low end of the scale, say pH 4, plants seldom flash symptoms. Certainly growth could be reduced, but there is typically no basis for comparison. The Dirr "adaptable" means the plant grows without obvious discontent over a wide berth from 4 to 7, perhaps a half unit +/– either way.

Soil testing labs may provide an additional pH number called a **buffer pH**. This is designed to help determine liming requirements by measuring inactive or reserve hydrogen in the soil. Consult the lab recommendations for liming requirements, but do not use the buffer pH when evaluating a soil's ability to support particular plants.

Why Is Soil pH High or Low?

A number of factors establish the pH of a soil. Soil to some degree reflects the acidity of the parent material. Granite, sandstone, and shale produce acid soil; soft limestone produces calcareous, or alkaline, soil. Plant growth tends to acidify soil, as do nitrification and water leaching through soil. All of these factors tend to concentrate acidic soils in the eastern half of the United States and the Pacific Northwest.

In areas where the evaporation rate exceeds the precipitation rate, evaporating water pulls dissolved calcium and sodium to the surface. Organic accumulation is lower, as is the rate of root growth. All of these factors tend to make the soil more alkaline. In the eastern part of the Great Plains, the factor of low annual rainfall converges with the limestone bedrock to produce large areas of alkaline soil.

In urban areas, concrete and masonry construction leach lime into the soil, raising pH. The pH of irrigation water can change soil pH over time and should be checked.

pH and Essential Element Availability

As pH changes, the plant availability of each essential element in the soil changes. Iron deficiency in pin oak is a classic example of this change. Leaves may turn yellow due to a lack of iron in the tree, even as the soil test indicates plenty of iron but an elevated pH.

Adding a chelated iron supplement to this soil is only a temporary solution. (Chelating an element attaches it to an organic molecule so that it is readily available to the plant.) Trees may be able to absorb some of the chelated iron, showing an initial improvement, but as time passes the excess iron is again immobilized in the high-pH soil. Under these conditions, it may be necessary to treat the soil every four to six weeks during the growing season—a solution that is both expensive and impractical.

Plants that exhibit a wide range of pH tolerance can lower the pH of a thin (1 mm wide or less) area of soil around the absorbing root known as the **rhizosphere**, allowing the uptake of elements that are immobilized at higher pH levels. In the next chapter, we'll go into more detail about the rhizosphere.

Table 1.4.5. Availability of essential elements at different pH levels. The gray box shows the range of pH for adaptable plants.

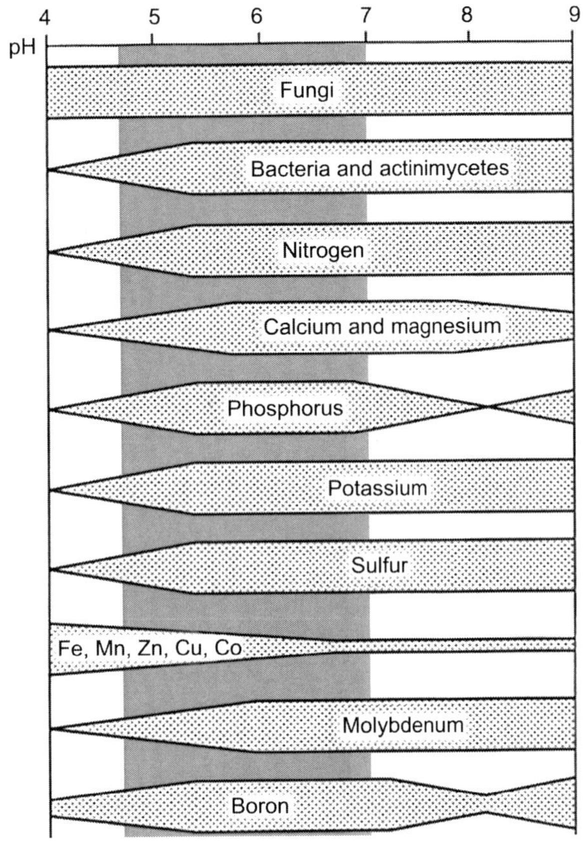

Figure 1.4.5. Salt crusting on top of soil.

While high pH can keep chemicals from entering the plant, low pH can concentrate certain elements. A pH of 5.5 or lower can cause aluminum, manganese, and iron to reach toxic levels in soil. Depending on soil types and other conditions, these elements may begin to occupy too many soil cation exchange sites, displacing other essential elements. Root growth slows, and water and element absorption declines.

Changing pH

pH is difficult to change because it is tied to the fundamental composition of the soil. It is almost always best to select plants that are compatible with the existing soil pH. However, if soil pH must be changed, applying lime will raise the pH, and applying sulfur will lower it.

Lime produces stable changes in the pH, while sulfur's pH-lowering ability is only temporary. Clay soils and soils with high organic content require more lime or sulfur to achieve the same effect than would be needed in sandy soil, due to the higher number of cation exchange sites in clay. Tables in many sources can help calculate the approximate amount of lime or sulfur to be added to raise or lower the pH, but it is best to follow the recommendations of the soil-testing lab.

Lime and sulfur are most effective when worked into the top 6 inches of the soil, and most rate charts assume this method. If planted areas are mulched, remove the mulch before applying the material. Incorporating amendment material into the soil is difficult in established planting areas, and regular applications of amendments are required to lower pH. Working the soil around existing plants does great damage to the surface roots and may offset the advantage of the application. Water-mixed forms of lime or sulfur products can reduce the need for working the soil, but also increase the frequency of application, the risk of overapplication, and the cost. Lowering the pH of irrigation water has been effective in large sites where the water supply can be manipulated.

Compost manufactured from sanitary sewage sludge often has a high pH resulting from the use of lime to de-water the sludge. This type of compost may be used to raise pH, or may inadvertently raise the pH if not accounted for in the soil design.

SALT

Salts break down soil structure and aggregation of the surface soil particles. This can create surface crusting that reduces infiltration of water. Salts also damage the soil food web. If absorbed by the plant, they can cause leaf scorch or bud deformity. Most importantly, salts reduce the plant's ability to move water into the roots, limiting available water in the soil and causing drought symptoms in the plant. This last factor causes significant decline and death of plants, particularly urban trees.

Several different elements contribute salt to the soil. The three most common elements are calcium (Ca), magnesium (Mg), and sodium (Na). Any compound that includes one of these elements can raise the salt level of the soil. Mg- and Na-based salts are common in arid regions. Na-based salt is a more common problem in regions where winter ice conditions require the spread of salts on roads and walks.

Some salt is present in all soils, but reaches toxic levels in several ways. Synthetic fertilizers contain significant amounts of salt, and irrigation water also contains some salt depending on its source and treatment method. Bio-solids composted from sewage sludge can contain high levels of salt. De-icing salts contribute to salt levels in cold areas.

Fertilizers have published salt indexes and different fertilizers have significantly different salt amounts. In most soil, a salt index of 25 or below is considered low. Indexes above 50 in sandy loam soils and above 75 in silty clay loam soil are considered high. Printing salt indexes on fertilizer labels is not required, but the information is often available on the Internet.

Salt and Climate

In arid areas where evaporation exceeds rainfall, salts tend to build up on the surface of the soil due to evaporation of capillary water. This is particularly severe in irrigated soil. Water dissolves salt in the soil and fertilizer. As the soil dries out, these salts are left behind in the soil and can accumulate to toxic levels. Flushing the soil periodically with large amounts of water can lower salt levels if the dissolved salt can drain out of the soil.

In cold and wet climates, soil absorbs winter de-icing salt. While the soil temperature remains below about 45°F, trees normally do not absorb water, so salt levels are not damaging. Above this temperature, trees try to absorb water, but are limited by the salt concentration. De-icing salt may be flushed out of the soil during spring rains, particularly in soils that are well drained either through rapid percolation rates or steep topography. When spring rains are not early enough, the amount of rain not high enough, or a late-season ice storm is followed by rapidly warming temperatures, salt damage can be severe.

In cold and dry climates, soil may get salt from winter de-icing operations and then be faced with insufficient water availability to flush it away. Yearly accumulation of salts in the root zone should be expected and flooding of the soil in the spring may be required to mitigate the damage.

Is There Salt in the Air?

Michael Dirr observes that some trees are damaged by windblown salt while being tolerant of salt from soil water, while others exhibit the opposite traits. Salt blown inland from nearby ocean water or road salt water becomes a mist and blows into adjacent trees, coating the branches. This salt kills needles in many evergreen trees and stunts bud development in deciduous trees. There has not been sufficient work to produce a list of the sensitivity of different trees to aerial or soil-borne salt. Local knowledge and observation must play a role in selecting trees in vulnerable locations.

Salt Tolerance by Plants

The range of salt that different plants will tolerate is fairly broad. Factors include the type of soil, the time of year, weather cycles when the salt is applied, how quickly it is leached away, and the health of the plant before the salt application. A stressed tree in confined, compacted, or heavy soil might die from a relatively small dose of salt, while the same species that is healthy and growing in generous volumes of well-drained soil might not be affected by even larger doses of salt.

The measurable level of salt in the soil will change dramatically with time, especially if the soil is well drained. Salt levels in early spring that are high enough to kill trees might be at normal levels in the soil several months later after a period of rain or activation of an irrigation system. A tree may die from winter salt applications, but soil samples taken once tree decline is noticed may indicate low levels of salt. Collect soil samples to determine salt just before the earliest tree bud break.

Salt levels are normally measured by electric conductivity, expressed as mmhos/cm. This type of soil test can look at all forms of salt in the soil, regardless of the source. Some soil testing labs may test for parts per million (ppm) of sodium (Na). This is a reasonable test in areas of the country where de-icing salt is the primary cause of salty soil, but is not useful if other sources such as calcium (Ca) or magnesium (Mg) are suspected.

Table 1.4.6. Soil salt concentrations.

Salt concentration (mmho/cm)	**Interpretation**
0–2	Low level
2–4	Slightly saline; sensitive plants will be restricted
4–8	Moderately saline; many plants restricted
8–16	Strongly saline; only tolerant plants will grow
>16	Very strongly saline; very few plants will grow

Salinity (Na) above 600 ppm is considered to be limiting for some plants, and more than 1,000 ppm limiting for many plants. Table 1.4.6 shows the interpretation of plant sensitivity to several levels of soil salt concentration.

Managing Salt

When managing soils that are experiencing or expecting salt accumulation, use one or more of these techniques:

- Choose salt-tolerant plants.
- Develop well-draining soils by installing drainage systems three feet or more below the root zone and/or installing deep, well-draining soil.
- Use fertilizers with low salt indexes and reduce synthetic fertilizer use.
- Switch to non-sodium de-icing salts. Reduce salt usage and mix one part of salt to three parts of sand to reduce salt content. Salt loses its effectiveness below 15°F. Switch to an alternative de-icing method at colder temperatures.
- Flush soils with fresh water in the early spring before soil temperatures reach 45° F. Be aware that soils on the north sides of buildings tend to get more salt, and that retail and commercial districts often get heavier salt applications than residential areas.
- Mix gypsum into the surface of sodium-salted soils before flushing with water.
- In arid climates, apply mulch to the soil to reduce evaporation rates.

- In wet climates, at the end of the winter, remove mulch that contains salt accumulations and re-mulch.
- In arid climates, maintain irrigation to keep the soil evenly moist and avoid letting the soil dry out. Salt concentrations will be highest at the edge of the wet area of soil.
- Salt concentrations will be highest at the point where there is the greatest evaporation. Do not plant at the very tops of mounds where salt may accumulate.
- In cold climates, design low curbs along edges of planting beds, lawns, and tree openings in sidewalks to divert sidewalk water away from the planting soil.
- Increase soil volumes of planting areas to increase the health of trees.

CHEMICAL CONTAMINANTS IN URBAN SOILS

Many chemical elements in urban soils can cause concern for plant growth and may also limit human activity on these soils. Developers have a due-diligence responsibility to make reasonable efforts to determine if toxic levels of hazardous chemicals exist in the soil, and financing companies may require chemical investigation reports on commercial properties. These determinations are beyond the expertise of most design firms, and usually require hiring specialty investigators.

Call the testing lab before samples are taken to determine the required sample-collecting methods, and be sure to wash your hands after handling any soil.

Designers exploring a site during the analysis phase of a project may discover signs of hazardous material. A designer should be aware of the most basic signs of chemical contaminants. Ignorance of these materials does not absolve a designer of responsibility to alert the owner when signs of their likely existence are found.

In urban soils, hazardous material may turn up at anytime. In his book, *Urban Soil in Landscape Design*, Phillip J. Craul discusses this topic in great detail. The following is a general overview, starting with a review of common contaminants.

Heavy Metals

Heavy metals are residual materials from industrial and automotive activity. Fortunately, heavy metals are relatively immobile, but they can be absorbed into plants. They are dangerous to humans if ingested or if the plants are burned where people can breathe the smoke. They rarely cause problems with plants at the levels found in urban soils. Metals can be transferred to humans if they eat plants grown in these soils.

Lead is the most common pollutant metal. For many years, lead was added to gasoline. Although this practice ended in 1995 in the United States, soils along highways built before the ban contain varying amounts of lead. In urban areas, soil within 500 feet of congested interstates and heavy traffic arteries has been found to exceed the maximum acceptable EPA levels for lead. Lead also builds up in significant amounts around the base of old painted buildings. Soil should be tested at any site in areas where there is a possibility of vegetable gardens or children's play areas. Imported or purchased soils for these types of projects should also be tested for lead.

The presence of other heavy metals is difficult to predict. A good understanding of the human activity on the site, the result of a through historic soil analysis, will provide the best information on the probability of metals in the soil.

Testing soil for metals is expensive. It is impractical to test for all metals in all soils. Site analysis and degree of risk should be used to determine when these specific soil tests are warranted.

Hydrocarbons

Most hydrocarbons vaporize fairly quickly when exposed to air. The greatest danger is if they enter groundwater or contaminate surface runoff. At low concentrations, there is little impact to trees, but at high concentrations these pollutants can limit growth or even kill plants by filling pores with oils or gas. Buried fuel tanks, landfills, industrial sites, dry cleaner locations, and spills are the most frequent sources of hydrocarbons. Abandoned fuel tanks often let small amounts of fuel seep out as the tank corrodes. This oil will move into the root zone during rainy periods. Leaks in natural gas lines will quickly kill large trees by displacing oxygen in the soil. If a low-level leak is under the root zone, the tree may produce small leaves and stunted growth.

A petroleum odor in the soil when taking soil samples indicates hydrocarbons. Hydrocarbons seeping out of the ground will make an iridescent sheen on standing water, but note that this can be confused with the sheen made by decaying organic matter. Testing for hydrocarbons is too expensive for all sites. A sensitive nose and knowledge of the site's history are the best ways to determine the need for additional investigation.

Figure 1.4.6. Gassed tree.

Pesticides

Thousands of pesticides have been sprayed into the environment. Most have short active periods and will not hurt plants or people at the rates normally encountered. A few can remain active in the soil for long periods, limiting plant growth.

In some soil conditions, a few general-purpose herbicides have the ability to limit plant growth for up to three years. A few others may remain in the soil for longer periods under certain conditions.

Powerful herbicides were used along old railroad beds and at some industrial sites that are still active many years after application. Trees planted in this soil will establish but then die once the roots penetrate to the herbicide level.

Testing for the presence of pesticides is not practical without some indication that there is a problem. Observing the site's plant patterns and understanding its history may be the best starting points to determining the presence of pesticides. When purchasing soil, require documentation of all pesticides applied over the previous three years.

Is There Anything Nasty in the Soil?

Inexpensive germination tests can prove effective to see if there are chemicals in the soil that may impact plants. Place three samples of each soil and three samples from known, good-quality garden soil in small cups and spread annual rye grass seed on the surface. Moisten the soil in each cup with the same amount of distilled water each day, but do not overwater. Observe the germination and growth of the grass for about a week after germination. Slower germination and initial growth in one or more site samples may signal the need for further investigation.

Elevation of Manganese from Hardwood Mulches

Repeated yearly use of mulches from hardwood trees has reportedly caused an elevation of manganese in the soil, causing symptoms of iron chlorosis in plants. There is no effective way to reduce the manganese levels in the soil. Manganese should always be included in soil test requirements. Mulches from pine sources or yard waste compost, which uses leaves as a primary source, are low in manganese.

FERTILIZER AND MANAGEMENT OF SOIL CHEMISTRY

Construction and maintenance of urban landscapes invariably results in the interruption of chemical cycles. Fertile soil is replaced with less fertile soil, organic matter is removed, chemical-balancing soil food web relationships are damaged, soils are tilled or compacted, salts and other harmful chemicals are applied, soil is covered with impervious surfaces, and soil volumes are restricted. At each step the soil will become more dependent on human intervention to maintain a fertility level that supports plant growth at acceptable levels.

On the other hand, established trees can adapt to relatively low levels of nitrogen, phosphorus, and other elements and still appear healthy. Most fertilizer rates are designed to improve crop yields or lawn quality, which does not factor in to improving long-term health. Young or recently transplanted trees may benefit from some fertilization after they have recovered from initial transplant shock. But maintaining adequate water in the root ball is the most effective therapy for newly transplanted trees. Fertilizer application at planting should be guided by soil test results.

There is quite a bit of controversy about the effectiveness of fertilizer in urban tree maintenance. A committee of expert arborists convened at ISA's 2000 conference to discuss this subject could only manage to conclude that "fertilizer may, or may not, help, or harm, trees." The bottom line is: Only apply fertilizer if good data indicate low levels of essential elements in soil. Use fertilizer with slow-release, organic origins whenever a fertilizer is indicated.

Shrubs may require more fertilizer to keep plants flowering, especially in the shade of large trees where there is stiff competition for resources. Lawn areas require the most fertilizer, especially if irrigated, shaded by large trees, or subjected to compaction.

The first step in soil chemical management is testing to establish the existing levels of each essential element. It is surprising how often this step is omitted. The initial test should examine a broad area of information, while later tests can look at specific areas as needed. Retest the soil about a month after applying any supplemental chemicals. Yearly testing for specific areas of concern is generally useful for intensely managed projects. Less intense projects might need limited testing only when plants are not performing to expectations. Take a full battery of baseline tests every five years.

See Part 1, Chapter Seven for a full discussion of testing and sampling soil for chemical properties, and Part 2, Chapter Four for specification of fertilizer and soil additives.

REFERENCES

Key References

Brady, Nyle C., and Ray R. Weil. 1999. *The Nature and Properties of Soils.* 12th ed. Prentice-Hall, Upper Saddle River, NJ. 881 pp.

Costello, Laurence R., Edward J. Perry, Nelda P. Matheny, J. Michael Henry, and Pamela M. Geisel. 2003. *Abiotic Disorders of Landscape Plant: A Diagnostic Guide.* University of California, Division of Agriculture and Natural Resources, Oakland, CA. 242 pp.

Craul, Phillip J. 1992. *Urban Soil in Landscape Design.* John Wiley & Sons, New York, NY. 396 pp.

Gershuny, Grace, and Joe Smillie. 1999. *The Soul of Soil: A Soil-Building Guide for Master Gardeners and Farmers.* 4th ed. Chelsea Green Publishing Company, White River Junction, VT. 173 pp.

Lloyd, John, ed. 1997. *Plant Health Care for Woody Ornamentals: A Practitioner's Guide to Preventing and Managing Environmental Stresses and Pests.* International Society of Arboriculture, Champaign, Illinois, and University of Illinois Extension, Urbana, IL. 223 pp.

Plaster, Edward J. 2003. *Soil Science and Management.* 4th ed. Delmar, Clifton Park, NY. 384 pp.

Sinclair, Wayne A., Howard H. Lyon, and Warren T. Johnson. 1989. *Diseases of Trees and Shrubs.* Cornell University Press, Ithaca, NY. 575 pp.

Other Information

Derr, Jeffery F., and Bonnie Lee Appleton. 1988. *Herbicide Injury to Trees and Shrubs: A Pictorial Guide to Symptom Diagnosis.* Blue Crab Press, Virginia Beach, VA. 72 pp.

Harris, Richard W., James R. Clark, and Nelda P. Matheny. 2004. *Arboriculture: Integrated Management of Landscape Trees, Shrubs, and Vines.* 4th ed. Prentice-Hall, Upper Saddle River, NJ. 578 pp.

Johnson, Warren T., and Howard H. Lyon. 1991. *Insects That Feed on Trees and Shrubs.* 2nd ed. Cornell University Press, Ithaca, NY. 560 pp.

Roberts, John, Nick Jackson, and Mark Smith. 2006. *Tree Roots in the Built Environment.* Crown Copyright, The Stationary Office, Norwich, England. 488 pp.

Singer, Michael J., and Donald N. Munns. 2002. *Soils: An Introduction.* 5th ed. Pearson Education, Upper Saddle River, NJ. 429 pp.

Trowbridge, Peter J., and Nina L. Bassuk. 2004. *Trees in the Urban Landscape: Site Assessment Design and Installation.* John Wiley & Sons, Hoboken, NJ. 205 pp.

PART ONE

5
Tree Biology

A tree moves water from the ground to the leaves, where it combines with air during photosynthesis to make sugar molecules. This sugar is used to support the tree's growth and reproduction. Every part of the tree supports this basic function. Knowing how these parts work can add to a larger understanding of how to successfully grow trees in the urban environment.

TREES GROW

A tree must increase in size each year. Branches must get a little longer and the tree must form an entire layer of new wood on all surfaces each year. Most trees used in urban landscapes can be expected to grow to a very large size. It is surprising how many designers do not consider this simple fact when designing spaces for trees.

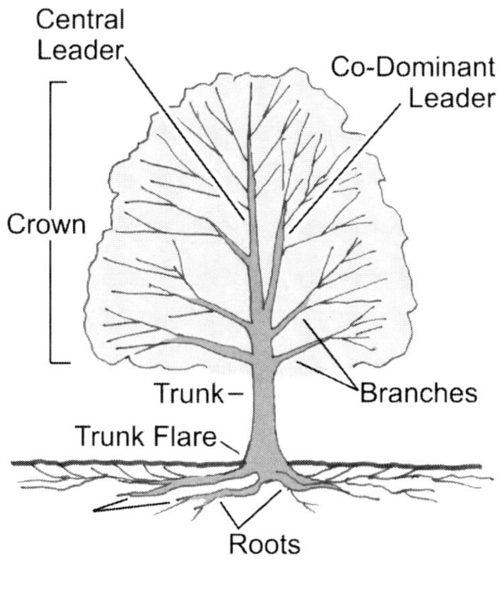

Figure 1.5.1. Primary parts of tree structure.

Figure 1.5.2. As trees grow, lower branches are either shed naturally or removed by pruning. Almost none of the branches that are on the tree when it is planted will remain at maturity.

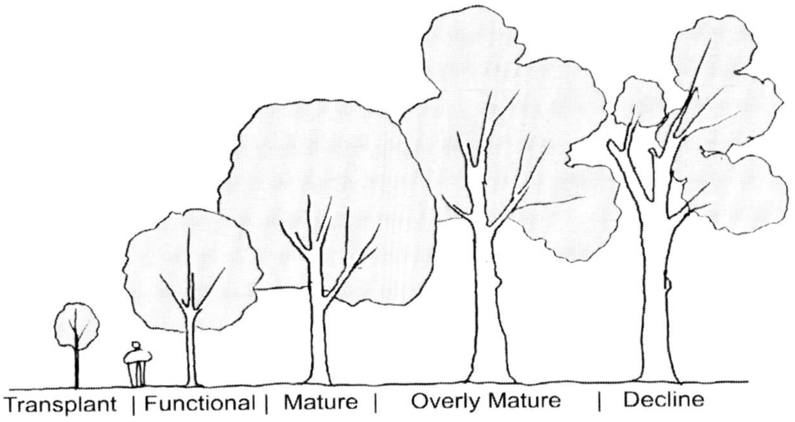

Figure 1.5.3. Trees mature and decline.

Trees Grow Old and Die

Trees are some of the largest organisms on earth. There are some fungi that are considered larger, but trees are by far the tallest and heaviest objects in nature. Trees also grow to be very old, with many individual trees living more than 1,000 years. These are special trees, blessed with being the right tree in the right place. The vast majority of trees live for shorter periods of 100 to 400 years. Trees in sites heavily influenced by human activity have even shorter life expectancies of 20 to 100 years.

Some books and professionals will tell you that trees in urban areas live for an average of around 10 years. Yet there is little data to support that assumption. Regardless of the exact average age of urban trees, the fact remains that despite widespread tree planting over the past 20 years, central business districts have sparse tree canopies.

The average age of a tree population is also a bit elusive, as one can easily tweak numbers to give results not relevant to the discussion. In nature, tens of thousands of seedling trees may sprout per acre each year, but only a few thousand of these live to see the first winter. The mortality rate remains dramatic for a few more years until small trees are established. Once the trees reach canopy closure, competition continues to kill off weaker trees at the rate of about 1/3 of the stand every ten years, until by age 300 or so a single tree may occupy several acres of ground. Factoring the entire stand of trees from those thousands of seedlings, the average life of all the trees sprouted may only be a few years.

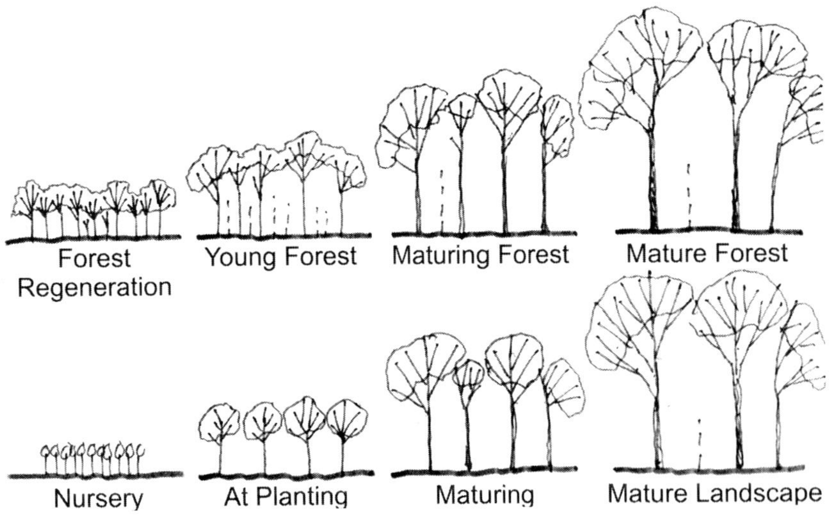

Figure 1.5.4. Natural and human-influenced tree aging. Competition is removing trees in both natural and human-managed stands of trees.

On the other hand, urban trees planted at wide spacing, in even average soil, might live to an average age that far exceeds the natural model. This is because wider spacing after the tree is transplanted from the nursery eliminates natural competition during the first decades of growth. The closer the tree spacing, the sooner the urban tree model begins to function like the natural model. Stands of trees in urban landscapes should be designed for the types of spacing in stable, mature forest, which is 35 to 50 feet. Figure 1.5.4 indicates the difference between natural and human-influenced tree aging.

So what are the important parts of trees' biology that allow them to reliably reach large sizes in landscape settings? Tree biology examines the factors that affect the growth, maturity, decline, and death of the tree. Tree physics looks at the structure of the tree, what keeps it upright, and what prevents large limbs from falling. While biology and physics are interrelated, they are often considered separately in the design process. This chapter will view them as inseparable.

ESSENTIAL PLANT FUNCTIONS

The two essential life functions of a tree are

- Photosynthesis, the production of the needed chemicals for growth processes.
- Respiration, the use of those chemicals in growth and decay.

During photosynthesis, the plant stores energy in the sugar molecules it makes. During respiration, the plant releases that stored energy as it uses the sugar molecules or when they decay.

Photosynthesis combines water and carbon dioxide in chlorophyll cells energized by sunlight to produce sugar and oxygen and storing energy. Respiration uses those molecules and oxygen to change the sugar molecule from one form to another, releasing energy and producing excess water and carbon dioxide.

Photosynthesis creates and stores sugar reserves as sequestered carbon-based molecules over the life of the tree. Respiration decays those reserves, continuing to release carbon long after the tree has died.

Photosynthesis

Photosynthesis can be seen as a fairly simple process of tearing apart and then recombining CO_2 from the air and water, using the energy of the sun to make sugar and oxygen. The tree uses the sugar and the oxygen goes back into the atmosphere. Life on earth could not exist without that excess oxygen, which comes from organisms as small as single-cell algae in the sea to the grandest of trees. All other non-green organisms reap the benefits. Figure 1.5.5 shows a simplified model of the photosynthesis process. It is probably not necessary to know how many C's and H's move through the plant to successfully design a landscape, but a simple understanding of this most basic of all life functions should be within the vocabulary of people who depend on it for the success of their work.

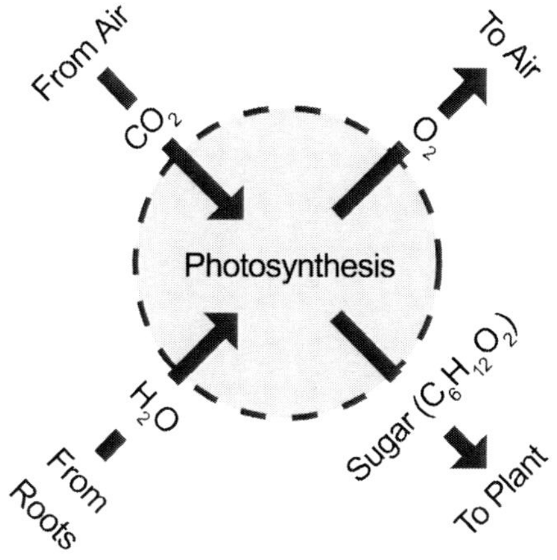

Figure 1.5.5. Photosynthesis.

Notice that only three elements, O, H, and C, actually show up in the final molecule. Why then is it so important to have all those other elements we discussed in the previous chapter? As these simple sugars move through the plant, they combine with essential elements, forming more complex and specialized molecules to build plant structure and use other chemicals to facilitate plant functions. There is very little nitrogen in the wood of a tree, but it is in the leaf helping with the work of creating sugar.

Photosynthesis in trees is not restricted to the leaf. There is a great deal of chlorophyll in the stem of a tree. You can see it as a green tinge on the wood when the stem bark is scraped off. This chlorophyll produces as much as 20 percent of the tree's sugar and functions as long as the air temperature is above 40°F.

Sugar, Glucose, Carbohydrates, Starch, Cellulose, Lignin

Sugar as used in this text is another name for **glucose**, the chemical produced by the leaves during photosynthesis. **Glucose** is a **carbohydrate** and is the basic building block of all tree cells. These molecules combine in more and more complex forms, eventually becoming **starch**, which can be stored in the tree for future use. Trees can break down starches into glucose when needed. **Cellulose** is a complex starch and makes up much of the rigid fiber in the tree. **Lignin** is a particular molecule in the cell walls of wood. It biodegrades more slowly than cellulose and is found in larger quantities in some bark, particularly of conifer species.

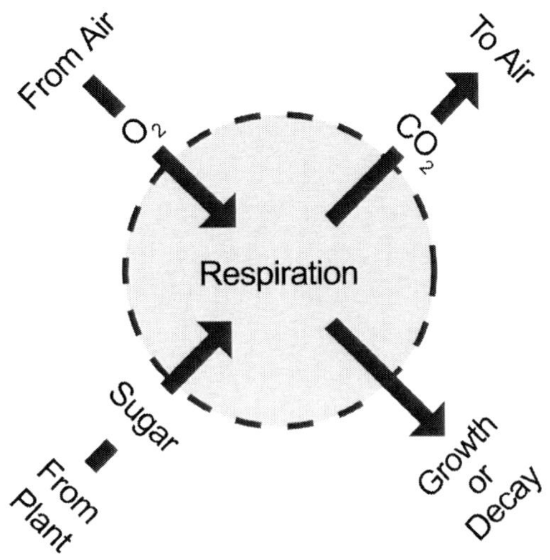

Figure 1.5.6. Respiration.

Respiration and Plant Growth

Photosynthesis creates the molecules that build the tree. Each molecule contains stored energy. The process of moving these molecules around the tree, combining them to form new molecules, and the ultimate decay and oxidation of the tree require the use of that stored energy. Imagine that each molecule is held together with small paper clips. The spring in the metal stores energy, which holds the object together. To change the shape of the molecule, the clip has to be released and, in doing so, the energy in the clip is released.

In plants, oxygen is required to break down these bonds. The molecular change uses oxygen, releases energy, and produces byproducts of water and carbon dioxide. The energy being released creates heat. The heat in a compost pile is the released energy during the decay process.

Notice that the process is circular, so that the substances needed for photosynthesis at the beginning become the products of respiration at the end. Energy, carbon, hydrogen, and oxygen work in a balanced, circular motion.

Respiration is most active in areas of rapid cell division. The root tip is one such area and requires an oxygen source within the soil to respire. As soil oxygen falls below 10 percent of soil air, cell division slows and eventually stops. Soil oxygen can be limited by either too much water saturating the soil for long periods of time or by soil compaction, which limits the exchange of air within the soil.

Water normally contains a significant amount of dissolved oxygen, and roots can continue to respire under water if the dissolved oxygen levels are high enough. Oxygen is constantly being replenished in slowly flowing water, such as in swamps, in amounts sufficient for some species to survive; but in a poorly drained soil without flow (as in bog), trees quickly use up the dissolved oxygen, making it difficult to survive. Very few plants can grow in bogs.

Water enters roots by passing through cells near the root tips. But how does all that water get up to the top of a very tall tree? Capillary action does some of the work. Surface tension tends to draw water up into small spaces or capillaries, similar to the way water runs up between two pieces of glass placed in contact with one another. Trees have a series of thin overlapping cells called **xylem** that run from the roots all the way to the leaves. Water passes from cell to cell along the xylem. But capillary action alone is not enough to move the water hundreds of feet up. Transpiration within the leaf finishes the job. As water evaporates out of the leaf surface, it forms a negative pressure in the xylem, providing just enough pull that when added to the force of capillary action, the water rises to the top of the tree.

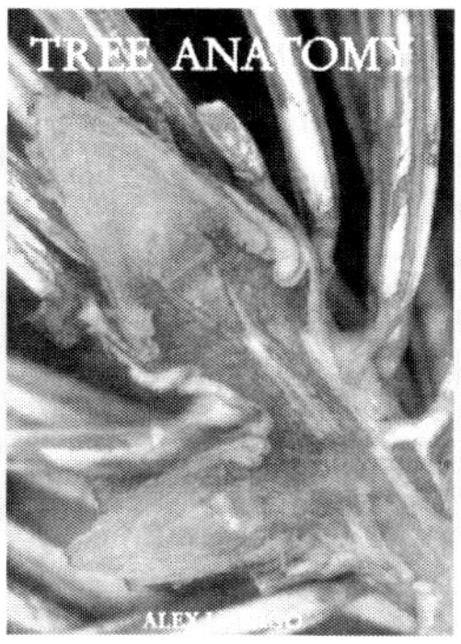

Tree Anatomy in Color

To really understand tree anatomy, great color photographs are very helpful. Dr. Alex Shigo produced a wonderful little book, *Tree Anatomy*, full of the color photos that will be helpful when reading the rest of this chapter.

TREE ANATOMY

Leaves

Along with the other green parts of the tree, leaves perform photosynthesis and help cool the tree. When leaves die, they contribute organic matter to the soil, providing carbon and energy to many soil organisms.

Each leaf is designed to support photosynthesis. Water moves up from the roots and into the leaf cells through veins within the leaf. Air enters the leaf through holes on the leaf surface called **stomata**. The inside structure of a leaf is somewhat open, allowing for air movement. Figure 1.5.7 shows an enlarged section through a leaf.

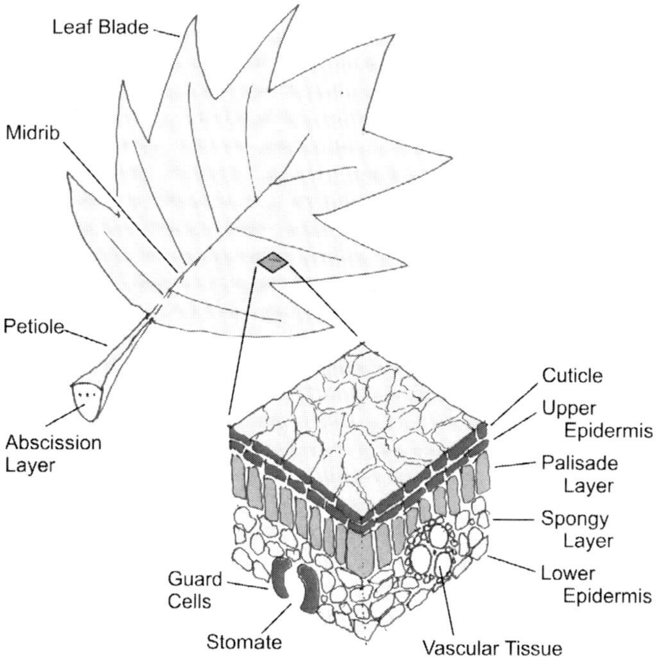

Figure 1.5.7. Leaf anatomy.

Leaf Color

Leaves are green because of the dominance of chlorophyll. In the fall, leaves of deciduous trees slow down photosynthesis and the green fades away, revealing the other colors that have been in the leaves all along. In some trees, glucose that was produced at the end of the season is trapped in the leaf and turns red in the cooler temperatures. Red fall color may also be anthocyanin pigments in the leaf. Yellow indicates a dominance of xanthophylls, and orange indicates carotenoids within the leaf cells.

In the spring, the leaves of some trees will emerge with a red color. These leaves may become green as the chlorophyll content increases or remain red or purple, depending on the species. Red-leaved trees like Japanese maple will appear redder longer if they are growing in shade or are in soils of low fertility. Variegated plants can either be genetic variations or symptoms of a virus. Some yellow plants have a specialized form of chlorophyll that is yellow instead of the normal green.

Leaf Attachment

Each leaf stem is attached to the tree branch at a structure called a **petiole**. This joint is intentionally weaker than the rest of the leaf stem to allow the leaf to separate from the branch. Between the petiole and the branch is a thin layer of cells called the **abscission layer**. This layer controls the flow of fluid to the leaf and the strength of the attachment. When the leaf is removed, a small mark called the leaf scar is left on the twig. In fall or when a tree is stressed, a healthy tree will slow the flow of fluids and the layer will weaken. The leaf may develop a fall color, and will eventually fall off.

During rapid onset of stress, such as drought or transplant shock, the abscission layer may not have time to function. Leaves may turn brown and not fall off the tree. This is a good indicator that those branches or even the entire tree may not recover. If the leaves go into early fall color and fall off easily, this is a good sign that the tree is reacting normally to stress and has a good chance to recover if proper water balance is restored. Buds on this branch may be able to sprout once the tree has recovered from the stress. A tree that goes into early fall color year after year is often signaling a soil problem or some other stress factor such as a girdling root.

Sugar Movement from Leaves to Storage and Roots

Sugar is produced in a dissolved state and moves through **phloem** cells to other parts of the tree to be used or stored. The tree converts simple sugar into starch molecules, which can immediately become part of the plant structure or can be saved for later. Starch needed for spring growth of new leaves and flowers is stored within the branch cells. Some is stored in the trunk and branch sapwood for the next year's growth, and some is stored in the roots for future root growth. The notion of most of the starch being transferred to the roots for winter storage is not correct.

The tree's roots release some of the sugar-starch molecules directly into the soil. These secretions are called **exudates** and provide a carbon source for bacteria in the rhizosphere, the area of soil directly around the absorbing part of the root. Exudates may be a critical factor in the success of urban trees where there is little to no leaf decomposition into the soil to provide an alternate source of carbon.

Twigs and Branches

Tree branches grow longer each year and tend to develop an increasingly complex structure. The terminal bud at the end of each twig controls growth. At the very end of the twig is an area of rapid cell division called the **apical meristem**. Behind the terminal bud, additional buds will form locations for flowers, leaves, and lateral stem locations. Lateral branches multiply the complexity of the branching structure.

Until the branch bark becomes quite thick, bark cells contain chlorophyll and photosynthesize. Since chlorophyll is sensitive to water stress, a green color is a good indicator of the vitality of a branch. The bark exchanges air to the cells by means of **lenticels**, small openings in the bark that function like the stomata in a leaf.

The location of each year's terminal bud will normally be marked on the stem, with a series of circular marks formed when parts of the terminal bud fall off. This is called the **terminal bud scar.** These scars remain visible for many growing seasons on most species. The distance between terminal bud scars can be used to measure previous years' growth rates.

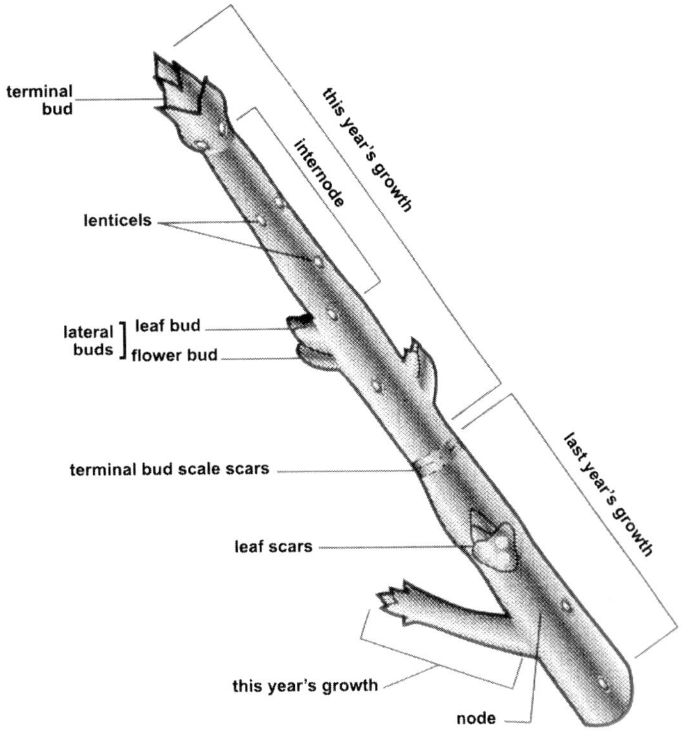

Figure 1.5.8. Twig anatomy

Normally, the year that a tree is transplanted is recorded by a short space between bud scars. Healthy trees have longer spaces than stressed trees. A partial record of the health of a tree can be observed by comparing the growth rates of known healthy trees with known stressed trees.

The number of lateral buds also relates to stress factors in the tree. The more buds and the wider their spacing, the healthier the tree. A really stressed tree growing in a restricted soil environment might have no lateral buds and almost no internodal distance. This reduction in buds and shortening of internodal distance results in twigs becoming somewhat irregular and misshapen when compared to twigs of a healthy specimen. Most twigs gracefully stretch out to the edge of the tree, while stressed trees of the same species have stunted, more angular branching habits. Figures 1.5.9, 1.5.10, and 1.5.11 show several different stress levels in the same species of tree.

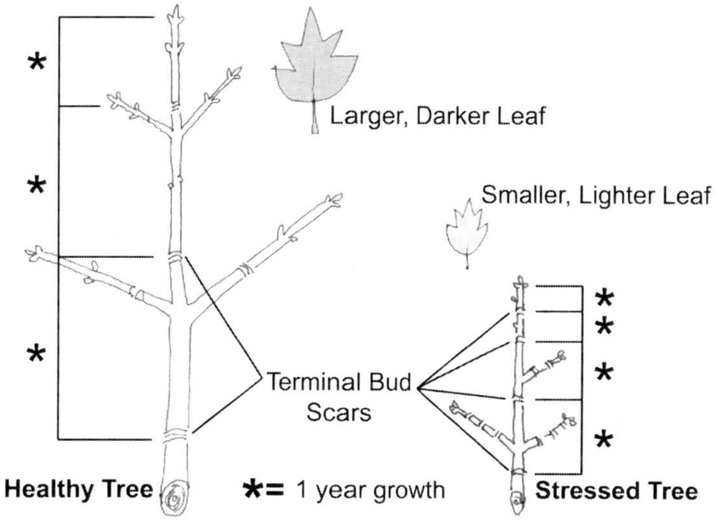

Figure 1.5.9. Comparing the incremental yearly growth distance on twigs can help an observer estimate the stress level and growth rates of the trees.

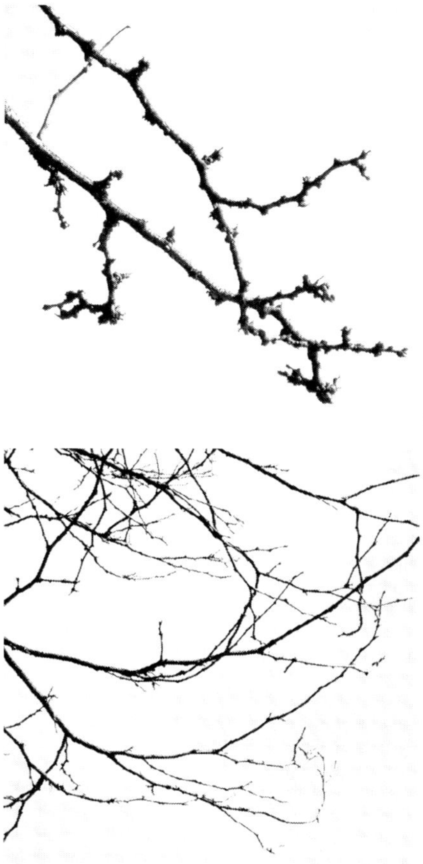

a

b

Figure 1.5.10. Comparison of stressed and healthy twigs showing shortened node distance with stress.

a. Twigs of stressed honey locust.

b. Twigs of healthy honey locust.

Figure 1.5.11. Stressed tree compared to less-stressed trees.

Stressed trees grow more slowly and are often misshapen. Stressed trees can be identified in the landscape by comparing them with trees of similar age growing in good soil conditions.

Figure 1.5.12. Multiple lateral branches after pruning the terminal buds.

Terminal Bud Dominance

Trees often grow primary leaders with a dominant terminal bud on the central branches. As long as these terminal buds remain viable, they tend to suppress the growth of the terminal buds on lateral branches further down the branch. Some genera like spruce (Picea) or sweetgum (Liquidambar), suppress the lateral branches dramatically, producing trees with single central leaders. These are called **excurrent** trees. Other genus like maple (Acer) or many of the oaks (Quercus) tend to have weak dominance and develop multiple leaders. These are called **decurrent** trees. Most trees start out as excurrent trees, and in a forest stand will remain excurrent until the canopy matures. An open-grown tree will often take on decurrent attributes due to the abundance of light on all sides.

If the terminal bud is removed, the lateral buds will grow into new terminal buds, forming several side branches. Each of these new branches will try to become the dominant branch. Pruning terminal buds results in dense clusters of branches, as shown in Figure 1.5.12, and may introduce structural defects by creating co-dominant branches. See further discussion of co-dominant branches later in this chapter.

Wood Growth Layers and the Vascular System

A tree adds an entire layer of wood each year to all surfaces of the trunk and branches. Along the outer surface of the tree are several layers that protect the tree and provide for its growth, as shown in Figure 1.5.13.

The outer layer is the bark, which is the protective surface of the tree. The cells of the outer bark layer are produced in the **cork cambium** layer of the inner bark.

Inside the inner bark layer are the three layers that make up the most crucial part of the tree. The first layer is the phloem, which carries sugar from the leaves to other parts of the tree. Phloem cells are living cells while they are functioning to transport fluids. Once they are replaced in the yearly growth cycle, the expanding tree crushes them and incorporates them into the cork cambium.

Immediately inside the phloem is the **cambium** layer, which is the principal layer of cell division. This layer produces both phloem and xylem cells.

The **xylem** cells inside the cambium layer accumulate each year, forming growth rings that become the wooden structure of the tree. In the spring, when water is plentiful and growing conditions are good, the first cells produced are large. As the cycle moves into summer, there is less water available and leaves become less efficient, resulting in smaller, darker cells. The process stops completely with the loss of leaves and resumes abruptly with the onset of new leaves. This quick change is what produces annual rings in a tree trunk. The thickness of each annual ring is determined by the amount of sugar a tree produced that year, in direct correlation to available water.

Xylem cells carry water up the tree to the leaves and hold starches in reserve. Several years of growth rings can transport water and store starch. This area of xylem is called sapwood. The remaining wood inside the sapwood is called heartwood and has no fluid transport function. Often, the heartwood is a darker color than sapwood.

Maple Sugar

Sugar to make maple syrup comes from the xylem of the tree. During the winter, stored sugar dissolves into the sap and flows in the xylem when temperatures rise above freezing. Warming early spring temperatures make the sap easy to tap, giving rise to romantic images of maple sap collection amid melting snows in the New England woods. By late spring, the tree is absorbing more water, which dilutes the sugar content of the sap and ends the sugaring season.

Within the xylem, a series of **ray lines** are visible in the cut cross-section of a trunk. Ray cells cross the cambium between the phloem and the xylem and can carry fluids between the phloem and the interior of the tree. They are also a critical part of the tree's defense against decay. Ray lines are visible in Figure 1.5.14.

Tree Trunk Enlargement and Tree Stress

Trees in good growing conditions will add more wood than trees in stressed sites or stressful climates. Historians have used tree rings to track weather patterns for many centuries in a process known as **dendrochronology**. This same technique can be used to assess tree health and the growing conditions at a site.

Figure 1.5.14 shows two trees planted in the same year, growing for 30 years in slightly different site conditions. Notice that the initial tree rings up to the time of planting are nearly identical, indicating that they probably grew in the same nursery and were of equal health. The larger tree suffered a slight setback in the year of transplantation, recovered and

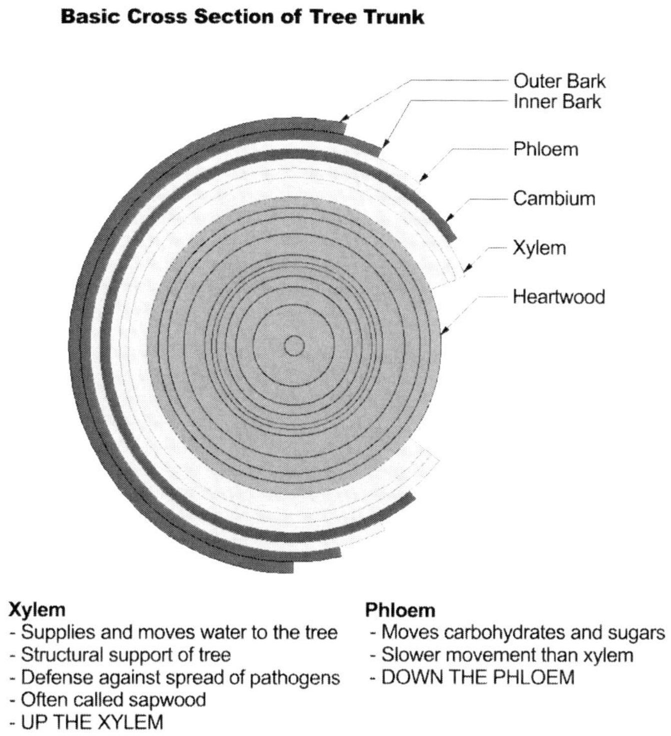

Figure 1.5.13. Anatomy of bark and wood within a tree.

Figure 1.5.14. Trunk sections from two honey locusts of the exact same age growing in the same park, one in a stressed site and one in a site with better soil conditions.

continued to grow at a rate close to the rate in the nursery. The smaller tree never appeared to recover from transplanting and continued to grow very slowly.

Tree growth rates vary considerably by species, tree age, tree size, weather, and site stress factors. Healthy, open-grown canopy trees in a maintained landscape should be expected to add approximately 1/2 inch to 1 inch of trunk diameter per year. (Because trees tend to add wood at a faster rate near their bases, trunk diameter is normally measured at about 4-1/2 feet above the ground.) Smaller trees will increase in diameter faster than larger trees. Trees in natural forest will grow more slowly, adding less than 1/4 inch of trunk diameter per year as they cope with the competition of closely spaced trees and the resulting small canopies. Trees in forest with thin or dry rocky soils may grow so slowly that the annual growth rings may be invisible to the naked eye and many urban trees.

Decay Resistance

Storms, insects, birds, animals, and humans are constantly damaging trees. Unlike animals, whose skin, bone, and muscle can repair themselves, once a tree's xylem wood is wounded, the damaged wood will not heal. New wood will grow over the wound, but the damage inside the tree remains, subject to decay by invading organisms.

The tree responds to this decay by attempting to wall off or block the area of the wound to slow the spread of decay. This process is called **compartmentalization**. The tree plugs many of the vessels in the wood ring around the wound site. This is called the **barrier zone wall**. New cells, added to the xylem growth ring after the wound, form stronger cell walls to resist decay from the inside. Existing internal ray cells also form walls. The cells of the growth ring inside the barrier zone wall form weaker walls to slow decay penetration further into the interior. Compartmentalization above and below the wound site is more difficult for the tree, but weak plugs can form in the vertical xylem cells.

Some forms of decay are stronger than others, while some trees are better at compartmentalization than others. Decay progresses through the walls and the tree forms more walls in an effort to slow the advance. Wood may become darker once it is walled off, although not all darkened heartwood is dark due to compartmentalization. Rot and decay tend to move first vertically, and then into the center of the tree. Ray walls are the next to be penetrated, and finally decay breaks down the outer barrier zone wall.

While the inside of the tree slowly decays, the outside continues to grow. The process becomes a race between the tree's ability to grow additional wood and put up walls faster than the decay breaks them down.

Fortunately, the material inside a cylindrical structure is not as critical to its strength as the thickness of the outer wall. Arborists use a device called a **resistograph** to measure the thickness and strength of the outer layers of the trunk and the progression of decay to determine whether a tree is structurally sound.

Indications of decay within the tree may be subtle and are easily overlooked. Designers who are contemplating preserving a large tree should have its structure surveyed by an ISA Certified Arborist before investing in a design dependent on the tree's long-term health.

Branch Structure

Branches provide support for leaves, maintain the flow of material between roots and leaves, and are the primary storehouse of chemicals the tree needs for continued growth.

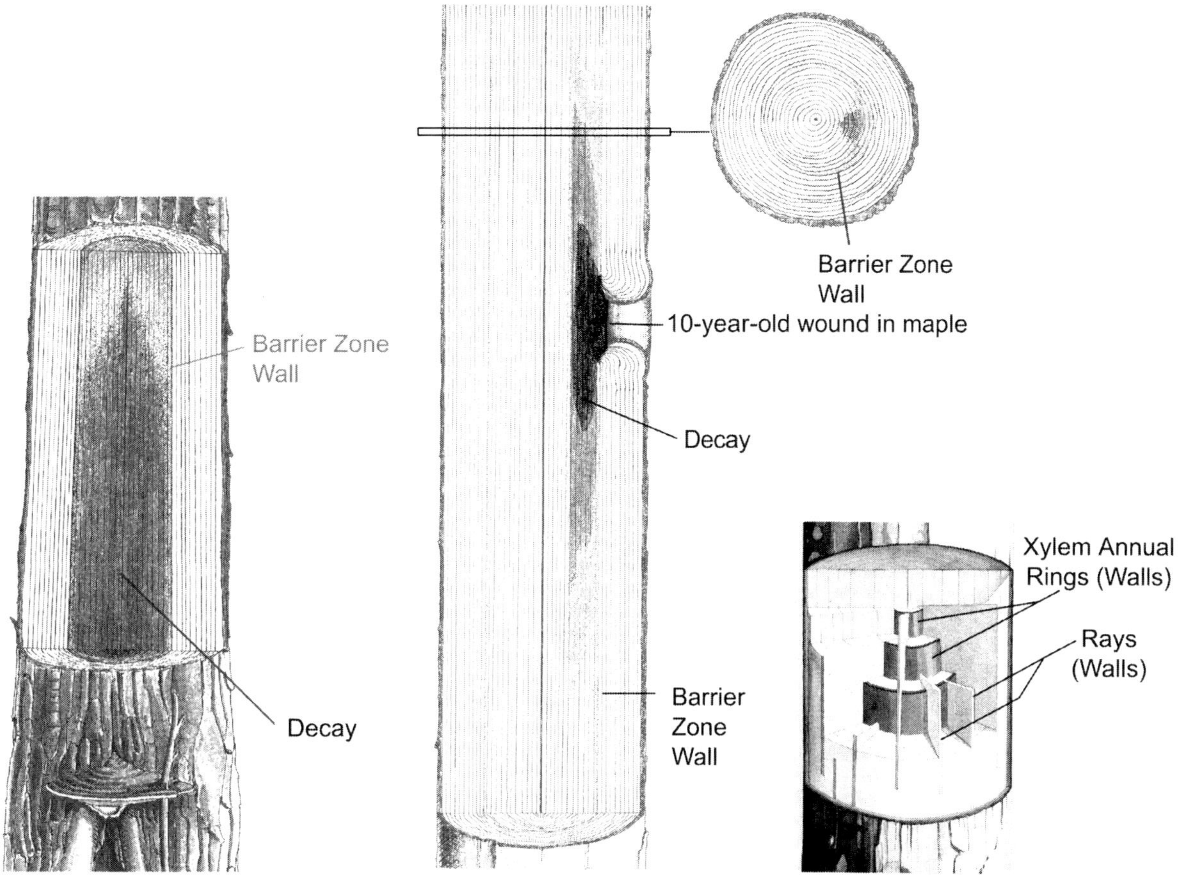

Figure 1.5.15. Compartmentalization of decay in trees. *(Source: USDA Forest Service Bulletin No. 405)*

Trees typically add more branch divisions than they actually need. As the tree matures, especially in a forest or tightly spaced planting, lower branches no longer receive enough light to support photosynthesis, so the upper branches take over primary leaf production. Lower branches may also conflict with the development of trunk structure to support the increasingly heavy tree mass. This means the tree must find a way to eliminate lower branches over time.

A tree has two mechanisms to facilitate this self-pruning, terminal bud dominance and a branch collar structure. In a forest and in groves of closely spaced trees, these result in trees with very long trunks and no lower branches.

Most trees develop a single trunk supporting increasingly heavier weight and resisting great loads at the base. As the tree matures, wind loads increase and apply a twisting force on the trunk. If the branches are not symmetrical, gravity will pull the tree toward the heavier side. This adds stress within the trunk. The tree responds by adding wood where it needs to resist the stress. This wood is called reaction wood.

As the trunk leans, the side in the direction of the lean is in **compression** while the side away from the lean is in **tension**. In hardwoods, reaction wood forms on the tension side of the tree, while in conifers more wood forms on the compression side.

Problems develop when there is a rapid change in the forces at work on the tree. This might include removal of adjacent trees or a portion of a tree's canopy, construction or removal of a building that redirects wind, cutting of

Figure 1.5.16. Reaction wood forming on the tension (smooth) side of the trunk, while bark forms buckling ridges on the compression side.

Figure 1.5.17. Trees that failed as a result of changing dynamics and insufficient root space to resist the force.
(Photo credit: Kevin Campion)

roots, or removal of curbs or walls on which the tree relied for support. Trees are not able to respond quickly enough to these changes. The larger and older a tree, the more trouble it will have reacting. A trained arborist can help assess the effect of planned changes when evaluating a tree for preservation.

Branch Collars

Terminal bud dominance tends to make lateral branches behind the terminal buds smaller in diameter. As the tree adds layers of wood, the layer covering the trunk or a dominant branch forms a small bulge in the wood around the lateral branch. This bulge is called the branch collar (Figure 1.5.18). The branch attachment is stronger on the bottom of the branch than on the top. This difference in strength results in a large rip in the wood on the bottom of the branch when it is torn away by high wind or mechanical damage.

In many species, the bark on top of the branch collar pushes up as the tree adds wood, forming a ridge at the union of the two branches. A bark ridge indicates a strong branch attachment. If the branch angle is narrow, the bark will begin to get caught between the two enlarging branch structures, forming a crease. This trapped bark is called **included bark** and keeps the two branches from forming a strong attachment. Over time, the branch connection gets weaker and weaker to the point where it fails.

Just inside the collar around the lateral branch, a compartmentalization layer forms that will slowly seal off the lateral branch as it is no longer

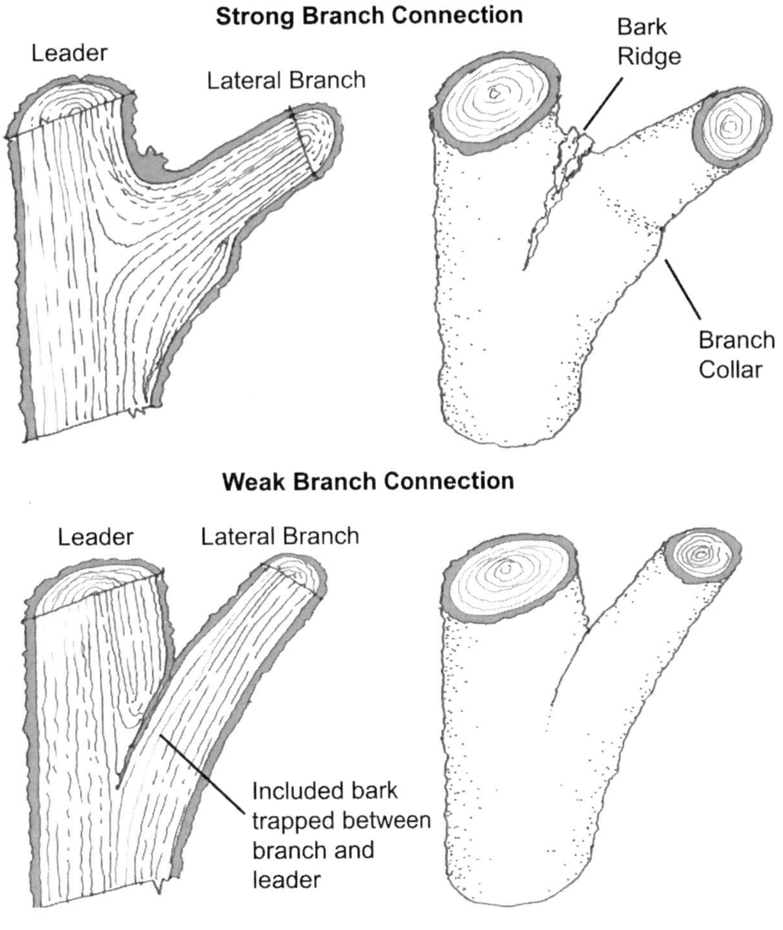

Figure 1.5.18. Strong and weak branch connections.

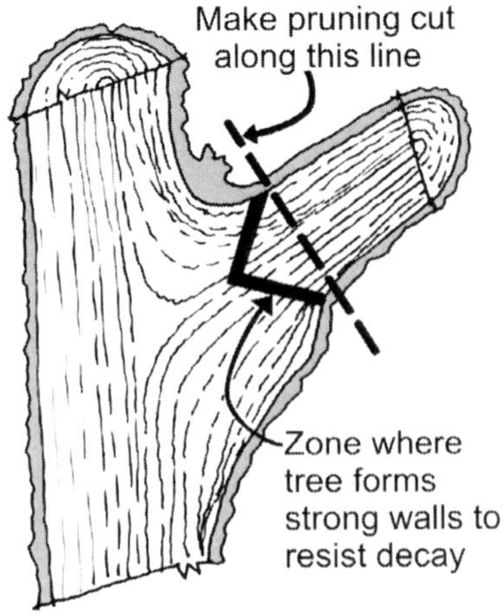

Figure 1.5.19. Compartmentalization within the branch collar.

needed. When pruning a tree, it is important to keep all the parts of the branch collar intact. This will allow the pruning wound to heal quickly.

Co-Dominant Leaders

If a dominant and a lateral branch are about the same diameter, or two leaders emerge after the terminal leader is removed, they are in conflict. Especially when the angle between the two branches is tight, wood layers bump into each other and begin to form included bark between the two expanding limbs. The wood layers of each branch cannot structurally join due to the bark, and a weak point develops in the tree. These branches are called **co-dominant leaders**.

Co-dominant leaders occasionally happen in nature, but are quite common in nursery-grown trees due to pruning practices. Nurseries often prune the terminal bud to make the crown of the tree fuller. This makes the tree appear larger, giving it higher sales appeal. If a nursery tree exhibits this pattern, remove one of the co-dominant branches. In mature trees, consult an arborist to determine appropriate remedies.

A forest canopy tree like river birch (*Betula nigra*) is often specified as a multi-stemmed tree. However, what many nurseries provide are really trees with multiple co-dominant leaders. Expect problems of a weak connection and loss of one

Figure 1.5.20. Co-dominant leaders.
a. Co-dominant leader with included bark.
b. Mature tree split as a result of a co-dominant leader left at planting. The included bark on split trunk lying on the right side of the tree was 11 feet long.
c. Multi-stemmed river birch is actually a triple co-dominant leader tree. One by one, each of these leaders will be lost and the tree will become a single-stemmed tree. Do not specify multi-stemmed river birch!

a

b

c

Figure 1.5.21. Grown upside down, these red maples formed branches that grow up, oriented toward the light.

or more trunks as the tree matures. When a clump form is desired, it would be better to specify multiple single-stemmed trees to be planted with touching root balls. Figure 1.5.20 shows the problem with co-dominant leaders.

Branch Structure and Light

Tree branches will grow toward the light. In low light, the branches will grow longer with fewer lateral branches. Lower branches that receive insufficient light will die. If the light is from one side, the tree will grow with a bend in its trunk and all its branches on the lighted side.

In urban areas, there is usually more light and space for branches, thus greater weight, on the street side, but not enough space for roots to hold up the tree on the sidewalk side. Slowly, the tree develops a lean in the direction of the street.

Trees can grow in reflected or diffused light, which sometimes results in trees on the north sides of buildings with all their branches facing north.

Epicormic Branches, Suckers, and Watersprouts

As a tree ages, dormant or latent lateral buds remain embedded in the bark. When a portion of the canopy or an adjacent tree is removed, formerly shaded

Figure 1.5.22. Epicormic branches and suckers.

a. Epicormic branches on the trunk of linden.

b. Suckers sprouting from poplar roots below the paving.

c. Maturing epicormic branch. Note included bark at top of branch.

bark is exposed to sunlight. These dormant buds can activate forming new branches called **epicormic** branches or **watersprouts**. These branches are not strongly attached and are easily broken until they become well established. Epicormic branches can form on a tree below a stress point such as a girdling wire, and will often emerge just below the graft union on trees propagated by grafting. Surface roots of some species may also have latent buds embedded in the root that can develop into branches or new trees. These are called suckers.

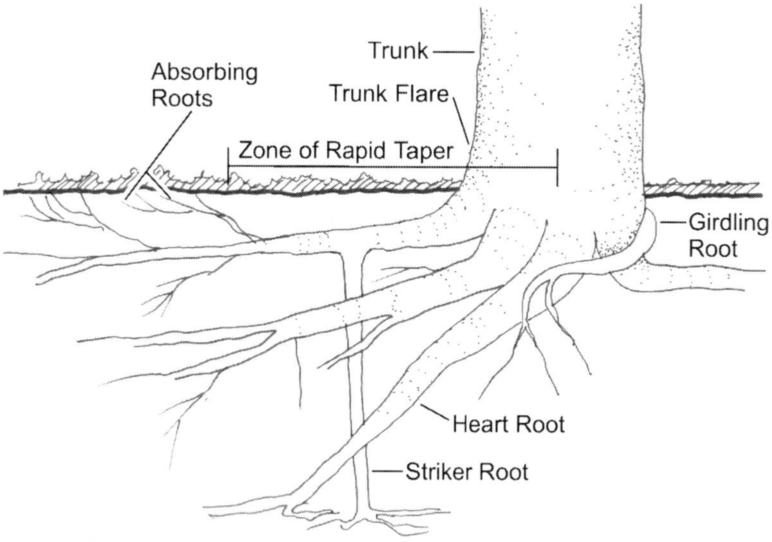

Figure 1.5.23. Root anatomy.

Roots

Roots absorb water and chemicals from the soil, conduct those elements to the tree, and anchor the tree in the soil. They also inform the parts of the tree above ground about conditions below ground. Charles Darwin wrote, "The root is the brain of the tree." Modern biology in part supports Darwin's hypothesis. Roots respond to water, oxygen, and chemical levels in the soil that are the primary determinants of tree health and survival, and send chemical messages thorough the tree to regulate growth and reproduction. Competition from other plants, soil disturbances, and changes in weather patterns affect soil directly, making root observations the best predictors of the future prospects of the tree.

Trees have horizontal root structures. Dr. Thomas Perry, the renowned urban forester, often said, "A tree is structurally like a wine glass on a dinner plate." This analogy is quite apt. It includes a root crown with its trunk flare and zone of rapid taper at the base of the glass, and the proportion of glass height to plate size is close to the natural model for forest trees.

Figure 1.5.24. Wine glass on a plate. Compare this to the diagram of a tree in Figure 1.5.1.

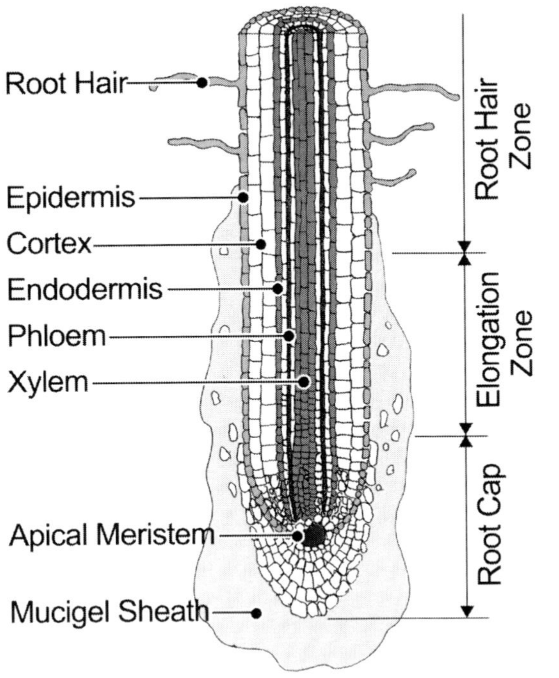

Figure 1.5.25. Absorbing root anatomy.

Absorbing Roots

Roots begin as non-woody, **absorbing roots** (also incorrectly called "feeder roots"). At the very end of the root tip is a layer of cells called the **root cap**. These cells break off the cap and lubricate the soil as the expanding root crushes them.

Roots secrete carbohydrates called **exudates** into the soil. These carbohydrates are produced in the leaf. There is wide disagreement on how important exudates are in the overall carbon cycling of a tree; they may represent anywhere between 10 percent and 50 percent of the tree's total photosynthesis production. Exudates and the bacteria immediately around the root influence the chemical composition of fluids around the root, may change pH, and help dissolve chemicals for absorption. Soil bacteria around the root consume the carbohydrates added to the soil. These bacteria provide many chemicals needed by the tree. All this activity happens in a thin layer of soil around the absorbing root called the **rhizosphere**.

Behind the root cap is a meristem similar to the meristem on the branch tip. This is the area of rapid cell division, producing a supply of cells for the root cap and new root cells. These new root cells expand in the "zone of elongation," which extends up to 1/4 inch behind the root cap. It is this elongation that pushes the root forward into the soil. Once elongated, the cells begin to differentiate into xylem, cambium, phloem, and other specialized cells. A portion of the root behind the tip remains capable of absorbing fluids.

Absorbing roots often grow upward into the surface layer of the soil from deeper lateral roots. The surface layer normally has a higher organic content, more water, and oxygen. Absorbing roots are considered ephemeral, meaning that they grow into an area when conditions are suitable for absorption. Clusters of absorbing roots may live for only a few days or weeks, then die when it becomes too dry, wet, cold, or hot. These dead roots contribute significant amounts of organic matter to the soil. Other tree roots may return to the same site once conditions again become favorable. A few roots in areas where growing conditions persist for the longest periods may become a part of the expanding lateral root system.

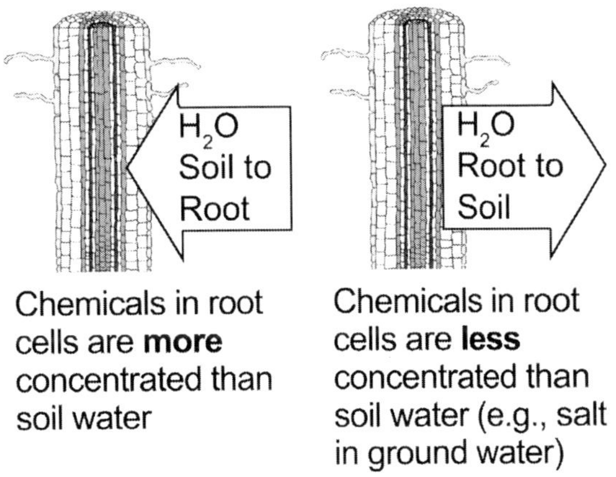

Figure 1.5.26. Water moves into the root by osmosis or out of the root when salt concentrations in the soil water increase.

Water Absorption and Osmosis

The epidermal cells of absorbing roots obtain most of the water and chemicals required by the plant. Water and dissolved chemicals move from the soil through permeable cell walls and into the root by osmosis. As illustrated in Figure 1.5.26, osmosis into the root occurs when the water on the soil side of the root has less chemicals than the water within the root. Soil water always contains some chemicals, but usually less than the chemical concentration within the root cells.

If the amount of dissolved chemicals in the soil water increases—for instance, if soil water is polluted with salt from de-icing—osmosis slows or stops. If salt concentration in the soil water becomes high enough, water will flow from the root cell into the soil water.

In some species, epidermal cells extend to form root hairs. Trees generally have fewer root hairs than smaller plants, and rarely look like the radish seedling many people studied in high school biology. With fewer root hairs, trees' absorbing roots are less efficient than those of smaller plants.

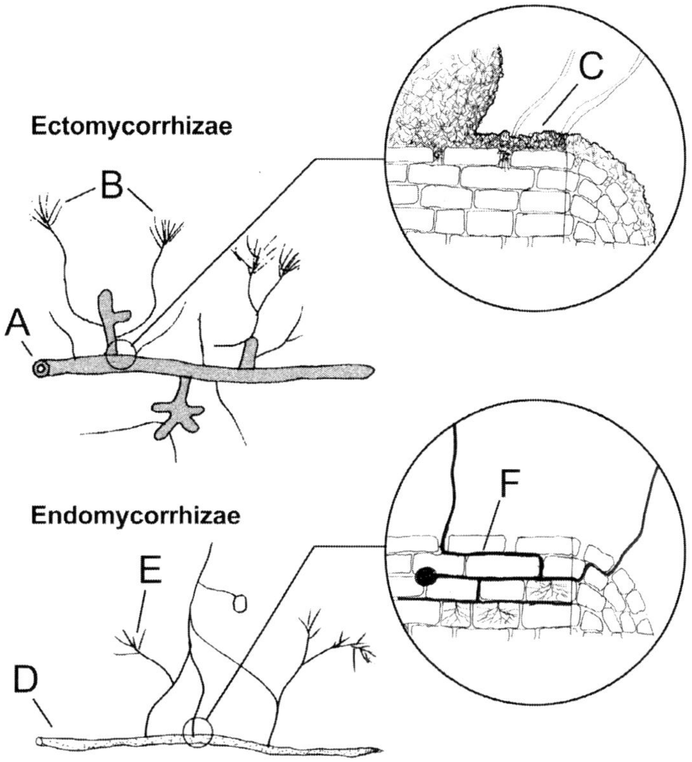

Figure 1.5.27. Ectomycorrhizae grow around and between the cells of the epidermis of the mycorrhizal root. Absorptive hyphae (A) are sent out into the soil, helping transfer fluids from the soil to the cell (B). A thick covering of mantel hyphae (C) protects the root. Endomycorrhizae grow into the cells of the mycorrhizal root. Absorptive hyphae (D) extend out into the soil (E) to bring water directly to the root cell through intracellular hyphae (F). *(Source: Adapted from Harris)*

Mycorrhizae

Because trees have few root hairs, they may rely on the formation of mycorrhizae to assist in the absorption function. **Mycorrhizae** are structures formed by a symbiotic relationship between the tree root and certain species of fungi. These fungi extend a network of root-like structures (**hyphae**) into the soil, bringing water and nutrients to the root. Figure 1.5.27 explains the two kinds of mycorrhizae found in association with trees.

There are hundreds of species of mycorrhizae in nature. Some are generalists and others are quite specific to a particular species of tree. The spores of mycorrhizae are found in most natural and urban soil, but the soil conditions to make them flourish must also be present in order for them to associate with tree roots. Active mycorrhizae are easily damaged or may fail to exist in soils that are too wet, too dry, compacted, overly fertilized, or contaminated.

Commercially produced mycorrhizal spores are available, but adding them to a poor soil may not improve the growth of the plant. Adding mycorrhizae to soil in combination with fertilizer has been shown to have a greater effect on the plant than adding mycorrhizae alone. Other studies indicate that the commercial products may not have viable spores. Trees may also use other mechanisms to compensate for lack of mycorrhizae.

Improving the organic content of the soil and loosening soil compaction can permit spores already existing in the soil to become active in the plant root. Locally produced compost may have sufficient species of mycorrhizae to inoculate the soil. Duff, or salvaged topsoil taken from woodland areas, is an excellent way to inoculate a soil with a wide variety of soil organisms including mycorrhizae. This is especially true for native tree species that may be dependent on specific species of mycorrhizae. In this case the collected duff or topsoil should come from an area where the tree species in question is already growing.

Nitrogen Fixers

Certain trees and plants are known to be able to "fix" nitrogen in the soil, converting nitrogen gas to a stable mineral form usable by the plant. The tree does not actually fix the nitrogen, but accommodates special types of bacteria, called actinorhyzal bacteria, that live within the roots and do this processing. These bacteria live in small nodules that are extensions of the root. While nitrogen-fixing trees and plants are interesting, much of the nitrogen used by plants is processed into an available form by bacteria already in the soil.

Figure 1.5.28. Distinctive ringed ridges of root epidermis. Note the point where trunk bark changes to root. Plant the tree so this point is at the soil line.

Lateral Roots

As the epidermis of the root develops a corky protective barrier and the xylem turns woody, the absorption function slows. The roots become lateral or framework roots that connect the absorbing root system to the trunk. These roots transport the absorbed material to the tree, store starches, and anchor the tree against wind and gravity. New absorbing roots will emerge out of these roots. Tree roots grow much faster than branches, up to 10 feet per year depending on species and conditions.

Lateral roots are made of woody xylem. Although roots have annual rings, the rings are thinner and less distinct than rings in the tree trunk. Annual rings may be thicker on the top of the root. Lateral roots do not tend to taper as fast as branches. When roots come in contact with an object, they will often increase diameter or form a callus at the contact point. The wood in roots tends to compartmentalize better than the trunk wood when damaged.

While trees generally have bark textures distinctive enough to aid in identification, the corky barrier of the roots of most trees is quite similar. Color may vary, but lateral roots of many species are similar in texture, developing a series of ringed ridges. These markings are helpful in determining the point where the root begins. Roots that become exposed to the surface will begin to develop bark similar to the tree. Figure 1.5.28 shows the distinctive markings of root covering.

Soil and Root Branching Habit

The branching habit and direction of lateral root growth is a function of both soil conditions and genetics. Soil moisture and compaction rates are often the greatest controlling factors in determining root habit. The optimum level of oxygen and water in the soil when the root became established controls its depth. Roots generally stay at approximately the same depth as long as conditions remain unchanged. Roots will appear to meander up and down if soil conditions change along the path or time period of growth.

Root systems tend to be more compact and fibrous in clay soils than in sandy soils. They will follow rock crevices, run down joints in paving, follow underground utility lines, and otherwise grow into the places where they can find acceptable levels of oxygen, water, compaction, and nutrients.

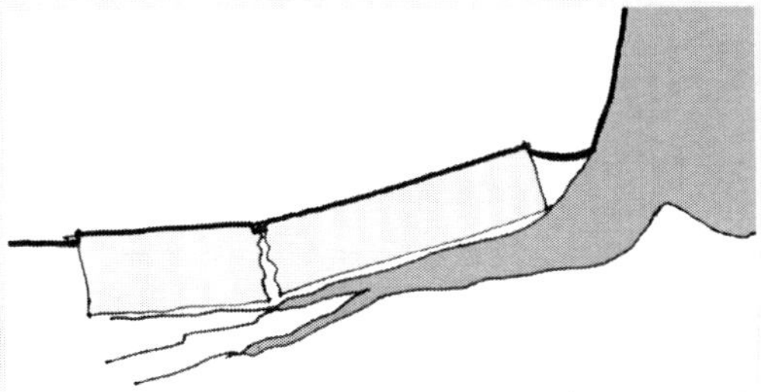

The Root Under the Pavement

The space between pavement and its compacted subgrade would not seem like a good place for a root, but roots grow there anyway. As the subgrade soil dries, it shrinks slightly, leaving a small air space between the underside of the paving and the soil. On hot days, water condenses on the underside of the pavement, and the paving allows little of this water to evaporate. Roots can take advantage of this situation of air and water, and grow into this space. Once roots find a good growing environment beyond the paving, they will grow larger, eventually lifting the pavement above.

In soils with significant seasonal moisture fluctuations, a multi-level root system may develop. Vertical striker or sinker roots that periodically branch off upper main lateral roots grow down to the lower level.

Suckers, new tree branches that can develop into new trees, can spout off lateral roots close to the surface in some species.

Figure 1.5.29. Roots grafting to form an interconnected web.

Root Grafting

When roots come in contact with one another, they can sometimes form graft unions and become one. This can happen between roots of the same tree and between two trees of the same species. Surface roots that have formed bark rarely will graft together. Vascular diseases and fungal infestations can be spread from tree to tree though these grafts.

Roots with Internal Compasses

A lateral root will tend to grow in the same direction once it has established its course. If it encounters an object, the root will grow around it and then continue in roughly the same direction as before. Experiments with Cornell Structural Soil (CU Soil) demonstrated this effect. Even though the roots in CU Soil constantly meet stone obstructions, they generally keep growing in their preset direction.

Experiments with root barriers suggest that roots can be turned 90 degrees and still return to their original course once they reach the bottom of the barrier. However, in soils that are compacted, roots redirected downward by root barriers normally grow back up to the elevations in the soil profile where growing conditions are favorable.

In soils that are compacted, the requirement to find oxygen and water will override the tree's internal compass, and the root will follow paths of least resistance through the soil. In urban areas, this may result in erratic and unpredictable root patterns.

Figure 1.5.30. Roots growing in CU Structural Soil.

Tap Roots and Heart Roots

Early in the life of a seedling tree, a single root may go straight down until it encounters a level of limited oxygen. This is called a **tap root**. In most species and soil conditions, horizontal roots overtake the importance of the tap root. In a nursery-grown tree, the taproot may be cut at several stages in production and does not exist when the tree is transplanted.

Other large roots emerge from the base of the tree at sharp angles to horizontal. These are called heart roots.

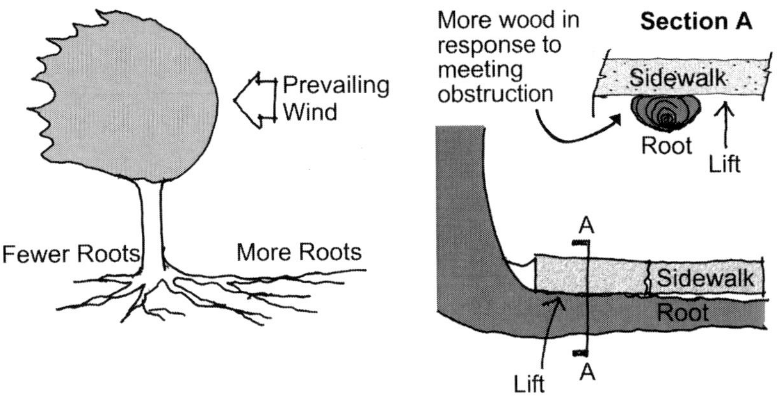

Figure 1.5.31. Root responses to load stress.

Root Response to Loading Forces

Roots respond to different load forces and form reaction wood. Roots in contact with an object, such as a curb or the underside of paving, will build up larger amounts of callus in response to the pressure of the object. The wood may start to wrap around the object and can eventually graft around it.

A tree adds more or stronger roots in the direction of a force. If wind regularly comes from one direction, larger roots will grow on the upwind side. If a tree is leaning or becoming gradually heavier on one side due to shading or loss of branches, more roots will develop in the opposite direction of the lean. When designing rooting spaces and making decisions about construction around large existing trees, this principle must be taken into account.

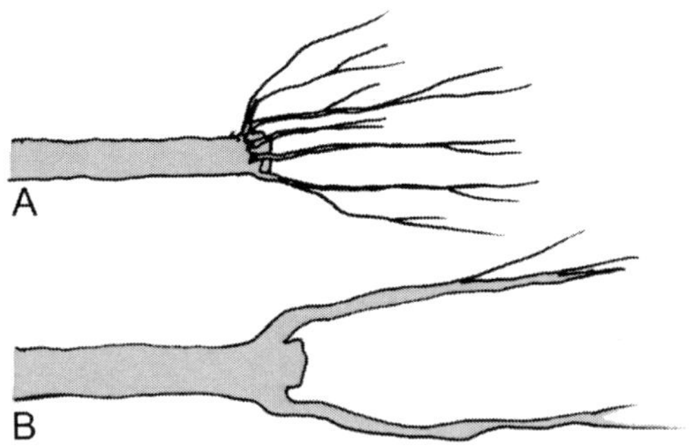

Figure 1.5.32. Root response to cutting.
A. Immediately after the cut, many roots sprout.
B. As root matures, only a few roots remain.

Root Response to Cutting

When roots are cut, several mechanisms come into play. First, the root begins compartmentalizing the wood behind the wound. Second, a series of small roots emerges from the cut end of the root to begin restoring the root system. Many of these new roots will die off, leaving just a few roots emerging from the stub of the cut root. When intentionally cutting roots, it is important to make clean cuts, perpendicular to the line of the root. Clean cuts offer a smaller surface for drying and compartmentalize better. Roots that are torn by large grading equipment can develop cracks that run laterally along the root, increasing the extent of damage. When grading near trees, always prune the roots in advance.

Root Crown

The **root crown** (or **root collar**) is the transition zone between trunk and roots. From the designer's perspective, this should be the second most important part of the tree after the roots. Where the tree meets the ground, the trunk wood and bark change to root wood and corky epidermis.

A tree is structurally a vertical cantilever, meaning the vertical portion of the tree resists overturning by relying on the anchoring of the horizontal roots. This puts great stress on the point where the vertical member, the trunk, joins the supporting plate. To resist these stresses, the tree adds reaction wood to form a bracket called the **trunk flare** at this joint. Annual rings at the base of a tree are two to three times the thickness of the rings farther up the trunk. This rapid growth at the base must be factored into any design of paving around the tree, and nothing must be allowed to interrupt its growth.

As the trunk enters the ground, it subdivides into six to eight large **buttress** roots. These roots spread the loading of the tree over a much larger area. They taper rapidly once they are underground to the point where they are between 2 and 4 inches in diameter about 6 feet from the trunk. After that point the taper continues, but at a much slower

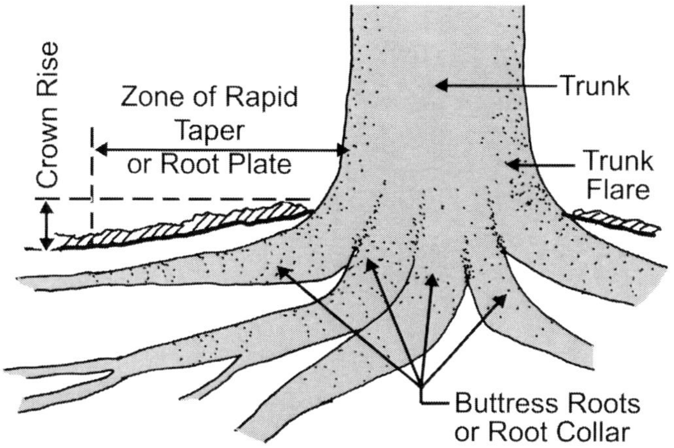

a

b

c

Figure 1.5.33. Root crown.

a. Root crown anatomy.

b. Urban tree with root crown lifting pavers. Any paving around a tree must accommodate this lifting.

c. Root plate revealed after an irrigation line was installed on the windward side of the tree. Note the flat upper edge of the root plate, which aligned with the irrigation line location.

rate. This area is called the zone of rapid taper or the root plate and is the area where the roots do the most damage to sidewalks and adjacent structures. When a large tree blows over, it exposes its root plate and the zone of rapid taper. Cutting or damaging roots in this area can seriously weaken the tree.

Girdling Roots

A root may grow around a portion of the trunk, at or near the surface over the top of the root collar. Once the trunk base encounters this root, the phloem begins to become compressed and the xylem can no longer add wood. Fluid flow is reduced and structural weakness begins to develop. The larger the area of compression, the greater the problem. If the root is slightly underground, the trunk will appear to enter the ground without a trunk flare.

Figure 1.5.34. Girdling roots.

Any time a tree does not have a trunk flare completely around the tree, a girdling root should be suspected. Arborists can perform a root collar investigation by removing soil around the base of the tree. Sometimes, the offending root can be removed. Under other conditions, the arborist may determine that removal of the root may cause too many problems with the tree and may leave it in place.

In a young or a nursery-grown tree, girdling roots should almost always be removed. In extreme cases, where a nursery tree has large amounts of girdling roots, the tree should be destroyed.

REPRODUCTION

Most landscape installations are not concerned with the reproduction of trees. As trees die, they are replaced with nursery-grown trees. Designers are concerned with flowers as a design feature, the ornamental value of fruit, and sometimes require the elimination of fruit. Occasionally, a project may involve the production of fruit for consumption. Each tree has particular requirements for the production of flowers and fruit. Consult the widely available literature for specific information about encouraging these features.

While designers rarely consider the natural reproduction cycle of trees as a landscape process, the manner in which trees are propagated in nurseries is of great importance to the specification of trees for the landscape. Nurseries propagate very few trees from seed, usually relying on asexual grafting, budding, or tissue culture reproduction. Propagation methods, early pruning practices, the requirement to transplant a tree several times, and the use of containers all change the natural form of a tree's root and crown structure. This process creates problems such as co-dominant leaders, root systems too deep in the root ball, girdling roots, and grafts that are later rejected. These conditions can cause failures of trees long after installation.

Flowers

Figure 1.5.35. A dogwood growing under the shade of a tree (left) will have a different form and far fewer flowers than one growing in full sun (right).

Flower production depends on available light and soil conditions. Larger trees are not generally grown for their flowers, and their great height usually allows them access to enough light once mature. Smaller trees can fail to produce dramatic flowers when overshadowed by larger trees and buildings. Shade-tolerant species may grow quite well, but will have reduced flowering in low light levels. Obtaining optimum pH, nutrient, and water levels can help improve the ability of small trees to flower in shade.

The shade of buildings is not as restrictive to some species as the shade from large trees. Large trees not only shade the smaller trees, but also compete for soil resources. Building shade allows some reflected light to reach the plant. Trees do not use the entire light spectrum and can still photosynthesize in the reduced spectrum of this reflected light. Buildings offer no competition for soil resources except for the building footprint and the compaction caused by its construction and use. So trees growing in good soil in the shade of buildings may grow at reduced but acceptable rates, with greatly reduced flower presence.

The timing of any pruning will affect the next flower production cycle. Most trees, particularly spring-flowering trees, should be pruned immediately after they bloom for the most prolific flower display the following year. Summer-flowering trees can be pruned in the fall or winter.

Sex and the Single Tree vs. Trees That Need Partners

Some trees are **monoecious**, meaning the tree contains the reproductive parts of both sexes on the same tree. Monoecious trees can produce fruit as a single isolated specimen. Other trees are **dioecious**, meaning the flowers of male and female plants are on different trees. When fruit production is important, dioecious trees need a partner in the general vicinity. If a particular dioecious tree is heavily utilized in a city, there may be sufficient pollen available to fertilize female dioecious trees without providing a male partner on the same site. Designers should consult a local horticulturist.

Ailanthus is dioecious, which opens the possibility of a male clone that would eliminate its label as an invasive tree. Ailanthus grows well in compacted poor soils, has few pests, and might be a great urban tree if its political image was improved.

Horticultural texts may note which plants are in each category or may use more cryptic terminology. In the widely referenced *Manual of Woody Landscape Plants*, author Michael Dirr often substitutes the word "perfect" for "monoecious" when both male and female parts are within the same flower. For dioecious plants, Dirr often uses a more descriptive discussion of the location of the stamens (male) and pistils (female) as a substitute for stating that the plant is dioecious.

Figure 1.5.36. Male ailanthus clone could make a great urban tree.

Pollen

Trees produce large amounts of pollen. Only female cultivars of dioecious trees produce no pollen. Seedless cultivars of trees are actually male clones of dioecious plants, and thus still produce pollen.

Pollen has always been a problem for people with allergies. Allergy activists in some areas of the country are promoting bans on the planting of pollen-producing plants. Unfortunately, there are only a few species of pollen-free, large trees, and a pollen-free world would be one with few trees. The type of pollen, means of dispersal, and other factors determine how detrimental pollen is to a person with allergies. If you want to avoid using trees that may aggravate allergies, consult *Allergy-Free Gardening* by Thomas Ogren. We'll go further into this topic in Chapter Seven of Part 2, but the urban forest must not be allowed to be cleared of pollen-producing trees.

Fruit Suppression

Sometimes it is necessary to find a way to suppress fruit production while still enjoying the benefits of the flower. Ethephon (Florel Fruit Eliminator), if sprayed during the flowering period at rates and timing recommended by the manufacturer, can be effective at yearly fruit reduction. Timing, species type, and weather are important variables in the success of this treatment. An arborist should be consulted as to the use of this approach.

INTERCONNECTIONS WITHIN THE TREE

Leaf/Root Balance

The individual growth functions described above are interrelated. Leaves cannot photosynthesize sugar molecules faster than the roots supply water. Roots cannot grow without the leaves supplying sufficient sugar to build more root cells. The tree must maintain a balance between the surface area of the absorbing roots and the surface area of all the leaves and other

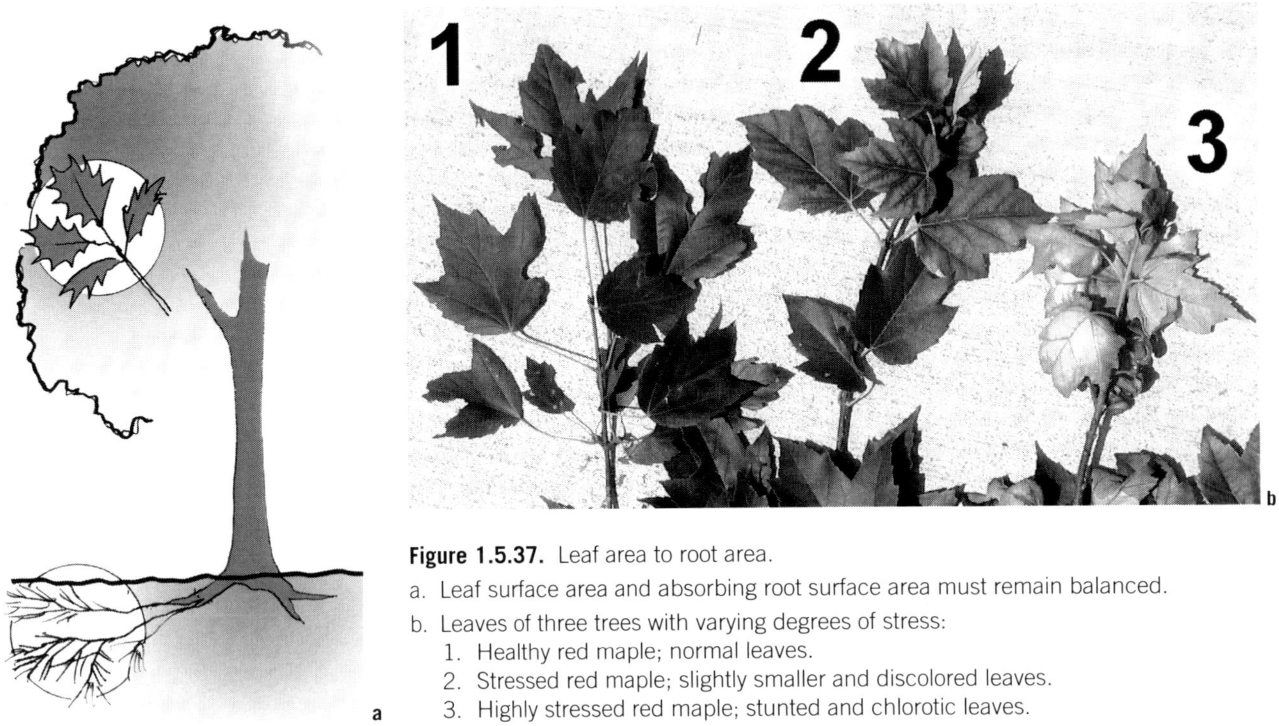

Figure 1.5.37. Leaf area to root area.

a. Leaf surface area and absorbing root surface area must remain balanced.

b. Leaves of three trees with varying degrees of stress:
   1. Healthy red maple; normal leaves.
   2. Stressed red maple; slightly smaller and discolored leaves.
   3. Highly stressed red maple; stunted and chlorotic leaves.

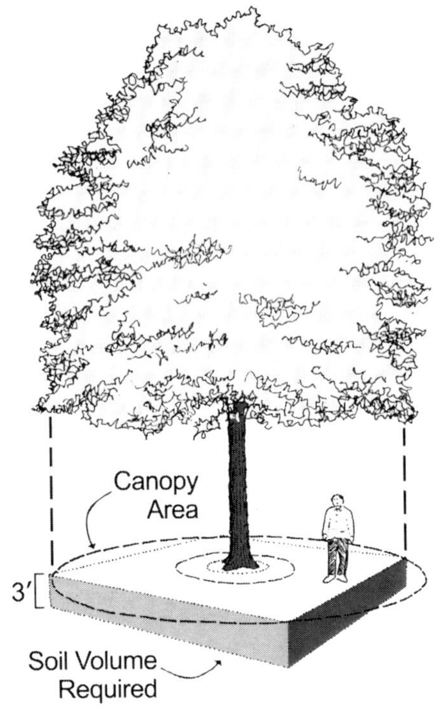

Figure 1.5.38. Soil and canopy size must remain in balance.

photosynthesizing surfaces. Trees use chemical messengers to communicate the balance, and the tree adjusts the balance by controlling its own size. These adjustments can be observed and indicate if the tree is healthy or stressed.

Soil Volume Requirements

A set volume of soil can support a limited amount of roots. This amount is determined by the degree of soil compaction and the ability of the soil to hold water and required elements. Soil that is regularly irrigated and fertilized supports more roots per cubic foot than soil subjected to the variations of weather and the natural cycle of the soil food web. Since the ability of the soil to support roots is a major factor in the size and health of the tree, it is possible to establish the relationship of available soil volume to projected tree size.

A rough formula states that a rooting volume of 1 to 3 cubic feet supports 1 square foot of tree canopy area. Tree canopy area is measured as the projection of the crown area onto the ground, and is often described as the area within the drip line of the tree. The lower figure of 1 cubic foot per square foot is for soil that is reliably irrigated. Three cubic feet of soil is for non-irrigated trees in drier portions of the United States. In much of the country, where rainfall is more than 30 inches per year, designers should plan approximately 2 cubic feet of soil per square foot of crown area.

These estimated volumes assume the soil is of good quality and not overly compacted. The calculations also do not assume the tree will immediately die once it reaches the size supported by the soil volume provided. Once the tree fills its maximum soil volume, it will slow its growth and become increasingly stressed. It may grow for a significantly longer time, but it begins to lose its resistance to disease and drought. In Chapter Four of Part 2, we'll go into detail about calculating soil volumes during the design process.

The Law of the Limiting

A tree's potential for growth is controlled by the most limiting factor within the plant/soil system. If any of the growth factors—water, soil volume, soil compaction, soil drainage, nutrient availability, structural support, or light—are compromised, the plant's growth will be limited to the extent that this one factor controls the plant. If nutrients are limited, increasing water without increasing nutrients will not improve plant performance. If nutrient deficiency is solved, the next most limiting factor will prevail. Thus, trees in differing conditions will grow at different rates. If a design calls for perfectly matched plants, the designer must arrange for perfectly matched growing conditions.

Drought Response

As the soil dries out, the flow of water to the leaf goes down. The tree can limit the loss of water by closing the stomata, but at some point the soil becomes too dry and the plant begins to be drought-stressed. Each species of plant has different resistance to drought based on its ability to control the evapo-transpiration of water or remain dormant during periods of low water availability.

Plants can manage periods of drought by growing deeper roots to draw on deeper water supplies. This response is dictated somewhat by genetic factors and by soil conditions. Some plants can shut down evapo-transpiration for long periods, reactivating those leaves when the water returns. These plants often have thick, waxy, or hairy leaves to reduce evaporation. Still other plants have the ability to shed leaves and go dormant during dry periods, growing new leaves once moisture improves. Finally, many perennial plants literally die back to the ground and re-grow during wetter periods. Few trees have this ability, and it is not a desireable trait for urban trees.

Nature vs. Nurture: Plant Stress Indicators

A tree's growth relationships—leaf size, shape, branch and bud development, overall growth rates, proportions, and bark features—are somewhat dictated by genetics. These will be roughly the same in trees of the same species growing in good quality soil of reasonable volume, especially if the trees are asexually reproduced in the nursery. However, as growing conditions become limiting, individual trees become stressed and cannot attain genetically determined growth rates. They will look different than their healthier cousins. The following are the primary stress indicators that can be used to tell if a tree is not performing to its potential.

Fewer, Smaller, and Thinner Leaves

When root area is restricted, the tree cannot draw on as many nutrients and as much water and must reduce its photosynthesis area to balance this limitation. Growing fewer and smaller leaves is the easiest way to limit this area. In addition to smaller leaves, the leaves may be slightly thinner or limper. Leaf size and condition may also change in relationship to the availability of light.

(Photo: Tom Perry)

Change in Leaf Color

Some trees might also produce fewer cells that can photosynthesize within the leaf.This shows up as a lighter green color that lets more of the red or yellow cells show up in the color spectrum. Leaf color shift might also mean a nutrient imbalance, low soil pH, or other biotic or abiotic stress.

Early Fall Color

A stressed tree may start the fall coloration period earlier than normal. This is a good indicator of how rapidly a tree is recovering from transplant shock and is an early indicator of the onset of stress.

Shorter Internode Lengths

Internode lengths can be "read" for many years along a stem, allowing the informed observer to see if the health of the tree has been increasing or declining. Drought also affects internodal length.

Smaller Trunk Diameter

Stressed trees add less wood each year. Trunk diameter as compared to age can be used to gauge the health and growing conditions of a large stand of trees. Trunk diameter is measured at 4-1/2 feet above the ground. The slowest urban tree I have ever measured was 1/32 of an inch per year trunk diameter increase over 20 years at Paley Park in New York. These trees died a few years after the survey.

Using Indicators to Manage Trees and Evaluate Past Designs

Some of the indicators of stress can show up years before the point where the untrained eye might suspect the tree was not growing well. A designer can look at past soil designs to tell if the current design is working before the tree dies, making it possible to incorporate changes into new designs sooner. Stressed trees are more susceptible to disease and insects. Disease and insect monitoring may be required or recommended.

To some degree, additional maintenance can improve the situation. Watering, regular application of mulch or other organic matter over the entire root zone (not just around the base of the tree), limited application of slow-release fertilizer if soil tests indicate chemical deficiencies, and applications of growth regulators can all provide temporary improvement. Longer-term improvements might include vertical mulching, soil compaction relief, removal of paving, or removal of competing trees.

There are other plant responses to environmental stress, many of which mimic diseases or are diseases brought on by stress. An excellent guide to these disorders is found in *Abiotic Disorders of Landscape Plants*.

Seasonal Tree Growth Cycles

Not all parts of the tree grow at the same time. Each part responds to seasonal fluctuations of light, moisture, and temperature. Table 1.5.1 shows how a tree

Table 1.5.1. Seasonal growth cycles of trees.

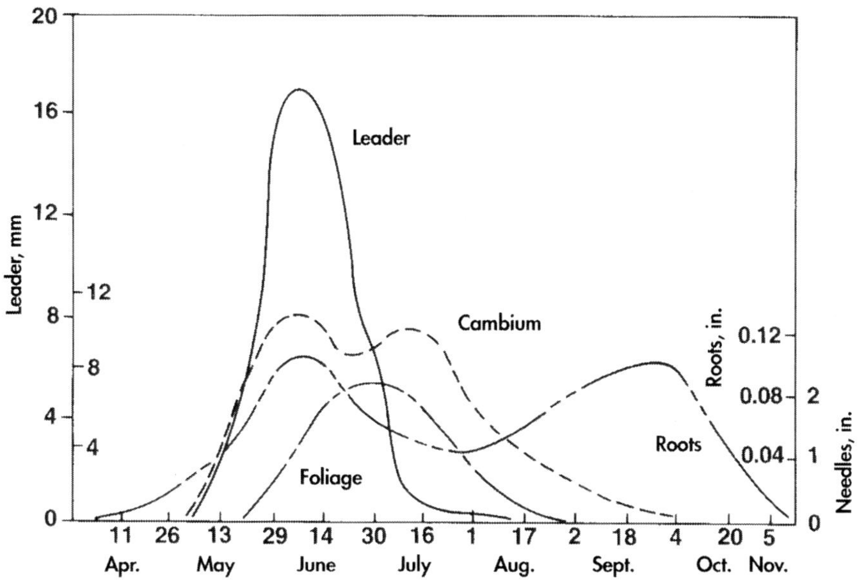

moderates its growing cycles. Species type, climate, and maintenance will affect the timing and durations of this growth cycle model.

TREE BIOLOGY AND PEOPLE

A number of other biological considerations relate specifically to the problem of trees in close proximity to human settlement, and can be caused by planting trees too close to buildings, pavements, roads, and footpaths.

Tree Structural Failures and Hazard Tree Evaluation

The topic of structural failures and hazardous tree identification is beyond the scope of this book, but it is nonetheless important. A good understanding of tree biology and physics is a useful skill for designers and maintenance providers. Clients and land managers often assume designers should be able to make this assessment, but in most cases it is not included in their training. A consulting arborist should be brought in to evaluate large trees. The ISA publication A *Photographic Guide to the Evaluation of Hazard Trees in Urban Areas* is a good reference on this issue. For those readers who may become fascinated with how a tree speaks to us about its structure, a small text by Claus Mattheck and Helge Breloer, *The Body Language of Trees*, is well illustrated and provides a tour of the physics of tree growth and failure.

Figure 1.5.39. Tree falling apart as a result of weak branch attachments.

Shade and Tree Establishment

Some trees are easier to establish in shaded situations, particularly trees that fill a climax position in the forest. Early successional trees are normally less shade-tolerant.

Figure 1.5.40. A tree in the shade of a much larger tree will have difficulty becoming established and will develop one-sided branch structure.

Also, most nursery trees are grown in full sun and adapted to that level of light. These trees, even if considered shade-tolerant, will undergo an adaptation period if planted in deep shade. The canopy will thin and the tree will produce fewer leaves. Individual trees will exhibit differences in branch structure compared to the same species growing with more light.

Two situations frequently encountered in the landscape require attention to this detail. The first is the planting of trees in the shade of a very tall building. There are places in large cities where the sun literally never shines. The second is when new trees are to be established under the shade of large existing trees. In both cases, it will be important to select shade-tolerant species, and to adjust one's expectations about the new tree's canopy density and ornamental value. Establishing new trees under existing ones may also require additional water to compensate for the ability of the larger tree to squeeze out the newer arrival. Good accounts of shade tolerance are available in *Native Trees* by Hightshoe and in *Agricultural Bulletin 65—Silvics of North America*.

Canopy Competition

As the canopies of similar-sized trees compete for the same space, they do not intertwine; instead, each establishes its own canopy area. All trees in this competitive situation suffer a reduced canopy area and resulting stress. In a grove of closely spaced trees, the trees inside the grove will be the first to die, thinning the stand. The trees on the perimeter may become loaded with too many branches on one side. If some trees have better resources and grow faster, the taller trees may grow over the shorter trees, causing them to further decline. As we have seen, in a forest, up to a third of a stand in close competition dies every ten years. With this in mind, planning wider spacing for groves of trees will yield longer periods when the stand is not in competition. Wider spacing becomes particularly important in triple or more rows of trees.

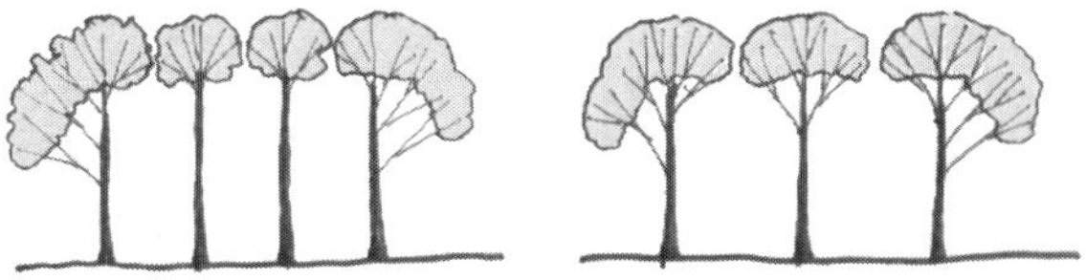

a

Figure 1.5.41. Canopy response to tree spacing.

a. Tighter spacing limits the canopy spread of interior trees.
b. Example of an interior tree growing within tightly spaced trees.
c. Tightly spaced double row of trees unable to grow sufficient interior branches to balance their own weight, resulting in trunk leans. Also note that approximately one-third of the original trees are gone due to the tight spacing.

b

c

Growth Regulators

Arborists have developed chemical treatments that can alter a tree's growth rate by slowing cell division in the bud and leaves. The principal chemical in this category is paclobutrazol (Cambistat).

Besides simply slowing the growth of the plant, paclobutrazol has been shown to increase the density of absorbing roots at the same time as it decreases twig and leaf growth. This may be useful in tree preservation projects, where roots have been or are going to be damaged. This chemical also can be a useful tool in the management of large, old, and stressed trees, and reduces the spread of some forms of fungus in trees and plants.

Application is by soil drench at the base of the tree. Dosage varies by species and amount is critical. Paclobutrazol does not work on all species, and it is easy to overdose a tree, especially in urban soils where root locations may be unknown. In an overdose situation, the leaves will become extremely small and it may take several years to recover. The treatment is relatively inexpensive. It may take up to a year to become effective, but may last three or more years.

Street Lights

Much has been written about the negative effects of street lights on trees, but it appears that there is little actual research on this subject. Contemporary papers all seem to reference one paper by Henry Cathy and Lowell Campbell, "Effectiveness of Five Visio-Lighting Sources on Photo-Regulation of 22 Species of Ornamental Plants," published in the *Journal of the American Society for Horticultural Science* in 1975. Cathy and Campbell report that some species were extremely sensitive to low levels of light, continuing to grow for some extended periods after control trees began to harden off for the winter. They speculated that this might result in an adverse impact, but no adverse impact was observed and trees normally harden off long before the onset of freezing temperatures. They also noted that all work was done on seedlings, which are much more sensitive to light than mature trees.

Figure 1.5.42. Trees do not seem to be harmed by artificial street lighting.

Plane tree (*Platanus*) was one of the species that appears to show the greatest impact in the study. One would then expect this would not make a good urban tree. However, throughout the northeastern United States and Europe, it is consistently one of the most successful urban street trees in areas of very high urban light levels. My own observations suggest the effect of lighting on plane trees is just as likely to be positive as negative, by allowing the tree a slightly longer growing season. More research is needed before a direct link between tree decline and proximity to street lights can be established.

Cold Hardiness vs. Photoperiod

Cold hardiness is the principal determinant used by designers to decide how far north a tree should be planted. To some degree, local knowledge decides how far south a tree is planted. Because cold hardiness is used as a primary selection determinant, particular cultivars of important urban tree species are planted over significant portions of the country. In some cases a single cultivar may be planted in places as diverse as northern Illinois and southern Georgia.

Yet there is more to the selection decision than temperature. Trees evolved to respond to different **photoperiods**, or the amount of sunlight per day and its changes throughout the year. Plants determine the onset of fall dormancy in part by photoperiod.

Not all members of the same species have the same photoperiod requirements. Red maple (*Acer rubrum*) is "native" from Canada to Florida. However, not all the red maples have the same exact set of genes. Red maples taken from North Carolina fail to harden off in New England before the frost arrives, while trees taken from New England to North Carolina go into early fall leaf drop, missing a portion of their growing season. Unlike the issue of street lights, which has at most a slight effect on photoperiod, getting latitudinal photoperiod wrong may make a big difference, particularly in situations where the tree is already under other stresses.

Select trees that are genetically from roughly the same latitude range as the location of the project site, or within the range where that cultivar has proven adaptable. Growers should be able to advise designers on the provenance—the geographic location of the genetic parent tree—of the trees they are producing.

Fire Resistance and Fire Breaks

Plants vary in their level of resistance to fire. The U.S. Forest Service has collected data on forest species and published fire break recommendations. In arid regions, much has been written about the ability of plants to burn and even survive fire. However, not all fires are the same. Soil moisture, season, and condition of the plants make it difficult to generalize about how plants will react.

The devastating fires in Oakland, California, in 2003, showed that further study is needed on the use of fire-resistant species, arid forest management, and standoff distances near buildings. An article in *Landscape Architecture Magazine*, "Crying Fire in a Crowded Landscape," March 2004, is an excellent starting point for anyone needing more information on this subject.

Air Pollution Tolerance

Trees growing in urban areas are subjected to the same air pollution as humans. It has been demonstrated that for trees that seasonally lose their leaves, most forms of urban air pollution have little impact on their health. Certain pollutants can impact pines and some other evergreen trees, but air pollutants are not a significant factor in most locations when compared to other urban tree stress factors.

Tree-Produced Air Pollution

In addition to producing pollen, molds, and particulate matter, trees contribute to air pollution in two significant ways. First are the emissions of vehicles and equipment required for installation and maintenance. The energy used in installing and maintaining urban trees is significant enough to offset much of the carbon sequestration benefits provided by the tree. Yet in the long term, there is still a net positive benefit.

A second source of air pollution is volatile organic compounds (VOCs) that contribute to the production of ozone and smog. Trees naturally emit small amounts of these compounds. However, the cooling and shading effects of trees in urban areas provide significant reduction in VOC emission from other sources, and there is a significant relationship between reductions in overall VOC levels and increasing urban tree canopy. Nine genera of trees—*Casuarina, Eucalyptus, Liquidambar, Nyssa, Platanus, Populus, Quercus, Robinia*, and *Salix*—have the greatest VOC emission levels. Some of these trees are the best candidates to produce large cooling tree canopies, so eliminating or reducing their use to reduce VOCs would have a net negative VOC effect, especially in areas where these species are the best choices for long-term large tree growth. *Prunus, Tilia*, and *Gleditsia* have the lowest VOC emission levels among species planted in cities.

Trees and Air Pollution Reduction

Overall, trees reduce air pollution in significant ways. Their impact is greatest when the trees are close to the places where humans live, work, and drive. Trees shade the urban heat island, reducing temperatures. Cooler cities use less energy. Trees absorb and filter dust and reduce other pollutants including ozone, sulfur dioxide, and nitrogen dioxide. Only large trees with a healthy canopy coverage make significant reductions. A 36-inch trunk diameter tree is 70 times as effective as one with a 3-inch diameter. For every 10 percent increase in a city's tree canopy area, there is a net decrease in ozone levels of approximately 3 percent to 7 percent.

Figure 1.5.43. Large trees are important to make cities habitable.

REFERENCES

Key References

Costello, Laurence R., Edward J. Perry, Nelda P. Matheny, J. Michael Henry, and Pamela M. Geisel. 2003. *Abiotic Disorders of Landscape Plant: A Diagnostic Guide*. University of California, Division of Agriculture and Natural Resources, Oakland, CA. 242 pp.

Harris, Richard W., James R. Clark, and Nelda P. Matheny. 2004. *Arboriculture: Integrated Management of Landscape Trees, Shrubs, and Vines.* 4th ed. Prentice-Hall, Upper Saddle River, NJ. 578 pp.

International Society of Arboriculture. 2005. *Introduction to Arboriculture: Tree Identification and Selection*. CD-ROM. International Society of Arboriculture, Champaign, IL.

Lilly, Sharon J. 2001. *Arborists' Certification Study Guide*. International Society of Arboriculture, Champaign, IL. 222 pp.

Mattheck, Claus, and Helge Breloer. 1997. *The Body Language of Trees: A Handbook for Failure Analysis.* 3rd ed. Robert Strouts, trans. Crown Copyright, The Stationary Office, Norwich, England. 240 pp.

Trowbridge, Peter J., and Nina L. Bassuk. 2004. *Trees in the Urban Landscape: Site Assessment Design and Installation*. John Wiley & Sons, Hoboken, NJ. 205 pp.

Other Resources

Burns, Russell M., and Barbara H. Honkala, tech coords. 1990. *Silvics of North America: Volume 2. Hardwoods.* Agricultural Handbook 654, Volume 2. U.S. Department of Agriculture, Forest Service, Washington, DC. 877 pp.

Dirr, Michael A. 1998. *Manual of Woody Landscape Plants.* Stipes Publishing, Champaign, IL. 1,187 pp.

Gilman, Edward F. 2002. *An Illustrated Guide to Pruning.* 2nd ed. Delmar, Albany, NY. 330 pp.

Hightshoe, Gary L. 1988. *Native Trees, Shrubs, and Vines for Urban and Rural America.* Van Nostrand Reinhold, New York, NY. 819 pp.

Lloyd, John, ed. 2002. *A Guide to the Plant Health Care Management System.* 3rd ed. International Society of Arboriculture, Champaign, IL. 150 pp.

Matheny, N.P., and J.R. Clark. 1994. *A Photographic Guide to the Evaluation of Hazard Trees in the Urban Areas.* International Society of Arboriculture, Champaign, IL. 72 pp.

Ogren, Thomas L. 2000. *Allergy-Free Gardening: The Revolutionary Guide to Healthy Landscaping.* Ten Speed Press, Berkeley, CA. 267 pp.

Shigo, Alex L. 1986. *A New Tree Biology Dictionary.* Shigo and Trees, Associates, Durham, NH. 132 pp.

Shigo, Alex L. 1989. *Tree Pruning: A Worldwide Photo Guide.* Shigo and Trees, Associates, Durham, NH. 186 pp.

Shigo, Alex L. 1991. *Modern Arboriculture.* Shigo and Trees, Associates, Durham, NH. 424 pp.

Shigo, Alex L. 1994. *Tree Anatomy.* Shigo and Trees, Associates, Durham, NH. 104 pp.

PART ONE

6
Urban Soils

Urban soils can be found on farms, in residential subdivisions, and in greenfield and brownfield development sites as well as on Main Street. They occur anywhere that soil has been moved, graded, compacted, or contaminated. Even when urban soils are highly degraded, they follow the same scientific principles that apply to natural soils. The urban soil-building process is similar to that in nature, but occurs in rapid, erratic progressions following the laws of finance and human irrationality, as well as more predictable laws of nature. The forces that build urban soils are more like meteor impacts, floods, earthquakes, glaciers, and volcanoes than like the long-term soil-building forces such as climate change and plate tectonics.

Urban soils may be degraded original or relocated soil. They are often manufactured or haphazard mixtures of sand, clay, silt, or other materials, from garbage and wood to plastic and toxic chemicals. Regardless of the way soil arrives at the site, it is often a less than ideal place to grow tree roots.

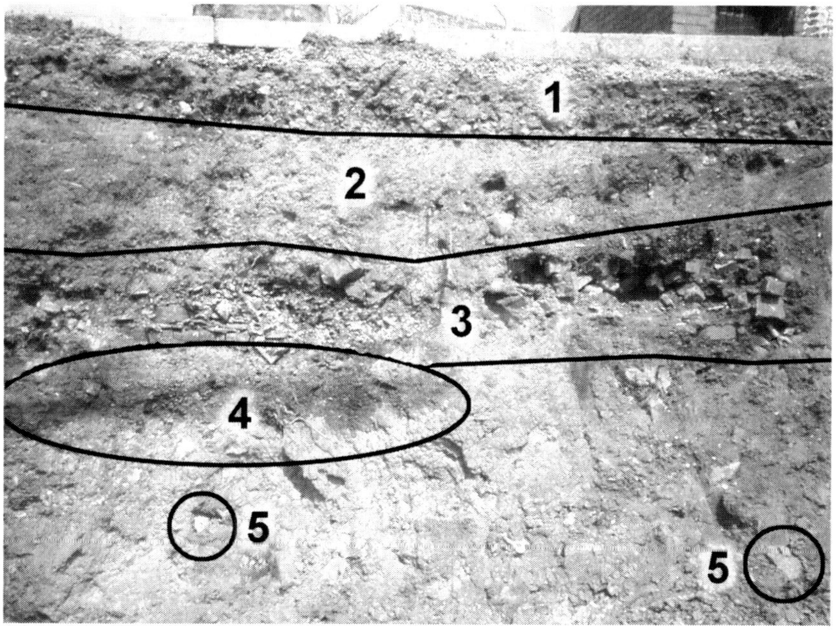

Figure 1.6.1. Urban soil profile, showing layers of previous human activity.

1. Current roadbed.
2. Fill soil.
3. Older roadbed.
4. Perched water seep.
5. Various brick pieces indicating that lower soil is human created.

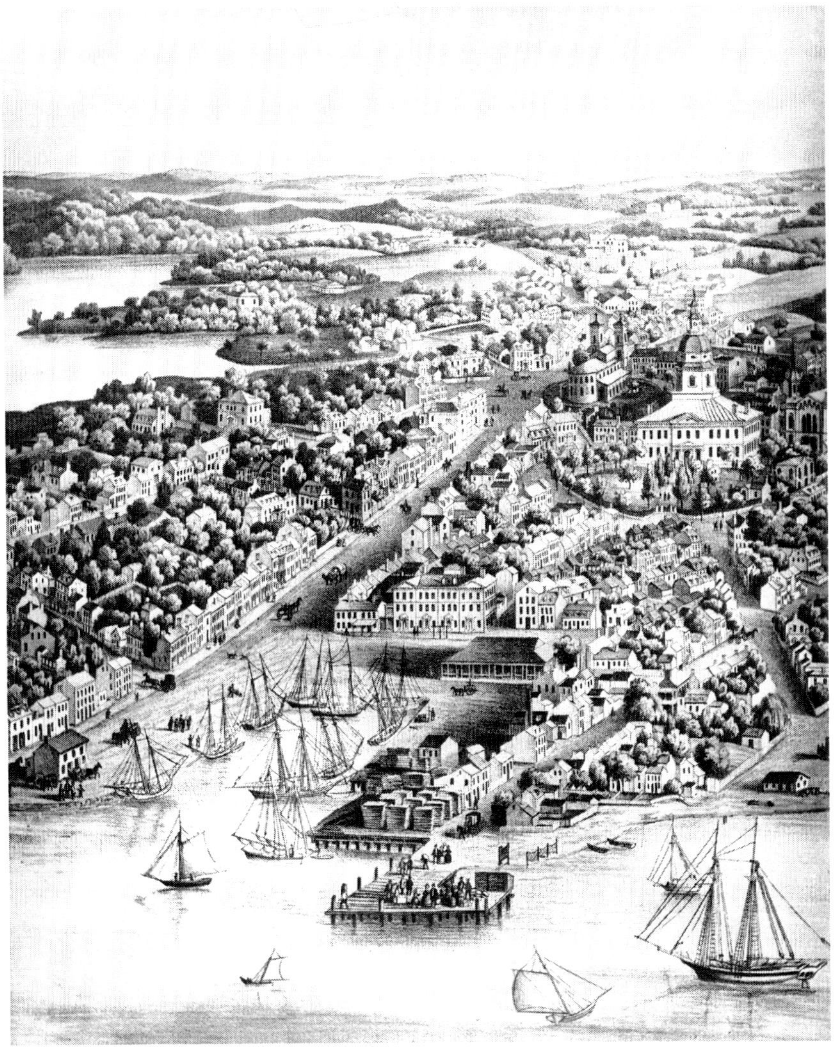

Figure 1.6.2. Trees come and go in urban spaces. *(Courtesy of the Maryland Archives.)*

HISTORICAL PERSPECTIVE

Human influence on soils began with intentional fires set to improve hunting, the clearing of land to farm, and the initial set of wagon tracks worn into the prairie. Early farming practices caused small but measurable changes to the soil. Even at subsistence levels, long-term impacts on soils by thousands of years of farming in Africa and Asia teach us that soil becomes highly degraded under the influence of human activity. Farming activity generally results in the erosion of topsoil, significant reduction in organic content, and compaction of subsoil. However, even after industrial farming and logging practices, the lower depths of the soil profile remain intact and the upper levels of the profile can still support trees.

Historically, there have always been motivations to move large amounts of soil. Wars, projects to support commercial and political power, and the fantasies of the rich might flatten a hill or fill in a valley. Indigenous tribes in the United States built large earthworks.

Before the advent of steam powered machines, people used human and animal muscle to move earth one small pile at a time. Deep compaction was difficult to achieve, and soil texture remained locally similar. Bits of original soil structure and organic properties remained in the moved soil, and the surface layer structure often recovered after construction. The process was slow, giving time for the restorative process of nature from frost, water movement, and the soil food web to heal the soil.

The invention of steam-powered engines at the beginning of the 19th century and the onset of the Industrial Revolution brought together forces that let humans move and compact soil in significant volumes. As people crowded together out of economic necessity, they disturbed greater amounts of soil. The speed of that movement increased, and larger machines broke the soil structure into finer particles. Paving covered greater and greater amounts of soil.

For a while, soil-restoring forces generally kept pace with human damage. Except in the most urbanized areas, trees still grew along streets and plants could be made to flourish with minimum efforts. Designers knew that soil was important, because they had firsthand connections to the land. Frederick Law Olmsted was a farmer first and a designer second. For New York's Central Park, most of which was built on disturbed soil, Olmsted imported large volumes of soil to support trees. Charles Street in Baltimore, by Olmsted's son, was designed with 3 feet of new soil in the street tree planting areas.

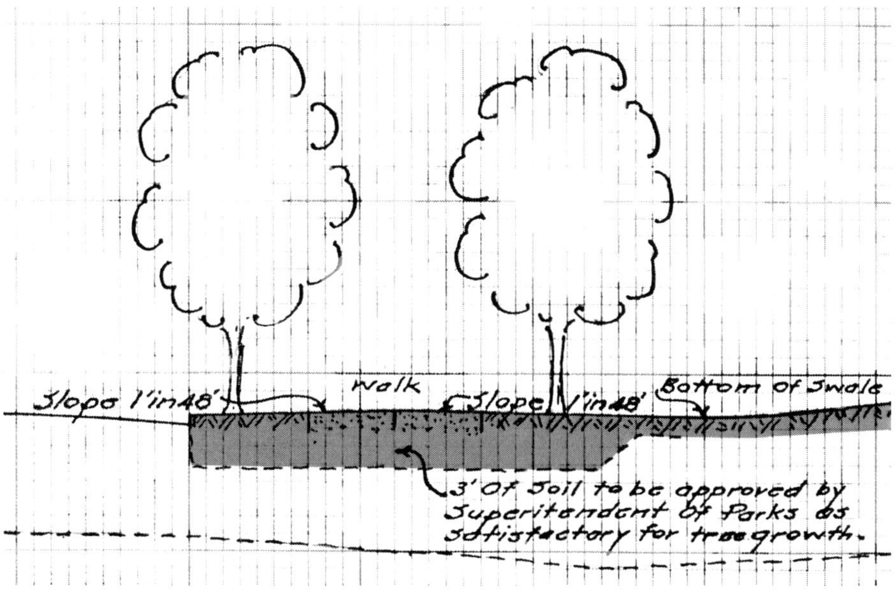

Figure 1.6.3. Olmsted drawing from 1907 for the design of Charles Street, Baltimore, showing large volumes of soil, 3 feet deep, "satisfactory for tree growth." *(Source: National Park Service, Frederick Law Olmsted National Historic Site archives)*

Early in the 20th century, forward-thinking arborists were beginning to see problems with urban trees. John Davey wrote in his 1907 book *The Tree Doctor* that a lack of soil was the primary cause of street tree failure in Cleveland. William Solotaroff's 1911 book *Shade Trees in Towns and Cities* echoes Davey: "A great deal, if not all, of the success in tree-growing depends upon the nature and preparation of the soil." These early references anticipate James Patterson's opening quote in the introduction to *Up By Roots* by more than 80 years. Solotaroff laments that there may be only about 12 tree species suitable for urban conditions, a situation that has not improved.

In the 1950s, Americans returned from war with new construction equipment and began building at a pace unprecedented in human existence. Hydraulic grading machines based on military tank designs aided rapid urbanization and began to move huge quantities of soil, compacting it to great depths. Legal rulings stimulated contractors to ensure that soil under paving was compacted to the maximum level attainable to avoid subsidence and potential lawsuits. Space for tree roots was squeezed out of the soil, and the number of locations where trees would not survive dramatically increased.

Figure 1.6.4. Independence Mall in Philadelphia, by Dan Kiley, 30 years after installation. A good example of trees planted in the 1960s with no consideration for soil. When Kiley's work was removed, landscape architects were outraged, but no one seemed to be aware that most of the trees had failed because of poor soil design.

At the same time that soil conditions became increasingly difficult, designers of landscapes, particularly landscape architects, began losing interest in the horticultural aspects of their profession. Landscapes were built to attain aesthetic results, but little attention was paid to the long-term success of the trees. Knowledge of trees and soils was lost.

By the early 1980s, the American Society of Landscape Architecture had adopted a policy not to include information on plants in its journal, *Landscape Architecture*. Around the same time, the profession of urban forestry was evolving in recognition that urban trees needed special attention. It was urban foresters who challenged the design profession to bring scientific principles into the design of the landscape.

URBAN SOIL AND TREE GROWTH

Urban soil disturbance generally reduces opportunities for tree growth. The process begins with grading the soil, cutting into existing soil profiles and filling over others. Relocating soil disrupts its structure. Surface soil is mixed with subsoil and other materials and often compacted. Some disturbed soil may be unstable due to low bulk density levels in deep fills. Irregular and discontinuous soil horizons may be created in the fill, while original soil horizons may become discontinuous, changing their hydrologic characteristics. Areas of exposed subsoil, low in fertility and already compacted from the weight of the soil above, are further compacted during the grading process. Soil thus damaged is not easy to repair.

Paving, soil crusting, and maintenance practices disrupt hydrologic and organic cycles. Toxic chemicals may be part of the fill or be added to the soil over time. Building foundations and other structures displace soil volume, divert the movement of ground water, and change the levels of available water in the soil.

URBAN SOIL CONDITIONS

The following are the types of degradation found in urban soils. We'll explore some techniques to mitigate urban soil problems in later chapters.

Remnant Soil

In any urban area, there will be soil that has not been highly disturbed and may still provide favorable rooting conditions, water holding, and nutrient supply. Remnant soils may be on the surface or buried under paving or layers of fill. These soils can often be depended on to grow better trees. Remnant soils generally have their B and C horizons intact and often do not have root-limiting bulk densities. Locating these soils and identifying their degree of disturbance is critical at an early stage of soil analysis so they can be protected as far as possible during construction. It is virtually always better to protect and enhance remnant soil where it exists than to excavate and replace with new soil.

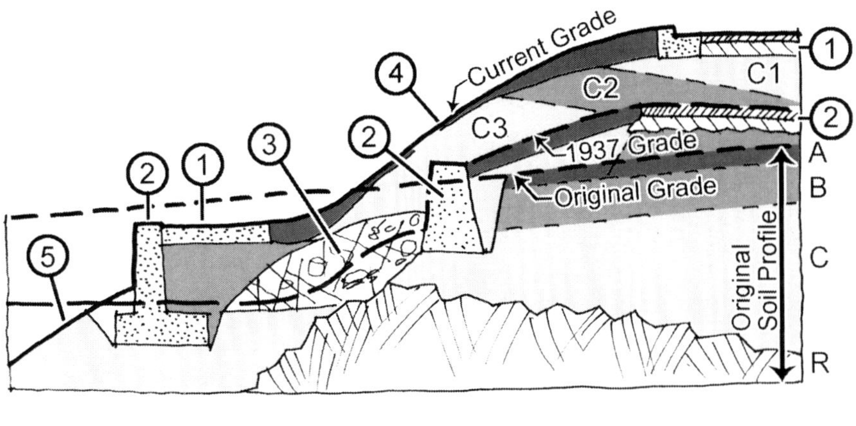

Figure 1.6.5. Urban soil profile.
A, B, C, R. Original soil horizons, may be graded and or compacted. Remnant and buried topsoil may be encountered.
C1–C5. Fill soils of various types, bulk density levels, and consistencies from heavy clays to sands. Expect soil interfaces between different soils.

1. Existing impervious surfaces.
2. Buried impervious surfaces and structures.
3. Buried trash and debris; may be unstable organic trash or compacted rock and gravel.
4. Eroded topsoil layer and exposed fills.
5. Exposed original subsoil with low organic content.

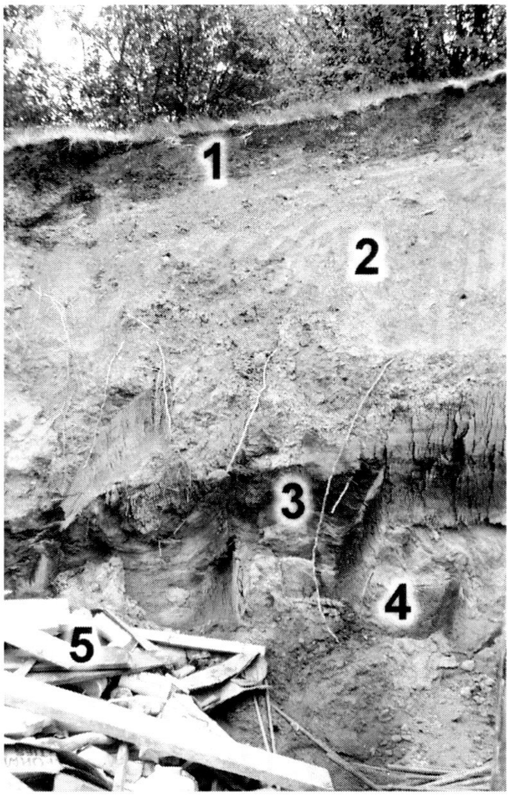

Figure 1.6.6. Remnant soil.

1. New topsoil. Note sharp interface between topsoil and fill material below.
2. Fill soil. Note lack of structure and fine roots.
3. Buried remnant topsoil. Note thick roots and angular structure preserved in the soil.
4. Original B horizon soil with strong structure and gradual transition between topsoil and subsoil.
5. Trash piled into the excavation, if not removed, will become a part of the urban soil profile.

Variability of Profile and Texture

The grading process cuts into existing soil profiles and adds fill layers, creating new profiles. These profiles may be difficult if not impossible to map. What might be under the ground? Conventional soil assessment techniques will not tell us. Part 1, Chapter Seven will discuss urban soil assessment techniques.

Soil texture within these profiles may also be highly variable, changing rapidly over short distances. Compacted layers may be buried. These differences result in changes in the hydrology of the soil and its ability to support root growth.

Discontinuity and Impedance Layers

Variability in soil profile and texture results in layers within the soil profile being discontinuous. Depending on the degree of textural difference between the soil types and their bulk density, each of these independent layers may form distinct hydrologic cells. When different soil textures are placed on top of or beside one another, an interface or impedance layer may form, slowing water movement. In a discontinuous profile layer, water may remain in the soil for long enough periods to become anaerobic.

These hydrologic cells can function like perched water tables and can be hard to find or predict. They may be a problem only in extremely wet years. Providing positive subsoil drainage in urban soils is particularly important in managing discontinuous soil layers.

Loss of Structure

Grading soil diminishes its structure. The mechanical action of digging up, moving, spreading, and compacting crushes soil peds, crumbling them into small

Figure 1.6.7. Urban soil with compacted, massive structure.

pieces. If the soil is graded when the water content is too high or low, the damage is worse. Damaged structure is very difficult to restore, especially if the soil is compacted. The structure of heavily compacted urban soil is described as massive and looks more like concrete than soil. Tree roots cannot easily penetrate massive soils.

Compaction

Compaction causes the greatest difficulty for trees in the urban landscape. The nature of urban construction requires significant bulk density levels. Compaction continues after construction through vibration and traffic. As soil particles are pressed together, root penetration, water infiltration, and drainage rates are reduced. Bulk density may vary with depth. Buried compacted layers can get in the way of drainage. Or, as depicted in Figure 1.6.8, bulk density in urban soils can decrease with depth due to heavy surface compaction over improperly prepared subgrade, while natural soils increase in bulk density with depth due to the weight of the soil above.

Simply digging up a natural soil with good structure and placing it back into the hole compacts it through loss of structure and subsequent settlement. Because they compact the soil as it is installed, engineers normally add between 10 and 20 percent more soil to fill the same volume of cut. Soil used for planting is also compacted as it is installed. Figure 1.6.9 illustrates the loss

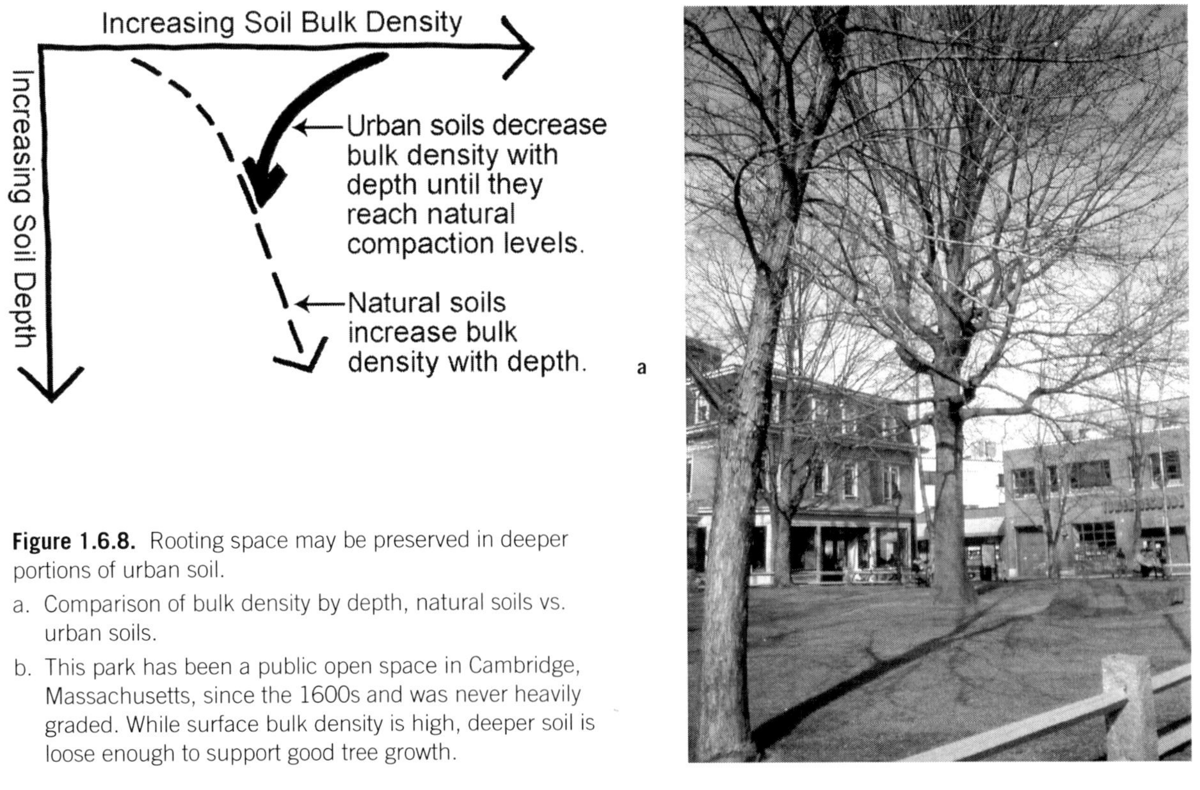

Figure 1.6.8. Rooting space may be preserved in deeper portions of urban soil.

a. Comparison of bulk density by depth, natural soils vs. urban soils.
b. This park has been a public open space in Cambridge, Massachusetts, since the 1600s and was never heavily graded. While surface bulk density is high, deeper soil is loose enough to support good tree growth.

of soil volume in an excavation through settlement. The compacting process is widespread and difficult to correct. At some point, the soil reaches root-limiting bulk density levels.

Surface Crusting

The surface of bare, low organic soil can form a thin layer that will repel water and impede drainage. The most common cause of soil crusting is the dispersal of fine soil particles during rain. The force of the rain breaks down soil peds into individual particles. While in a fluid condition, larger soil particles become aligned with their flat surfaces horizontal to the surface, and the smallest particles settle into voids. The resulting crust can be quite thin, less than 1/8 inch. Light compaction, the accumulation of airborne hydrocarbons from cars and jet airplanes, or lime dust from the construction process can render the crust almost impervious to air and water exchange.

A second form of crusting common to construction sites is the accumulation of fine clay and silt deposits. Excavated low areas collect silty water. A thin film of sediment forms a crust, lining the bottom of the excavated area and reducing infiltration.

A third form of crusting occurs at locations where concrete trucks or mortar mixers are cleaned, leaving thin films of impervious cement.

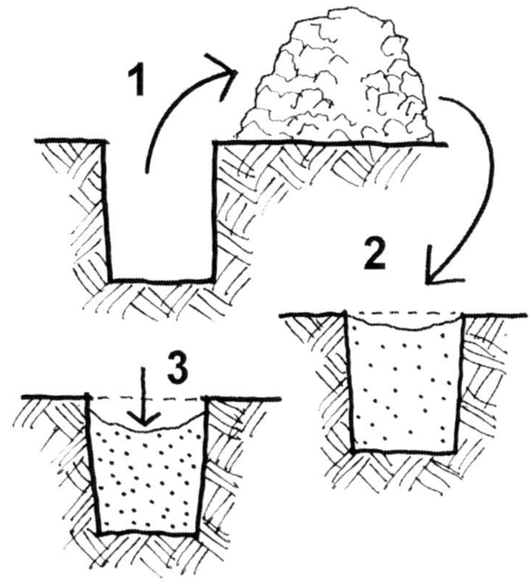

Figure 1.6.9. Loss of soil volume through settlement.

1. As the soil is removed, important soil structure is lost.
2. The same soil pile will not fill the hole back to the original level, indicating an increase in bulk density.
3. With time, additional settlement of this soil indicates an even higher bulk density.

a

b

c

Figure 1.6.10. Soil crusting.

a. Smooth appearance and characteristic cracking of dry, crusted soil.
b. Crust of cement slurry from concrete mixer washout.
c. Ponding water on top of a thin soil crust.

If a soil with a strong surface crust is buried, the impervious layer can cause significant reductions in drainage. Light tilling or roughening with backhoe teeth of any subgrade surfaces to be filled and surfaces to be planted can relieve this problem. Maintaining a layer of mulch, thick ground cover, or lawn will prevent surface crusting on finished grades.

Hydrologic Cycle/Drainage

Most of the previous discussion is about various ways that disrupt the hydrologic cycle. Moisture flow into the soil may be reduced, creating dry conditions, or water movement out of the soil may be reduced, causing wet conditions. When drainage rates are reduced, the soil's oxygen level can remain low for prolonged periods. Under these conditions, soil will begin to turn gray and eventually develop an anaerobic sour smell. Too much water is more often the cause of urban tree decline than too little. Since mapping urban soil drainage is extremely difficult, all soil installations should include provisions for drainage systems to ensure positive movement of water through the root zone.

Soil Particle Migration

In soils where fine particles are mixed with coarse sand and gravel, the fine particles are sometimes insufficient to fill all the spaces between the larger particles. In these cases, the fine particles may migrate down into these pores. This migration will be slight when the soil is dry to moist, but increases as the soil becomes wetter and as compacting pressure squeezes wet soil from above.

As soil moisture approaches saturation, water forms a lubricating film around the particles. If there is enough space between the large soil particles, the finer particles may begin to flow through the soil, following the laws of fluids by responding to the pressure flow of the water within the soil. Cavities at lower levels within the soil will fill up. When rubble and gravel are under or adjacent to finer-grained soils, particle flow can be so pervasive that the surface of the soil will subside.

This principle is a cause of much of the settlement in soil that was excavated and then replaced without attaining sufficient bulk density. Small soil clods act like gravel, bridging over gaps that then become filled with finer material as the clods break down. The soil mass slowly collapses into itself.

If migrating fine particles encounter an impedance layer in the soil, such as a compacted layer, two layers of different soil textures, or a piece of filter cloth, they may form a layer that further restricts drainage and water movement. Filter cloths used in drainage systems have been known to clog or "blind over." When specifying a filter cloth, take care to use material that will pass small soil particles that might collect on its surface. Filter manufacturers should be consulted in selecting fabrics for different soil types and applications.

Particle flow can also have a beneficial effect. When fine-grained soil is placed over gravel or rubble without a separating filter fabric, the migration of finer particles will form a natural transition layer, breaking the impedance to water flows. While the stone may appear clogged, the fine particles never compact to the point where drainage stops. Drainage through the stone is reduced, but drainage between the stone and soil is increased. Some amount of soil settlement should be expected, as the soil migration into the gravel will reduce the volume of the soil above. The amount of settlement is related to the volume of the gravel. Gravel drain systems have functioned for many decades before they slow to the point where they are not serviceable.

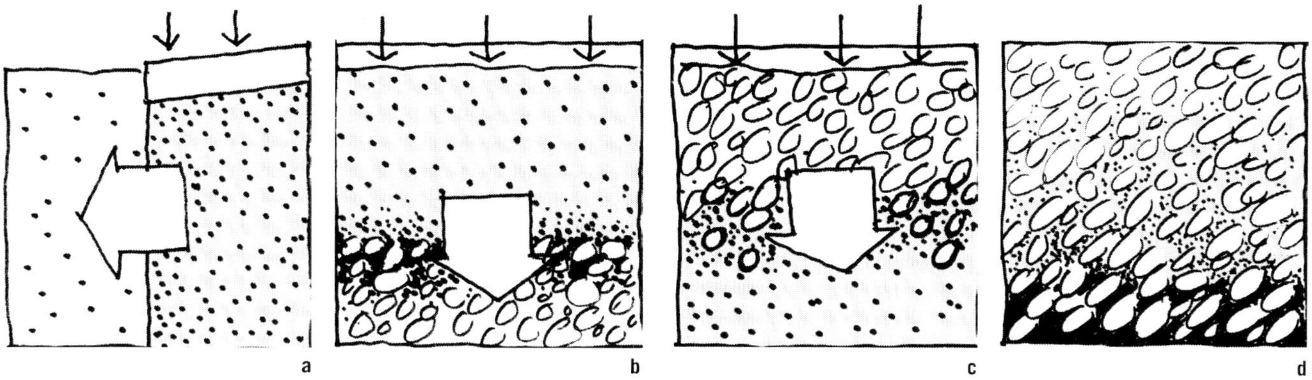

Figure 1.6.11. Saturated soil particle migration.

a. Compacted soil next to loose soil. Particles migrate horizontally, causing settlement of roadbed.
b. Fine-grained soil over coarse-grained soil. Fine particles migrate into coarse-grained soil, causing settlement.
c. Gravel over fine-grained plastic soil. Aggregate pushes into the lower soil, causing settlement.
d. Gap-graded soil such as CU Structural Soil. Fine particles compress into lower levels or into drainage system, leaving the top void of soil.

Particle migration can occur when soils with two significantly different textures or bulk density levels are placed next to or on top of one another. Soils that are gap-graded, such as CU structural soil or sandy soil mixes, may experience particle migration within the soil mix if the material becomes saturated. Fine particles will migrate out of the upper zones of these soils into lower areas or into the drainage system.

Particles from pavement subgrade soils can migrate into loosely compacted planting soils causing pavement failure. Providing a sloped angle of repose from the toe of pavement edges into and under the planting soils should retain the soil.

Anthropogenic Material and Rubble

Anthropogenic material is anything made or modified by humans. This material—bricks, masonry rubble, coal ash, plastic cups, clothing, etc.—litters urban soil horizons. Finding such material is a good indicator that the soil was placed there as part of previous construction. The objects can sometimes be used to date a particular soil disturbance and aid in soil assessment. They are similar in function to rock fragments in natural soil. The larger the percentage of anthropogenic material in the soil, the greater the impact on soil quality.

Until the quantity of anthropogenic material reaches about 15 percent of the soil volume, it can be ignored, provided it is evenly distributed within the soil.

Figure 1.6.12. Urban soil with anthropogenic material.

Figure 1.6.13. Rock or anthropogenic material in soil at concentrations of 15, 50, and 75 percent. As rock increases, there is less room for root development and more total volume is needed.

Figure 1.6.14. Plants can grow in extreme soil environments, but species are limited and growth rates slow.

a. Pines growing on top of solid rock outcrop. *(Photo credit: Bill Fountain)*

b. Locust growing in 2-inch-thick sand bed between brick paving and the gravel sub-base. These trees' trunk diameters increased just 2 inches in 30 years.

When solid fragments exceed 15 percent of the volume, they begin to reduce the ability of the soil to support roots by taking up space that could otherwise contribute to plant growth. When objects are between 50 and 75 percent of the volume, the effect on soil volume is significant and the fragments may contribute to making a soil that is highly compactable. Between 75 and 80 percent, the objects, assuming that they are solid, begin to touch, and compacting forces bridge over the remaining soil, leaving fine-textured soil with lower bulk density, even though the overall material may become compacted. This is the principle of structural soil developed by Cornell University. Roots will continue to grow in this soil but the soil volume itself becomes the limiting factor.

Often, anthropogenic material is found concentrated in layers, such as buried paving rubble fill or vertically as old walls and foundations. These layers of material often cause failures in the urban plantings. Sheets of buried gypsum wallboard were found to be the cause of a mysterious and significant plant decline at an office park in Virginia. Buried paving can conduct water into unintended places. Roots of existing trees often concentrate in the rubble/soil interface of old foundations. Roots can also redirect themselves around solid objects, changing assumed growth patterns.

Extreme Concentrations of Particle Size: Clay, Sand, Gravel, and Rock

Concentrations of a particular soil particle size classification appear in nature in places such as clay bogs, sand dunes, gravel talus, and exposed bedrock. In each case, the range of plants that can grow in these environments is severely limited. In urban areas, construction also creates concentrations of clay, sand, gravel, or rock. Unlike the natural models, bulk density often is significant and the cycling of organic matter is cut off. The number of plants that can survive becomes severely limited.

Areas of solid or decaying bedrock may be found near the surface, the result of previous grading activity. The type and structure of this rock may form a barrier to roots or may offer channels within the rock layers that can be good places for roots to grow. In nature, trees can be found on very thin soils over rock outcroppings and even growing directly on the face of the rock if conditions are adequate. Replication of those conditions in built landscapes is difficult, as such trees start from seed and even in nature, growth rates are slow and mortality rates high.

Utilities

In extreme cases, utilities become dense enough to impede soil volume and water flow over a significant portion of the landscape. In addition to the simple loss of space, backfill around pipes and vaults sometimes consists of special granular fills that are not good places to grow tree roots. Utilities compete for space and limit the opportunities to take corrective action in urban situations.

Nutrient and Organic Cycles

Urban soils are often shut off from nutrient cycling. As we saw in Part 1, Chapter Three, large areas of paving and buildings reduce the supply of leaves. Those leaves that do fall to the ground are often removed. Lawn clippings are bagged, dead limbs and trees taken away. In some instances, wood- and bark-based mulch is added back, but this material lacks the biological complexity of the forest floor. Composted green waste will rapidly decompose when applied as a mulch. Chemical fertilizers may be applied in garden and lawn areas, but the water-soluble nature of the nitrogen in these products makes the treatment temporary, requiring repeated application. Inorganic chemical fertilizer does not supply the organic matter that is the foundation of the soil food web.

Losing these organic layers makes it difficult for damaged urban soil to recover. The type and number of organisms in the soil are reduced as the flow of organic matter slows. The processing of many important chemicals needed by the tree is cut off, making it difficult to maintain soil structure and continuing the downward spiral of urban soil. Restoring the organic cycle is one of the easiest ways to start a damaged soil on the road to recovery.

Figure 1.6.15. Exposed utilities. The number, location, and depth of urban utilities, particularly in older cities, are difficult to predict and conflict with the goals of improving soil.

Figure 1.6.16. Organic matter is removed from urban sites. Compost as a part of site management must be added on a regular basis.

Figure 1.6.17. A mason found this tree pit an easy place to work, leaving lime dust behind. Unless removed, this dust will raise the pH of the soil around the tree.

pH

Urbanization changes the pH of soil. A high (above 9) or low (below 4) pH can indicate previous intensive industrial activity or toxic material in the soil. Urban soil normally has an elevated pH, above 7, because concrete, masonry, paint, and other building products are alkaline-based materials. Even mulch and compost can have elevated pH, depending on the source of the organic matter. Mulch and compost made from composted sewage sludge often have a high pH due to the lime used in the processing of the sewage. See Part 1, Chapter Four for a more in-depth discussion of pH and soil.

Salt

Elevated salt levels are often present in urban soils. Sodium-based salt compounds are water-soluble and may not show up in soil tests after heavy spring rains, but may still be the cause of serious decline in trees.

Toxic Chemicals

Toxic chemicals are difficult to find without significant specialized testing. Small spills or random chemical use during the history of a site may create levels of toxicity harmful to plants or dangerous to humans. Sites of known industrial activity may be easier to recognize and assess, but also present large cleanup issues. Land adjacent to major transportation routes often has elevated chemical toxicity, particularly lead near highways. Studies have found that soil as far away as 500 feet from inner-city interstate highways can carry lead levels toxic to humans.

Even chemicals that plants need to grow can be found in concentrations that are toxic to those plants. Any chemical in high enough concentrations will at some point be toxic to the plant.

Temperature

Urban soils, especially those directly under pavement, next to dark masonry walls, and near steam lines, can be hot enough to prevent roots from developing or even kill existing roots. Soil temperatures in rooftop planters over unheated spaces in cold climates can reach levels that can damage roots. However, this is rare when soil volumes are large enough and deep enough to support large trees.

Figure 1.6.18. Grading at an urban site.

Soil Stability

Construction and reconstruction are nearly continuous in urban areas, posing a significant problem for existing trees. Soil is being disturbed on a regular basis to install or repair utilities and sidewalks, or to reshape the land for new uses. Any roots thus disturbed will be damaged. If the soil was of good quality before the disturbance, its quality is often degraded after the work is completed.

URBAN SOILS AND ROOT PATHWAYS

Any one of the abovementioned problems may not be fatal to the tree, but when two or more combine they can accumulate to stress levels that can be fatal.

Fortunately, tree roots are opportunistic. If better soil is available and roots can find a way past degraded soils, they will exploit the better resources. Not all trees can escape past areas of poor soil, and some will grow better than others. Roots can follow pathways in the soil over pipes, along the backsides of curbs, or along cracks in the pavement for great distances to exploit a remote soil resource. Unfortunately, as the roots follow these pathways, they can do great harm to paving, structures, and utilities. Designers can prevent much of this damage by using design and construction techniques to remove inconsistencies in the soil and provide for more consistent tree growth.

a

Figure 1.6.19. Roots will follow pathways of suitable growing conditions.

a. Roots finding enough water and air in the seams of solid rock.
b. Roots following the pathway created by the installation of a utility conduit.

b

REFERENCES

Key References

Craul, Phillip J. 1999. *Urban Soils:Applications and Practices.* John Wiley & Sons, New York, NY. 366 pp.

Craul, Phillip J. 1992. *Urban Soil in Landscape Design.* John Wiley & Sons, New York, NY. 396 pp.

Harris, Richard W., James R. Clark, and Nelda P. Matheny. 2004. *Arboriculture: Integrated Management of Landscape Trees, Shrubs, and Vines.* 4th ed. Prentice-Hall, Upper Saddle River, NJ. 578 pp.

Scheyer, J. M., and K.W. Hipple. 2005. *Urban Soil Primer.* United States Department of Agriculture, Natural Resources Conservation Service, National Soil Survey Center, Lincoln, NE. 74 pp.

Trowbridge, Peter J., and Nina L. Bassuk. 2004. *Trees in the Urban Landscape: Site Assessment Design and Installation.* John Wiley & Sons, Hoboken, NJ. 205 pp.

Other Resources

OpenAg.info's Soil Science Encyclopedia. 2007. http://www.openag.info/wiki/index.php/Soil_Science_Encyclopedia.

PART ONE

7
Urban Soil Assessment

Landscape design normally begins with an assessment of site conditions. As part of their preliminary work, responsible designers seek to gain an understanding of sun angles, views, topography, land ownership, zoning regulations, and other factors that will affect the design. At undisturbed sites, a study of existing soil conditions, as taken from the natural Resources Conservation Service (NRCS) Soil Surveys, is also included in the analysis.

At a disturbed urban site, however, existing soil conditions are often not considered. Information about these soil resources is thought not to be readily available, or the resources are considered a damaged commodity with little value. Neither of these assumptions is correct, and accepting them can lead to increased project cost or to the poor growth of trees and other plantings.

Urban soils can be assessed, mapped, and incorporated into project designs, and such assessment contributes valuable information to the success of those designs. Often, soil resources can be improved with little effort, at a savings of time and money over the life of the project. Ignoring soil quality during the design process leads to environmental harm, increased cost, and reduced chances of growing the long-lived, large, healthy trees that contribute so much to an urban environment.

It may be obvious from the start that the existing soil is not a good candidate for reuse, and extensive soil analysis is not justified. This might be the case, for example, where most or all of the site must be dramatically disturbed and relocated. Large urban buildings sometimes require the excavation of the

Figure 1.7.1. NRCS soil surveys, the sole source of most site soil analysis, are not adequate for urban sites.

entire site to build basement space. What little land is not built upon is used for infrastructure and construction staging. Required topographic changes may leave only small areas of the site undisturbed. In these cases, it would be of little value for the designer to consider the existing soil resource. However, the designer must still anticipate soil conditions at the end of the construction process, and plan and budget for their restoration.

Understanding urban soil requires the use of a different set of tools and skills than those used to assess natural soil. On most NRCS soil maps, urban soils are designated as Urban Land Complex, described only at the soil association level, or with historic soil designations mapped before development disturbed the soil. Internet sources and GIS mapping technology also provide little information.

Effective urban soil assessment takes place on a site-by-site basis and uses a wide range of tools brought together by an informed designer. Designers must use their creative skills to understand soil just as they analyze other complex site relationships. Using the recommendations outlined in this chapter, landscape designers will be able to conduct urban soil assessments as a necessary part of the design process. Urban soil study is part anthropology, archeology, forensics, and historical discovery. If you watch *CSI* or The History Channel, you will love urban soil work.

DEVELOPING A SITE-SPECIFIC ANALYSIS

Firsthand knowledge of the soil at urban sites may be difficult to obtain. Soil is often covered with paving and may be highly compacted, making the insertion of hand-operated soil probes difficult or impossible. The layers of greatest interest may be deeper than can be easily observed. Since urban soil disturbance is highly variable and the opportunity for sufficient soil sampling is limited, designers must employ a combination of physical sampling and investigative inquiry. This requires synthesizing information from many sources. The primary sources of urban soil information include

- existing soil surveys
- physical sampling of existing soil
- existing plant types and condition
- site history
- site utility survey
- aerial photography
- existing and historical topography and mapping
- geotechnical boring reports

Each source helps reveal what kinds of soil may have existed at the site before human occupation, and what changes to the soil have resulted from human activity.

Figure 1.7.2. Urban soils are dramatically modified from natural soils. Circled piles are remnants of the existing grade left in place to hold grade stakes.

SOIL ASSESSMENT QUESTIONS

A good urban soil survey seeks to answer the same questions a soil scientist asks when evaluating a natural soil. What is the combination of soil texture, drainage, compaction, and chemical and biological properties that makes up each soil type? How are different soil types or layers arranged?

From a textural classification perspective, urban soils are still just a combination of clay, silt, sand, and gravel-size particles. However, the particles may not be of natural origin, and there may be considerable non-soil material included, such as garbage, building material, and other human-produced debris. In most cases, these objects simply function as a different particle size and shape. For instance, a crushed can or a brick is simply a large piece of aggregate. In other situations, human-produced material can carry chemicals that change soil composition, pH, or aggregation in ways that influence plant growth. See the previous chapter for details on human disturbance of soil.

A good urban soil analysis must answer six fundamental questions:

1. What are the soil textures?
2. To what extent has the soil been disturbed by grading, cutting, and filling?
3. To what levels has the soil been compacted?
4. How well does the soil drain?
5. What barriers and interfaces are within the soil profile?
6. Are there chemicals within the soil that will be hazardous to plants or humans?

The answers to these questions set the limits to how the existing soil can be used and to what extent it must be modified during the construction of the new landscape.

EXISTING SOIL SURVEYS

NRCS soil surveys, available from the county of each project, will form a beginning point for more in-depth analysis. While these surveys may not provide much information on the site in question, they are full of useful data. The introductory portions of the survey contain information about the regional soil forming process; they also include extensive descriptions of the different kinds of natural soils and soil associations that could be encountered in the surrounding geography. Since it is expensive to move soil very far, it is likely that these soils will form the basis of those encountered at urban sites. Pay careful attention to the lower soil horizon descriptions, since the upper horizons (topsoil) are often removed. NRCS maps may be useful in establishing the location of remnant soil—predevelopment soils that are still in place, with B and C horizons intact and relatively low compacting.

Often, the NRCS offices have copies of the historical surveys that precede the current version. Some of these surveys go back to the early part of the 20th century, when many urban areas were still agricultural. While these documents are not available for distribution, most NRCS local administrators will grant access to them, and they can be a valuable source of information on predevelopment soil conditions.

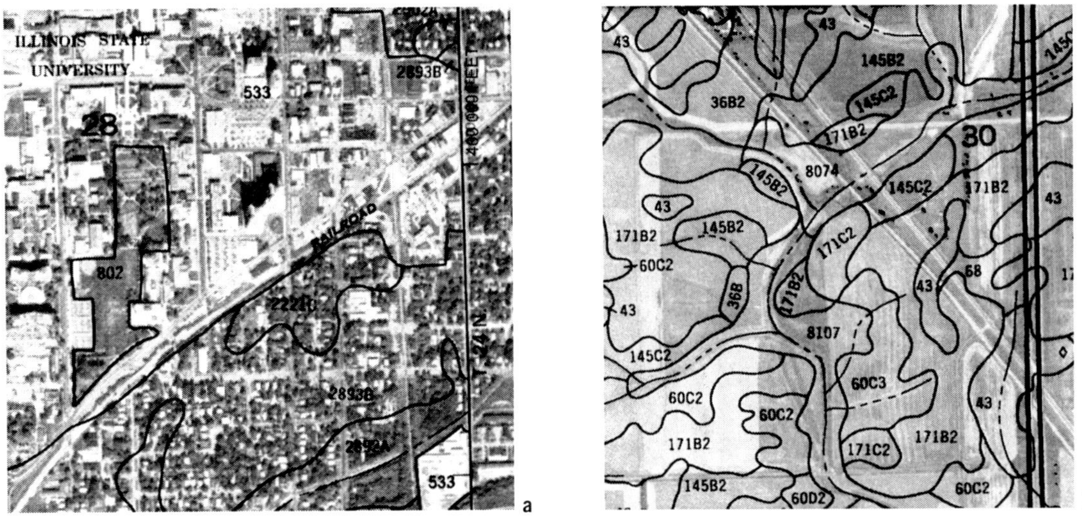

Figure 1.7.3. NRCS soil survey of an urban area.

a. Downtown area of Normal, Illinois. Soil in this area is classified as "Urban Land Complex" and not described.

b. Farmland immediately outside of Normal with similar topography and relationship to watercourses. Study of the soil descriptions and limitations in this area can provide clues to the urban land complex soil that may be found within the urban development.

Money Is on Mars, Dirt Is on Earth

In her book *Under Ground*, Yvonne Baskin (2005) notes that the United States has spent more money studying the soils of Mars than it has studying the soils on Earth—a sad commentary on our priorities as a nation.

The NRCS is developing ways to map large areas of urban soil, but is only beginning to establish the descriptive terminology for various urban soil conditions. Surveying methodologies are being tested on a few pilot sites, but the work of accurately mapping large areas of very diverse soil conditions, much of which are covered by impervious material, will take decades.

PHYSICAL SAMPLING OF THE EXISTING SOIL

Physical sampling should be a part of onsite evaluation even though it may only produce limited data.

Sampling Tools

Different soil conditions demand different types of sampling tools. Here are some of the most common.

Figure 1.7.4. Soil sampling tools.

1. Small-bore sampling tube.
2. Helix auger.
3. Dutch auger.
4. Shovel.
5. Post-hole digger.

Shovel, Post-Hole Digger, or Trowel

While these tools are readily available, they offer only a limited ability to penetrate the soil to sufficient depths, especially in compacted soil.

Small-Bore Sampling Tube

This is the basic investigative tool, and one that should be found in every design office. It extracts a cylinder of soil about 1 inch in diameter and 12 inches long. A "T" handle allows the tube to be pushed into the ground.

Various configurations of this tool allow greater depth of sampling, up to about 4 feet. Foot jacks can be added to increase leverage. Twisting the probe during insertion increases efficiency. This probe allows the quickest sampling of upper soil layers when compaction is limited or when soils are moist. Dry soils, even when not overly compacted, may be difficult or impossible to penetrate with a sampling tube. If a large root or stone stops the probe, move it to another location a few inches away. Inspection of the debris on the end of the tube will often reveal the nature of an obstruction.

Helix Auger

Helix augers are available as an alternate tip to a small-bore sampling tube. They can penetrate stony or compacted soil, but are slow, and sampling frequency is greatly reduced. Soil removed from the hole tends to become mixed with the soil higher in the sample section, and the interpretation of the resulting soil samples must account for this contamination.

Dutch Auger

This tool is the most efficient in most urban soils and my personal favorite. It can penetrate compacted and dry soil. It is less efficient in stony soil where a stone can stop the auger. This auger removes large samples from a 3-inch diameter hole, and can penetrate to 5 or 6 feet with persistence and extender pipes. Longer, padded, and ratchet handles are available to increase leverage and make taking samples easier. Purchase several extension rods to allow adjustment in the length of the auger.

In sandy soil, the soil tends to fall out of the auger during the extraction process. Adding water to the hole as you dig can solve this problem. A variation on the Dutch auger is the bucket auger, which is useful in sandy soil to hold the soil in the tool.

Tools and other useful soil analysis equipment are available from forestry, nursery, and soil science equipment suppliers, such as Ben Meadows (www.benmeadows.com) or Forestry Suppliers (www.forestry-suppliers.com).

In addition to the sampling tools, other items will be needed that make up a soil sampling kit. A basic sampling kit will contain:

- plastic bags to hold soil samples
- black markers and pen
- clipboard and note pad
- a plan of the site to record sampling locations
- measuring tape
- camera
- a sheet of white plastic to lay out samples for photography
- paper towels and water to clean hands and tools

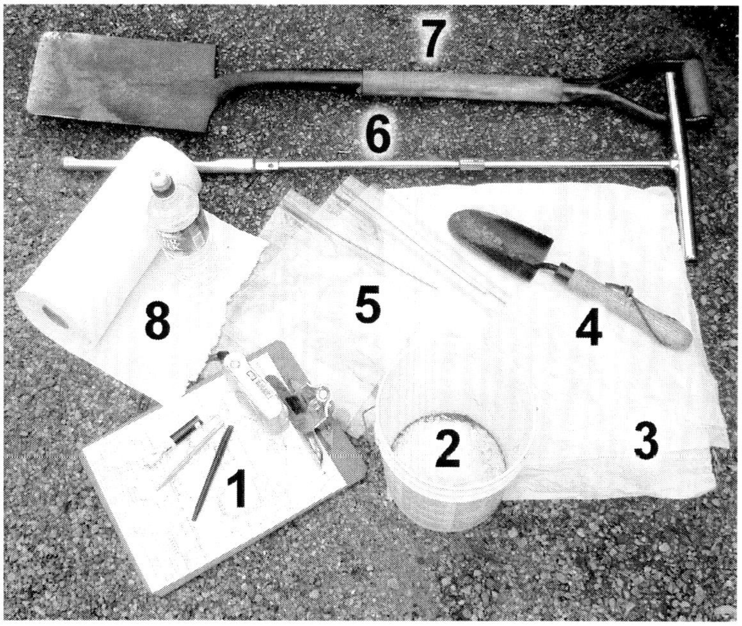

Figure 1.7.5. Soil sampling kit.

1. Camera, paper, plans, markers.
2. Two-gallon pail.
3. White plastic sheet.
4. Trowel.
5. One-gallon locking plastic bags.
6 Soil probe.
7. Shovel.
8. Water and towels for cleanup.

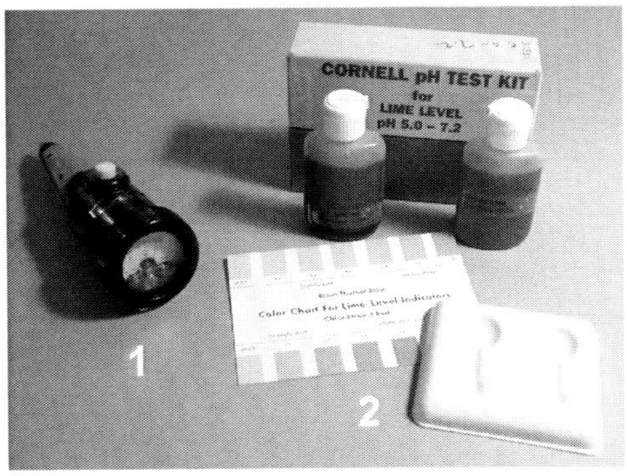

Figure 1.7.6. pH testing tools.
1. Kelway pH meter—rapid measurement; also measures moist soil.
2. Cornell pH testing kit—slower but more accurate.

Figure 1.7.7. Correct starting position for a Dutch auger. Select an auger length that is a little taller than your waist. Use extension rods to bore deeper holes.

Field pH Testing

A handheld pH meter, such as a Kelway pH meter, can be useful to gather readings in the field, but the readings are not as accurate as those obtained by pH tests that saturate soil samples with color-rated chemicals. A Cornell pH testing kit gives accurate results from soil samples back at the office, if rapid results are needed. The testing procedure is easy and requires no real training. The Cornell pH testing kit is available at www.css.cornell.edu/soiltest/soil_testing/products.asp. For complete pH testing, it is important to purchase both the high and low pH range Cornell kits.

Soil Sampling Techniques

With some knowledge and practice, you can learn to construct a fairly accurate first impression of the accessible soil at a site by feeling the soil texture (see Part 1, Chapter Two) and observing its compaction, color, and odor.

None of the soil tools is easy to use in compacted soil. Soil investigators need to be prepared for a good workout, as soil sampling is physically demanding. Wear gloves to reduce blisters. Keep tools clean and sharp, including filing the edges of shovels and probes. If possible, schedule your investigation when the soil is moist. This will reduce the effort needed to dig in the soil, allowing moisture to lubricate soil particles and tools to slide into the soil more easily.

Selecting Sampling Locations

Taking each sample may require considerable effort, so take time to carefully choose each site. Understanding the site and the project's goals before taking samples can narrow the choices. Before starting extensive sampling, it is worthwhile to investigate the soil history of the site, along with other sources of soil information described later in this chapter. This may point you toward sample sites of particular interest.

When looking for places to observe, do not be confined by the actual site. If there are places in the general vicinity of the site where the development history might be similar but the soil is more accessible, take samples there to record additional information. There is always a considerable amount of utility work and other construction in a city, and finding holes and trenches others are digging in the area can save time and provide useful information even if the excavations are not actually on the site in question.

Use topography and drainage patterns to help you choose the right sites. Try to determine what may have been original topography and what is obviously graded material. Low places, ridges, and slopes often have different soil. Water staining on pavements and at wall weep holes may indicate saturated soil conditions. Using the type and quality of existing plants as an indicator of soil quality, take samples from places where plants indicate a difference in soil quality.

A good location for a sample site is at the property line adjacent to neighboring property. Often the two sites are graded at different times by different owners, but neither can disturb the grades at their common property edge. Original soil profiles can often be observed there. Soils under large, old trees are also candidates for finding original soil profiles.

At sites where existing soil is covered by paving, begin by taking samples from easy-to-reach places like tree pits and other open locations. Inserting a probe at a slight angle next to the paving will help you take samples from under the paving, giving a better example of the types of soils to be expected. Finally, potholes or other damaged paving at the site can be large enough to insert a soil probe for a limited sample.

As you remove samples, carefully examine the removed soil for color and smell. (See Part 1, Chapter Two for more information on soil color and soil odor.) Note overly dry soil as well as wet soil. Record anthropogenic or human-introduced material found in the soil. Everything from bricks and broken china to cigarette butts and human hair indicate that the soil was not naturally placed. Some anthropogenic material can be used to date the disturbance and confirm other historical information.

Record all the information in a field book. Number each observation site and note the location on a plan. Take numerous photographs of the site, soil extracted, soil profiles and the conditions of trees. Modern digital cameras have amazing resolution and the camera should be set to the highest resolution practical. Mark all soil samples and place in food storage bags. All this effort requires considerable work, and an assistant is normally needed.

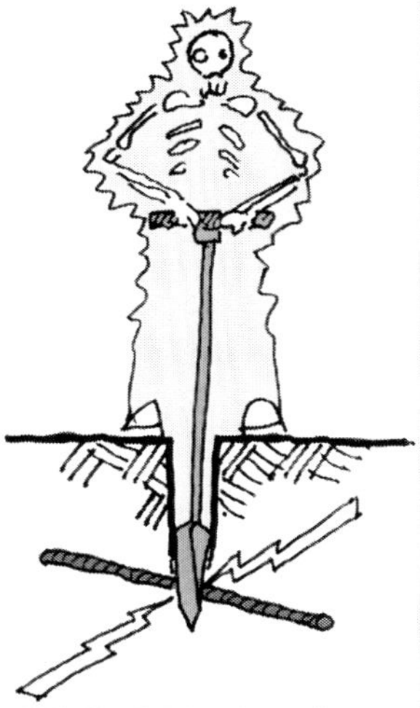

An Electric Experience

All soil investigators need to be wary of underground electric lines. They are rarely in the spots where they are indicated on plans. Unmapped lines are common. Local utility services can locate underground service. If time and the size of the project permit, it is a good idea to have the locations marked on the ground before starting soil investigations. An electric line will feel similar to a root, which makes a soft thump on the probe. (A rock, on the other hand, makes a grinding noise.) A soil probe will easily cut through the insulation on a wire. Do not ignore an encounter with a soft, resistive object. Play it safe and move to another location.

Figure 1.7.8. Observe soil in holes dug for other purposes around and near the site to gather useful information. It is much easier to look down a utility hole than to dig with an auger.

Compaction Terminology

The words *compaction, bulk density,* and *penetration* resistance become intertwined when evaluating soil for reuse as a planting medium. Compaction as it impacts plant growth is the soil's bulk density (weight divided by volume) and is a measurable quality if the proper tools are available. Penetration resistance, or how hard it is to push an object into the soil, is moisture-sensitive but can give some compaction feedback when not too wet or dry. A penetrometer, shovel, or soil probe will each give some information on penetration resistance.

COMPACTION

Compaction is a significant factor in how useful the soil will be. Do not be fooled into thinking soil that is easy to dig is not compacted. The more moisture in the soil, the easier it is to dig and insert probes. As the soil dries out, almost all soil will feel compacted, so be aware of soil moisture when evaluating compaction. Even good garden soil can be impenetrable when dry, and heavily compacted clay soil easy to penetrate when wet. The presence and depth of small roots in the samples can help indicate the compaction level at below root-limiting levels. Old, dead roots, normally black, may be found in recently compacted soil, a residue of a time when the soil was less compacted.

Undercompaction of the soil can be as significant a problem as overcompaction. Patterns of differential settlement, pavement cracking, out-of-plumb walls, lights, and leaning large trees can indicate undercompaction. However, pavement lifting and subsiding may also be caused by expanding clay soil or roots or both. If there are sharp, architectural limits to the cracking, there may be a basement or vault below ground, supporting some areas of pavement more than others.

Bulk density levels can be assessed using methods described at the end of this chapter. This is time-consuming and tedious work. Sharpen your skills at observing site conditions and using soil assessment tools to help you make approximate soil compaction assessments needed for better design decisions.

PROFILE SAMPLING WITH A DUTCH AUGER

Carefully dig into the soil with the Dutch auger to record the soil profiles. Record the layers of soil. Lay each portion of the soil sample on white plastic sheets in the order that it is removed from the hole and at the correct depth so the soil profile is visible. Break apart any remaining soil peds to look at structure. Photograph the profile and make notes of your observations of its color, texture, odor, and compaction. Include measurements of the depths of different observations. For each soil that is significantly different, collect samples in plastic bags marked by both location and depth. These samples should be sent to a lab for analysis.

The number of samples needed will depend on the size of the project, its soil history, and the different types of soil uncovered. Since the biological nature of soil changes with time, biological testing may be done later in the construction process.

Figure 1.7.9. Soil profiles removed by a Dutch auger probe, laid on a white plastic sheet for examination. These images will be come part of the soil report.

Natural soil profile (left). Note gradual color shift from dark to light and increasingly larger soil peds with depth.

Constructed soil profile (right). Note lack of soil peds and sharp interface between two soil types at the midpoint in the profile.

The holes made by a small-bore sampling tube may be left open, but the hole made by a Dutch auger or other tools may be large enough to be a tripping hazard. It is always important to fill in the holes after recording the data. If the soil from the hole is collected on a plastic sheet, it is easier to gather the removed soil and place it back into the hole. If the soil removed from the hole is being collected as a sample, use soil from a nearby shrub bed or other location to fill the hole. Use the probe to push the edges of the hole inward to make a softer depression and partially fill the hole.

SOIL STRUCTURE

Samples extracted with small-bore probes and augers will reveal little about the structure of the soil, most of which is destroyed as the sample is removed. The samples from a Dutch auger can, with experience, provide some limited information about structure. To really examine structure, it is necessary to dig up a large shovelful of soil and break it apart to see how it fractures and crumbles. Looking in holes dug by a backhoe is the best way to observe soil structure.

EXISTING PLANTS AS SOIL INDICATORS

Trees, shrubs, lawns, and even weeds growing in cracks can provide information on soil quality. The condition and species of these plants will indicate the growing conditions of the soil. By evaluating the growing requirements of the healthy plants and plants in decline, it may be possible to make assumptions about drainage, pH, and fertility. Subtle changes in the size and vigor of similar plants across the site will indicate changes in soil. When evaluating plants, be aware of recent weather patterns. Weeds may look lush during an extended period of rain and be nonexistent during a drought.

Figure 1.7.10. Vertical platy soil structure revealed in excavation dug by a backhoe.

The health and stress levels of existing large trees are often the best long-term indicators of soil conditions. The plant stress indicators described in Part 1, Chapter Two can guide the interpretation of patterns and rates of plant stress. The book *Soul of Soil*, by Smillie and Gershuny, contains a list of weeds and what they may indicate about the soil. This reference is full of other low-tech ways to evaluate soil properties and is a great reference to learn more about natural soil.

Figure 1.7.11. Using plants as indicators of soil problems.

a. Change in grass type and stressed maple tree suggest soil compaction between the two paths.
b. Weeds in parking lot and healthy trees on the edges indicate remnant soil resources left undisturbed by the original construction.

a

b

SOIL HISTORY

In addition to historic and current soil surveys, the land-use history of a site can shed light on the kinds of soil disturbances that may be encountered. The local planning office is a good beginning source for historical material. They may have a series of maps used for insurance purposes, called Sanborn Maps that date back to the 19th century. These maps show the location and sizes of buildings as well as other human modifications to the landscape. Aerial photography of towns, available at the planning office, may date back to the 1920s. The city may also have permit records that show previous site construction and disturbances.

Local libraries and historical societies are also good sources of information. Historical maps are often available dating to the first settlers. Books on the history of the area contain many drawings, maps, and photographs that depict the character of the land from its earliest settlement. Key remaining features can be used to pinpoint the location of the site being investigated.

Cameras recorded much of America from the time of the Civil War. Before that, artists made numerous landscape drawings that are very accurate in portraying site conditions of that period.

Drawings of old construction projects are normally available for review. This investigation usually leads to a basement room full of treasured drawings with useful information. An hour of digging here can replace many hours of hard work in the field.

Oral histories and interviews with people familiar with the site—neighbors, previous contractors, janitors, groundskeepers, or building managers—can provide significant data on the history of the soil. Non-professional people who have connections to the site can sometimes offer very

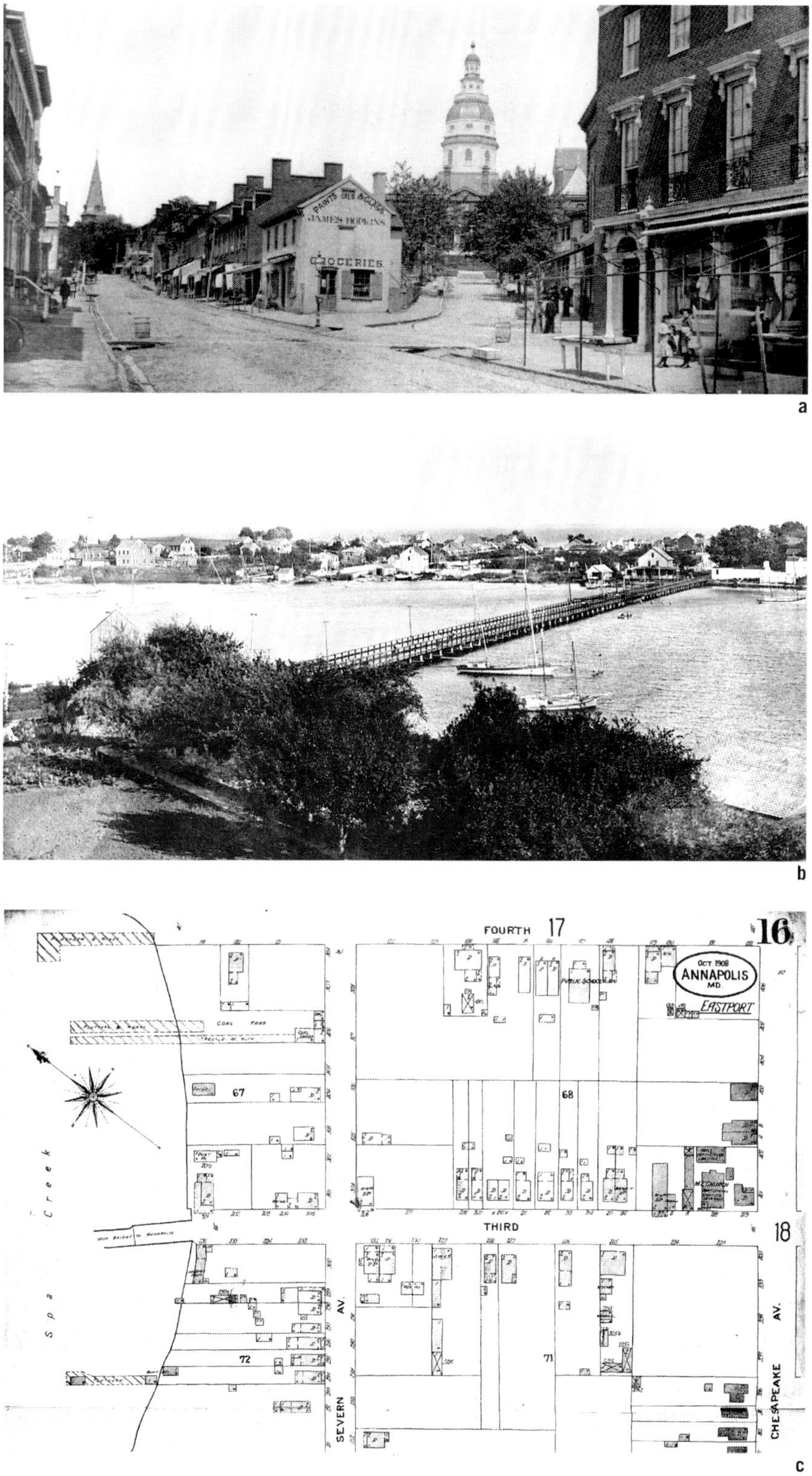

Figure 1.7.12. Sanborn maps, historical aerial photos, and old maps can reveal past uses of a site. (Source: Courtesy of the Maryland Archives)

a. Main Street, Annapolis, Maryland, circa 1888–1890. The trees are in soils that have not substantially changed in 100 years.

b. Eastport, Maryland, circa 1890. The location of large trees indicates good soil locations.

c. Sanborn map depicting the location of buildings and other important physical features that hold clues to soil disturbance.

accurate and important information. Their answers to questions about drainage, flooding, plant replacement, past grading, and construction can lead to a better understanding of the site conditions.

Site history investigation may be the only way to detect subsurface barriers and interfaces. Record the location of all previous buildings, roads, paving, and major utilities. Try to determine whether these objects are still present in the soil. Even if they have been removed, the compacted soil that supported them remains.

The more tools and sources of information, the clearer your picture of the existing soil conditions. All this may seem like a lot of effort, but it can save many hours of back-breaking digging to look at soils, and can save many thousands of dollars in design fees and construction costs.

SITE UTILITY SURVEY

The site utility survey records a significant amount of soil disturbance data and is an excellent resource to begin to understand soil disturbances. A survey drawing that includes site utilities is a good base to record other soil information gathered in the field.

AERIAL PHOTOGRAPHY

Low-altitude, high-resolution aerial photography can provide significant soil data for large urban sites. Its precise color rendering reveals subtle changes in plant colors. An infrared photograph is more difficult to obtain but provides more information if available. These photographs can be taken without the expensive ground measuring and stereographic features of traditional aerial photography

Figure 1.7.13. Aerial photographs can assist in identification of soil conditions. This photo, when viewed in color, easily indicates seven conditions that should be investigated with field probes. (Photo: David Wallace)

1. Dark green grass; probability of good soil.
2. Erratic tree growth and light green/ brown grass; dry slope soil.
3. Scalped brown patch.
4. and 5. Several types of poor soil or compacted soil.
6. Wet soil.
7. Heavily fertilized and watered soil.
8. Healthy forested area; good soil.

used to prepare aerial topography. Often local photographers with a love of flying take commercial-quality aerial shots for the development community at lower cost than engineering firms that specialize in photogrammetry.

Pictures taken in mid- to late summer will reveal significant data on wet and dry patterns in the soil, but the tree canopy cover may obscure ground detail. Photos taken in late summer, particularly in dry years, will indicate wide variations in tree canopy, which normally is a good indicator of soil quality. Lighter green coloration and signs of early fall color will be easily spotted. Winter photos give more information about ground conditions below trees, but are less useful in determining soil drainage patterns. Photographs printed on large-size cibrachrome paper will have the best resolution and show excellent detail. Digital images must be a very high resolution to achieve the same results, and require lots of memory. A good photographer can shoot from directly overhead and size the prints such that they come close to a measurable scale if given distances between known points on the photograph. Oblique photos are less useful.

EXISTING TOPOGRAPHY AND DRAINAGE

Natural soils tend to develop consistent slope contour patterns over broad areas. Human activities such as grading tend to disrupt those patterns. Contour patterns on the survey maps and old construction drawings for the project can reveal areas of previous grading. Sudden changes in slope rate, rectilinear contour patterns, and overly steep (2:1 or greater) and overly flat (less than 2 percent) slopes will often indicate human grading activity.

Obviously, topography impacts drainage and rates of wetting and drying. Note steep, likely dryer, south-facing slopes vs. damper north-facing slopes. Also note low flat areas and observe the soil moisture. How long does each area stay damp after a rain?

Take special note of areas that remain wet long after other soils have dried out. These may be caused by residual springs, covered over during previous development, or manmade springs or seeps where drainage is interrupted and water builds up behind an inadvertent soil dam, slowly releasing water over time.

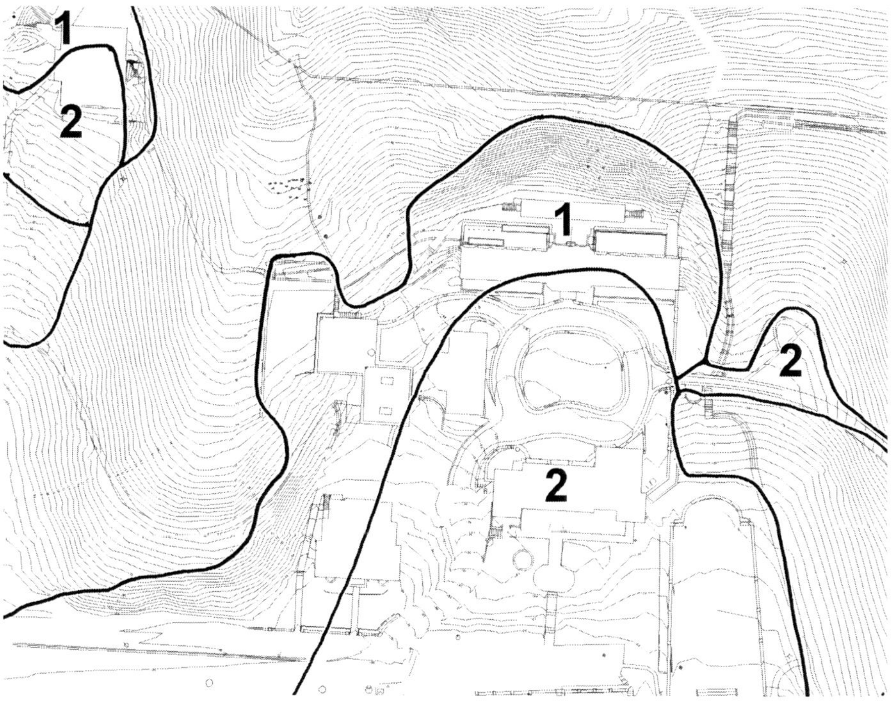

Figure 1.7.14. Use of a topographic survey to find significant soil disturbance. Contours that are not consistent with natural topography such as overly steep or flat areas were likely human fabricated grades.

1. Fill area.
2. Cut area.

GEOTECHNICAL BORINGS

Most large projects include deep geotechnical soil borings made before the beginning of the design process. These soil reports are focused on the ability to support foundations, and provide scant information on surface conditions. They do indicate groundwater depths and subsurface drainage patterns. With careful study, they can reveal previous soil disturbances deep in the soil profile.

The Unified Classification System used by engineers in describing soil borings is different from that used in agricultural soil reports. It has different gradation sizes for sand, silt, and clay, and uses a different set of soil names. Soil boring reports should include a description of the system used, but if not, the geotechnical engineer who prepared the report will be able to give you that information.

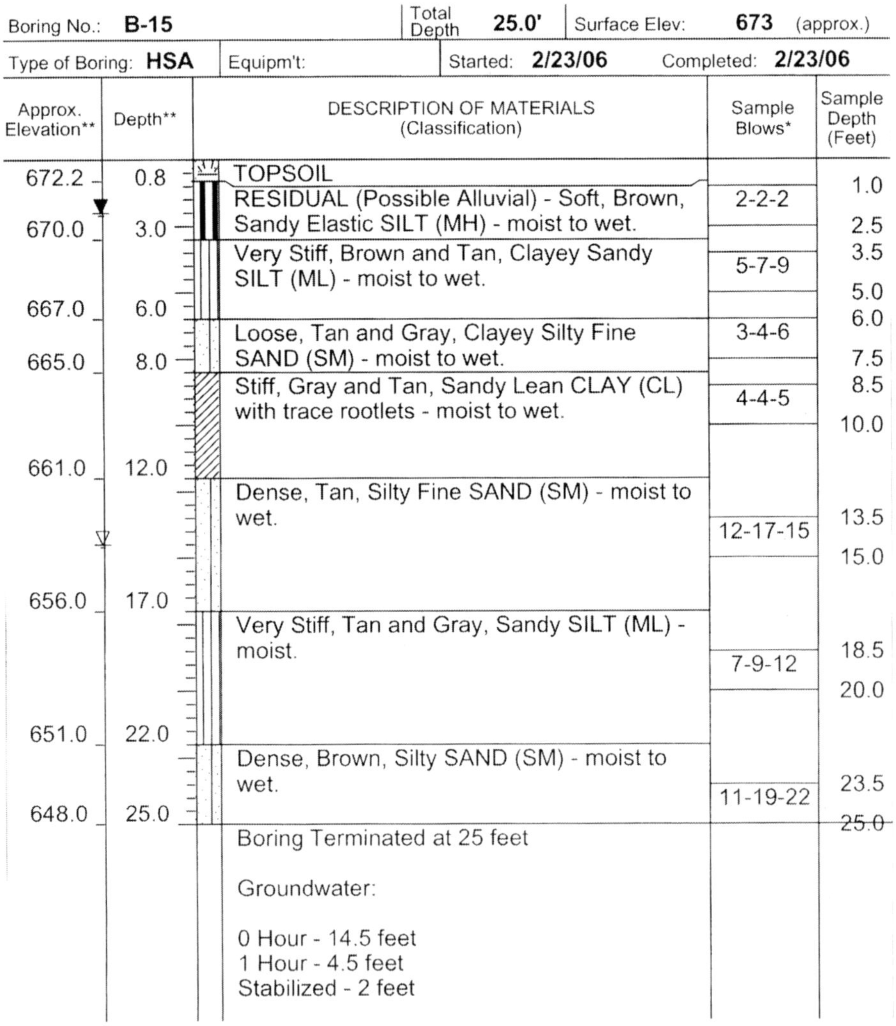

Figure 1.7.15. Soil boring logs, with soil names in Unified Classification System. This log indicates significant water problems that will require subsurface drainage be added to the project.

MAPPING AND ANALYSIS

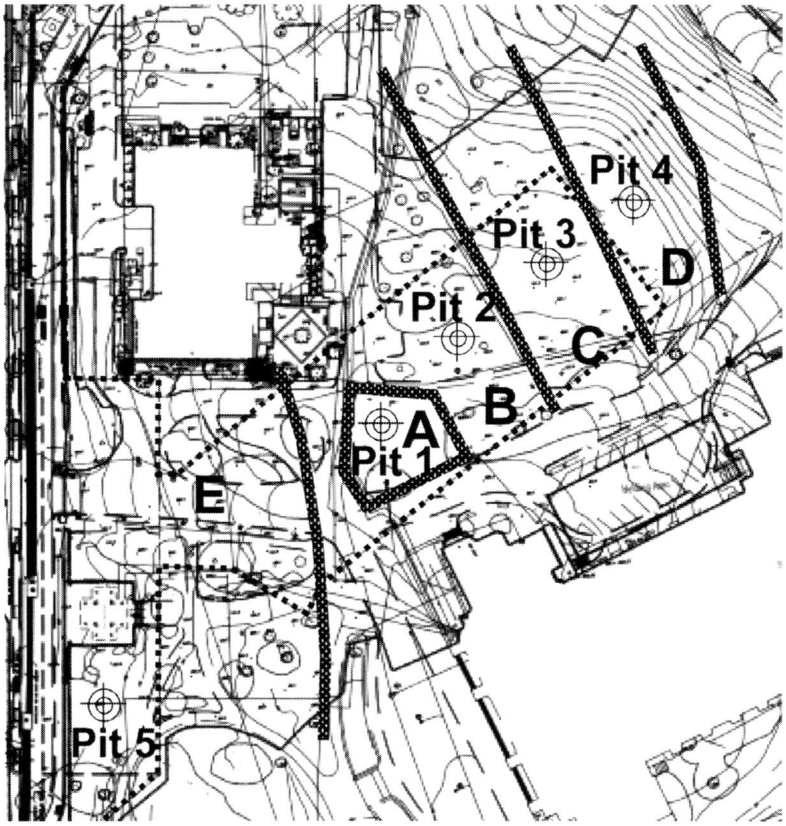

a

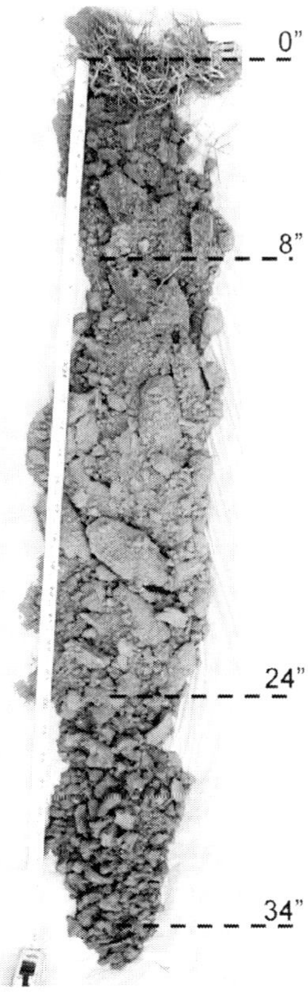

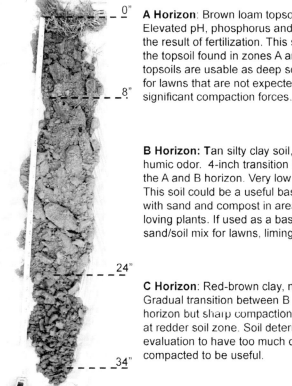

A Horizon: Brown loam topsoil, humic odor. Elevated pH, phosphorus and potassium, likely the result of fertilization. This soil is similar to the topsoil found in zones A and E. These topsoils are usable as deep soils for trees and for lawns that are not expected to have significant compaction forces.

B Horizon: Tan silty clay soil, slight humic odor. 4-inch transition layer between the A and B horizon. Very low pH (4.8). This soil could be a useful base to mix with sand and compost in areas of acid-loving plants. If used as a base for a sand/soil mix for lawns, liming is required.

C Horizon: Red-brown clay, no odor. Gradual transition between B and C horizon but sharp compaction encountered at redder soil zone. Soil determined at field evaluation to have too much clay and is too compacted to be useful.

b

Figure 1.7.16. Composite soil report.

a. Soil map summarizing findings into different soil zones.

b. Example of a soil zone description.

As information from different sources is collected, it should be recorded on the survey of the property. A survey drawing that includes both utility and topographic information is the best document to use as a base for this map, unless it is so cluttered with data that it becomes too confusing. The following information should be mapped:

1. Soil textures encountered
2. Soil disturbance
    - Undisturbed soil or areas of minimum disturbance (good soil)
        - Depths of usable topsoil
    - Cut soil
        - Subsoil with replacement topsoil
        - Subsoil
    - Fill
        - Topsoil fill over natural soil layers
        - Buried topsoil layers
        - Subsoil fill with topsoil fill
        - Subsoil fill
        - Rubble fill with topsoil fill
        - Rubble fill
3. Soil compaction
    - Surface compaction (top 12 inches)
    - Deep compaction (deeper than 12 inches)
    - Buried compacted layers
    - Undercompacted (visible surface subsidence)
4. Soil drainage
    - Anaerobic odor
    - Gray soil
    - Overly dry soil
5. Barriers and interfaces
    - Solid barriers—walls, building foundations, and concrete and asphalt paving
    - Semi-pervious barriers—road subgrade, compacted layers, interfaces of two different soil textures
6. Chemical contaminants or suspected areas of contamination
    - Toxic to humans and animals or may translocate to the ground water
    - Toxic to plants

As the soil analysis map is being prepared, the designer must make value judgments about the soil resources at the site. Soils should be categorized as one of the following:

1. **Good soil:** Soil that can be used with little or no amendments or modifications, or which may be able to be stripped and reused.
2. **Usable soil with significant amendment:** Soil where the texture, chemical, biological, or compaction rates could be corrected and still use the base mineral material. These soils generally fall into three types ranked from the easiest to hardest to remediate.
    - ***Compacted soil:*** The natural soil profile remains intact, and the problem is simple surface compaction; the soil may be fractured or coarsely tilled to restore much of its previous quality.

- ***Graded soil:*** The soil profile has been disturbed, but the resulting grades are not heavily compacted. The deeper the soil disturbance, the greater the damage. The more the O and A horizons are mixed with B and C horizon material, the greater the damage.
- ***Graded and compacted:*** The soil profile has been disturbed, and the soil, as it is graded, has been compacted. The deeper and more forceful the compaction, especially when combined with greater amounts of profile disturbance, the greater the damage.

3. **Unusable soil:** Soil where the texture, chemical, biological, or compaction levels will have significant impacts on plant growth and will be difficult or impossible to correct at reasonable cost.

Once you have made your map, use it to guide the design and develop construction documents.

Develop a soil protection plan to preserve good soil resources where possible. Protecting good soil is just as important as saving the root zones of existing trees. Good soil is valuable and hard to re-create once damaged by construction. Solutions to soil problems should be incorporated into the project and eventually be delineated on a soil improvement plan, a separate drawing sheet in the contract documents, supported by its own section on the specifications.

Urban soil analysis will remain an inexact science, but the simple tools outlined above increase the knowledge of the site. The longer designers work in a given region, the better they will know the soils of that region. On very large projects, the fee may allow the hiring of a soils expert to analyze and design soils. The majority of projects, however, are too small to hire a soil specialist, yet the need for existing soil information remains. Landscape architects should be expected to be able to do basic soil investigations to support their work.

SOIL TESTING FOR PHYSICAL PROPERTIES

This section outlines protocols for testing the physical, chemical, and biological aspects of soil. These protocols can be used during the initial site investigation period through to construction to assure quality control. Testing of soil mixes is a separate discussion in Part 2, Chapter Four.

Soil Texture

Specification: For natural soils and loamy soil mixes, *Methods of Soil Analysis, Part 1,* Particle Size Analysis (hydrometer method). For high sand soil, *Methods of Soil Analysis, Part 1,* Particle Size Analysis (pipette method).

All references to soil texture in this book are based on USDA nomenclature. There are engineering ASTM tests for soil texture, but these are reported in Unified Classification nomenclature, which uses different break points between sand, silt, and clay and different soil names. Most soil tests for agricultural purposes use the hydrometer method. For most natural soils and soil mixes, the different soil testing methods do not yield differences in results that are significant for tree and shrub growth.

The standard soil textural analysis measures only sand, silt, and clay. For the USDA test, gravel and any organic particles larger than 2 mm are removed before the test. The sand, silt, and clay will equal 100 percent, with any gravel reported as

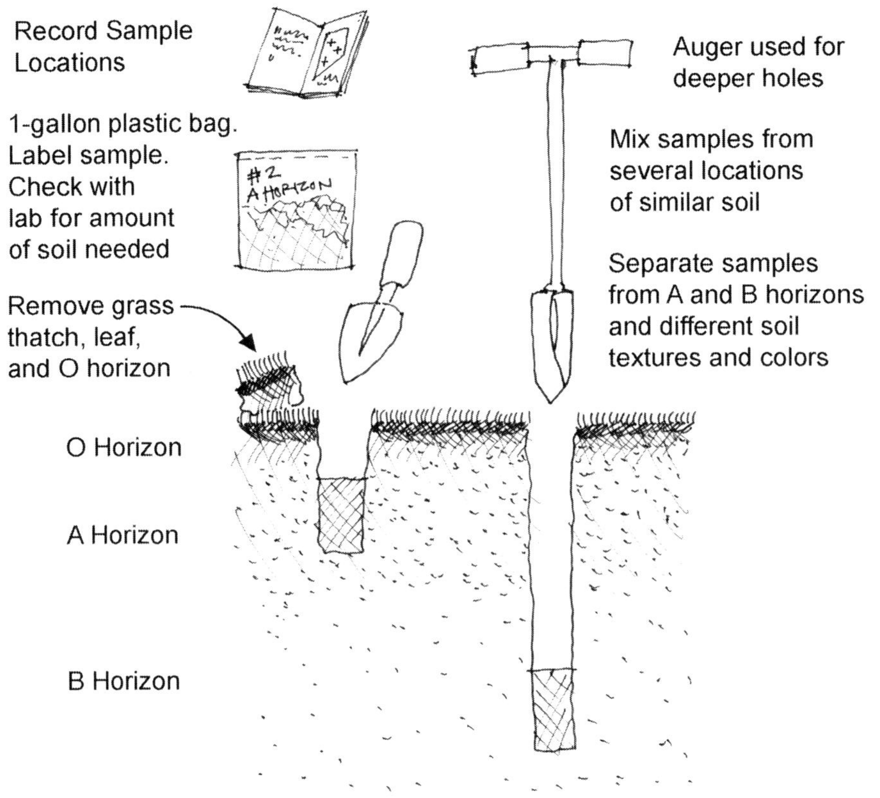
Record Sample Locations
Auger used for deeper holes
1-gallon plastic bag. Label sample. Check with lab for amount of soil needed
Mix samples from several locations of similar soil
Separate samples from A and B horizons and different soil textures and colors
Remove grass thatch, leaf, and O horizon
O Horizon
A Horizon
B Horizon

Figure 1.7.17. Collecting soil samples.

a separate amount above 100 percent. The elimination of large organic particles will alter the organic matter calculation.

For each test, approximately 3 cups or more of soil are required. Each lab will have its own requirements, and many will have special bags to send the samples. Always contact the lab to confirm the requirements for the test needed. Make sure to use the forms provided by the lab in requesting testing services.

Sand Fractions

Specification: *Methods of Soil Analysis, Part 1,* Particle Size Analysis, Sand Fractions (dry sieve method).

In addition to the normal particle size analysis, in some cases it is advisable to test for sand fractions. This would include sandy loam soils and any soil that is being considered as a base to mix with sand as a planting soil blend or mix. This is always a separate test. Use a lab that specializes in golf, athletic turf, or planting mixes. Many state agricultural labs do not do sand fraction testing.

Knowing the sand fractions is critical to developing designs for adding sand as an amendment and estimating the compaction resistance of a soil.

Compaction

Most soil experts can identify overcompacted soil by feel or by observing the quality of plants growing in the soil, but this does not provide quantifiable data necessary to justify the expense of compaction reduction. Such data are obtained by measuring compaction using either the Proctor test, penetration resistance, or bulk density. Each one will be discussed in the following sections.

Compaction Measurement by Proctor Test

Specification: Standard Proctor Test ASTM D698.

The **Proctor test** is the most common standard to measure compaction in the construction industry. This test defines the compaction rate as the percent of a soil's maximum density with that soil at optimum moisture level. A geotechnical soils lab must determine the maximum soil density and optimum moisture curve. With that information, the soil can be tested in the field using a nuclear densiometer or other devices.

Percentage Proctor is based on known bulk density of a soil compacted using a specific compaction protocol developed from the engineer's Proctor curve data. Once the 100 percent number is determined, it is easy to convert a bulk density requirement to the Proctor percentage. Often the engineering data are in pounds per cubic foot. One Mg/m^3 equals 62.43 pounds per cubic foot.

A Proctor test is most often used to determine if a soil is compacted to the minimum level to support structures. Ninety-five percent of maximum dry density is considered adequate for most structures, and 90 percent is a standard for many residential sidewalk applications. Eighty-five percent is often quoted as the density for planting soil, yet research indicates that 85 percent is on the edge of root-limiting for most plants in most soils. A percentage lower than 85 percent, more likely lower than 80 percent, is a better standard.

The advantage of the Proctor test is that it is precise and accepted industry-wide, but there are a number of problems associated with its use. A geotechnical lab is needed to test each soil type prior to conducting the test. Testing equipment is expensive and requires a trained technician to operate it. Only limited samples will be studied, and there is a time lag to obtain the results. A nuclear densiometer, a devise used to measure field soil, can only read soil compaction to the depth of the probe, or about 6 to 12 inches, and does not give reliable readings in soils with elevated organic content. Densiometer readings in organic soil are generally higher by 5 to 15 percent over actual density. Finally, maximum and minimum Proctor densities for organic soil use as a planting medium have not been researched sufficiently. Part 1, Chapter Two discusses the relationships of different soils' Proctor values and bulk density.

The Proctor test is a poor way to analyze soil compaction in existing soil in the site analysis phase, but a useful tool during the construction phase when the installed soils are uniform and a technician skilled in the use of the equipment is available.

Figure 1.7.18. Nuclear densiometer.

Compaction Measurement by Penetration Resistance

Specification: *Methods of Soil Analysis, Part 1* (cone penetrometer method)

Penetration resistance is measured by a cone penetrometer. This device can provide instant readings of relative soil compaction to depths of 24 inches or greater. It is pushed slowly through the soil, and resistance is measured on a gauge. A penetrometer is easy to use and relatively inexpensive to purchase. The soil's ability to resist

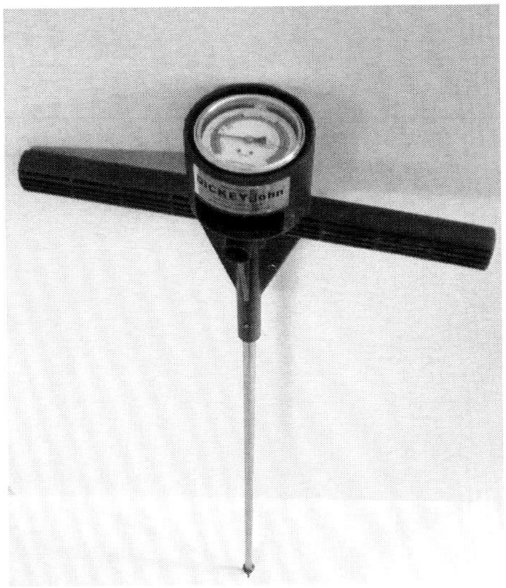

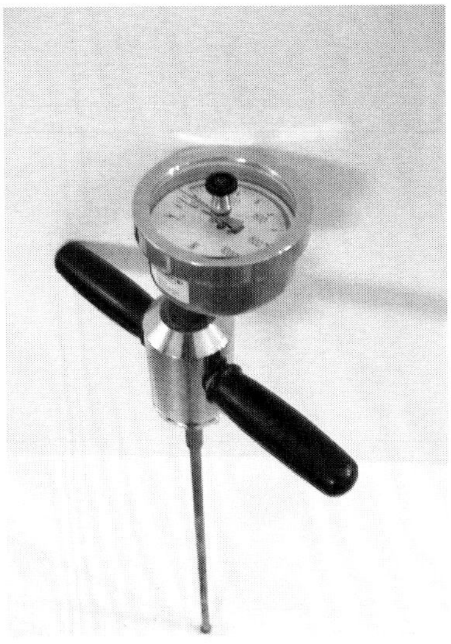

Figure 1.7.19. Penetrometer.

penetration is measured in mega Pascal (MPa). Moist sandy loam soil lower than 2 MPa is considered appropriate resistance for root penetration. The problem with using a penetrometer to analyze or specify soil compaction is that readings vary significantly with changes in soil moisture or soil type. Soil will read low when it is wet and high when it is dry. A perfectly good garden soil may resist all attempts to insert the penetrometer when dry. Compacted fine-grained soil will read acceptably low when it is close to saturation levels. When soil moisture is below field capacity, penetrometer readings may provide rough data.

To date there is not sufficient data on the relationships of these two variables of moisture and soil type to make this tool useful in site assessment. With a little practice, the small-bore soil probe can provide about the same level of information on soil compaction as a penetrometer.

Penetrometers may have value during the installation of new soil, as we will see in Part 2, Chapter Four.

Compaction Measurement by Bulk Density

Specification: *Methods of Soil Analysis, Part 1* (core method or excavation method).

Bulk density of an undisturbed sample is a common measuring standard used by agronomic soil scientists and is the most useful method to measure the compaction levels on most soil during the analysis phase.

Bulk density is the soil's dry weight divided by its volume, most often expressed as megagrams per cubic meter (Mg/m^3) or grams per cubic centimeter (g/cm^3). Note that in metric nomenclature, these two designations give the same unit value for equal compaction: 1.5 Mg/m^3 equals 1.5 g/cm^3. Part 1, Chapter Two summarizes the data on the relationship of bulk density and root penetration of various soils.

Obtaining bulk density is time-consuming and requires that each sample be taken to a lab, dried, and weighed, a process that takes several days or longer. Special equipment is needed to collect the samples, and special care taken in their shipping. Often, the timing of construction does not allow for processing multiple bulk density tests during the soil installation phase. Despite these problems, this method is still easier than a Proctor test and much more accurate than a penetrometer during the site analysis phase. Designers can make their own bulk density measurements if they invest in a limited amount of equipment. Approximately $500 will buy a scale, slide hammer, and other sampling tools. Figure 1.7.20 shows the process of measuring bulk density. The sample is taken back to the office, measured, removed from its tube, and placed in an oven set at 215°F to dry overnight. A few simple measurements and calculations determine the weight and volume. Make all measurements in metric. Having the capability to determine bulk density in the office speeds up the process to just one day. Samples can be removed in the afternoon, dried overnight, and a report issued the next morning. This is well within the schedule constraints for most projects.

While an office-generated bulk density test is useful, the authority of a test performed by a soil testing laboratory may be required if the results are likely to be challenged or used to defend an action.

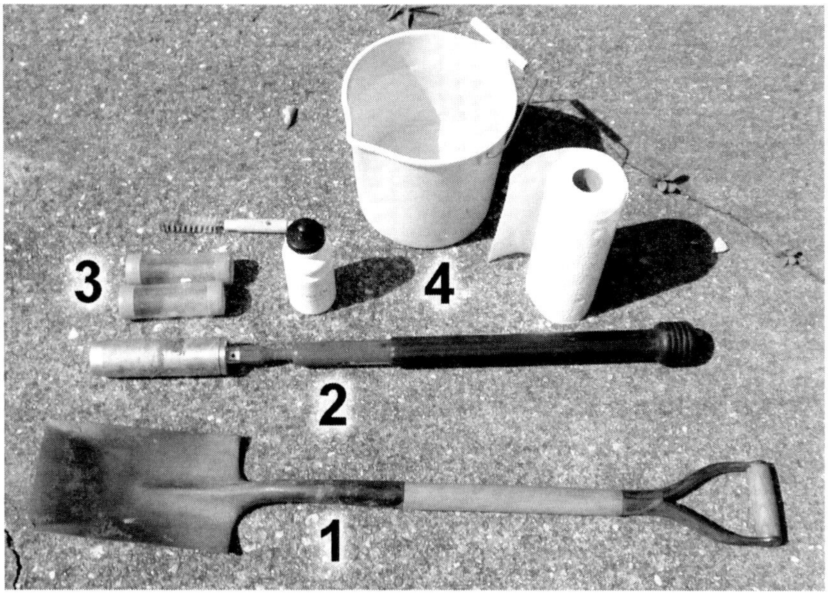

a

b

c

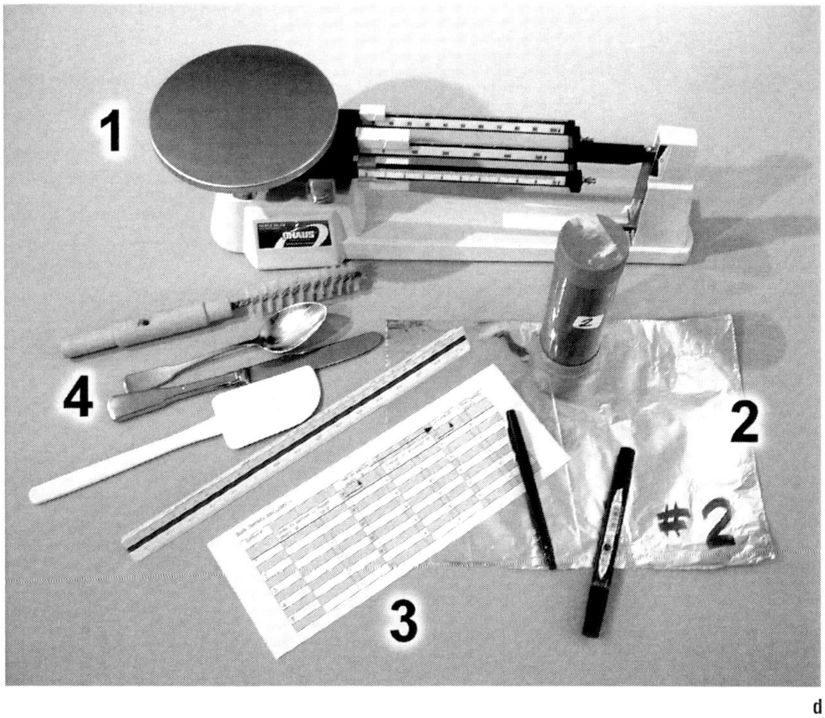

d

Figure 1.7.20. Bulk density sampling method.

a. Tools needed in the field:
   1. Shovel to remove organic layer.
   2. Core sampler and slide hammer.
   3. Plastic core liners with caps.
   4. Cleanup tools. Water required for tool cleanup and to make it easier to remove the sampling tool from soil.

b. Taking an undisturbed sample with a slide hammer and core tube. Note that the cylinder is driven only to the level of the bottom of the cap inside the core, so as not to change the compaction of the sample. Mark this depth on the outside of the tool.

c. After the sample is removed, the length of the sample in the sleeve is measured. The soil may not completely fill the sleeve.

d. Tools needed in the office:
   1. Metric balance scale.
   2. Aluminum foil, marker.
   3. Bulk density calculator form.
   4. Metric ruler and tools to remove soil from tube (oven not shown).

Figure 1.7.20. continued on page 138

Figure 1.7.20. continued from page 137

e

f

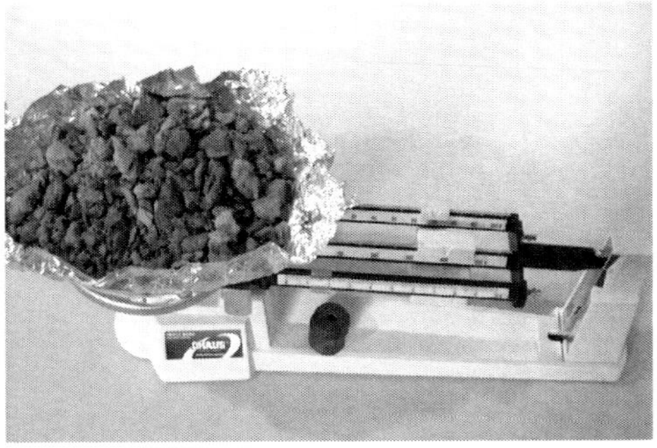

g

Sample #	Sample gross dry weight (g)	–	Foil weight (g)	=	Sample net dry weight (g)	÷	Volume - cm^3	=	Bulk Density g/cm^3
	Tube radius (cm) squared	X	3.141	X	Sample length (cm)	=			
	(g)		(g)	=	(g)	÷	cm^3	=	g/cm^3
	(cm)	X	3.141	X	(cm)	=			

h

Figure 1.7.20. Bulk density sampling method.

e. Weigh foil and remove soil from tube. Crumble soil apart.

f. Dry sample in oven for 12 hours at 215°F.

g. Weigh sample.

h. Fill out bulk density calculation form.

Several helpful hints to improve the making of bulk density test:

- Do not screw the sampling core tight to its top piece to make it easier to remove.
- Spray the inside of the plastic liner with silicon lubricant to ease the removal of the soil.
- Clean out all soil from the liner and threads of the tool between tests.
- If the sample is weighed before it is dried, the moisture content of the soil can be calculated.

In their book, *Trees in the Urban Landscape*, Bassuk and Trowbridge describe a lower-tech method of measuring compaction that requires less expensive field equipment. A small hole is dug in the soil and filled with a plastic bag. Water is poured into the bag to fill the space and a record made of the amount of water required to fill the hole. This gives a reasonably accurate volume of the soil removed. The removed soil can then be dried and weighed to calculate the bulk density as shown in the illustrations above. It is critical that the volume of water be accurately determined, and that the water be filled precisely to the level of soil removal.

Soil Moisture

Soil moisture relationships including infiltration, hydraulic conductivity, moisture content, and moisture-holding capacity must be tested in the field. Infiltration is a function of texture, structure, compaction, and conditions in the subsoil. Soil moisture content changes significantly with time and must be tested in the field. Infiltration and hydraulic conductivity rates of a specified soil to be installed at a given compaction rate can be tested in the lab.

Field Testing Infiltration

Specification: *Methods of Soil Analysis, Part 1,* Intake Rate (cylinder infiltrometer method).

An infiltrometer is used to test the infiltration rate of existing soil and subgrade conditions. This can be performed by a soil scientist or geotechnical engineer. With the purchase of a ring infiltrometer, designers can obtain reasonable results. The diameter of your measuring ring should be 6 inches or larger. Both single and double ring infiltrometers are available. There are no statistical differences in the results obtained.

Infiltration is highly influenced by compaction and soil structure. Infiltration rates measured before the start of construction should be expected to drop as construction proceeds. It is more important to measure infiltration rates in the subsoil just prior to installing planting soil than during the design phase, if that soil is to be graded or removed.

Start by removing grass and thatch. Drive the infiltrometer into the ground. Fill the ring with water. Record the rate of drop over time.

For subsoil observations, an excavated pit must be dug to the desired elevation. Care must be taken during the excavation not to compact or disturb the soil where the measurement takes place. This requires hand-digging that last several inches of the excavation in the area around the infiltrometer.

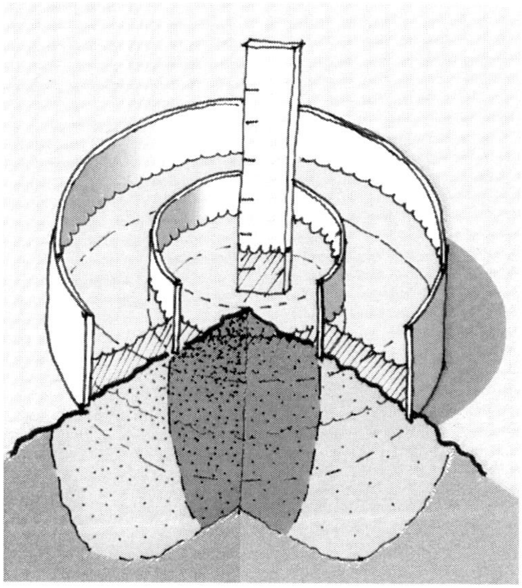

F.1.7.21. Double-ring infiltrometer. Outer-ring water saturates soil around the inner measuring ring.

Hydraulic Conductivity

Specification: ASTM F 1815-97 with sample compacted to 80 percent and 85 percent of maximum dry density standard Proctor method ASTM D698.

Soils samples can be lab tested for their drainage rate (hydraulic conductivity) if a compaction rate is specified. Typically, a Proctor value range of between 80 and 85 percent is used, as these are the compaction rates where root penetration becomes limited. Check with the soil lab for instructions on test specifications and requirements.

Moisture Content

Specification: *Methods of Soil Analysis, Part 1,* Water Content (gravimetric method).

Remove a sample of known volume, weigh and dry it, and then reweigh it to determine the water loss. This test uses the same tools as the bulk density test. It is not practical for making soil management decisions in the field such as determining if a contractor should stop work because the soil is too wet.

Moisture content in existing soil can also be measured by an array of portable instruments, which give moisture in percent or relative wet/dry scales. They generally work on the principle that more moisture passes greater amounts of electricity. The readings from these instruments may be skewed by high amounts of salt and other chemicals in the soil.

Most of the time, whether soil is too wet or dry is all that is needed. Soil probes and augers may be the quickest and most informative way to look at soil moisture by simply feeling the moisture in the soil.

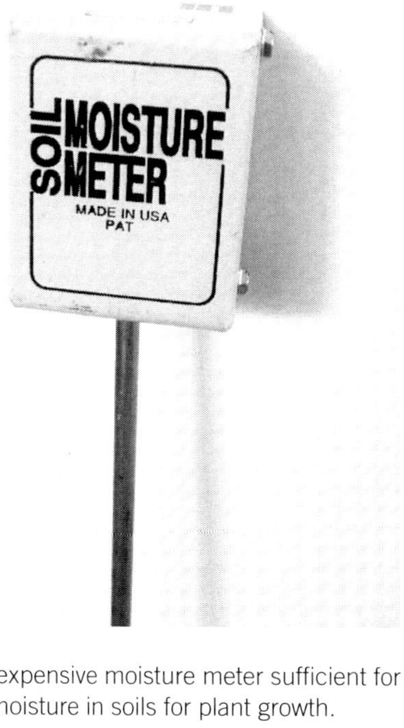

F1.7.22 Inexpensive moisture meter sufficient for assessing moisture in soils for plant growth.

Moisture-Holding Capacity

Specification: ASTM F 1815-97 with sample compacted to 80 percent and 85 percent of maximum dry density standard Proctor method ASTM D698.

The moisture-holding capacity of a soil is tied to its compaction rate and structure. Samples of sandy soil used for golf greens and athletic turf can be compacted to known levels and the macro- and micropores calculated. Contact a soils lab that specializes in golf and athletic turf soil for requirements. This protocol does not provide useful information on fine-grained soils due to the importance of structure, which is destroyed when preparing the sample.

Structure

There is no test for soil structure, which can be observed when digging into an undisturbed soil.

Color

Soil color can be observed and compared to the Munsell soil color charts.

Odor

Soil odor must be observed in the field. Good observation skills take practice.

Temperature

Soil temperature can be measured in the field by one of many available soil thermometers. Normally, temperature is not an issue in plant health. Human influences, particularly steam lines in northern cities, can affect plants. If soil temperatures

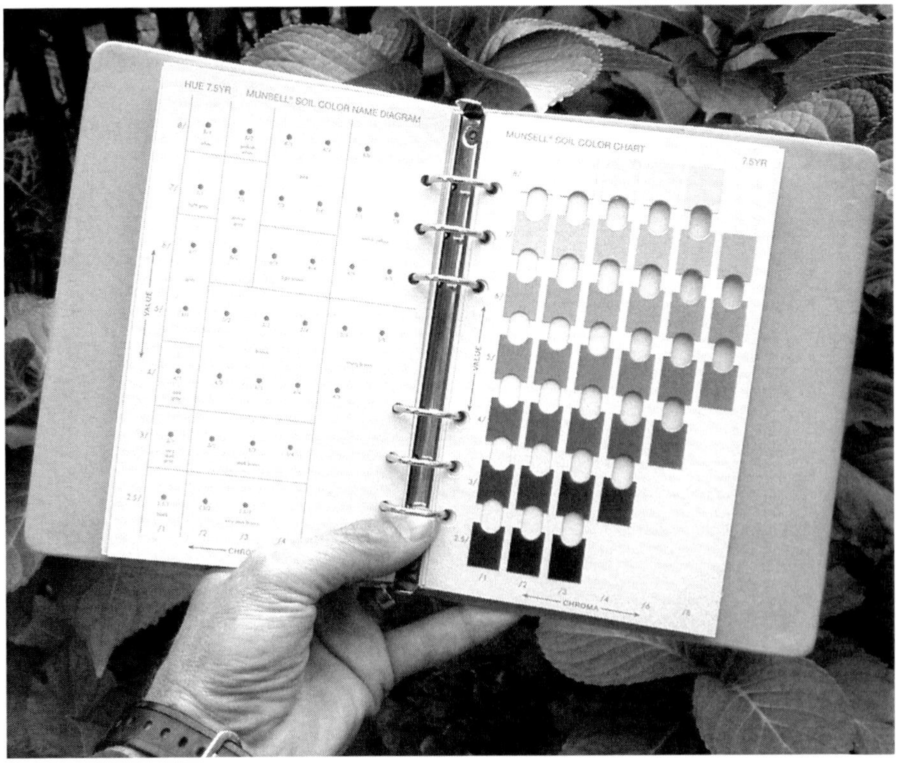

F1.7.23 Munsell charts compare actual soil color with standard color chips and nomenclature.

are near root-limiting levels, it should be possible to detect a potential problem simply by feeling the soil in the auger as soon as it is extracted. Soil temperatures more than 6 inches from the surface should feel cooler than the ambient air.

SOIL TESTING FOR ORGANIC MATTER AND SOIL BIOLOGY

Soil Organic Matter

Specification: *Methods of Soil Analysis, Part 3,* Direct Estimation of Organic Matter (loss on ignition method).

Soil organic matter is measured by burning the sample to remove the carbon-based component and calculating the difference expressed as a percentage of oven dry weight. This test indicates the amount of carbon-based matter but reveals little about the health of the soil food web. Standard soil labs can perform this test.

Organic amendments added to the soil are not organic matter as determined by this test! When compost is added to a soil, less than half of the compost weight is going to show up as organic matter in the soil test. Large pieces of organic amendments are removed during the preparation of the sample as required by the protocol. Around half of the weight of the remaining organic amendment is composed of non-carbon elements that are not lost in the burn. Adding 10 percent compost by volume to a soil mix is only going to raise the measured organic content by about one or two percentage points by soil weight.

This situation would change if the soil test were conducted without removing the large particles of organic matter. However if the sample is not screened or the screen is opened to a larger size, it will be difficult to evaluate the test results against existing data.

Because of the physical difference between naturally occurring organic matter in the soil and organic amendments, it is impossible to use a soil test to determine whether a soil mix has the correct level of added organic amendment. A better tool to evaluate whether a given sample of a soil mix meets the specification requirement is to compare the color and feel of the final mix to samples mixed under controlled conditions. Specification for testing organic amendments is discussed in Part 2, Chapter Four.

Soil Organisms

Tests have been developed to measure key indicator species of the soil food web. Testing labs such as The SoilFoodWeb, Inc., will provide recommendations for appropriate levels of critical elements of the soil food web based on soil type, drainage, and plants to be grown. They will also recommend methods to modify the soil to achieve organism balance. Specialty blends of compost teas can be applied in conjunction with the application of different types of organic matter to adjust soil biology.

Adjusting soil biology at the end of construction can be specified as part of the soil installation. Proper soil and drainage improvements will be critical to the success of this adjustment. Soil biology cannot be improved in compacted, poorly draining or droughty soil or soil with low organic matter. Healthy soil biology also depends on a continuing supply of organic amendments (mulch and compost) to feed the biology in loose well-drained soil.

SOIL TESTING FOR CHEMICAL PROPERTIES

Chemical Elements

Specification: *Methods of Soil Analysis, Part 3.*

State extension and commercial soil testing labs provide chemical soil testing services. Commercial labs usually are slightly more expensive, but can be more responsive to schedules and particular testing requirements. The lab will need to know what plants are planned for the site. Request the lab's recommendations to correct deficiencies. Each lab will have particular requirements and protocols. Be sure to follow all the instructions provided by the lab.

Essential element levels by parts per million including:

- Macronutrients: phosphorus, potassium, magnesium, calcium, and sulfur
- Micronutrients: boron, manganese, iron, zinc, and copper

Nitrogen is normally not tested. Soil nitrogen recommendations are normally estimated from organic content in the soil. Organic matter in the soil may indicate the ability of soil biology to transform nitrogen into plant available forms.

Nitrogen and other elements can be tested by leaf analysis. This method is more expensive but often more accurate to determine the soil chemistry around existing plants. It has no application for soil for new plantings.

Total soil nitrogen can also be determined using several methods, but results must then interpret plant-available nitrogen. Contact you soil lab for more information.

Sample Number: GP-1 **Lab Number:** 987 **Date Received:** 10/20/2005 **Date Reported:** 10/24/2005

GRAPHIC SOIL ANALYSIS REPORT

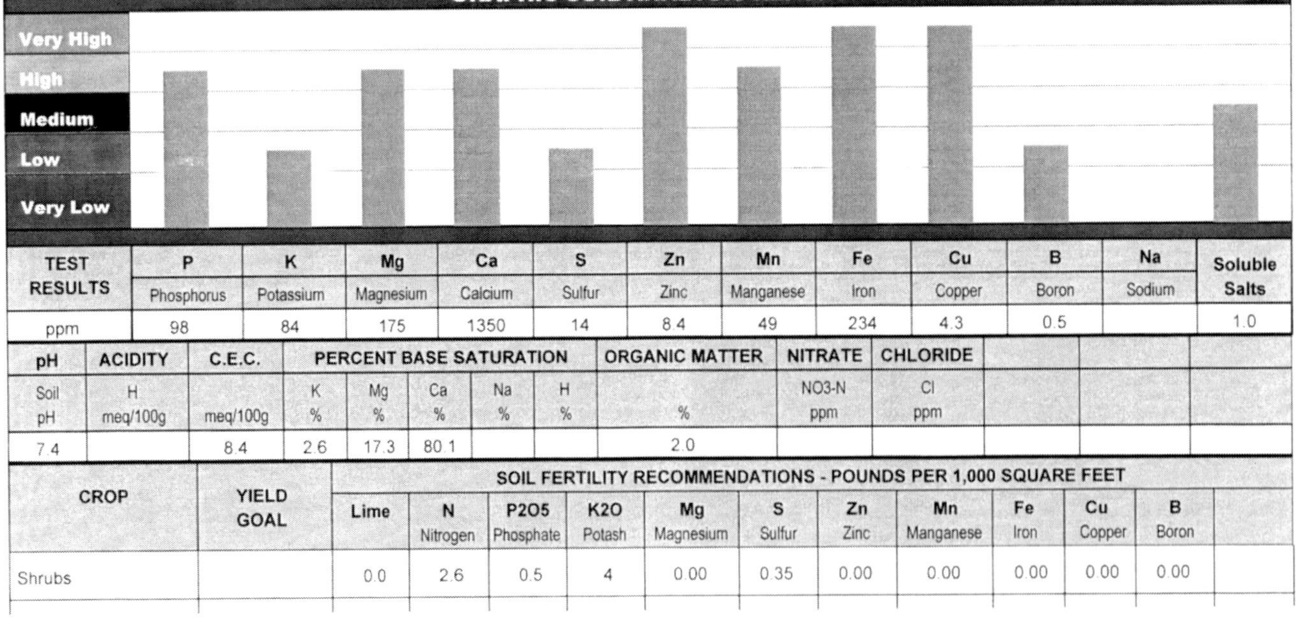

TEST RESULTS	P Phosphorus	K Potassium	Mg Magnesium	Ca Calcium	S Sulfur	Zn Zinc	Mn Manganese	Fe Iron	Cu Copper	B Boron	Na Sodium	Soluble Salts
ppm	98	84	175	1350	14	8.4	49	234	4.3	0.5		1.0

pH	ACIDITY	C.E.C.	PERCENT BASE SATURATION					ORGANIC MATTER	NITRATE	CHLORIDE			
Soil pH	H meq/100g	meq/100g	K %	Mg %	Ca %	Na %	H %	%	NO3-N ppm	Cl ppm			
7.4		8.4	2.6	17.3	80.1			2.0					

CROP	YIELD GOAL	SOIL FERTILITY RECOMMENDATIONS - POUNDS PER 1,000 SQUARE FEET											
		Lime	N Nitrogen	P2O5 Phosphate	K2O Potash	Mg Magnesium	S Sulfur	Zn Zinc	Mn Manganese	Fe Iron	Cu Copper	B Boron	
Shrubs		0.0	2.6	0.5	4	0.00	0.35	0.00	0.00	0.00	0.00	0.00	

Figure 1.7.24. Typical chemical soil test results. *(Source: A&L Labs)*

pH and Buffer pH

Specification: *Methods of Soil Analysis, Part 3,* Soil pH (1:1 soil:water method).

Use a soil testing service when documented, accurate results are required. This takes several days and normally is done in conjunction with other tests. Lab tests will often report both pH and buffer pH. Buffer pH is used only to determine liming requirements and is not the actual soil pH.

Field pH test kits using chemical solutions can gather pH data quickly. pH meters are subject to inaccuracies imposed by other chemicals in the soil. Accuracy of the results depends on how skillful the observer is at following the procedure and recognizing subtle color changes in the fluids.

Cation Exchange Capacity (CEC)

Specification: *Methods of Soil Analysis, Part 3,* Cation Exchange Capacity.

This test is performed by all agricultural soil labs and gives an estimate of the soil's ability to hold nutrients.

Soluble Salt

Specification: *Methods of Soil Analysis, Part 3,* Salinity (electroconductivity method).

Salt is measured by electrical conductivity of a 1:2 soil:water sample, measured in milli-ohm per centimeter, or mmho/cm, also written as deci-siemens per meter, or dS/m. mmho/cm and dS/m are different names for the same value.

Hazardous Chemical Elements

Heavy metals, hydrocarbons, and pesticide content are normally tested if there is information that they may be present in limiting quantities or if the use of the site may indicate a high sensitivity, such as children's play spaces or the cultivation of food crops. Metals, hydrocarbon, and pesticide testing are completed by specialty testing services and require special sample handling techniques. These tests are expensive, and broad-spectrum analysis requires many tests. Knowing the general types of potential toxicity sources can limit the cost. Consult with specialty chemical testing labs.

REFERENCE

Key References

Baskin, Yvonne, and the Scientific Committee on Problems in the Environment (SCOPE). 2005. *Under Ground: How Creatures of Mud and Dirt Shape Our World.* Island Press, Washington, DC.

Bassuk, Nina, et al. 2003. *Recommended Urban Trees: Site Assessment and Tree Selection for Stress Tolerance.* Urban Horticulture Institute, Cornell University, Ithaca, NY. 127 pp.

Brady, Nyle C., and Ray R. Weil. 1999. *The Nature and Properties of Soils.* 12th ed. Prentice-Hall, Upper Saddle River, NJ. 881 pp.

Craul, Phillip J. 1992. *Urban Soil in Landscape Design*. John Wiley & Sons, New York, NY. 396 pp.

Klute, Arnold. 1986. *SSSA Book Series 5: Methods of Soil Analysis: Part 1; Physical and Mineralogical Methods.* 2nd ed. Soil Science Society of America and American Society of Agronomy, Madison, WI. 1,188 pp.

Macbeth Division of Kollmorgen Instruments Corporation. 1994. *Munsell Soil Color Chart.* Revised ed. Kollmorgen Instruments, New Windsor, NY. http://usa.gretagmacbethstore.com.

Sparks, D. L., ed. 1996. *SSSA Book Series 5: Methods of Soil Analysis: Part 3; Chemical Methods.* Soil Science Society of America and American Society of Agronomy, Madison, WI. 1390 pp.

Trowbridge, Peter J., and Nina L. Bassuk. 2004. *Trees in the Urban Landscape: Site Assessment Design and Installation.* John Wiley & Sons, Hoboken, NJ. 205 pp.

Weaver, R.W., et al. 1994. *SSSA Book Series 5: Methods of Soil Analysis: Part 2; Microbiological and Biochemical Properties.* Soil Science Society of America and American Society of Agronomy, Madison, WI.

Other Information

Craul, Timothy A., and Phillip J. Craul. 2006. *Soil Design Protocols: For Landscape Architects and Contractors.* John Wiley & Sons, New York, NY. 339 pp.

Derr, Jeffery F., and Bonnie Lee Appleton. 1988. *Herbicide Injury to Trees and Shrubs: A Pictorial Guide to Symptom Diagnosis.* Blue Crab Press, Virginia Beach, VA. 72 pp.

Gershuny, Grace, and Joe Smillie. 1999. *The Soul of Soil: A Soil-Building Guide for Master Gardeners and Farmers.* 4th ed. Chelsea Green Publishing Company, White River Junction, VT. 173 pp.

Lilly, Sharon J. 2001. *Arborists' Certification Study Guide.* International Society of Arboriculture, Champaign, IL. 222 pp.

Klute, E.A., ed. 1986. *Methods of Soil Analysis: Part 1. Physical and Mineralogical Methods.* 2nd ed. Soil Science Society of America and American Society of Agronomy, Madison, WI. 1,188 pp.

Roberts, John, Nick Jackson, and Mark Smith. 2006. *Tree Roots in the Built Environment.* Crown Copyright, The Stationary Office, Norwich, England. 488 pp.

Scheyer, J.M., and K.W. Hipple. 2005. *Urban Soil Primer.* United States Department of Agriculture, Natural Resources Conservation Service, National Soil Survey Center, Lincoln, NE. 74 pp.

Singer, Michael J., and Donald N. Munns. 2002. *Soils: An Introduction.* 5th ed. Pearson Education, Upper Saddle River, NJ. 429 pp.

Other Resources

Soil Foodweb, Inc. 2007. http://www.soilfoodweb.com.

Part 2
Applying the Science of Trees and Soils

Part 2 presents a ten-step process to guide the design and installation of trees in urban spaces. The steps offer the designer techniques for responding to sites with increasing density, keeping in mind both the need to limit budgets and the goal of providing functional trees for the future.

These steps are grouped into three sets of strategies:

Soil-based strategies set out requirements to work with existing soil resources, protect and improve those resources, and recognize when to abandon the existing soil in favor of replacement soils.

Tree-based strategies evaluate the needs of the tree and accommodating those needs in the design.

Management-based strategies provide tools to fund and implement the ideas presented in the first two sets.

INTRODUCTION
Soil-Based Strategies

Ignoring soil properties during the design process can lead to significant landscape failures. Leatzow Associates, a major malpractice insurer of landscape architects, reports that more than 80 percent of claims involve some type of soil failure. Designers and their clients cannot afford to ignore this essential element during the design process.

To successfully implement these principles, it is important to read Part 1 of this book.

In the soil assessment phase (see Part 1, Chapter Seven), we looked at how to map and evaluate existing soil resources. Once the resources are known, the designer must determine how useful they are. At high-density urban sites, there may be no usable resources, or the ability to reuse them may be limited. Often, the entire site is needed for project requirements, or space for the project may be at such a premium that the contractor cannot justify preserving or stockpiling soil. At other sites, existing soil may be usable but will become highly degraded during construction. There are ways to improve degraded soil, but it will never attain preconstruction quality.

This photo shows several stages of soil disturbances from undisturbed farm soil (on the edges of the site) to deep, imported fills placed over remnant soil profiles near the top.

SOIL-BASED DESIGN PRINCIPLES

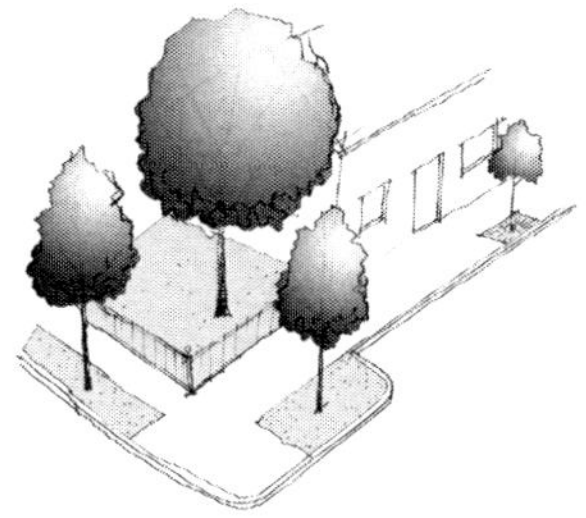

In the next four chapters, we'll look at ways to address these challenges. Briefly stated, these are based on the following principles.

Principle 1: Plant the Easy Places First

Directs early design decisions to locate the tree within the plan in the best and largest soil resources.

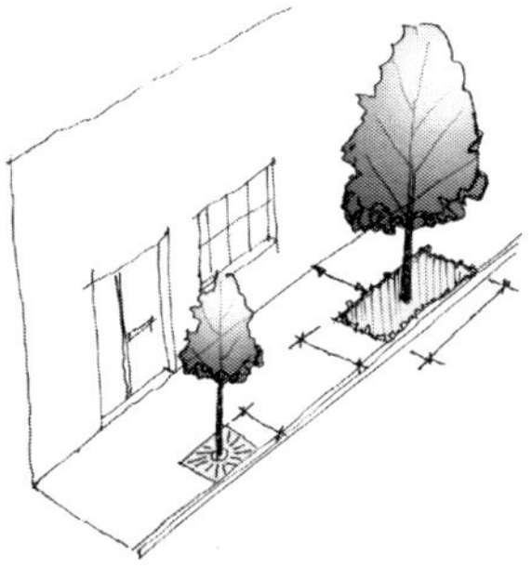

Principle 2: Make Larger Planting Spaces

Explains the importance of making the planting space as large as possible when there is a conflict between the tree and paving around it.

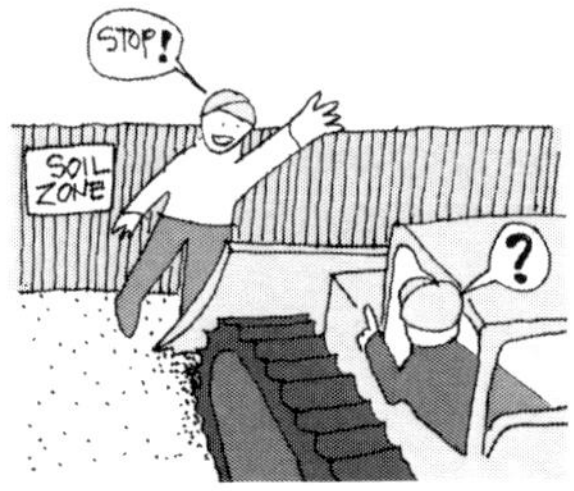

Principle 3: Preserve and Reuse Existing Soil Resources Whenever Possible

Develops a strategy to use, preserve, and reuse existing soil.

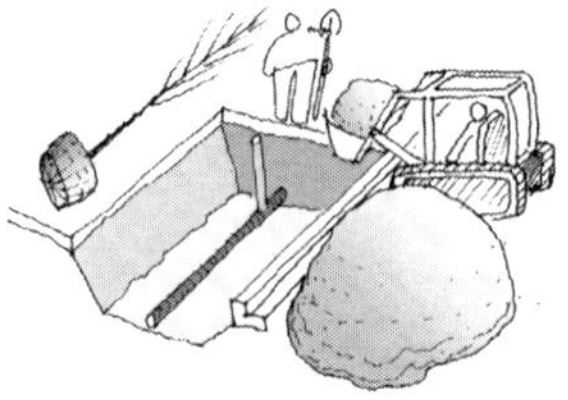

Principle 4: Improve Soil and Drainage

Describes specific techniques for improving soil and drainage and importing new soil.

Could Not Stop Myself

"The three trees that died were in a soil situation that is most difficult, in the smallest pits over the garage entry." This statement was made by a well-known landscape architect in response to criticism that trees had died on his award-winning project. He added the trees "were remnants of an earlier design effort that we could not change." Why couldn't the design be changed to accommodate the difficult conditions over the garage entry? If the designer knew the design was dependent on soil, why was the soil condition not considered? A design professional should have the skills, and certainly the obligation, to know when a design concept cannot be successfully implemented. Designers must adopt a "just say no" policy to planting trees in locations where they will not grow.

Implementing Soil Strategies

Landscape architecture is about changing land for human use. In the process, significant portions of the soil will be modified. The following factors determine the amount of soil that is disturbed and the ability to secure resources for its restoration.

Program Requirements

The space required for program requirements of the project impact the opportunities to preserve soil resources. The proposed uses of the site may also be incompatible with either the type of soil or the existing grades. For example, a high-use sports field, which needs sandy soils to support constant impact, will not succeed on clay loam soil without changing the soil type. Hilly topography may require significant grading and soil disruption to accommodate parking and road alignments. At sites with poor or no soil resources, imported soil may be the only option.

Plant Selections

Matching plant selections to the existing soil and drainage conditions is preferable at sites with usable soil resources. At sites with poor resources, it might be better to modify the soil and drainage to fit the plants desired, because the number of usable plant types may be otherwise too limited.

Soil Sustainability

Removing and then re-importing soil should not be considered a sustainable practice. Once soil is thrown away, more must be mined and transported to the site, leaving another site robbed of its soil. This process uses significant energy, degrades the imported soil, and creates a situation in which silt will migrate out of the system regardless of the care taken in construction.

The Green Building Council's "LEED certification" claims leadership in sustainability, but its certification requirements do not include preserving or restoring site soil. Without including soil, requirements such as credits for the use of native plants ring hollow. Native plants, like any other plant selections, must be matched to the correct soil type in order to grow with minimum maintenance. As of this writing, the American Society of Landscape Architects is working to add soil requirements to the LEED certification.

Cost and Constructability

Sustainability principles must be reconciled with issues of cost and constructability.

Protecting and improving soil resources become more expensive as site density intensifies. Preserving existing soil requires space, which translates into higher cost. Stockpiling takes up valuable room at urban sites. It is cheaper to grade slopes than to build walls or install sheeting. A soil preservation area is a potential contractor's staging location. Trucking soil offsite, storing it, and bringing it back may be more expensive than removing it and purchasing new soil.

Soil Budgets

The cost of soil and drainage improvement in a typical urban project is normally, at a minimum, equal to the cost of the plants. At dense urban sites, it can be two to four times the plant cost. This amount must be budgeted into the project's earliest cost estimates.

Soil Disturbance History

The more times the soil in a given area has been disturbed, the more likely it will limit root growth. Soil disturbed after the middle part of the 20th century will be more limiting to root growth than soil disturbed before the advent of modern, mechanized construction. To determine soil disturbance, designers must incorporate the principles of urban soil analysis discussed in Part I into their early design studies.

Soil Change During Construction

Compaction, contamination, inadvertent fills, and grading during construction alter the soil in significant ways. The designer must anticipate these changes when preparing a soil plan.

Client Commitment

Often, it is up to the designer to educate clients about the importance of soil preservation and modification, obtaining and nurturing client support for soil improvement. As with tree preservation, soil preservation cannot be successful without a client's commitment. Unlike tree preservation, the things needing protection are largely invisible. Of all the factors affecting the success of soil preservation, this is the most difficult to manage.

Designer Fees

It takes more design and administration time to save and modify soil than to throw it away and start over. The designer must convince the owner to pay for this additional work. Much of this extra time occurs during the construction oversight phase, when client fatigue is high and little sympathy exists for slowing construction to protect or fix "dirt." Designers can build on past success with soil to increase fees for future projects.

A designer must anticipate each of these factors when developing soil strategy. There is always going to be some level of compromise, and even the best plan may fail if any of these factors is underestimated.

Many factors determine whether the soil resources for a project can move successfully from concept to construction.

PART TWO

1

Principle 1: Plant the Easy Places First

This principle should inform the very first design sketches and will influence the aesthetic form of the project. More than any other principle, this one is dependent on understanding the information found throughout this book. Planting the easy places first almost always reduces the cost of construction and maintenance. It is less expensive and more sustainable to plant trees in large areas of good soil than in small spaces confined by paving and compacted soil, walls, and curbs. Designers should take into account the information gathered in the soil assessment, and avoid designs that force trees into restrictive soil conditions when better locations are available (see Part 1, Chapter Seven). All too often, we see landscapes built with trees in small holes adjacent to better, but unused, spots.

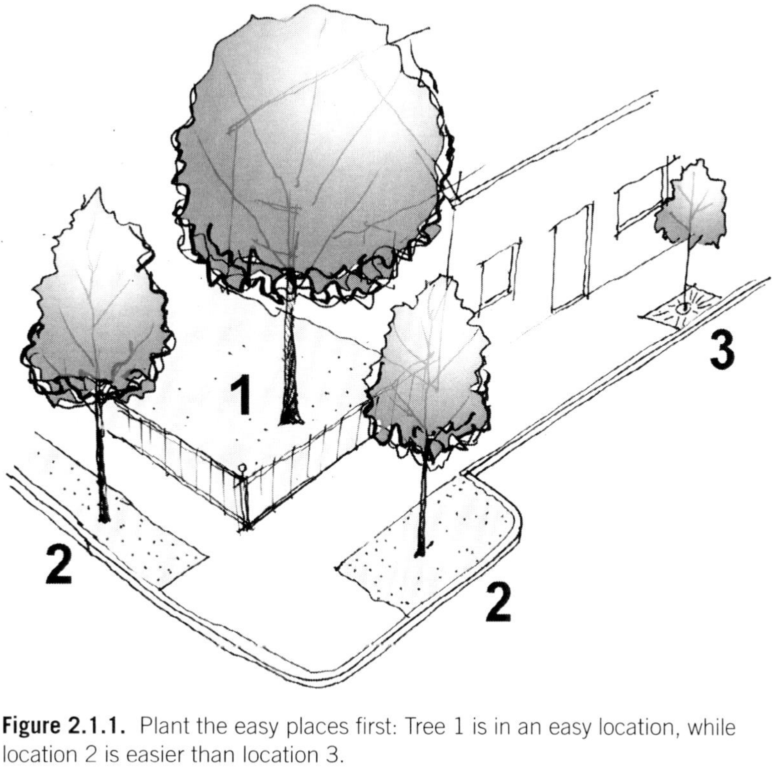

Figure 2.1.1. Plant the easy places first: Tree 1 is in an easy location, while location 2 is easier than location 3.

Figure 2.1.2. Easy vs. difficult planting places:

a, b, and c. Three trees at the same property in easy to increasingly difficult places.

d. Designer failing to achieve matched trees in easy and difficult places. What argument was made to plant the trees in the tree grates? Could the design have been changed to widen the planter in this large plaza to incorporate all the trees in an easy planting space?

FINDING THE EASY PLACES

Identify areas of soil with the least compaction and soil disturbance—places where existing plants, lawns, and mature trees are vigorous—as places to locate new trees. Soil not covered by pavement can be improved at lower cost than soil under pavement. Existing mineral soil may only need to be loosened and supplemented with organic matter.

Understand that soil conditions will change during construction.The good soil that was there during the design phase will likely be compacted and changed by contractor activity. If the design calls for protecting the soil, confirm that the contractor is following the requirements. Make alternative soil plans if conditions change. Note where soil disturbance is likely to occur during construction, and avoid areas that will become compacted or disturbed. Ensure that the soil is in good condition at the end of construction (see Principles 3 and 4).

At sites without good soil, designers can still respect this principle by designing easier places. Cluster trees in areas of contiguous soil volume. Simplify the design of pavement-to-tree relationships, with tree soil areas consolidated and distinctly separate from paved areas. Avoid surrounding individual trees with pavement (see Principle 2).

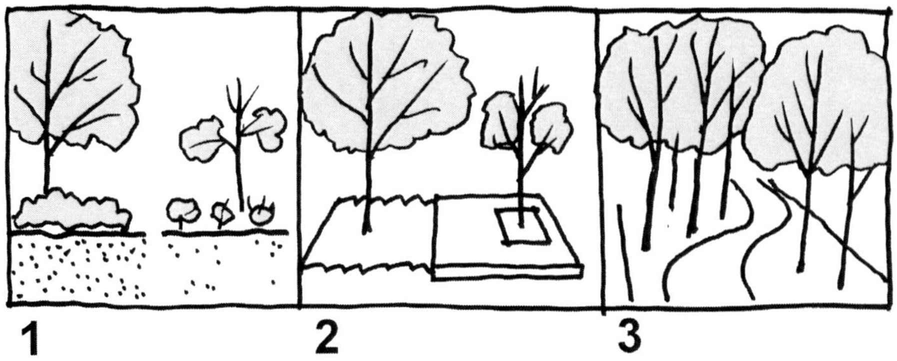

Figure 2.1.3. Finding and designing easier places.

1. Plant in places where existing vegetation is healthier.
2. Plant in larger soil areas, avoid confined spaces.
3. Cluster trees separated from paving.

a

b

Figure 2.1.4. Protect soil resources.
a. "Cow path" compaction caused by a design that failed to reflect pedestrian movement.
b. Curbs control pedestrian compaction in the planting space.

PROTECTING SOIL RESOURCES

Respect the circulation of people and vehicles at the site, and avoid designs where tree-rooting space is likely to be compacted. Low curbs or fences between planting soil and walks are effective to keep pedestrians on paths. Make walk alignments as direct as possible. People will always try to take the shortest path, even if that is through a turf or planting area. Predict where vehicles may use turf areas as temporary parking. Develop strategies to prevent the resulting compaction, using turf reinforcement, barriers, or soil aeration (see Principle 4).

DESIGN IMPACTS

Even slight changes to soil conditions will affect tree growth. Design symmetrical planting areas if symmetry of canopy growth is desired. This includes symmetry of plan configuration, grading, drainage, and soil improvement. Do not design formal rows or grids of trees where some trees are in large beds and some are in restricted spaces. They will always grow at different rates. No matter how much soil under pavements is improved (see Principle 6), it will not produce the same tree growth as a similar soil exposed to the sky.

Planting the easy places first will often result in planting fewer trees. Traditional design theory often relies on tightly spaced geometries that look pleasant and inviting

Figure 2.1.5. Trees in easy (right) and difficult (left) places will never grow at the same rate and already show differences in growth after just a few years. This designer added grates around the street-side trees, making an already difficult place even more difficult for the tree.

Figure 2.1.6. A single tree in an easy place can have greater impact than a row of declining trees in difficult places.

on the plan sketch, but ignore the reality of site conditions. Placing trees in the easy places improves the chance of producing large, healthy trees, and fewer trees may be required to achieve a cooling canopy. Avoid the temptation to fill gaps in difficult places with additional trees for the sole purpose of creating a particular visual rhythm, unless sufficient project resources exist to improve the growing conditions.

TREES AND TURF

Planting trees in the easy places often means planting in turf areas. When planted together, trees and lawn are in fierce competition. Many turf grasses secrete chemicals into the soil that are harmful to the roots of other plants as a defense mechanism to slow the growth of larger plants that would block out the sun. Turf also forms thick root mats that absorb available water and nutrients from the soil before they can reach the tree roots. In nature, tree seedlings overcome these defenses by quickly producing large root systems to compete with the grass. Nursery-grown trees, however, arrive as stressed plants with small root systems and large crowns. The grass has all the advantage, and a tree planted in lawn often declines or takes years to recover.

When a tree must be planted in turf, give the tree a better chance by installing a 6- to 10-foot-diameter mulched area around it, and arrange to keep that area weed free for a period of three to five years to increase the tree's recovery rate. This mulch should be well-aged or composted to a dark brown color. Avoid fresh bark mulches.

Once a tree produces enough shade, the grass declines. Too often, people then begin their own chemical offensive to keep their lawn perfect, at great cost to the tree. If a vigorous lawn under trees is important, keep the spacing between trees wide, 50 feet or more, to allow light to come through. As the trees mature, more water will be needed to keep the lawn green in dry periods. If narrower spacing is desired, select trees with open canopies or require canopy thinning as the trees mature.

a b c

Figure 2.1.7. Trees in mulch grow better than trees with lawn close to the trunk.

a. Large mulch ring around specimen tree in lawn.

b. Tightly spaced trees in mulch beds.

c. Tightly spaced tree originally planted with lawn ground cover, now mulched due to tree shade and root competition.

SUMMARY

- Plant large trees in areas of large soil resources.
- Separate planting areas from paved areas.
- Cluster trees in areas of contiguous soil volume.
- Recognize that restricted soil volumes lead to smaller trees.
- Design symmetrical soil areas if uniform trees are desired. Avoid designing formal rows or grids of trees where some trees are in large beds and some are in restricted spaces.
- Ensure that soil is in good condition at the end of construction.
- Avoid designs where tree-rooting space may become compacted. Design curbs and fences along planting areas. Make walking path alignments as direct as possible.
- Keep lawn 3 to 5 feet from the trunks of newly planted trees until the tree is established.
- Avoid designing lawns under the canopies of large, closely spaced trees.

REFERENCES

Costello, Laurence R. and Katherine S. Jones. 2003. *Reducing Infrastructure Damage by Tree Roots: A Compendium of Strategies.* Western Chapter of the International Society of Arboriculture, Cohasset, CA. 119 pp.

Trowbridge, Peter J., and Nina L. Bassuk. 2004. *Trees in the Urban Landscape: Site Assessment Design and Installation.* John Wiley & Sons, Inc., Hoboken, NJ. 205 pp.

Urban, James. 2000. *Ramsey/Sleeper Architectural Graphic Standards.* 10th ed. John Ray Hoke, Jr., ed. John Wiley & Sons, Inc., New York, NY.

PART TWO

2

Principle 2: Make Larger Planting Spaces

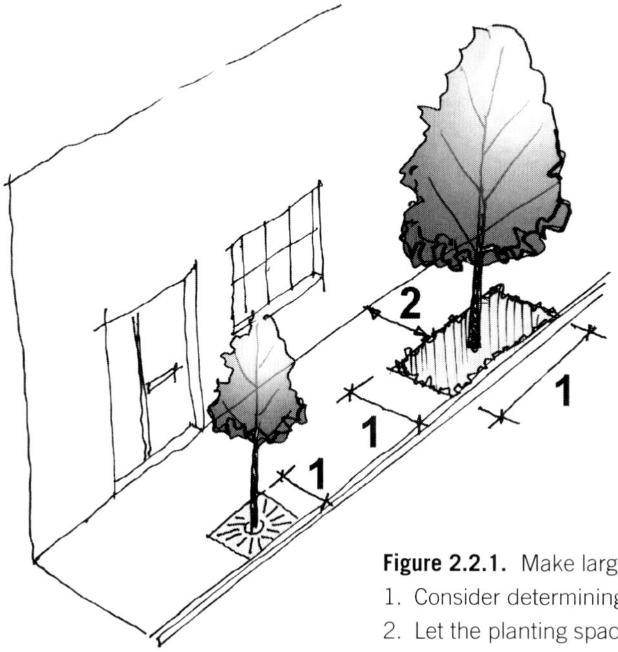

Figure 2.2.1. Make larger planting spaces.
1. Consider determining minimum paving dimensions.
2. Let the planting space fill the space available.

When trees must have paving or structures on all sides, design the largest planting spaces possible. Larger planting spaces, filled with good soil, will produce healthier, longer-lived trees. A single successful tree in a consolidated planting space is much better than many trees struggling in small holes.

As the landscape becomes more urban, it is more difficult to design adequate soil volumes. Pavement needs more ground to handle more pedestrians and vehicles. The result? Spaces for trees tend to be as small as possible.

Larger planting spaces should be used even if there are resources to accommodate roots under the paving. Larger spaces are more sustainable, using fewer resources to improve soil and reducing paving conflicts. Like planting the easy places first, making larger planting spaces is a design decision that must begin with the very earliest sketches.

Figure 2.2.2. Minimum tree planting space. This is not to say that smaller spaces cannot be designed, only to recognize that smaller spaces are not optimum.

MINIMUM TREE SPACES

What is the minimum size hole for planting a tree? Ideally, 20 feet or larger in diameter is a reasonable minimum to support a functional, large-canopy tree. Anything smaller will compromise the tree at some point in the future, but a 20-foot space for a tree is prohibitive in most urban areas. What then is a realistic size for an urban setting? The practical answer is that the space for the tree and the paving should be developed together, with the paving designed to provide the minimum width needed for the use of the space, and the area for tree planting designed to be the largest size practical. The size of the space for the tree should vary within the design, putting a premium on design approaches that allow flexibility of geometry.

This approach is counter to fundamental urban design principles, which put a premium on consistency and rhythm in paving and other urban features. A craftily designed paving pattern around a small tree opening remains one of the hallmarks of a "good" urban streetscape plan, even though such standards most often predict failure for the tree. The design community must acknowledge that a healthy, large tree provides significantly greater value to the space than a clever paving pattern and visual rhythm.

If there is no practical minimum size for the tree opening, is there a minimum dimension into which a tree should not be planted? Unfortunately, there is no simple answer to this question. Factors in such a decision include:

- The type of tree
- Surrounding soil conditions, existing or constructed
- Project goals
- Willingness to compromise the tree
- Client tolerance for risk of losing the tree and/or damaging the pavement

A Hot Dog or a Tree?

Often it is argued that the spaces for street trees cannot be larger because of the need to accommodate pedestrians on a busy street. In New York City, the typical street tree is allowed a 4-foot by 4-foot hole. However, the typical hot-dog vendor occupies a space more than twice as large. These vendors are usually at the corner, where the greatest numbers of pedestrians collect. So why is a larger space for a tree, which provides greater value to the community, a problem but a larger space for a hot-dog stand is not?

Figure 2.2.3. Long planting spaces allow the largest open soil space while accommodating other urban functions.

Figure 2.2.4. A good balance between trees and other urban requirements

Most of the conflicts in a very small planting space are related to the future growth of trunk flare and zone of rapid taper (see Principle 5 for discussions of these constraints).

Although developing a larger width for the planting area is critical, in areas of linear pedestrian traffic, making the tree space longer in the direction of travel has significant advantages. The longer space provides additional soil volume at low cost, and the trunk flare and zone of rapid taper will adapt somewhat to the shape of the space.

In areas of intense pedestrian activity, providing a curb or fence around the planting space is a reasonable alternative to installing a tree grate or paving over the planting soil. The curb has the added advantage of reducing salt intrusion into the soil around the tree in northern climates.

TRUNK-TO-PAVING TRANSITION

The ground immediately around the base of a tree is subject to relatively rapid and constant change. The adequacy of the planting hole depends on how the design accommodates the tree's trunk flare and the roots' zone of rapid taper as required in Principle 5, "Respect the base of the tree." The zone of rapid taper is the area 15 feet or more in diameter around the trunk where root diameters are the largest. Although it is best not to have rapid-taper roots under paving, this may be unavoidable in dense urban areas. The more paving is near the expected zone of large roots, the more conflicts a designer can expect, and the more it will cost to accommodate them—or to repair damage if the designer fails to do this planning. Principle 5 must guide decisions on the minimum size of tree openings.

Figure 2.2.5. Trunk base transition. Long-term changes in the base of the tree are best accommodated with larger planting spaces.

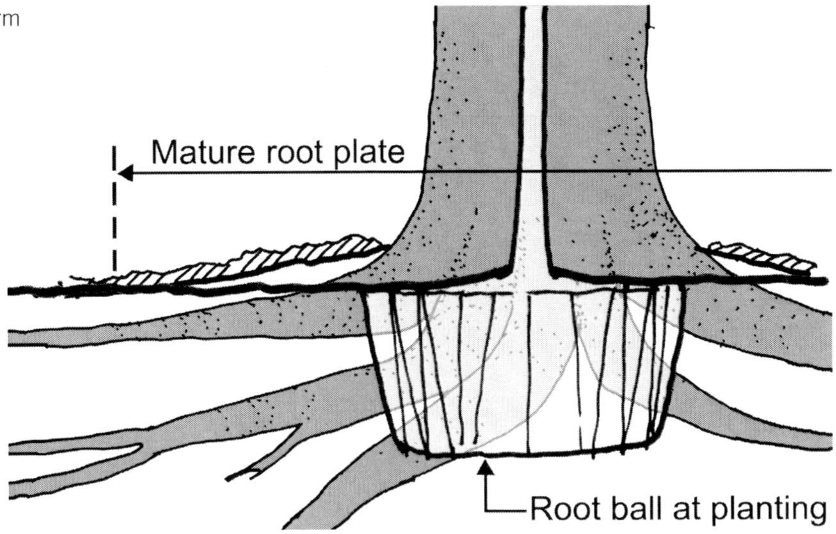

When the tree is young, the bare soil between the trunk and the paving needs some type of covering such as mulch ground-cover plants, gravel, or loosely laid pavers. Designers need to think of this space as a transition zone that will gradually fill with trunk wood and roots. The less flexible the material that is used to fill the space, the more conflicts will occur as the tree grows. Therefore, tree grates should never be used.

Although a planted understory is the preferred alternative, never plant ground-cover plants within the root ball of a newly planted tree. This damages critical roots at the precise time when the tree is most stressed. The area directly above the root ball at planting must remain mulch. Plant ground covers around the edge of the root ball and allow them to expand over the root ball with time.

As the tree grows, the available light, water, and nutrients within the soil will change. Select understory and ground-cover plants that can survive these more difficult growing conditions. At the time of planting, the area under the tree may be in full sun, and few plants can thrive in both full sun and full shade. Wider spacing of trees reduces this conflict. If the planting can change as the tree matures, the landscape will be more successful. Designers should make clients aware of this need for change and incorporate modification recommendations into their plans.

SOIL WITHIN AND AROUND THE PLANTING SPACE

Once the designer has determined the size of the tree growing space, the next step is to optimize the quality of the soil and drainage within and around this area. Principles 3, 4, 5, and 6 will discuss strategies for this optimization. Principles 3 and 4 provide methods to reuse or improve the existing soil. Principle 5 sets requirements for the ever-enlarging trunk flare and zone-of-rapid-taper roots. Principle 6 provides ways to improve the roots' growth potential under the pavement.

Start by calculating the volume of soil that is available or provided to determine whether it is adequate for the expected growth. Use the soil volume chart presented in Part 2, Chapter Four, "Improve soil and drainage." Remember that improved soil covered by pavement is never as useful to the tree or as sustainable to install as good soil without pavement. Following the strategies in Principle 6, "Make space for roots," does not remove the requirement to follow Principle 2, "Make larger planting spaces."

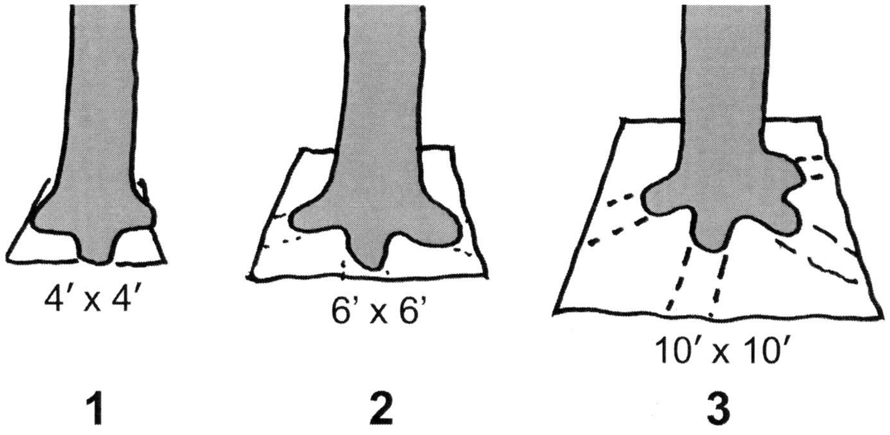

Figure 2.2.6. Bigger spaces offer less conflict, but none of these options provides sufficient soil volume. Where possible, make the spaces longer in the direction of pedestrian travel.

1. 4-foot space: Conflict with mature flare and ZRT roots
2. 6-foot space: Conflict with mature ZRT roots
3. 10-foot space: Conflict with ZRT roots only when tree becomes quite large

If the space for planting becomes too small and budgets are insufficient to provide for the requirements of the tree, it may be best to plant fewer trees to allow for adequate conditions with the available resources or, in extreme cases, to plant no trees.

SUMMARY

- Improving soil within the area of the planting hole is the cheapest and most sustainable way to improve growing conditions for a tree.
- The minimum planting space size is 20 feet or greater in diameter.This size is an impractical standard for most urban areas.
- Consider minimum paving space as opposed to minimum planting space.

Figure 2.2.7. Mature tree in a small space, successfully altering the paving around its base. Though planted in a 4-foot space, the tree has enlarged the hole many times and lifted the ground almost a foot. Several generations of sensitive landowners have reset bricks to accommodate the tree's needs. Unfortunately, not everyone is this considerate.

- Optimize soil and drainage within and around the planting space.
- Allow planting spaces to grow as circulation requirements vary. Avoid uniform planting spaces designed to fit the most restrictive dimension.
- In areas of linear circulation, make the holes longer in the direction of travel.
- Use fences or curbs to elevate and separate planting areas from foot traffic and salt applications.
- Provide for plants, mulch, gravel, or other flexible materials on the ground around the tree. Never dig into the root ball of a newly planted tree to plant ground-cover plants.
- Ensure that shrubs and other plantings under trees are compatible with shade and drought conditions that can be expected as the trees mature.
- Calculate the soil volume. Develop sufficient volume to support the long-term growth of the tree.
- Eliminate the tree if the need for paving overly restricts space for it and budgets are insufficient to allow soil for roots under the pavement.
- Follow the strategies in Principle 6, "Make space for roots." Remember that improving the soil under the paving is not a substitute for larger planting spaces. The two concepts are complementary.

REFERENCES

Key References

Costello, Laurence R. and Katherine S. Jones. 2003. *Reducing Infrastructure Damage by Tree Roots: A Compendium of Strategies*. Western Chapter of the International Society of Arboriculture, Cohasset, CA. 119 pp.

Craul, Phillip J. 1999. *Urban Soils: Applications and Practices*. John Wiley & Sons, Inc., New York, NY. 366 pp.

Ferguson, Bruce K. 2005. *Porous Pavements*. CRC Press, Boca Raton, FL. 577 pp.

Harris, Richard W., James R. Clark, and Nelda P. Matheny. 2004. *Arboriculture: Integrated Management of Landscape Trees, Shrubs, and Vines*. 4th ed. Pearson Education, Inc., Upper Saddle River, NJ. 578 pp.

Trowbridge, Peter J., and Nina L. Bassuk. 2004. *Trees in the Urban Landscape: Site Assessment Design and Installation*. John Wiley & Sons, Inc., Hoboken, NJ. 205 pp.

Urban, James. 2000. *Ramsey/Sleeper Architectural Graphic Standards*. 10th ed. John Ray Hoke, Jr., ed. John Wiley & Sons, Inc., New York, NY.

Other Resources

Roberts, John, Nick Jackson and Mark Smith. 2006. *Tree Roots in the Built Environment*. Crown Copyright, The Stationary Office, Norwich, England. 488 pp.

Watson, Gary W., and Dan Neely, eds. 1994. *The Landscape Below Ground*. International Society of Arboriculture, Savoy, IL. 222 pp.

Watson, Gary W., and Dan Neely, eds. 1998. *The Landscape Below Ground II*. International Society of Arboriculture, Champaign, IL. 265 pp.

PART TWO

3

Principle 3: Preserve and Reuse Existing Soil Resources

Figure 2.3.1. Soil, one of our most precious resources, is a building block of sustainability.

Whenever natural soil is disturbed, it loses some of its ability to support plant life by losing its structure, its one irreplaceable attribute (see Part 1, Chapter Two). Loss of structure is incremental: Even a little compaction or grading will damage a small portion of the structure. Once structure is lost, it cannot easily be restored. The one exception is very sandy soil, which generally lacks a definable structure.

Designers must not fool themselves into thinking they have healed a piece of land by importing or re-spreading "good" soil. The site may be better than if they had done nothing about the damage, but the new soil will never be as good as it was in its undisturbed state. The preservation of good soil is as important as the preservation of fine historic architecture or healthy, mature trees. Good soil is an irreplaceable resource.

Figure 2.3.2. Finding space to preserve and stockpile soil can be challenging in urban sites.

Soil preservation or soil reuse? Principle 3 assumes the existing soil is healthy and can be preserved or reused with minimum modification or amendment. Preservation of the soil means guarding its plant-supporting qualities and protecting it from grading, compaction, and contamination during the proposed construction. Reused soil is soil that can easily be made to support plants, and that may be maintained in place with minimum grading, compaction, or contamination, or may be reused after being stripped and stockpiled, an option preferable to importing new soil from another site.

Soil and drainage plans. All requirements for soil preservation and reuse should be recorded on a contract document drawing titled "Soil and Drainage Plan," separate from the planting plan, which includes its own set of details and specifications. These documents are described in Principle 9. Soil and drainage plans are a recent addition to a standard set of contract documents.

SOIL PRESERVATION

The less soil is disturbed, the better. Preserving it in place should be the first option, but it takes passion and long-term will to convince landowners and contractors to undertake the compromises needed for preservation. At urban construction sites, the pressure to use all the available space is great, and vacant space to remain as "landscape" is viewed as a prime staging area for contractors. Community environmental values respecting the importance of soil will need to change before this approach can receive a wider application. For now, the following recommendations may be just a dream for the future.

Client Commitment

Preserving existing soil in place has significant impact on design and construction options, construction cost, and schedules. It will not succeed without the commitment of the owner and contractors. This commitment must be cultivated through the construction period. At the end of the project, goals tend to shift, and the urgency of completing the project may outweigh the need to preserve some "dirt."

Design and Coordination

To be successful, soil preservation goals must become a part of the design program. This will guide the location of paving and structures, utility alignments, grading, planting, and irrigation systems, as well as all other aspects of the site work in the vicinity of the soil to be preserved. Those invested in these goals must coordinate with the work of other consultants on the project and must educate others about the importance of preserving the resource. Designers interested in this level of sustainability must often take on this effort without compensation.

Figure 2.3.3. The economy of mass grading of sites makes it hard to add the subtleties of soil preservation into the construction sequence.

Cost and Schedule

In purely economic terms, we cannot justify preserving existing soil at urban sites .The owner may have conflicting and shifting schedule requirements that make soil preservation difficult. The small cost saved by not having to restore damaged soil is offset by additional construction cost. Soil preservation means less space and more restrictions for the contractor, including longer schedules, sheeting and shoring requirements, and required controls over subcontractors. The benefit of reduced environmental damage must be embraced as the primary justification. Preserved soil may also be better quality than purchased soil. With these factors taken into account, soil preservation becomes a more prudent choice.

Protection provisions are often compromised at the end of construction. When fences that guarded soil from harm are removed before construction ends, contractors will use the newly released space to park vehicles, store supplies, and construct parts of the finished project. Landscape contractors are often the worst offenders, especially because they are charged with making modifications to the planting in the area. Once the contractor is in the preservation zone, it seems, anything goes.

Requirements

Soil protection includes protection from compaction, grading, filling, contamination by chemicals and silt, the loss of organic functions, the formation of surface crust, and changes to drainage patterns. Keep specifications simple. Avoid requirements that may be difficult to enforce in the field, because unrealistic restrictions will often cause all requirements to be ignored. Provide contractors with enough room to work, and be flexible in allowing them into an area for certain activities.

Figure 2.3.4. Soil preservation requirements are similar to those needed for tree root preservation, but are harder to enforce, lacking a tree to serve as the visual rationale.

Fencing

Use fences to prevent intrusion into the preservation zone, with signs on the fence that say "Keep out—Soil preservation area." Coordinate silt fencing with the civil engineer to control silt intrusion.

Preserve Existing Plants

If there are plants and grass within the area, leave them in place until the end of the project, even if they are to be removed. Stop mowing the grass and allow it to grow. All existing vegetation will serve as a barrier to the contractors and make it less likely that they will see the soil preservation area as available construction space.

Sheeting and Shoring

Sheeting and shoring temporarily support the sides of excavations to reduce the size of the excavation and the amount of grading required to

a

b

Figure 2.3.5. Sheeting and shoring to reduce soil disturbance.
a. Building requirements for sheeting can be extended to include soil areas.
b. Pipe trench boxes and other temporary measures can reduce the size of excavations.

construct subsurface elements. To ensure that sheeting and shoring are included in the bid price, they must be delineated on the architect's or civil engineer's drawings.

Mulching, Matting, and Geotextile

Spread mulch or wood chips to protect soil from the occasional inadvertent or necessary intrusion. The mulch will decompose during the construction period, adding organic material to the soil. Mulch will also absorb dust, silt, and other contaminants, which can then be easily removed by removing the mulch layer. If the mulch is not contaminated, it can be reused at the site.

Plastic or plywood mat boardwalks over mulch are needed where vehicles or repeated access to soil preservation zones is required. A pre-engineered system called Alturnamats is very effective and can be reused for multiple projects.

For resistance to severe compaction during intense construction, add a layer of geotextile or geogrids under the mulch or wood chips. This must be removed along with the mulch above when the project is complete. The surface of the soil that was under matting and geotextile may need to be lightly tilled to remove surface crusting.

a

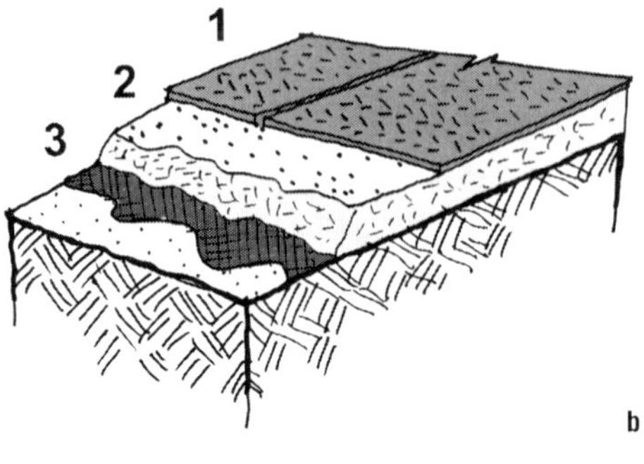

b

Figure 2.3.6. Protecting soil from compaction.
a. Matting (Alturnamats) over wood chips and geotextile to protect soil from compaction.
b. Matting detail:
1. Alturnamat.
2. Six inches of wood chips or bark mulch.
3. Geotextile.

Weather and Soil Moisture

It is not always possible to keep all construction off a good soil area. The timing of access relative to soil moisture content is critical. Require wet-weather restrictions on access to the soil.

Inspection

In a large construction project, there are long periods when it is not anticipated that the landscape designer will be at the site. Soil damage can happen at any time by any of the subcontractors on the job site. Support of the owner or client to allow consistent site inspections is critical. If inspections must be limited, be sure to include at least one at the end of the project, when significant soil damage often occurs.

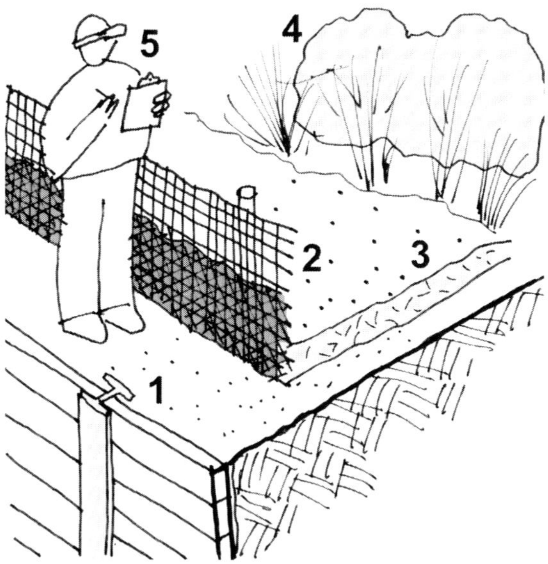

Figure 2.3.7. Soil protection details
1. Sheeting and shoring.
2. Fencing and silt fencing.
3. Mulch or wood chips.
4. Retain existing vegetation even if it will be removed at the end of construction.
5. Inspection.

SOIL REUSE

At most projects, the mineral soil resource may be reused, but requires some modification or grading. Soil damage before and during construction includes compaction, grading, or contamination caused by contractor equipment. Whatever the situation, the soil's ped structure is damaged and chemical and organic composition likely changed. Compaction reduction and organic soil amendments may be needed to restore it to a useful state.

If good records have been kept on the extent and depth of soil resources during the analysis phase, it will be easy to prepare a soil improvement diagram (see Principle 9). This plan should delineate what is to be restored or removed, and the depths of soil harvesting. While the designer may identify a location for the soil stockpile area, most contractors will determine how they want to manage the site during construction. It is difficult for the designer to direct the process of a project, because construction contracts are designed to measure outcome, not to direct means and methods.

Design and Coordination

Be conservative in evaluating soils for reuse and predicting the level of damage expected during construction. Plan and prepare specification documents for the worst-case scenario, and set milestone reviews during construction to monitor decisions on the extent of reuse and what will be required. The soil amendment process usually cannot be implemented until the very last stages of construction, at which time the finished surface, paving, walls, lighting, irrigation system, and utility lines will limit the size and type of equipment that can operate, as well as the depth to which tilling and subsoiling can extend. The more intensive the site development, the fewer options are available.

Cost and Schedule

Reuse of soil on large sites can be cost-effective, but the savings diminish as sites become smaller. Impact of reuse on construction schedules is normally limited, because it is assumed that the contractor can enter these areas with minimum restrictions. Compaction caused by activity must be mitigated. Once soil has been tilled and amended, it must be protected.

Figure 2.3.8. Compaction reduction.

Requirements

Different soil types will require different amendments. The greater the clay level in soil, the more difficult it will be to improve soil quality.

Work with the contractor to reduce the damage from construction by limiting the area needed for parking, storage, and work. Use of tracked grading machines and machines with large, low-pressure (4 pounds per square inch or less) tires during soil work and other construction will result in less damage. Tracked machines of all sizes are now common in most markets, making it easier for the contractor to require them on site. The trucks that haul materials, however, are not low impact and must be restricted to specific areas.

The goal of soil preservation is to reduce compaction, amend damaged texture and structure, improve drainage, and restore organic functions. Principle 4, "Improve soil and drainage," provides an in-depth discussion of soil improvements. The following are the most common modifications for soil that is to be improved in place.

Figure 2.3.9. Amending soil texture.

Reducing Compaction

Compaction is the most common form of soil damage, and compaction levels in both topsoil and subsoil must be reduced before installing plants at the end of construction. Breaking up compaction requires considerable effort. At intensely developed sites, there may not be space for large equipment to operate, and significant conflicts with utilities may complicate the job. Subsoil compaction reduction, if required, should be completed before installing utility lines within the top 36 inches of soil. Fine-grained soil will tend to recompact as it settles under the forces of gravity and water movement. Detailed descriptions of compaction reduction techniques are found in Principle 4.

Figure 2.3.10. Sand added to existing clay soil. Dark center of broken ped (top) reveals that sand is simply coating the clay peds, not mixing into the soil. Drainage and soil texture is not improved.

Amending Soil Texture

Adding organic matter, or materials such as expanded shale or calcined clay, to the soil during turning or tilling will introduce an artificial "structure" and help reduce the tendency toward recompaction. These materials can be spread over the surface to be subsoiled or backhoe-turned. As the soil is fractured and turned, organic matter or shale material will fall into the cracks and keep them open. The organic matter should be stable compost, preferably from a source high in lignin such as pine bark. See Principle 4 for further discussion on soil amendments.

Do not add small amounts of sand to fine-grained soil to improve texture and drainage. It is difficult to mix sand into clay or silt, and, if insufficiently mixed, the sand just surrounds soil peds. Unless the sand is quite coarse and added in large enough quantity (more than 50 percent of the volume), it may make the soil drain less rapidly and become more compacted, taking on the quality of concrete. Adding composted organic matter is usually the best method of improving soil texture and drainage.

Improving Drainage

The compaction reduction and soil structure techniques outlined here will improve drainage. If the underlying subsoil is not well drained, further steps may include grading to introduce steeper slopes, planting on mounds with a minimum of 10 percent slopes after soil settlement, or adding a subsurface drainage system.

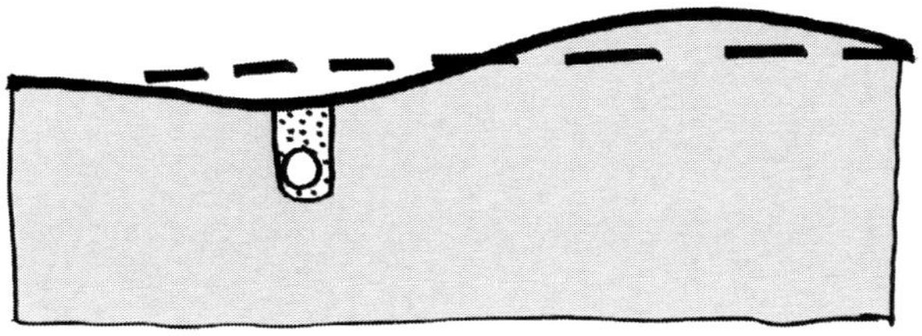

Figure 2.3.11. Improving soil drainage.

Restoring Organic Functions

Generous amounts (3-4 inches) of locally produced yard waste compost, applied to the surface and lightly tilled into the top 3 to 4 inches of soil, will improve the organic content of the soil and create conditions for improvement in the soil food web. Avoid extreme cultivation that breaks down soil into very fine particles.

Well-composted products high in humic acid and/or lignin are the best products to use as soil amendments. Applications of compost tea can provide specific organisms that are identified through a soil biology assay as deficient.

Organic restoration is the final step in soil improvement. Making changes to organic soil functions in the top layer of compacted or poorly drained soil will do little to improve the soil if nothing is done to correct problems in the layers below.

Fencing and Sediment Control

Fencing areas to be protected during construction may be helpful, but this is harder to justify if the soil is already partially damaged and compaction reduction requirements are specified at the end of the work. Temporary fencing should be required around areas of completed soil work if work is ahead of the rest of the construction. Permanent and temporary fencing should be indicated as required on the soil and drainage plans.

Require sediment control to segregate preserved soil resources from graded areas. Because regulations require sediment control only at the project perimeter, it may be a challenge to justify internal sediment control.

Figure 2.3.12. Do not grade or move soil when it is wet.

Weather and Soil Moisture

Perform all these soil improvement processes when the soil is friable. Avoid cultivation when the soil is at extremes of moisture or dryness. Where possible, restrict activity during construction in areas where the soil is to be improved. Refraining from heavy traffic and/or grading during wet weather is important.

Lime Stabilization Applications

Increasingly, site engineers are applying lime during construction to stabilize wet soils. The lime helps to aggregate the soil together and allow traffic during wet weather. The lime increases the pH of the soil to more than 8 and contributes to the formation of a dense, compacted crust. Soils treated in this way will not be usable for planting trees. Designers should discourage this practice and recommend alternative ways to allow construction to proceed in wet weather. These include:

- Restricting lime applications to proposed road and parking subgrade areas.
- Using mats, geotextiles, and aggregate or wood-chip blankets to allow circulation over wet soil.
- Restricting contractor activity to stable surfaces and dry weather.

SOIL REMOVAL AND STOCKPILING

Soil removal and stockpiling is the most common form of soil reuse, especially at large sites. The effort to strip, stockpile, and spread topsoil and subsoil does considerable damage to soil structure, profile, and biology.

Design and Coordination

Evaluate existing soil resources, and map the areas and depth of usable topsoil and subsoil to be stockpiled, using the procedures for soil assessment in Part 1, Chapter Seven. Use soil probes to determine the depth of the A horizon and usable B horizon soils. Make this plan part of the contract documents.

Cost and Schedule

Reuse of removed and stockpiled soil is a cost-effective way to improve growing conditions. The larger the site, the greater the advantage of removing and stockpiling soil. Assuming there is storage space, there is little impact on the construction schedule. On tight urban sites, room for soil storage may preclude reusing the existing soil. Trucking the soil to an off-site storage area may be more costly than removing it and purchasing new soil at the end of construction, particularly for projects that will take more than a year.

Requirements

Small changes to standard procedures can make a big difference in the level of damage that occurs to soil during moving and storage. The less it is moved, stored, and graded, the less damage will occur.

Stripping Topsoil and Subsoil Material

Before starting stripping operations, remove woody plants, stumps, and large root mats of trees. At sites where noxious or invasive plants are growing, develop a plant removal and herbicide program to control these plants before stripping the soil. Also, mow the area before stripping the soil. The root mat of herbaceous and grass plants may be left in place, if the soil is to be stockpiled for more than one growing season.

Perform soil removal and storage only when soil moisture is such that the soil is friable, neither overly moist nor overly dry. Soil should hold together in clods as it is being handled. Strip and stockpile topsoil (O and A horizons) and subsoil (B, E, and C horizons) separately. See Part 1, Chapter 2 to understand these conditions.

On sites with multiple topsoil types, segregate sandy soils from finer-grained clay or silty soils. Indicate use of each soil type in the final soils plan. Place sandier soils under lawn areas or locations with the highest potential for compaction impact. Use finer-grained soils under planting beds, on mounds, and in places that require higher water-holding capacity or have low potential for compaction impact. If different soil types are discovered during the excavation process, be flexible about modifying soil plans to take advantage of available resources.

Use tracked grading machines or large, low-pressure-tire loaders to spread the machine's weight to reduce the compaction of subsoil.

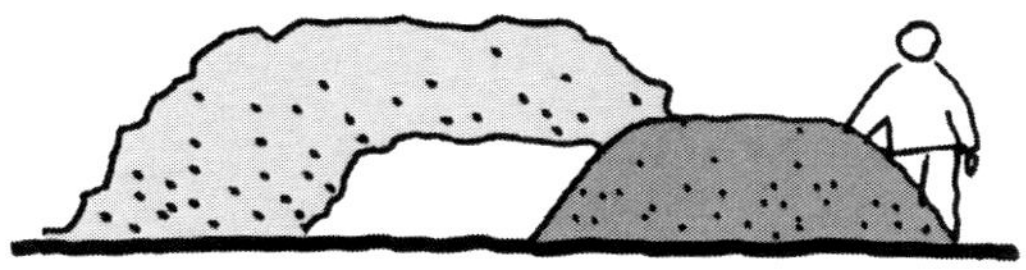

Figure 2.3.13. Separate different soil types.

Stockpiling and Storage

Maintain separate stockpiles for each soil type and reuse in different applications. Where practical, maintain many small piles rather than one large pile to reduce compaction of soil peds and loss of soil biology. The optimum size of stockpiles is 6 feet maximum height for sandy loam soil and 4 feet maximum height for clay loam soil. This is substantially smaller than typical standards and may be difficult to achieve.

Refrain from moving the soil pile during the construction period. Each time soil is moved, soil ped size is reduced.

Few sites have the luxury for ideal soil storage conditions. The longer the soil is stockpiled and the larger the piles that must be accommodated, the longer it will take to reactivate soil biology properties. Compost tea application and composted yard waste tilled into the soil, once re-spread, can assist in this reactivation.

Soil under the stockpile will become compacted. Such compaction will increase the longer the pile is in place and the greater the pile height. If the pile location is to be used as a planting location, compaction reduction of that soil may be required after the pile is removed.

Do not cover the stockpile with an impervious cover such as a tarp or plastic. These materials will reduce air penetration and increase soil temperature, which may kill soil organisms. An impervious layer over the soil may actually increase soil moisture by wicking moisture through the pile from below. This may leave the soil too wet at the time it is to be spread.

If the soil contains noxious or invasive plants that sprout during the storage period, use a selective herbicide to kill the plants so that they are not spread with the soil. Several treatments may be needed.

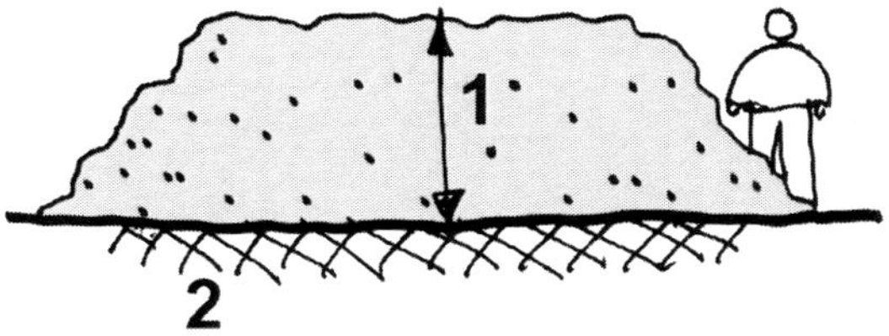

Figure 2.3.14. Soil stockpile.

1. Optimum height 6 feet for sandy loam, 4 feet for clay loam.
2. Reduce compaction under the pile area after it is removed.

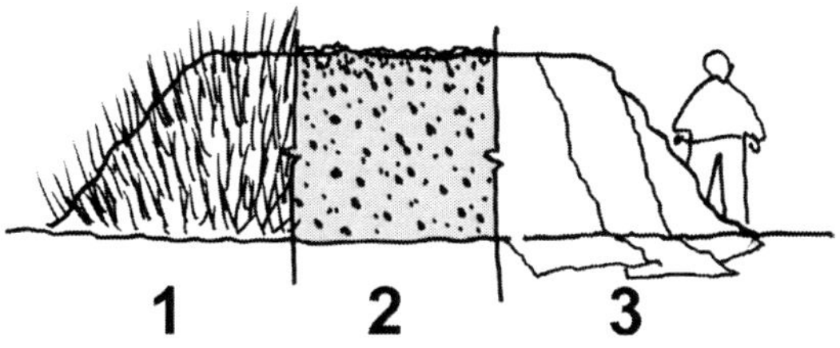

Figure 2.3.15. Protect the soil stockpile from water and wind erosion. Depending on the season and length of time of storage, provide one of the following covers:

1. Annual or perennial grass cover crop.
2. Compost or mulch blanket.
3. Pervious, needle punched geotextile.

Reusing Stored Soil

Prepare subgrades and spread stockpiled soil as required in Principle 4. The soil may require amendments at the time of installation. Organic matter incorporated into the soil as it is being spread will improve drainage, biological activity, and introduce an artificial structure into the soil. If the soil is to be applied in beds deeper than 12 inches, restrict the added organic matter to 10 percent of total soil volume. Additional organic matter (3 to 4 inches of compost) can be tilled to the surface after the soil is rough graded.

Figure 2.3.16. Maintaining vegetative cover on soil stockpiles is challenging. Temporary covering such as mulch or geotextiles may be preferable.

SUMMARY

- Evaluate the condition of the soil before construction, predict the types of damage that may occur during construction, and evaluate it again after construction.
- Make recommendations at each stage of the construction process based on these evaluations.
- Work with the contractor to limit the damage to the soil.
- Preserve good and usable soil resources, in place, where practical.
- Stockpile and reuse soil where there is room for storage.
- Break up surface and subsurface soil compaction.
- Amend soil texture with organic additives.
- Improve soil drainage.
- Restore organic soil functions.
- Maintain smaller soil stockpiles.

REFERENCES

Key References

Costello, Laurence R. and Katherine S. Jones. 2003. *Reducing Infrastructure Damage by Tree Roots: A Compendium of Strategies*. Western Chapter of the International Society of Arboriculture, Cohasset, CA. 119 pp.

Craul, Phillip J. 1999. *Urban Soils: Applications and Practices*. John Wiley & Sons, Inc., New York, NY. 366 pp.

Craul, Timothy A., and Phillip J. Craul. 2006. *Soil Design Protocols: For Landscape Architects and Contractors*. John Wiley & Sons, Inc., New York, NY. 339 pp.

Trowbridge, Peter J., and Nina L. Bassuk. 2004. *Trees in the Urban Landscape: Site Assessment Design and Installation*. John Wiley & Sons, Inc., Hoboken, NJ. 205 pp.

Urban, James. 2000. *Ramsey/Sleeper Architectural Graphic Standards*. 10th ed. John Ray Hoke, Jr., ed. John Wiley & Sons, Inc., New York, NY.

Other Resources

Craul, Phillip J. 1992. *Urban Soil in Landscape Design*. John Wiley & Sons, Inc., New York, NY. 396 pp.

PART TWO

4

Principle 4: Improve Soil and Drainage

Principle 4 develops the detail about soil modifications, soil mixes, drainage improvements, and improvements to soil within the root zone of existing trees.

As the volume of available soil becomes smaller, the quality of the soil becomes more important to the tree's long-term success. Working with existing soil should be the first option, but replacing this soil with imported topsoil or soil mixes may be a reasonable, or even preferred, choice. Specialized program requirements such as constructed wetlands, storm water filtration areas, rooftop planters, and turf will benefit from soil mixes that are not easily created from existing resources.

Figure 2.4.1. Improve soil and drainage.

KEY FACTORS IN SOIL AND DRAINAGE IMPROVEMENT

For this step, more than any other, it is crucial to have a thorough understanding of soil and drainage, both in general and on the specific site in question. Review Part 1 if needed, and be sure you have conducted a soil assessment as outlined in Part 1, Chapter Seven.

As with Principle 3, it is critical to check assumptions during and at the end of construction to determine how much the soil, subsoil, and drainage conditions have been altered and whether the design assumptions remain valid.

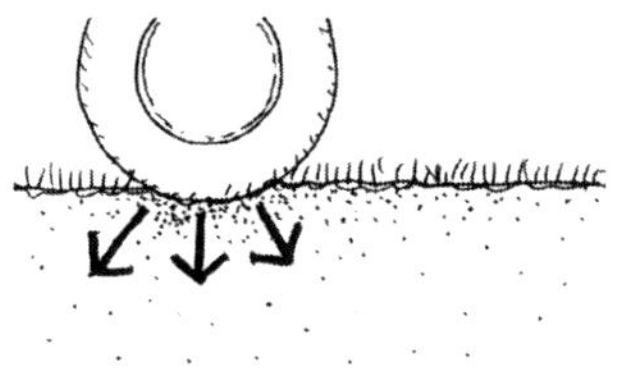

Soil Compaction

Compaction is one of the primary causes of urban plant failure. Clay soil that has become massive in structure due to compaction will be difficult to remediate, as will soil where compaction runs so deep that it limits drainage at depths greater than 24 inches. Compacted, sandier soils will be easier to amend.

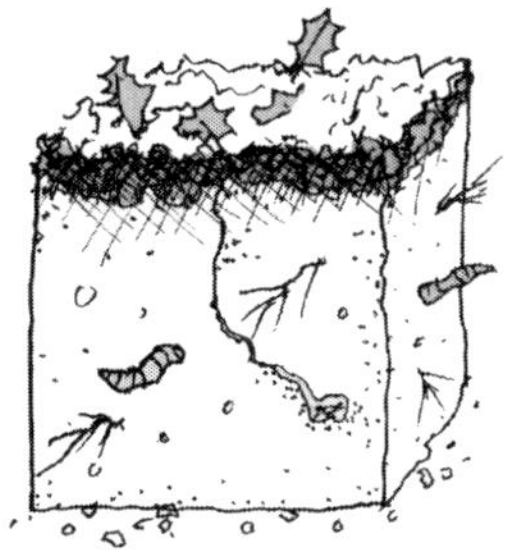

Soil Organic Matter

Lack of organic matter is a common deficiency in urban soil. Organic matter levels below 1 percent by weight reduce soil organisms, percolation, and chemical balance. Improving organic matter levels is relatively easy and very cost-effective. Adding organic amendments that raise the total soil organic matter content to over 5 percent by weight may cause problems in some soil types and drainage conditions. Avoid too much of a good thing.

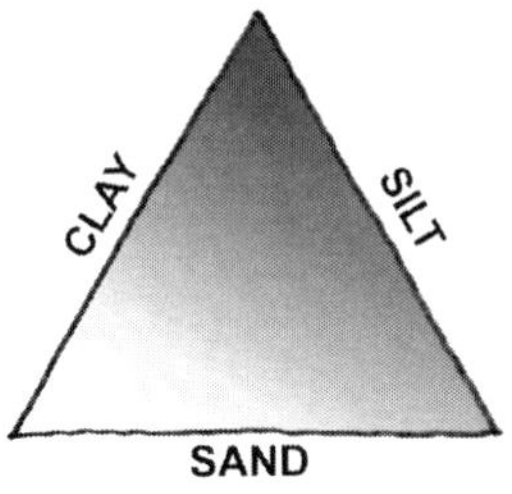

Soil Texture

Soil texture is difficult to change. The more clay, silt, rubble, gravel, and rock in the soil, the harder it will be to compensate for textural problems. Self-compacting, silty soil and soil with even-graded textures are also difficult to remediate.

Silty and fine sand loam topsoil, prevalent over much of the United States, requires special care. They over compact easily, settle significantly if under compacted, and drain slowly, even when there is good subsurface drainage.

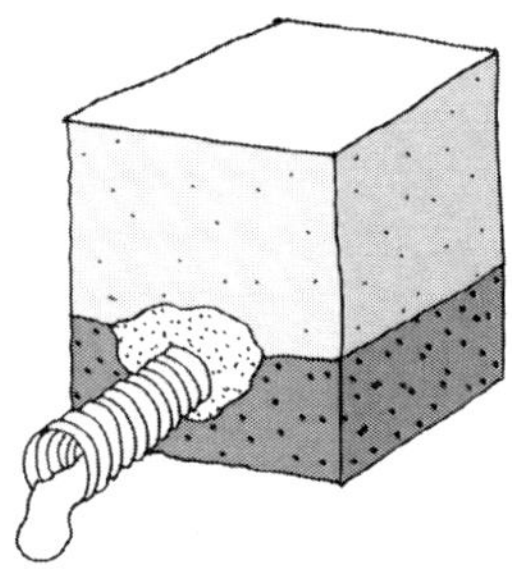

Drainage

Many factors affect soil drainage, including soil type, compaction, topography, and vegetative cover. The greater the clay and/or silt content, or the higher the compaction rate, the more slowly water will move in and out of the soil. Steep slopes result in greater runoff, while flat areas infiltrate more water. Healthy plants lower soil moisture levels. By understanding the soil type and the need to make the soil wetter or dryer, a designer can take steps to control soil moisture without necessarily changing the soil type.

The goal is to remove water fast enough to permit the exchange of gas in the root zone, but still retain enough water to support the plant between rain or irrigation cycles. Too much water kills plants much faster than too little. A poor drainage situation in a completed landscape is difficult to fix. On the other hand, too little water can be addressed by applying more water. Always err on the side of too much drainage rather than too little. See Part 1, Chapter Two.

Soil Biology

Soil biology may be easy to remediate if compaction levels are improved and organic amendment can be added. Soil chemistry problems can make soil biology difficult to modify.

Soil Chemistry

Soil pH and excessively high levels of chemicals with low water solubility, such as phosphorus and manganese, are difficult to change. High levels of hazardous chemicals may be difficult to reduce or stabilize, but may be equally difficult to remove legally. Correct chemical deficiencies by adding the necessary element, and flushing salt from the soil. Soil biology can also be used to change soil chemistry.

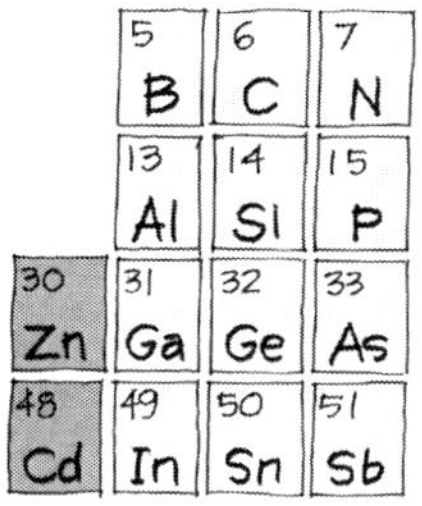

Existing Trees

Improving soil within the root zone of existing trees is especially challenging. Changes to soil beyond light surface treatments are not recommended. Avoid lowering grades, and respect the requirements of existing roots when adding new soil.

Budgets

Soil replacement and amendment are almost always more expensive than soil reuse if there is room to store the soil during construction. The reverse may be true on sites with limited storage space.

Construction Schedules

Soil amendment normally has less effect on schedules than replacement if there is room to work with the soil. The reverse may be true if space at the site is constrained.

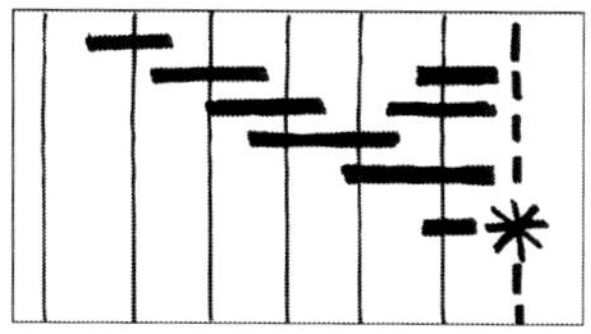

Sustainability

Amending existing soil is often more sustainable than replacement. Reusing soils on the site requires less resources and energy to improve plant quality. Often the mineral component of the soil is reasonable and simple changes to compaction, organic matter and drainage can make the soil acceptable.

SOIL AND DRAINAGE PLANS

All required modifications should be recorded on a soil and drainage plan that is separate from the planting plan and includes its own set of details and specifications. These documents are described in Principle 9.

SOIL AMENDMENT DESCRIPTIONS

Soil amendments are items added to improve the soil's condition. Amendments are added in large amounts to change texture, and may improve biological or chemical aspects. Some amendments are added in small amounts (less than 1 percent of soil volume) and change the biological or chemical balance in the soil. These amendments include fertilizers, compost, biological inoculants, and highly processed mineral products.

For the purpose of clarity, we'll define all soil amendments used in this book here, though they may be discussed in other chapters.

When specifying any addition to the soil, be sure you understand and can document what deficiency exists in the soil, why the product is being added, and how it works to achieve the desired effect. Improper combinations of amendments and soil types, or amendments used in too small or too large amounts, can have negative effects and unintended consequences.

Most soil amendments are natural products that are regionally produced. Designers must be aware of regional and vendor variations in availability, nomenclature, cost, and quality.

These are the amendments most commonly used in the landscape industry:

- **Organic:** Composted plant residues that increase the organic matter content of the soil.
- **Mineral:** Natural or processed mineral products that change the texture of the soil.
- **Physical:** Plastic, manufactured products designed to replace soil structure and improve its resistance to compaction or erosion.
- **Biological:** Condensed organic compounds and biological inoculants used in small amounts to alter soil biology or soil chemistry.
- **Chemical:** Compounds used in small amounts to add nutrients or change pH.

Figure 2.4.2. Organic soil amendments.

Organic Soil Amendments

Organic soil amendments are various forms of composted organic material. They improve drainage rates and water- and nutrient-holding capacity of silty, clay, or sandy soil, and can be inexpensive and effective. Organic amendment is the easiest material to blend into the soil, with little consequence if mixing is not uniform.

Organic soil amendments improve the soil food web, both by introducing organisms and by providing the carbon source to support those organisms (see Part 1, Chapter Three). The type and source of feedstock (the material being composted), length of composting time, and weather during the composting and storage period will alter the composition and quality.

Organic soil amendments should be well composted or matured, meaning that the product has reached a relatively stable state of decomposition. Such amendments are dark brown to black in color, with few or no identifiable pieces of the feedstock. A reasonable standard for organic soil amendments is that they should be dark brown to black—the color of a dark chocolate candy bar with at least 70 percent chocolate content or darker black. Good-quality compost should have a strong, musty, sweet earth odor.

Incomplete or poorly composted material will draw nitrogen from the soil temporarily as bacteria complete the composting process. Material that has not been composted to maturity will also shrink more than mature compost.

It is important to note the difference between organic amendments and organic matter. Organic matter is the amount of stable carbon based compounds that are in the soil, usually measured as a percentage of dry weight after ignition of the soil. Organic amendments are products that contain carbon-based compounds, but they are not stable and continue to breakdown after being added to the soil. They are usually discussed as percentage of the volume of the total soil mix. The difference between volume and weight and the difference between stable organic material in the soil and a pile of compost are regularly confused within the design profession.

All organic amendments will continue to decompose, and the soil will shrink (or re-compact) as a result of this decomposition. This loss in volume will seldom reach root-limiting levels unless the soil is subjected to foot or vehicle traffic. Shrinkage will be greater as amended soil depth or amount of organic amendment in the mix increases. The more stable the organic amendment the less the material will shrink. The loss in volume is due in part to the carbon in the material being released as carbon dioxide gas into the atmosphere. Methane can also be produced from organic amendment as it decomposes particularly when it is too wet. In large enough quantities this gas in the soil can limit plant growth and even kill the plant.

Organic amendments that are high in lignin will shrink less and at a slower rate than material low in lignin. Lignin is the part of the cell wall structure that resists decay longest. Bark and other hard plant structures have more lignin than softer parts of the plant such as wood and leaves. Types of high-lignin material are described later in this section.

High-lignin organic amendment mixed at 10 percent by volume into the soil should cause the soil to shrink by about 5 percent of the depth of the installed soil. Shrinkage will be greater with low-lignin organic amendment such as yard waste. Compost that has not matured will shrink more than mature, stable compost. The more compost is added to the soil, the less mature the compost, or the lower it is in lignin, the higher the initial finished grades must be set to allow for additional settlement. Settlement of 12 inches or greater has been observed in soils 30 inches deep with excessive organic content.

Many specifications still call for up to one-third organic amendments by volume as an amendment, which is far too much. Because of the predicted soil settlement, organic amendments in soil deeper than 12 inches should not exceed 10 to 15 percent of the soil by volume. High-lignin compost is recommended for this application.

Much larger amounts of organic amendment (25 to 35 percent by volume) can be added to the top 6 inches to increase soil biology and contribute to the formation of new topsoil. Organic amendment from diverse feedstock, such as composted yard waste, is preferred in the top 6 inches of the soil profile, provided that the soil finished grades are set high enough to compensate for the future loss of volume.

Organic-Amendment Specification

Specifying organic amendment is not a precise art. In the simplest terms, organic amendment must be stable, meaning that it is well composted. Such material has a carbon to nitrogen (C/N) ratio of 25 or less. A C/N ratio of 15 or lower is considered high-quality compost. An organic soils laboratory can determine C/N ratio. It is generally black or dark brown in color, passing the dark chocolate test. It should have a musty sweet earth odor and should not have an anaerobic odor.

The Solvita maturity test is a measurement of CO_2 and ammonia from the compost, and rates compost on an index of 1 to 8 as a measurement of stability or completeness of composting. To be classified as "mature," compost must rate 7 or higher. Solvita test kits are available with instructions to test your own samples.

Compost pH varies and will change soil pH. Biosolid-based compost (compost made from sewage feed stock) often has an elevated pH (above 8) and should be used only when it is acceptable to raise soil pH. Some leaf compost can have a pH below 5. Compost with specific pH levels can be specified. Since the pH is dependent on the feedstock source material, sources must be identified during the specification process. Check with local suppliers.

The U.S. Composting Council (www.compostingcouncil.org) sets standards for compost. Incorporation of the requirements of their Seal of Testing Approval (STA) program is an excellent standard to adopt for specifications. However, as of the publication of this book, few suppliers in each region have applied for the STA, and quality suppliers may not be members. Requiring that compost meets STA requirements rather than requiring that the supplier be an STA certified supplier is one way to allow good quality compost in a region where there are no or few STA certified suppliers.

A summary of approved suppliers and the testing parameter requirements can be found at the USCC Web site. The testing parameters include pH, soluble salt, nutrient content, organic matter, moisture, particle size, and compost maturity and stability. Allowable content of inert material, trace metals, weed seed, and soil pathogens is specified.

The feedstock is important to identify in any specification. Following are the different classifications of sources as developed by the USCC. Only a few of these sources are useful as textural amendments. Plant-matter compost is preferred. Local agricultural extension services and soil suppliers are excellent resources for information on available sources.

- *Food-processing residuals*—compostable material remaining after fruit, vegetables, grains, nuts, and meat are processed for consumption.
- *Manure and agricultural byproducts*—originate at racetracks, feedlots, farms, and greenhouses.
- *Forestry and forest product residuals*—include bark and sawdust, fiber fines residue, and biosolids generated by lumber or papermaking processes. Bark, wood, and sawdust can be used as carbon sources with other feedstock material or as bulking materials to increase porosity of the feedstock mix. These products often have a lower pH. To get a high-lignin material, specify barks from pine and other conifers.
- *Biosolids, or sewage sludge*—the solid material generated by the biological treatment of sewage at a wastewater treatment plant. It often has a high pH.
- *Leaves, brush, and yard trimmings (yard waste)*—leaves, brush, grass clippings, plant trimmings, and plant remains. An excellent source for organic amendment added to the top of the soil profile.
- *Source separated organic waste (SSOW)*—the compostable and composting-compatible fraction of municipal solid waste. This is a broad category and many of these materials may not be useful.

Next we'll look at the most common composts used for soil amendments.

High-Lignin Composted Organic Amendment

This comes from sources such as bark from pine, spruce, fir, or other conifers. Rice hulls, coconut husks, or other plant residues with hard, fibrous structures also make good high-lignin compost. High-lignin compost has greater longevity in soil, decomposing more slowly and holding soil particles apart longer.

In much of the United States, pine bark fines are widely available as a high-lignin textural amendment. Ideally, this material should be well composted; however, demand is high for this material as mulch and alternative fuel. Finding well-composted material is difficult. Even without being fully composted, pine bark fines remain an excellent high-lignin material. Select from a source that has the darkest brown color and the least pine odor. This material composts slowly, and the nitrogen drop in the soil is not root-limiting when added to the soil at the 10 percent level. Some sources of pine bark fines include large amounts of wood in the bark material. Avoid pine bark fines with more than 10 percent wood. Wood pieces can be identified by breaking into the pieces of compost. Wood will be white inside, while bark will be brown.

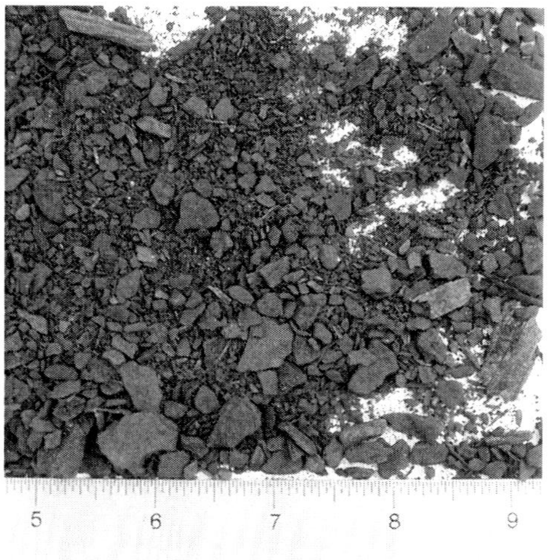

Figure 2.4.3. Composted pine bark, a high-lignin organic amendment.

Composted Yard Waste

This is derived from leaves, brush, grass clippings, plant trimmings, and plant remains. It is the most commonly available compost, but quality varies widely. Good yard-waste compost should be black, with few identifiable plant parts. The soil food web that composted the material will be varied due to multiple feed stocks. This is a superior product for the top of the soil, because it provides a great variety of organisms. A renewable waste product, it is a very sustainable option. Wood-based compost is better for trees; leaf-based compost is better for perennial beds.

Figure 2.4.4. Composted yard waste.

Mineral Soil Amendments

Non-organic amendments include sand; expanded shale, clay, and slate (ESCS); perlite; diatomaceous earth products; plastic grids that bind the soil together to resist compaction; and even ground expanded polystyrene (EPS). Mineral soil amendments are generally permanent and dimensionally stable in the soil, and may increase drainage if used in sufficient quantity. Some of these products have internal pore space that can hold water and small amounts of nutrients. The deeper into the soil profile the material can be incorporated, the greater the effect on drainage. Use rates will vary widely, depending on the product and its application. Since

A Petite Word on Peat

Peat moss is often specified as an organic soil amendment. Peat is a consistent, easy-to-obtain product. It is not a good textural amendment because it is very low in lignin and oxidizes rapidly in the soil, causing the soil to shrink. Peat is not a renewable resource, and there are better, cheaper, and more stable organic materials available.

Figure 2.4.5. Blowing compost onto the soil. This must then be tilled to obtain contact with the soil.

product weights vary, always specify the material as a percentage of total soil mix design volume. Application rates will be discussed later in this chapter.

Mineral soil amendments are processed products. Processing can range from simple sieving and washing of sand to molding, heating, crushing, and sieving of products such as expanded shale, clay or slate. Since most of these products must be purchased in large quantities, using locally available material is critical to control cost. Products change from region to region, and specifications must be region-specific.

Sand

The type and grade of sand used to make concrete is the best material to use. It must be incorporated at rates sufficient to bring the total medium and coarse sand in the soil to greater than 50 percent of the soil volume. It should be quartz-based with sharp, angular shapes.

Avoid round sand, manufactured sand from sedimentary rock (particularly high-pH, limestone-based sand), and finer sand, including masonry sand. These products may not improve the soil mix and can slow drainage or change the pH of the final mix. In regions lacking in naturally coarse, sharp, quartz sands, work with local aggregate suppliers to determine the best alternative specification. Look for the coarsest, most angular sand with the lowest pH.

The ideal sand for a soil mix is specified as coarse concrete sand, ASTM C-33 Fine Aggregate, with a Fines Modulus Index between 2.8 and 3.2. The Fines Modulus Index is a measure of the average size of the aggregate, and test data is normally available from the supplier of sand. Masonry sand, while sometimes used as an amendment, is slightly smaller and makes soil less compaction-resistant.

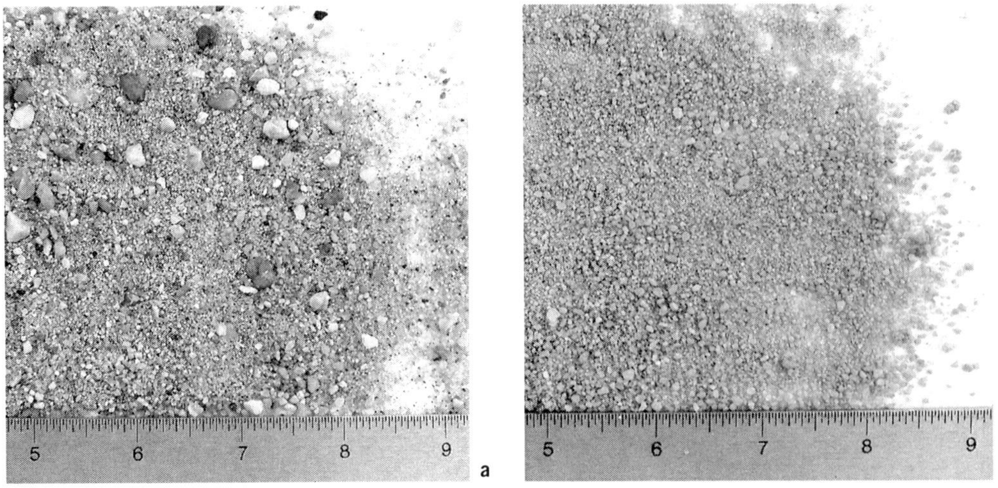

Figure 2.4.6. Sand.
a. Coarse concrete sand.
b. Masonry sand.

Expanded Shale, Clay, and Slate (ESCS) and Calcine Clay

These natural aggregates are heated to increase porosity, and include a class of products known as calcine clays. Internal airspaces in these products absorb water and have a higher cation exchange capacity than other aggregates. The spaces also help increase soil drainage rates. ESCS aggregates improve drainage when mixed with soil at a rate of approximately 25 to 30 percent by volume. The optimum particle size is 1/4 to 1/2 inch. Larger aggregate, 3/4 inch, is used in structural soil.

The light weight of these aggregates makes them ideal to reduce the weight of soil mixes over structures (see section on rooftop soils at the end of this chapter). These amendments have also been mixed with sand, organic amendment, or fine ESCS materials to make very coarse and highly compaction-resistant soil. They can also be a part of compacted aggregate/soil or aggregate/sand structural soil mixes, which are described in Part 2, Chapter Six.

ESCS material is produced at a limited number of locations. Shipping costs increase with distance from the plant, limiting the area in which these products are practical to use. The Expanded Shale, Clay, and Slate Institute (www.escsi.org) can provide source locations for different products.

Figure 2.4.7. Expanded shale, clay, and slate. Left 1/4–1/2 inch, right 3/4 inch.

Perlite

This is a natural siliceous rock that has been heated to expand it. It is the lightest weight-per-volume material available to reduce soil weight. It is used at rates similar to ESCS, but should not be used in structural soil applications. Perlite will hold water on its surface, but will not absorb water. It is not an ESCS material, and some breakdown of particles should be expected over time, which will reduce soil volume. Perlite floats, and particles on the surface tend to wash out of planters. Its use should be limited to extreme cases where great reductions in soil weight are required.

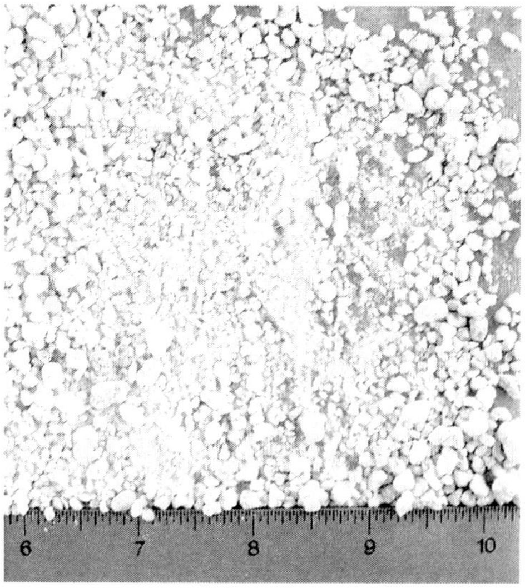

Figure 2.4.8. Perlite.

Vermiculite

This is similar to perlite but has less strength. Rapid breakdown in the soil and clogging of drainage fabric by fine vermiculite particles have been reported. Vermiculite is not recommended for planting soil mixes.

Expanded Polystyrene (EPS)

Marketed as Styrofoam by its original manufacturer, expanded polystyrene is now also produced by other manufacturers. EPS comes in different strengths, and stronger materials can support vehicles. 40 psi strength foam produced by Dow is strong enough to support loading in most commercial tree soil applications. Sheets and blocks of EPS can be used to fill space under planting soil in applications over building structures where there are weight limitations. Good drainage under the EPS is required. The Dow product comes with pre-molded drainage channels on its bottom surface.

Ground EPS may be added to the soil mix, but never more than 25 to 30 percent by volume. EPS will make a weak soil and trees planted in it may not be stable. It is usually better to achieve soil weight reduction by using a mineral soil mix, and put the EPS under the soil to reduce its overall weight.

Figure 2.4.9. Expanded polystyrene.

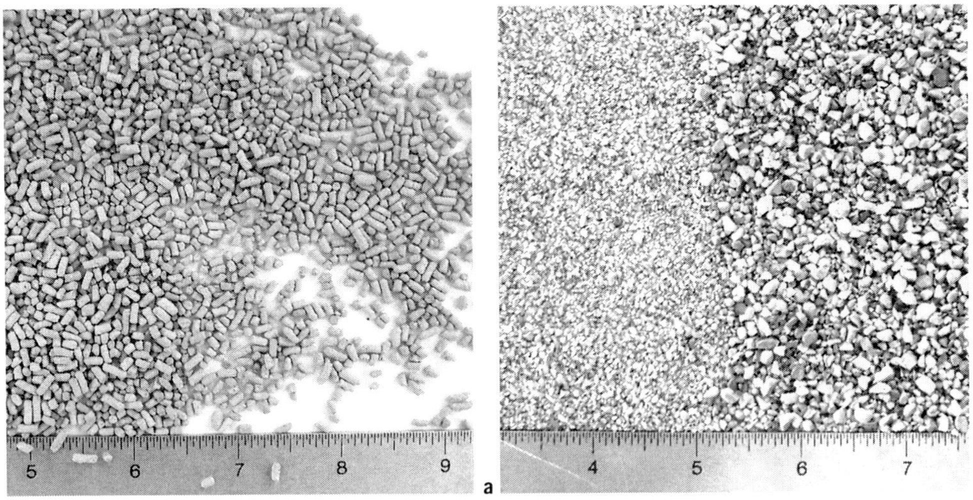

Figure 2.4.10. Diatomaceous earth.

a. Isolite.

b. Axis fine and coarse.

Diatomaceous Earth

Several products, including Axis and Isolite, are produced from rock containing diatoms, which are the shells of tiny sea creatures. These materials have significant pore space and a high cation exchange rate. This is an expensive additive and needs to be added at a rate of at least 10 percent by volume to be effective. These products are light in weight and can reduce soil weight where budgets allow.

Most often, these products are not part of a soil mix, but are spread over the soil and tilled into the top 6 inches of finished soil. Their cost often restricts these products to turf and garden applications where the highest quality soils are required. More research is needed to determine if their effectiveness for tree applications justifies the cost over alternative methods to improve pore space and cation exchange rate.

Polymer Gels

These include a number of synthetic products designed to hold water in the soil. Because gels are not biological amendments and are not intended to change the soil's chemistry, they are included among the mineral amendments. These products temporarily increase the plant available water-holding capacity of the soil. There have been reports of salt accumulation problems when soils that contain polymer gels are fertilized.

Polymer gels must be mixed into the soil in order to improve water-holding capacity. Their best application may be to assist in reducing transplant shock and improve water retention immediately around the plant. Use manufacturers' recommended application rates. Polymer gels are often a part of the mixture of biological amendment products such as mycorrhizal inoculants.

Polymer gels are effective at reducing water loss and transplant loss in bare-root transplanted material. The bare rootstock is dipped in a slurry of gel material before shipping from the nursery. Container trees that are stripped of their potting soil just prior to planting to reduce circling roots and correct other root problems will benefit from being dipped in polymer gels. This application is also a part of field collecting and transplanting larger trees that are being dug bare-root.

Figure 2.4.11. Polymer gel before and after adding water.

Physical Structures as Soil Amendments

Several products are available to hold loosely compacted soil in place for the root zone of a plant while allowing the transfer of compacting forces to a lower layer of soil. Some of these structures can also allow steep, almost vertical, slopes on soil and act as a kind of retaining wall.

With the exception of soil stabilizer grids, these products are generally only useful for turf and small plants, and have limited application for trees. They do not create the continuous horizontal soil volumes needed for tree roots, and the spaces between the webs and cell structures are not large enough for larger tree roots. Roots may be girdled and/or the soil layers may be too thin for tree support.

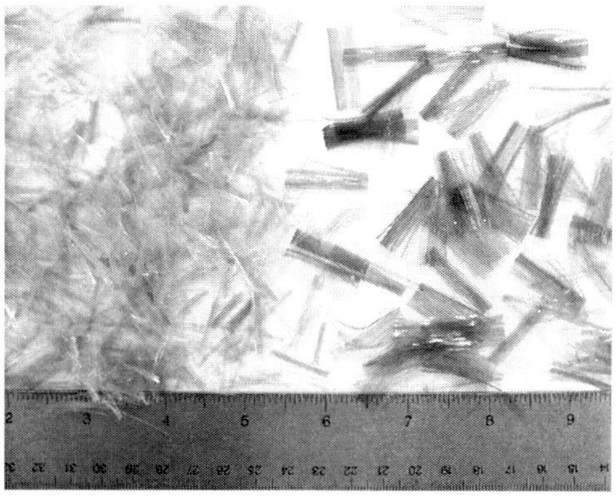

Figure 2.4.12. Stabilizer grids.

Soil Stabilizer Grids

These tiny plastic pieces of mesh are incorporated into the soil to help resist compaction. They were originally developed to stabilize fire lanes around buildings and to improve the compaction resistance of athletic turf. Grids may have an application in deeper landscape soils to create an artificial soil structure. They have been shown to be effective to permit steeper slopes on installed planting soil. (See www.stabilizersolutions.com.)

Figure 2.4.13. Geowebs. *(Photo courtesy Presto-Geosystems, Inc.)*

Geowebs

These large, webbed-cell structures are made of flexible material, which divides the soil into chambers that hold and reinforce it. The soil within the cells is only loosely compacted. These products provide a number of geotechnical and engineering solutions when small plants are to be grown on steep slopes. Applications as a tree-rooting system are limited due to the small size of the cell openings and the limited interconnections of the cells. (See www.prestogeo.com.)

Turf Cells

Designed to transfer compacting forces to a soil layer below the cell, these small plastic structures are filled with loosely compacted soil and are used to grow turf. Cell size, thickness, and limited interconnections make them unsuitable for tree root growth. Soil below the turf cells must be compacted, which limits the use of the sub-base for root area.

Figure 2.4.14. Turf cells. *(Photo courtesy Presto-Geosystems, Inc.)*

Biological Amendments

Biological amendments are added to the soil in small amounts (usually less than 1 percent of the total soil volume) to improve the soil food web. Some must be incorporated into the soil, while others can be applied to the surface. Products containing active inoculants or microorganisms may be intended to increase specific organisms, or may simply improve the conditions required by specific parts of the soil food web.

Biological amendments vary in their effectiveness, and product claims are sometimes exaggerated. The effectiveness of mychorrhizal inoculants depends on the viability of the spores at the time the product is

Figure 2.4.15. Biological amendment application. *(Photo courtesy The Care of Trees)*

deployed, and independent surveys of various products indicate a wide range of viability. One researcher found almost no viable spores in any product. Testing individual bags of product may not be practical, which leaves the specifier at the mercy of the distribution chain. This may be a critical factor in variations between product claims and results.

For all the hype, the academic data does not offer overwhelming proof that adding these mycorrhizae and kelp-based products changes the performance of plantings. Manufacturers often offer anecdotal endorsements. (See the sidebar, "Ivy Tower vs. Ivy Planters.") There are situations where biostimulants such as compost tea can be shown to make a difference, but if the soil has good drainage and organic functions, biological amendments offer limited value. This does not mean that they do no good, only that the effect on plant performance is small. Conversely, if the soil has poor drainage or is compacted or low in organic matter, adding biostimulant products will not improve these conditions, and the product will be ineffective. These additives may be most useful as a temporary measure when a tree is stressed from transplant or recovering from construction.

Bioassays

Biological amendments are best used in conjunction with a bioassay, a test to confirm that there are deficiencies in the soil and that a particular amendment will help. The bioassay will assist in determining application rates and types of products that would be the most beneficial. Biological assay labs can be located on the Internet.

Long-Term or Short-Term Effect

Soil biology is a dynamic force, and competition among microorganisms is natural and normal. Most biological amendments tend to spike biological activity in the soil shortly after application, which then dies down as easily available organic resources are consumed. Many of the products listed below evolved from either the turf or ornamental plant industries, where continuous peak performance is required and where there are resources to provide several applications per growing season. Any product that accelerates biological activity in the soil will also accelerate the breakdown of organic amendments in the soil, which may not be beneficial if there is no management program to replace organic amendments.

Organic amendments are long-term management tools. If the post-construction management team can be identified during the design period, applications of biological amendments at the time of construction should be coordinated with management directions given to that team. If the site is to be turned over to a contract maintenance provider or, worse, no maintenance is contemplated, use of biological amendments will have limited value, except in reducing transplant shock.

Confused? You're not alone. More research is needed to determine the effectiveness of different treatments. In the meantime, adding good old compost remains the simplest and most effective way to improve soil biology.

Ivy Tower vs. Ivy Planters

Academic researchers often tend to isolate limited variables in an experiment and look for measurable statistics to support their findings. Planting large trees is complex, with many stress factors. Biological additives are meant to reduce stress. A researcher may take quality trees, plant them correctly in good soil, making sure that each tree is watered the same. The trees may be marginally stressed, and all recover well. Little wonder that the product does not show effectiveness. Meanwhile, in the real world, the tree may be shipped 300 miles, left in the parking lot for a few days, planted too deeply, and not watered correctly. Under these circumstances, some of these products likely do make a difference. While scientific research, when available, can offer some insight into decisions about use of a product, it's also a good idea to talk to the people who actually use that product. Make sure these endorsers are using the product under similar conditions to your proposed application.

Following are the most common biological amendments.

Mycorrhizae. There are now many products on the market that include mycorrhizal fungal spores. Mycorrhizal products have been shown to be more effective if used in combination with fertilizer. While those organisms are an important part of the soil food web, they are only one small part of complex soil biology. Viable mycorrhizal spores are pervasive, even in disturbed urban soils, and mycorrhizae will develop on their own if soil is improved to support their development. Adequate composted organic amendment and water remain the best additives to reduce transplant shock and improve long-term tree growth.

Kelp extracts. Many products have kelp extracts listed in the ingredients. These products may offer short-term reductions in tree transplant shock. If used, they should be applied frequently before and every several weeks after transplanting, as a single application is not likely to be effective.

Humic acid. Humic acid is a stable form of carbon chain and remains in the soil for long periods of time, nurturing the soil food web. A single application will provide measurable benefit.

Organic fertilizers. Organic material can be refined and concentrated sufficiently to be classified as a fertilizer. There may be some ecological benefit to the use of these products over petroleum-based fertilizers; however, like any concentrated product, they can be over applied. Since these products are primarily used to change soil chemistry, they will be discussed further in the next section on chemical amendments.

Compost tea. Compost tea is used to manage soil biology and reduce or eliminate the need for other chemicals in the soil. This improves plant growth and serves as a defense against disease.

Compost teas are concentrated solutions of the various organisms in the soil food web. Specialty blends of compost and water plus sugars or other compounds are mixed together and "brewed" for about 24 hours so that the desired organisms increase dramatically in number. The tea is then spread over the soil to inoculate the desired organism. Use of compost teas assumes that soil tests have pinpointed which organisms are needed and that the foundations of the soil food web, sufficient organic matter, is available in the soil. For maximum efficiency, compost teas are custom-blended, and must be applied the same day they are brewed. For best results, work with a firm that specializes in this technique.

Growth Regulators

These chemicals are meant to be taken up by the plant. They slow down the growth rates of plants, but also increase the density of root systems. They are neither biological nor chemical amendments, but a unique category of treatment.

Growth regulators have been shown to help trees recover from construction damage, heal from other stressed conditions, and resist some types of diseases. Not all plants are receptive to this treatment,

"You say mycorrhizae, and I say mycorrhizal."

These terms are often confused and misused, but it is just a twist of grammar. Mycorrhiza literally means "fungus root," and its proper definition is "the symbiotic relationship between certain fungi and the roots of a plant." There is no organism called a mycorrhiza, just fungi having a relationship. Mycorrhizae is the plural form when there is more than one fungus involved. *Mycorrhizal* is the adjective form, usually preceding a noun as in "mycorrhizal fungi." And yes, for those old enough to remember it, you can remember how to spell mycorrhizae by singing the Mickey Mouse Club theme song.

Figure 2.4.16. Compost tea brewer.

and some are highly sensitive to overdosing, which can almost stop the growth of a tree and produce very small leaves. Treatment effects last about three years. Consult an arborist or Rainbow Tree Care, a product manufacturer, at www.rainbowscivance.com.

Chemical Amendments

Changing the chemical composition of a soil is difficult. Soils deficient in a particular element or exhibiting a pH level inappropriate for the specified trees will be a long-term management problem.

Review the basics of soil chemistry in Part 1, Chapter Four and obtain soil testing results before specifying any changes to soil chemistry. Wherever possible, match plant selection to the existing soil fertility and pH of the site and/or use organic and biological amendments to change soil chemistry. If a soil test demonstrates that chemical additives are needed, the best time to incorporate them is during soil mixing.

Salt and Fertilizer

The chemical processes that make fertilizer work produce salt. In dry regions this salt can build up in the soil to damaging levels. The amount of salt produced (salt index) depends on the fertilizer used. Manufacturers do not have to print the salt index on product packaging, but you can often find it online. If you cannot obtain this information from the supplier or on the Internet, find another product, as there are many alternatives. A salt index of 25 or below is considered low. Avoid fertilizer with a salt index above 50 in sandy loam soils and above 75 in silt clay loam soil.

Organic Fertilizer

There is much debate about the use of organic fertilizer as a part of sustainability efforts. A definition of organic fertilizer is elusive, and agribusiness has made great efforts to expand the official limits of the term "organic" in many areas, including fertilizer. Lacking a good definition, look for products derived from plant or animal residues or products mined from the earth with a minimum of industrial processing.

Specifying Fertilizer

Only add fertilizer if soil test results indicate it is needed. Once a soil test confirms that fertilizer may be beneficial, work with the soil testing lab and the maintenance team to make the best selection. The combination of different fertilizer products and soil requirements is too broad a subject to discuss in this text.

Use the least concentrated material at the lowest dosage possible. Consider compost and compost teas in place of concentrated fertilizers, reserving these more powerful products for times when quick or intense plant response is required.

Plant Disease, Insect Problems, and Fertilizers

Maintaining the correct level of chemical balance in the soil is difficult when using chemical additives, and they are often over applied. As plants become over fertilized, they will become more susceptible to certain insects and diseases.

COMPACTION REDUCTION

Compaction is the most common and lethal form of soil damage. It is difficult to prevent in a construction project and in areas subjected to intense use. Compaction levels will vary greatly over small distances and change with soil depth. Standards for determining when a soil is over compacted are not well established, and accurately assessing and measuring compaction is difficult.

Compaction reduction methods should vary depending on the site situation. The soil type, compaction rate and depth, and size of the site, as well as presence of obstructions and utilities, will limit options for treatment. Compaction reduction is moderately expensive, but cost effective in terms of its improvement to the soil.

Effective compaction reduction techniques include double-spading, backhoe turning, and subsoiling. These methods leave some of the soil peds intact. Within the root zone of an existing tree, specialized techniques are required to avoid damage to the roots. We'll learn about these root-zone techniques later in this chapter.

Many commonly used techniques to relieve compaction are of little help. Tilling machines penetrate 6 inches into the soil at best, may create a compacted plow layer under the tilled surface, and pulverize soil peds, eliminating soil structure. A fine-grained soil that is pulverized will easily recompact as it settles. Adding organic or mineral amendments to the soil can help reduce this recompaction.

Machines that inject blasts of compressed air to fracture the soil and relieve compaction have not been demonstrated to have any long-lasting impact. Injecting solid material into the fractures, just at the moment the air is injected, may be somewhat effective, but has a higher cost. Aerating the soil using machines with long tines is a little more effective, but has limited application when compaction rates become very high or deep in the profile. Adding mulch to the top of the soil to allow the soil's biological function to "open up" the soil is largely ineffective at high rates of compaction.

a

b

Figure 2.4.17. Compacted soil.

a. Smooth soil surfaces are an indication of surface compaction

b. Planting bed compacted to the point of no drainage. Minimal surface treatment may be insufficient to break deep compaction.

Measuring Compaction

In Part 1, Chapter Seven, we discussed how to measure compaction of soil. It is important to know when existing soil is over- or under compacted during the design phase. Compaction of all installed planting soil must be controlled and verified.

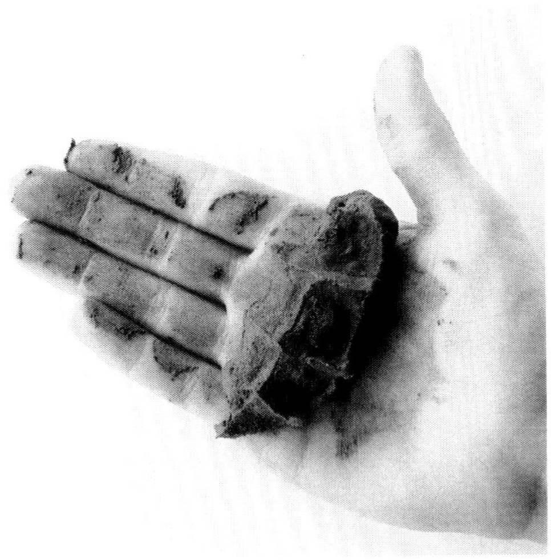

Figure 2.4.18. If soil is moist enough to stick mud on your hand and make impressions of your fingers when squeezed, it is likely too wet to till or grade.

Soil Moisture Levels and Compaction Reduction

Soil moisture must be between field capacity and wilt point during compaction reduction for maximum effectiveness. (See Part 1, Chapter Two for a description of these moisture levels.) This soil is considered friable, meaning it has adequate moisture to break into clods when lifted and turned with a shovel. Friable soil will make the hand dirty but not muddy when squeezed. If the soil is so wet that it makes a mud stain on the hand, compaction reduction efforts may be ineffective or even make things worse. If the soil is so dry that it does not break easily into clods, compaction reduction will also be limited.

In most soil, "too wet" is defined as within several days after enough rain has fallen to saturate the soil profile. If the soil is heavily compacted or in an area of poor drainage, this may take much longer. If the soil is dry, it will take several inches of water to hydrate the soil. One rainy day may not provide enough water.

Soil Amendments and Compaction Reduction

When modifying compaction, incorporate either organic or mineral amendments into the soil to reduce the tendency of the soil to recompact. High-lignin compost or ESCS products are most commonly used. ESCS products are preferable in areas that will be subjected to foot or occasional vehicle traffic, due to their permanence in the soil, but are much more expensive. When ESCS material is used, it should be specified at approximately 3/8-inch size. These amendments are placed on the surface of the soil and fall into the spaces between the soil peds as the soil is physically turned.

Compaction Reduction Techniques

Only mechanical disruption of a compacted soil will effectively change bulk density. In severely compacted soil, adding mulch or other organic material onto the top of evenly compacted soil will not reduce compaction. Letting the soil "rest," covered in organic amendment, takes many decades for slight reductions in compaction. Areas with extreme ranges of frost depths and frequent freeze/thaw cycles may show more improvement over a shorter time. Increasing the water level in the soil, combined with other treatments during the resting period, can increase the rate of compaction reduction.

Tilling

In areas of thin layers of soil compaction, traditional tilling to depths of 6 inches can be effective. Tilling may be the only option when there are utilities close to the surface. If the compaction layer is deeper than 6 inches, more aggressive techniques such as double-spading or subsoiling are required. Surface tilling a deeply compacted soil may not improve growing conditions for anything but small plants. In fine-grained soil, the upper soil structure is lost, and the tilled soil may recompact over time. A tiller can create a plow layer of compacted soil just below the tilled layer, which reduces drainage between the tilled and not-tilled soil.

a

b

c

Figure 2.4.19. Tillers have limited effectiveness in compaction reduction but may be the only alternative.

a. Conventional tiller.
b. Spading tiller lifts the soil in chunks rather than grinding the soil into small pieces. *(Photo courtesy Dwayne Stenlund)*
c. Tractor-mounted spading tiller. *(Photo courtesy Dwayne Stenlund)*

If you must till, consider using a spade tiller, available from the Italian company Gramegna (www.gramegna.com). These use small spading plates to break up the soil, reducing soil damage. They are not widely available, but specifiers should seek them out and include them in specifications.

If tilling is used to relieve compaction, add a soil amendment, as described later in this chapter.

Double-Spading

Gardeners use this method of bed preparation to renovate compacted soil. Remove the top 8 or 9 inches of soil from the bed, spread a 2- to 3-inch layer of organic amendment over the subsoil, and then turn the next 8 or 9 inches of subsoil. During this process, the organic amendment falls into the spaces between the loosened soil clumps. Do not attempt to till or break up the subsoil into small pieces. Then return the topsoil, incorporating a heavier dose of organic amendment (3 to 5 inches) loosely as the soil is moved. High-lignin compost is preferred for the lower level, while yard waste compost is preferred for the upper level. The topsoil is not tilled, but is broken into smaller clods due to moving it twice. The bed surface can be lightly tilled and graded. The bed will now have a pronounced crown, which will settle over time.

The important details are that the subsoil is not mixed with the surface soil and the lower soil is not broken into fine particles, just turned, leaving large but compacted soil peds intact. When soil is broken into overly fine particles, it will recompact as gravity and water settle the soil. The smaller the soil peds or clods, the faster this process will occur.

Double-spading is only useful in small gardens and is labor-intensive. Other soil restoration techniques that replicate the gardener's process should be specified.

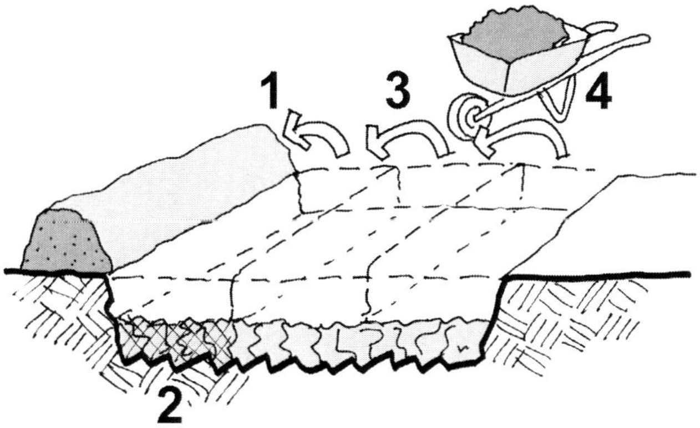

Figure 2.4.20. Double-spading.

1. Remove section of top 6 to 9 inches of soil and set aside.
2. Break up compaction in lower 6 to 9 inches of soil.
3. Move top of second section of soil to first section, repeat compaction reduction in lower section. Continue process across bed area.
4. Add 10 percent by volume organic amendment to both top and bottom layers as the soil is turned.

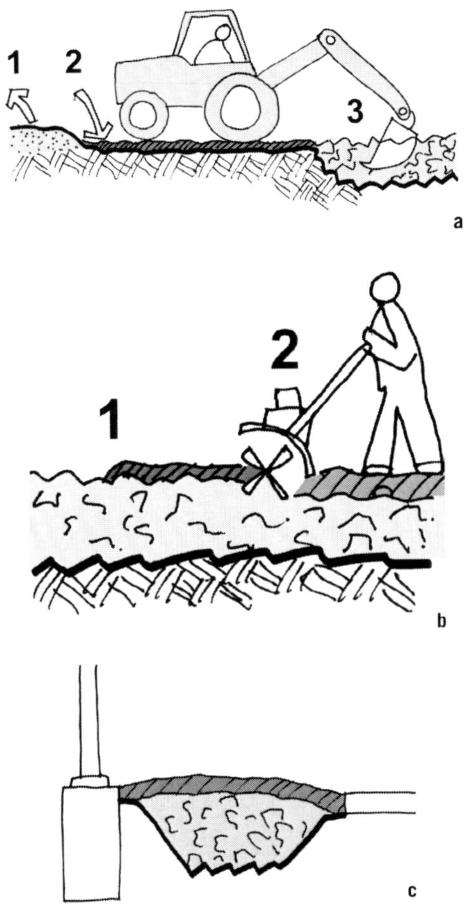

Figure 2.4.21. Backhoe turning

a. Turn the soil.
   1. Remove any A horizon topsoil.
   2. Spread 3 to 4 inches of organic or ESCS amendment over the area.
   3. Turn the top 24 to 30 inches of soil to break it into large peds and loosely incorporate the soil amendment.

b. Re-spread topsoil and add organic amendment.
   1. Spread 2 to 3 inches of organic amendment.
   2. Till amendment into soil.

c. Maintain safe subgrade slopes and distance from walks and footings.

Backhoe Turning

If there is enough space, a backhoe can replicate the double-spading process. Use a backhoe bucket to lift compacted soil and break it into large peds. This method allows for deeper compaction reduction, and the resulting soil may have fewer tendencies to recompact. This is very cost effective for small to medium-sized sites but may be an expensive way to fix large areas. Smaller backhoes mounted on skid loaders can operate in small spaces.

Before beginning the turning process, remove layers of good topsoil. If there is no significant topsoil layer, the backhoe can penetrate the entire soil depth in one action. In all applications, spread several inches of ESCS or high-lignin compost over the soil to be turned before lifting the soil to keep the broken particles apart. This improves drainage and helps resist recompaction.

Be sure the backhoe work does not get too close to walks or structures. Maintain a slope of compacted soil at the edge of paving so as not to undermine the paving sub-base. Require handwork along the edges of walls to a depth no greater than the bottom of footings. Have all utility lines marked prior to the start of work. A backhoe is not a good device to find utilities, wires, or irrigation pipes.

At the end of the process, the soil surface will be very rough. Spread 3 to 5 inches of yard waste organic amendment over the surface, and lightly till to break the soil into a texture suitable to fine grade. Complete the grading. There will be a considerable mounding of the soil, which will settle over time. Soil will expand between 10 and 20 percent of the depth of the turning. This mounding will quickly settle.

Subsoil Conditions

The thinner the topsoil and soil amendment on top of the subgrade, the more critical it is that subsoil compaction be reduced. Engineering specifications may require that subsoil be compacted to 90 or even 95 percent dry density in subsoil below planting areas. Designers must try to persuade engineers that subgrade compaction in the 2 to 3 feet of subsoil in planting and lawn areas should be 75 to 80 percent, or below the root-limiting bulk density values cited in Part 1, Chapter Two. Ninety percent density may be acceptable for deep fills and specialized situations. If high subgrade compaction has been created, deeper soil modifications sufficient to support tree roots will be required.

Compacted subsoil also may create an interface between the amended or installed soil and the subsoil. This slows drainage and root penetration. There are several methods for modifying a subgrade interface. Dragging the teeth of a backhoe through the subgrade surface just before installing the soil can break up the planar interface. Tilling a 3-inch layer of the new soil into the subgrade soil is more effective but is expensive. Subsoiling may be required to break subgrade compaction and modify the interface.

When subsurface drain lines are being installed, the subgrades must be sculpted to slope toward these lines. Inadvertent subsurface low points and areas of trapped water will occur behind footings, compacted subgrades under roads and walks, and other grading situations. It is up to the designer to plan and inspect subgrade elevations.

Subgrade inspections are critical to the success of soil installations. Once the soil has been placed, it is impossible to determine whether the contractor has followed the requirements. This may require many trips to the site, as subgrades will not be all prepared at one time. Typically, small sections of the project are made ready and then the planting soil brought into that area only. This requires client support for frequent site inspections.

Subsoiling

On large sites with limited underground utilities, subsoiling chisels can be pulled through the soil by heavy equipment, breaking up deep, compacted layers. Fracturing the subsoil to a depth of 24 to 30 inches is preferred. Larger equipment can break compaction to greater depths. The plow makes a series of passes in two directions, with the second pass perpendicular to the first.

Spreading several inches of ESCS or high-lignin compost over the soil before subsoiling improves the effect of the treatment, but the amendments are not as effectively incorporated with subsoiling as with the backhoe-turning method.

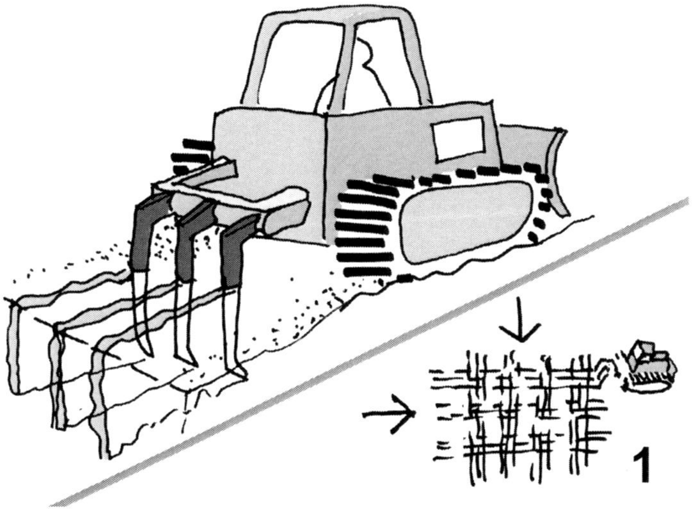

Figure 2.4.22. Subsoiling requires large equipment to pull chisels through the compacted soil. Subsoiling pattern requires tilling in two directions for best results.

Normally three chisels are attached to the tractor. In heavily compacted soil, the machine may only be able to pull one. To be effective, the machine must be quite large and powerful. Because of this requirement, this application is limited to sites that are large enough to operate such equipment. Any subsurface utilities will be damaged, and accurate location of existing wires and piping is critical. Existing utility conflicts are the most common reason why subsoiling is not applicable in urban areas.

Subsoiling is best completed when other work and operations that cause compaction at the site have stopped. Unfortunately, by this time, most of the site utilities have been installed, making subsoiling difficult. Subsoiling requirements must be coordinated with the civil engineer and the contractor.

Once subsoiling is completed, spread topsoil and other surface amendments, and till into the surface as described in the backhoe method.

Trench Subsoiling

A variation on subsoiling is trenching. A trenching machine digs narrow, 4-inch-wide trenches to the maximum depth possible through the compacted soil. The trenches are approximately 24 to 36 inches apart and are filled with high-lignin compost. A rod should be used to reduce air pockets in the compost within the trench. Topsoil is applied to the top 6 - 8 inches of the trench. This technique is labor-intensive but can be used in smaller spaces where bringing in large equipment such as a backhoe may not be possible. In lawn areas, this technique may result in the trenches appearing, over time, as sunken lines.

Figure 2.4.23. Trench subsoiling can be an effective treatment in small areas.

SOIL COMPACTION REDUCTION AND SOIL IMPROVEMENT NEAR EXISTING TREES

When compaction occurs within the root zone of large existing trees, the abovementioned methods of compaction reduction can damage roots, potentially doing more harm than good. (The same harm can be done by adding new plants within the root zone, which cuts roots to dig planting holes.) Within the root zone of large trees, make any soil changes incrementally over several years, and plant fewer plants on wider spacing. Tight schedules may be as harmful as the work itself.

Assessing Conditions

If a tree is mature, it is reasonable to assume that any compaction and soil degradation occurred at some point after it reached maturity. This normally means that the problem is close to the surface. Compaction may only be several inches deep, or there may have been fill added to the root zone of the tree. Larger roots may be on the surface in compacted soil. Absorbing roots may be under the compacted or fill layer. Even a thin layer of compacted soil will reduce water and oxygen movement into the soil. This condition is common after construction where a small amount of soil is spread and compacted over soil to be preserved.

Large roots can survive and function in compacted or poor soils. It is the soil around the absorbing root layer that must be improved or protected from compaction and disturbance. Protect larger roots from mechanical damage, including cutting or shaving roots.

Large roots can be damaged by increases in soil moisture that allow fungal diseases to flourish. Changes in grading outside the root zone can alter water flow within it. Adding automatic irrigation to trees that matured without irrigation will often start a decline. Part of the damage is caused by the installation of the system and part is from the increase in water level. Avoid adding irrigation to the soil under large existing trees.

The location of large and absorbing roots and the type of soil disturbance are both critical to determining the type of mitigation required. Make numerous soil probes and test pits to record soil profiles, compaction levels, and depths to uncompacted soil. Note the presence of fill soil over darker original A and O horizons. Estimate the extent of rooting activity, and record any visible surface roots. For important trees, use an air-excavating tool to locate the large roots. At a minimum, expose the trunk flare and zone-of-rapid-taper roots. If you encounter any girdling roots, remove them.

Ground penetration radar can help locate the larger roots of a mature tree, but the systems are not as accurate as removing the soil. Expect improvements to this technology in the near future.

Figure 2.4.24. Review both past soil disturbances and future construction impacts when making soil recommendations around existing trees.

Fill Soil over Roots

Fills may be inadvertently added to roots during construction. This soil should be removed as soon as possible using an air excavating tool and vacuum excavator to reduce root damage and improve soil compaction. Even hand shovels will nick root surfaces, causing damage that can be significant. If the soil cannot be removed, it should be loosened and mixed with organic amendment, as described later in this chapter.

Air and Hydro Vacuum Excavation

New tools such as the air excavating tool or air knife and hydro excavator can remove large amounts of soil with minimum damage to the roots. Both methods are much more expensive than conventional excavation.

An air-excavating tool uses compressed air to blow soil apart. The high-pressure air expands the pores in the soil. Since the air pressure does not penetrate the bark of the root, the root surface remains intact. The air pressure will damage finer absorbing roots and can damage bark by abrasion if the airflow is set too high, but impact to the tree appears slight.

This technique is useful in small spaces, in remote locations, and can be effective in most soils, except in fine-grained soil that is dry and tightly compacted. Wetting the soil will increase the rate of soil removal.

Dust and small rocks will fly over a large area, so be sure to specify barriers and protection of adjacent surfaces. Air excavators are more efficient when combined with a soil vacuum such as "vactor" trucks used to clean out sewers. Soil removed by air excavation can be reused, but will lose all soil structure and may need significant added organic amendment.

A hydro excavator uses high-pressure water to erode soil away from the roots and is most effective in extremely compacted, fine-grained soil and where large amounts of material must be removed. The process creates large amounts of mud slurry, which cannot be reused. Hydro excavator trucks are quite large and include a vacuum system. The equipment footprint and limitations of the air excavating tool are less than with the hydro excavator systems.

Figure 2.4.25. Vactor truck pipe, in the foreground, removes compacted soil from around tree roots loosened with an air-excavating tool, with water applied to assist in the process. *(Photo courtesy Chris Boyer)*

Surface Treatments Under Trees

Surface treatments within the root zone of trees, such as topdressing, composting, or mulching, will not by themselves reduce compaction, as noted earlier in this chapter. These treatments will improve the planting conditions for new ground-cover plants under trees, and some new roots from the tree may grow into this soil layer.

Figure 2.4.26. Vertical mulching around existing trees. Holes are about 3 feet apart. *(Photo courtesy Gary Johnson)*

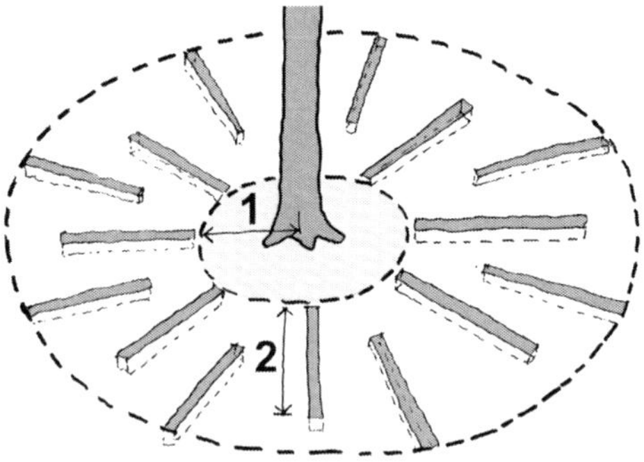

Figure 2.4.27. Radial trenching within the drip line of an existing tree can improve rooting in soil that has become compacted.

a. Radial trenching diagram.
   1. Do not trench within the zone of rapid taper roots (6- to 8-foot radius).
   2. Trenches 5 to 6 inches wide by 6 to 12 inches deep and 8 feet or more long to the drip line or beyond.

b. Radial trenching using water and hydro vac. *(Photo courtesy Rob Gross)*

Vertical Mulching

This is accomplished by creating a series of holes into soil that has become compacted, to invigorate root growth. Using an air-excavating tool, make holes in the compacted soil 5 to 6 inches in diameter and 6 to 9 inches deep. An air-excavating tool removes soil without damaging the roots, wires, or pipes. The holes should be between 2 and 3 feet apart. Fill the holes with composted yard waste in planting beds or a mixture of one part composted yard waste and two parts ESCS in areas where pedestrian traffic is expected.

This application has limited effectiveness at reducing compaction beyond the actual hole, but has been shown to marginally improve tree vigor in areas of surface compaction. It is relatively expensive.

Radial Trenching

Using an air-excavating tool and a vactor truck, make trenches in the compacted soil 5 to 6 inches wide and 6 to 12 inches deep by 8 feet or more long, radial to the tree out to the tree's drip line. Begin the trenches outside the tree's zone of rapid taper roots (6 to 10 feet from the trunk). Fill the trenches with composted yard waste in planting beds, or a mixture of one part composted yard waste and two parts ESCS in lawn areas where pedestrian traffic is expected. This treatment may be less expensive and more effective than vertical mulching, depending on the soil type and site situation.

A backhoe or trenching machine can be used to dig trenches. It costs less to use than an air-excavating tool but causes more root damage. The backhoe itself will cause additional compaction as it works in the root zone unless protective matting is in place. Adjusting the trench locations to avoid cutting large tree roots helps reduce root damage, but locating the roots before they are damaged is difficult. This is an application where ground penetrating radar would be useful.

Radial trenching and vertical mulching will be more effective if combined with surface mulching, liberal watering, and additions of biological amendments after treatment.

Organic and Biological Amendments

If the soil is not compacted to a root-limiting level, biological amendments such as compost tea, kelp-based biostimulants, mycorrhizal inoculants, humic acid, and chemical additives indicated by a soil analysis may improve the health of the tree. These supplements should be applied in conjunction with applications of 2 to 3 inches of yard waste compost over the root zone to improve biological activity. Biological amendments will be more effective if combined with water therapy, vertical mulching, or radial trenching. If the soil is compacted to near root-limiting levels or lacking in organic matter, adding biological amendments on top will generally not be effective by itself.

Soil over Existing Tree Roots

Adding soil over existing roots is not recommended to improve the growing conditions of the tree or new plantings, and should be avoided in favor of air excavation tools to loosen the soil. However, there will be times when grading requirements make it necessary to build up soil around a tree.

When adding soil or organic material, scarify the top surface of the soil with a steel rake or air excavation tool, remove any ground-cover plantings or sod, and add several inches of sandy loam topsoil to establish a better seedbed for lawn or ground cover. If the lower soil is fine grained, select a finer grained sandy loam to reduce the introduction of a soil interface. Several inches of organic leaf compost mixed into the soil can also make an excellent bed for ground-cover plantings. Deep watering at infrequent intervals may help force roots of the new plants into the existing soil and improve absorbing root growth.

Avoid adding fine-grained soils directly over tree roots. Do not aggressively till the new soil into the existing soil, as it will damage tree roots. Avoid adding soil over compacted layers without first reducing the compaction by vertical mulching, radial trenching, or air excavation soil improvement.

It is possible to add greater amounts of new soil over tree roots. Up to 12 inches of a sandy loam soil can normally be added, but many factors may change the depth of this recommendation. The more rapid the drainage rate of the underlying soil, the more soil can be added. Floodplain-tolerant trees will be more tolerant of increased soil. The lower the percentages of fine particles in the soil being added, the greater the possible depth. Trees with visible shallow roots may not be able to tolerate any additional soil. Soil up to several feet thick has been successfully placed on top of the existing grade if all conditions are favorable, while just a few inches of fine-grained soil have killed trees under unfavorable conditions. Compaction of existing soil during installation of the new soil may do more harm than the effect of the new fill. If existing soil is protected from compaction, greater amounts of soil can be added to the top of the root system.

For soil depths greater than 12 inches, install a 4-inch gravel mat on top of geogrid mats laid over the root zone. The geogrids help distribute the loading of the work above. The gravel must not include fines and should be similar to AASHTO #57 stone, to permit water and air flow through the material. Ensure that the gravel bed has positive drainage out of any low points in elevation and a means to get air into the gravel at the high point. Install a dry-laid retaining wall system, which needs no footing, several feet beyond the base of the trunk flare to maintain an open airspace around the base of the tree.

Before starting the work, remove any sod or ground-cover plants. If the soil is compacted, vertically mulch the root zone to invigorate the tree. Phase the work so that equipment does not work directly on the

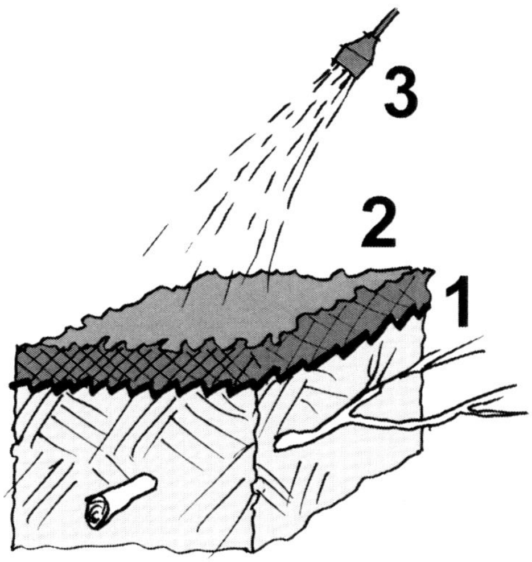

Figure 2.4.28. Adding organic and biological amendments to soil within a tree root zone that is not compacted to root-limiting bulk density.

1. Scarify soil surface.
2. Add 2 to 3 inches of yard waste compost.
3. Apply biological amendments recommended by soil test.

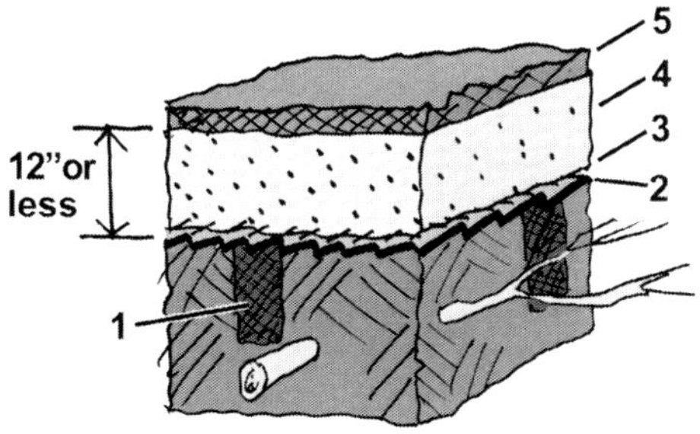

Figure 2.4.29. Adding 12 inches or less of soil within the root zone of large existing trees.

1. Vertical mulch if soil is compacted.
2. Scarify soil and remove plants and thatch.
3. Geogrids (optional).
4. Sandy loam soil.
5. Mulch or lawn.

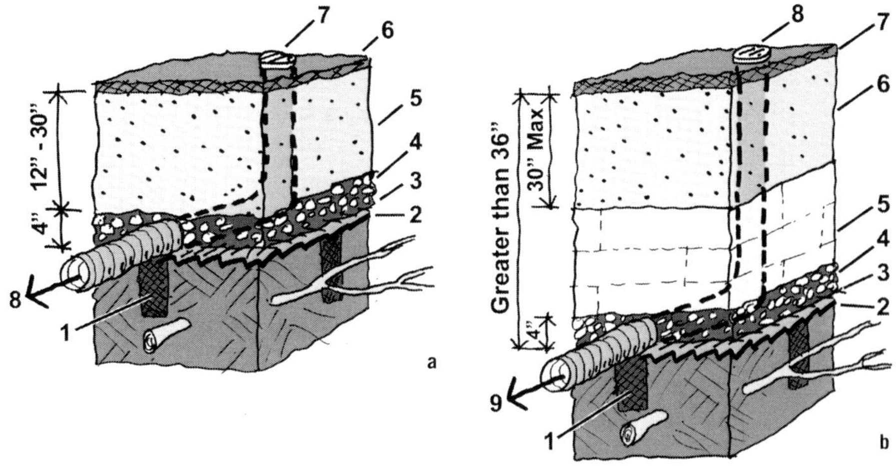

Figure 2.4.30. Adding more than 12 inches of soil within the root zone of large existing trees.

a. New soil 12 to 36 inches deep.
   1. Vertical mulch if soil is compacted.
   2. Scarify soil and remove plants and thatch.
   3. Geogrids.
   4. Gravel drainage layer.
   5. Sandy loam soil.
   6. Mulch or lawn.
   7. Riser pipe with grate for air flow.
   8. Perforated drain lines extend to positive outfall to remove water.

b. New soil greater than 36 inches deep.
   1. Vertical mulch if soil is compacted.
   2. Scarify soil and remove plants and thatch.
   3. Geogrids.
   4. Gravel drainage layer.
   5. EPS foam or ESCS light weight aggregate.
   6. Sandy loam soil.
   7. Mulch or lawn.
   8. Riser pipe with grate for air flow.
   9. Perforated drain lines extend to positive outfall to remove water.

soil within the root zone. If all these requirements are met, up to 30 inches or more of soil can be added with little impact to most tree species.

At soil depths greater than 3 feet, the weight of the new soil starts to become a significant compacting element to the existing soil. Techniques to lighten the soil weight, such as using an ESCS material in the fill or building up EPS under the soil above, can allow the addition of thick layers of material.

Air Excavation Soil Modification

Air-excavating tools can be an effective treatment to relieve compaction in the top layer of soil. All of the soil within the drip line of the tree may be loosened up to 8 inches deep in this manner. Spread compost and other soil additives over the loosened soil, then use the air-excavating tool to "stir" the compost into the soil. Mulch and water well. This method of soil modification is expensive but very effective for important trees where the surface soil has become compacted.

Figure 2.4.31. Air excavation of soil to reduce compaction and add soil amendments. *(Photo courtesy The Care of Trees)*

Air Excavation or Hydro Excavation Soil Replacement

Total replacement of soil around the roots is possible using an air excavating tool or hydro excavator to remove the soil. This procedure may be used in extremely compacted areas or in cases of toxic material spills. Remove soil one small section at a time, immediately replacing it with a compaction-resistant sandy loam soil. Keep roots moist by misting. Deep sections and broad areas of soil replacement are possible. Be wary of creating a water-holding low point; if the site is flat or the soil is fine-grained and slowly draining, consider installing a drainage system. This method is very expensive but effective.

Figure 2.4.32. Several feet of soil removed around the base of a tree by hydro excavation. *(Photo courtesy Rob Gross)*

Compressed Air Subsoiling

Injecting compressed air, with an air gun device, deep into the soil to relieve compaction is sometimes recommended for compacted soils near existing trees. This practice has not been demonstrated to have any long-lasting impact. Injecting solid material into the fractures after air has been injected may be somewhat effective but is more expensive. Other soil treatments recommended here are better options.

EXISTING SURFACE SOIL TEXTURE MODIFICATION AND AMENDMENT

Where no existing tree roots are encountered or in areas of grading, existing surface soil can sometimes benefit from modifications to its texture and the addition of soil amendments. This can increase the soil's ability to absorb, hold, and drain water; to remain friable; to resist future compaction; and to increase chemical and biological activity. Surface treatments are limited to the top 6 inches of the soil profile, which is as deep as most tilling equipment can penetrate. Treatments and amendments vary in cost.

Modifications to existing soil can cause problems if not done correctly. It is better to err on the side of less modification rather than more. Tilling will damage some or all of the soil structure. The benefit of improving soil texture must be balanced by the loss of structure. Farmers have recognized this tradeoff, and as a result have developed no-till farming techniques. The landscape profession can benefit by studying these techniques to learn better soil management. However, urban soils usually require more vigorous treatments than agricultural soils.

Drainage Between Amended Soil and Subsoil

Changes to soil texture may not improve drainage in flat or poorly drained sites. The amended soil may become a large bathtub, holding water. If lower-level drainage is poor, more aggressive drainage techniques, such as increasing the slope of the surface grades, adding perforated drain lines or subsoiling, may be needed. (See Soil Profile Design later in this chapter.)

Soil Moisture Levels During Mixing and Tilling

It is critical that soil moisture be at the correct level during soil mixing or tilling. This level is somewhere between field capacity and wilt point. (See Part 1, Chapter Two and the description of soil moisture requirements during compaction tilling earlier in this chapter.)

Soil Amendments

Organic Amendments

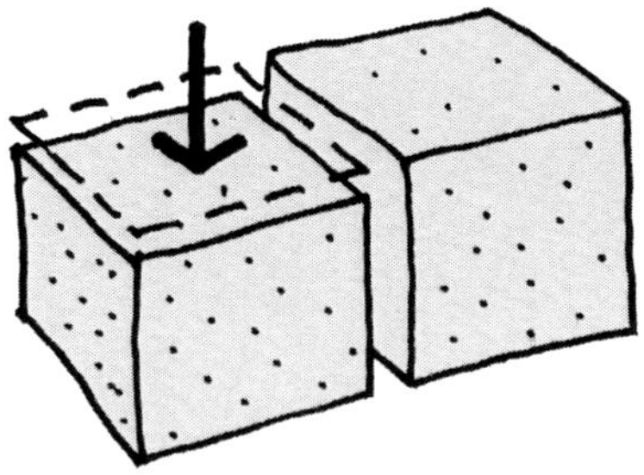

Figure 2.4.33. Organic amendments will shrink over time.

These are the most cost effective and likely the best amendments to modify soil texture. Compost, particularly yard waste compost, can be added to remediate excessively silty, clay, or sandy soil.

Organic amendment will increase drainage rates in clay and silt soils, and will also improve water-holding capacity in sandy soil. Organic amendment is the easiest material to blend into the soil, with little consequence if mixing is not uniform. It is normally added at rates of between 10 and 15 percent of the total volume of the soil.

Organic compost is not permanent and will shrink in the soil. The amount of shrinkage will be greater as amended soil depth and amount of organic amendment in the mix increase. At 10 percent by volume in the soil, pine bark fines should cause the soil to shrink by about 5 percent of the depth of the installed soil. Yard waste compost will shrink even further.

Mineral Amendments

Mineral amendments include expanded shale, clay, and slate (ESCS); perlite; and diatomaceous earth products. Sand is not recommended as a surface amendment. These mineral additions are permanent and generally increase drainage. Many can increase the cation exchange capacity of the soil, depending on soil type. Most of these products have internal pore space that can hold water and small amounts of nutrients. Non-organic soil amendments need to be incorporated into the soil at rates between 25 and 35 percent to be effective. The deeper the material can be incorporated, the greater its effect. Aggregate size of these materials should be approximately 3/8 inch.

Perlite and diatomaceous earth products are more expensive per volume than ESCS products but may improve the soil with lower rates of use. Because of their cost, their use has been limited to locations such as high-end gardens and golf and athletic turf. (See "Soil Amendments" at the beginning of this chapter for more information on different types of mineral amendments.)

Avoid adding sand as a surface treatment, particularly in clay soil. It is very difficult to mix by tilling sand into clay loam soil. Typically, the result is a matrix of clay balls surrounded by sand. Sand does not improve most soil conditions unless large quantities (at least 50 percent to as much as 70 percent of the total volume) are added. Sand should only be considered as a part of a soil mix when a soil-blending machine is available. See "Imported Topsoil and Soil Mixes" later in this chapter.

Surface Tilling Amendments

Surface tilling amendments improve the soil's organic functions and break up surface compaction, but may offer only limited improvement to poorly draining soils. The largest commercial tractor-mounted tiller can only penetrate 6 inches into the soil. In flat areas, if the underlying soil does not drain well, surface tilling may make drainage worse by creating a reservoir to hold larger amounts of water with no place for this water to go. Tillers also create a thin compacted layer just below the blades. Subsurface drainage must be added in these conditions. Increasing the slope on the site by mounding and sculpting may be the most cost-effective way to improve drainage conditions. Minimum slopes should be 2 percent in lawns and 5 percent in planting beds (10 percent in fine-grained soil).

Subsoiling may be required to improve soil drainage. Managing irrigation to the lowest level possible or even eliminating irrigation also helps improve soil water to manageable levels.

Amending the surface 4 to 6 inches with 25 to 30 percent ESCS has been effective in improving rooting capability in fine-grained soil, where only surface tilling is possible. To install surface amendments into existing soil, till the area 6 inches deep, add 2 to 3 inches of 3/8-inch ESCS on top of the tilled soil, re-till the soil to incorporate the amendment, and fine grade. ESCS material is relatively expensive, depending on the proximity to an ESCS supplier.

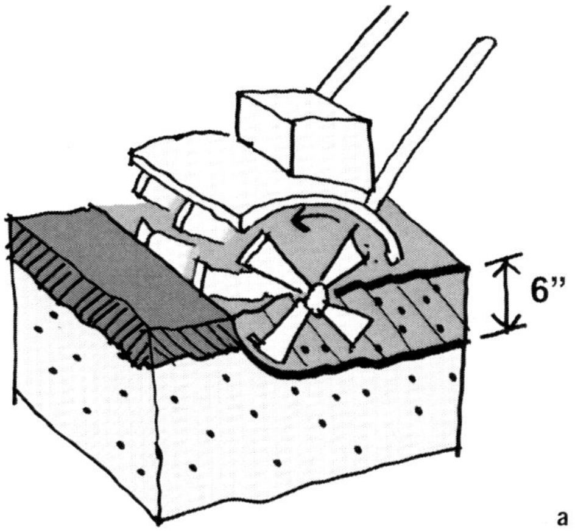

a

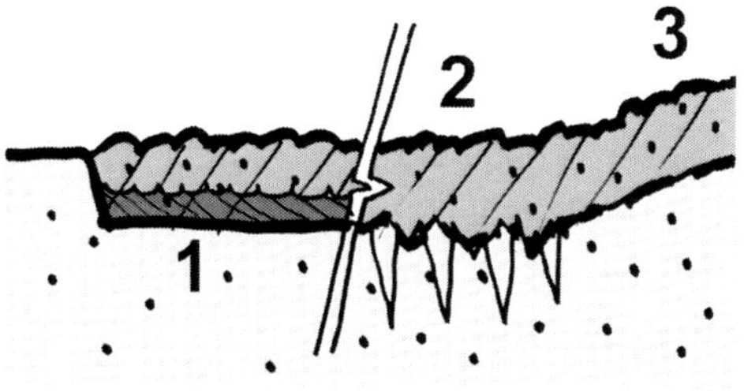

b

Figure 2.4.34. Tilling amendments into surface soil.

a. Improvement is limited to the top 6 inches and the tilling machine can increase compaction in the soil just below the tilled soil.
b. Surface tilling alone does not improve drainage.
   1. In flat areas, water layers can fill the tilled soil with no place to drain.
   2. Subsoiling may be needed in compact fine-grained soil before tilling amendments.
   3. Increasing surface slopes is an effective improvement when combined with surface amendments and tilling.

INSTALLED SOIL

On many projects, planting soil will be installed over a subsoil layer. The soil may be topsoil that was stripped from the site and stockpiled, or imported from another location. It may or may not be amended as a soil mix, or the amendments may be added after the soil is installed.

At each step in the process, the designer must make decisions related to the soil type, soil depth, volume, grades, drainage, compaction, and amendments. Soils may be designed to fit the plants required, or plants may be selected to fit the soils and amendments available.

Soil Profile Design

Natural soil has many layers that reflect its formation and make up the soil profile. These layers contribute to its effectiveness to support plants. Replicating soil profiles in modified or installed soil is important to soil improvement.

Whenever soil is added over existing soil, efforts need to be made to ensure that the underlying soil is draining and that a soil interface (see Part 1, Chapter Two) is not created between the two different soil textures. To improve drainage rates across the interface, the surface of the lower soil should be loosened and roughened before adding the new soil. This can be accomplished by dragging the teeth of the loader or backhoe before adding the new soil.

Design Goals for Soil Profiles

Four layers of natural soil profiles are important to include in the design of soil profiles.

- **O horizon:** Mostly organic matter, typically the mulch, leaf duff, or sod-thatch layer. The O horizon provides soil carbon to support the soil food web.

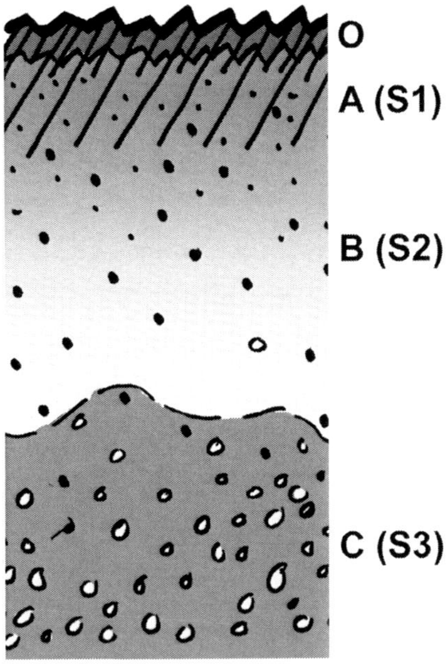

Figure 2.4.35. Soil profiles must be created in urban soils. *(S1–S3 nomenclature from Phillip Craul)*

- **A horizon:** Soil with a high level of carbon and organic matter, where soil biology converts and stores many chemicals plants need. This layer must support the delicate balance of water and air needed to support roots and soil biology. Water in the A horizon used by the tree is often wicked up from the B horizon.
- **B horizon:** Soil with less carbon. This layer primarily stores water and anchors large trees.
- **C horizon:** This layer's primary function is to drain away excess water, but it also acts as a long-term water source during dry periods. In the built landscape, the C horizon is the existing subsoil. In street tree applications, the C horizon may be the soil beside the tree pit. In a roof garden, the C horizon is the drainage board.

Transitions

Most natural soils have gradual transitions between layers, which are important to the movement of water, roots, and nutrients through the soil column. When there are sharp interfaces between horizons, water movement slows or even stops. Gradual transitions between soil layers are hard to replicate in constructed soils. On the other hand, because most constructed soils are well drained, the lack of gradual transitions between horizons should have limited impact on water and root movement. In deep soil profiles, the thin, perched water tables just above the C horizon may actually be beneficial, holding water that is usable by the plant.

Soil Profile Names: A Clarification

Phillip Craul has written extensively on specifying soil. Much of *Up By Roots* evolved from his writing. Dr. Craul refers to constructed profiles by a different nomenclature than natural profiles, using an "S-#" designation in place of the traditional soil science O, A, B, C nomenclature. Thus his S-1 is similar to the A horizon, S-2 is similar to the B horizon and S-3 is similar to the C horizon. This book chooses to retain the traditional names for constructed profiles since their function is similar.

Subgrade and C Horizon Drainage Rates

One of the more challenging tasks in the design of soil profiles is to determine the drainage rate in the subsoil, or C horizon, at the time the new soil is to be installed. At most construction sites, there is considerable compaction of subgrades, and often the soil that will become the C horizon takes the brunt of this abuse. The subgrade tends to be covered with a fine layer of silt and dust that can slow down or stop drainage.

The post-construction drainage rate of the subsoil cannot be predicted based on a preconstruction examination. A percolation test can be run immediately before new soil is placed, but if a problem is discovered, few options are generally available. A percolation test is a simple hole about 10 inches in diameter and 10 inches deep. The hole is filled with water and allowed to drain. Once it has drained, it is filled again, and the rate of fall of the water is timed. A rate of 1 inch per hour or more is satisfactory, half an inch to an inch per hour is slow, and less than half an inch per hour is normally unacceptable although rates as low as one quarter inch per hour have been found satisfactory. Rates will be faster if the test is made in dry soil, slower if the soil is wet from recent rains.

It is useful to observe the site during construction and after heavy rains, and note the places where there is poor drainage. These are the locations that will require some type of additional drainage. Be prepared to alter assumptions based on these observations.

The most practical approach is to assume that there will be little or no percolation and to design a subsurface drainage system for each project. This requires additional design time and construction cost, but is reliable. The second option is to require that in any area that drains less than 1 inch per hour, the subsoil compaction be broken up using any of the methods described earlier in this chapter. Be aware that there may be areas where these techniques are difficult to implement. The contractor may request more money to do this work unless it is clear in the contract that this work is required. It is always better to make positive subsurface drainage a requirement, not an option, and then delete it if it is not needed.

The problem of silt and dust on the surface of the subsoil is easier to correct. Require that all subgrades be disturbed either by tilling or dragging the teeth of a backhoe before the planting soil is put in place. This breaks up any thin surface interface and roughens the soil, which improves drainage between the two different soil types.

Confirming subgrade drainage assumes that the designer is at the project site on any day that soil is placed on the subgrade and has the authority to stop the work to change conditions if drainage rates are too slow. Unfortunately, this requires many trips to the site. Rarely is the entire site prepared for inspection at the same time.

Typical Soil Profile: Mulched Shrub and Tree Beds

Following is a profile for an installed soil to be planted with large trees. The soil bed under the tree may be mulched and/or planted in shrubs or ground cover. The profile assumes that soil mixes will be installed. The soil design is in the mid-Atlantic region and is not expected to be irrigated after establishment, except in summer drought. A minimum amount of fertilizer may be required based on the results of a soil test or this soil can be maintained organically with no chemical fertilizers. The exact composition of this soil mix would be refined to reflect the needs of the trees and plants included in the design and the availability of mix components.

- **O horizon:** 2 to 3 inches of mulch or compost. Provide for regular replenishment of organic amendment as a part of maintenance requirements.
- **A horizon:** 4 inches of yard waste compost tilled into the top 6 inches of the B horizon soil mix.
- **B horizon:** 30 to 36 inches of mineral-based sand/soil organic soil mix. (See discussion on soil mixes later in this chapter.) This soil mix includes 10 percent maximum by volume of composted pine bark fines or other high-lignin compost and is compacted to a bulk density of between 1.35 and 1.55 Mg/m^3. The 30- to 36-inch depth includes the A horizon.
- **C horizon:** Native soil that is confirmed to drain at a rate of at least half an inch per hour. Provide for a transition layer between the B and C horizons by roughening or tilling the interface zone before installing the B horizon. Provide for subsurface drain lines if the C horizon soil drains slower than half an inch per hour, and at the back of all site walls that block the horizontal flow of soil water.

Set design grades to anticipate approximately 2 to 3 inches of settlement over the first 10 years after installation, in addition to the initial settlement of the A horizon.

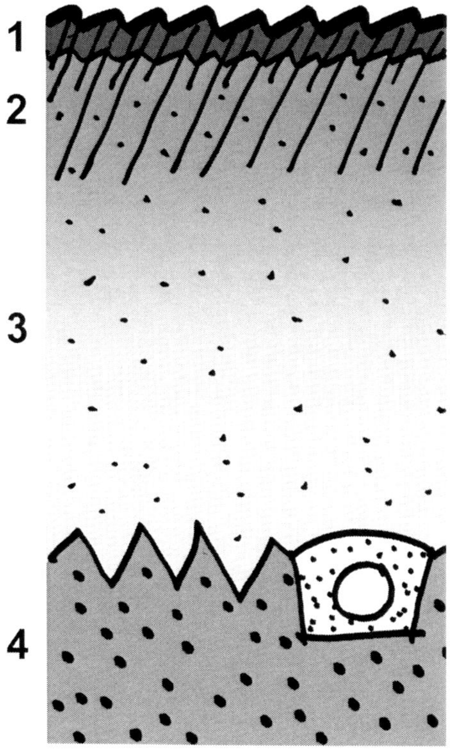

Figure 2.4.36. Soil profile for mulched tree and shrub beds.

1. O horizon, 2 to 3 inches mulch.
2. A horizon, 4 inches of compost tilled into the top 6 inches of the B horizon soil.
3. B horizon, 30 to 36 inches of mineral-based soil.
4. C horizon, subsoil, assure adequate drainage.

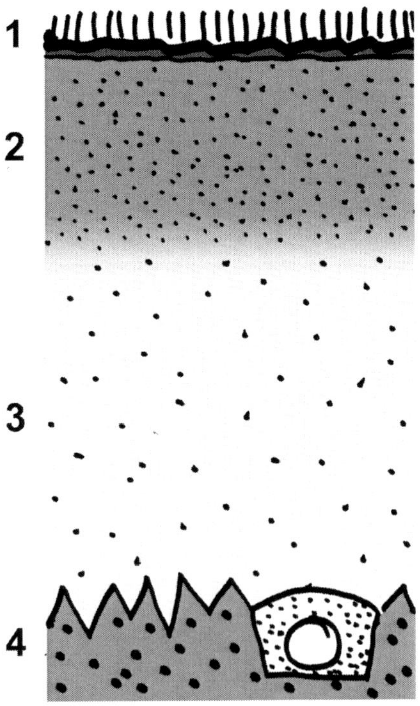

Figure 2.4.37. Soil profile for trees in lawn areas.

1. O horizon, sod thatch.
2. A horizon, 12 to 14 inches high sand soil.
3. B horizon, 24 to 30 inches sandy loam soil.
4. C horizon, subsoil, assure adequate drainage.

Typical Soil Profile: Trees in Lawn Areas

Following is a profile for an area in the mid-Atlantic region to be planted with large, mature trees with a surface of seeded or sodded lawn. The profile assumes that soil mixes will be installed, that the area will be irrigated and fertilized after establishment, and that it receives moderate foot traffic. A temporary perched water table may be formed between the A and B horizons needed to sustain water in the sandier soil. Fertilizer is primarily to support the lawn.

- **O horizon:** Sod thatch.
- **A horizon:** 12 to 14 inches of mineral-based sand/soil organic soil mix with between 5 and 8 percent clay. (See discussion on soil mixes later in this chapter.) For lawn areas subjected to only light foot traffic, 1 to 2 inches of compost may be tilled into the upper 4 to 5 inches of the A horizon. Compact to a bulk density of between 1.50 and 1.60 Mg/m^3. In this soil profile, a perched water table is desired in the sand layer, requiring a sharp interface between the A and B horizons. Do not roughen the soil between the A and B horizons.
- **B horizon:** 24 to 30 inches of mineral-based sand/soil organic soil mix with between 8 and 12 percent clay. (See discussion on soil mixes later in this chapter.) This depth does not include the A horizon. The soil mix includes 10 percent maximum by volume of composted pine bark fines and is compacted to a bulk density of between 1.45 and 1.55 Mg/m^3.
- **C horizon:** Native soil that is confirmed to drain at a rate of at least 1 inch per hour. Provide for transition layer between the B and C horizons by roughening or tilling the interface zone prior to installing the B horizon. Provide for subsurface drain lines if C horizon soil drains slower than 1 inch per hour.

Set design grades to anticipate 1 to 2 inches of settlement over the first 10 years after installation.

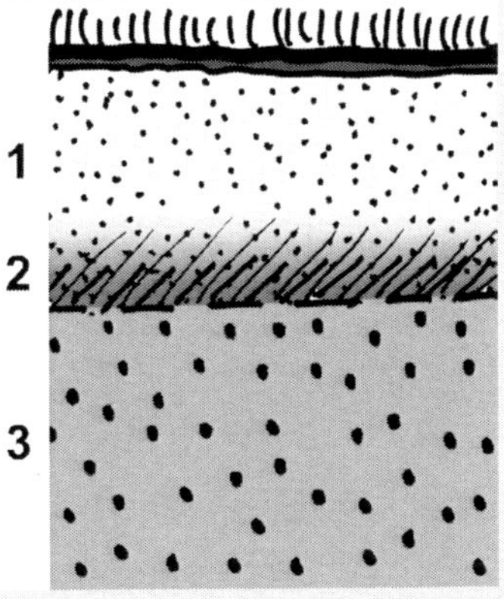

Figure 2.4.38. Perched water table.

1. Upper soil layer with a consistent texture and smooth interface with lower soil.
2. Temporary perched water layer.
3. Lower soil layer with a different texture than the upper layer.

Perched Water Tables—Good or Bad?

A smooth interface or a filter fabric between different soil types may result in a layer of soil that remains saturated for long periods of time. This is a perched water table. Is this a problem? Not always.

The roots of plants that require well-drained soils will stop above the saturated zone. Other plants may like the wetter conditions. In either case, as the plant uses water the perched water will wick up to replenish the soil water. In coarse, sandy loam soil supporting lawn, a perched water table may be preferred. The thinner the soil depth, less than 6 inches, and the finer the grain of the upper-level soil, the more likely a perched water table will be detrimental with trees becoming unstable. A perched water table can concentrate salts near the surface. As the slope of the soil increases, the perched water table will migrate to the bottom of the hill. Do not confuse a perched water table with water trapped on top of a very slowly draining layer. Trapped water is always bad if it turns the soil gray or becomes anaerobic.

Profile Variations

Variations on these horizon configurations and soil types should be developed to reflect multiple differences in conditions, requirements, budgets, and availability of materials.

Find local topsoil that is a suitable replacement for soil mixes. Avoid placing fine-grained and high organic topsoil at depths greater than 24 inches. Changing the depth of the profile changes the soil volume; ensure that adequate soil volume is provided. Soils with greater than 70 percent medium to coarse sand will likely require irrigation. Coarser soil types can be compacted to higher levels and have less settlement.

Horizontal Profile and Transitions Between Soil Types

In urban soil, the horizontal profile transition between soil types is as critical as vertical profile considerations.

The transition from one soil treatment to another must account for the movement of water between two soil textures and avoid trapping water in a low point at the joint between two soil depths. If the two soils are of significantly different textures or compaction rates, soil particles may move from the more compacted material to the less compacted soil. Vertical faces between two different fill soils or planting soil are difficult to build. Specify a gradual slope between two different soils. When digging the excavation, make holes with rough, sloped soil faces.

Compacted subsoil supporting paving, curbs or footings must always slope away from the paving to provide support for the paving and underlay softer materials. This required slope also applies to the installation of structural planting soil under pavement.

When planting soil abuts walls or other structures, adding drain board to the face of the wall will improve aeration and root growth deeper in the soil and may be less expensive that gravel backfills.

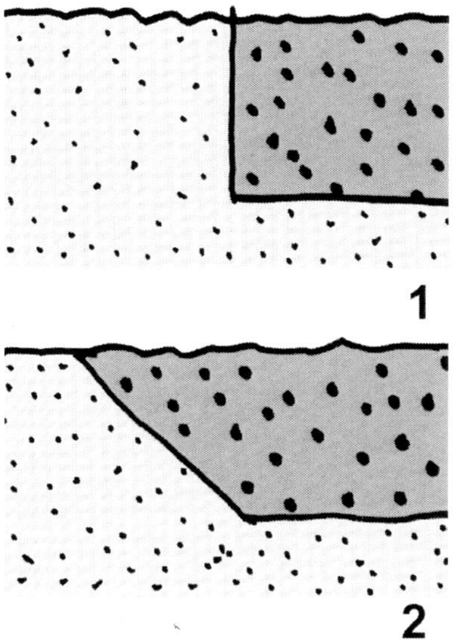

Figure 2.4.39. Horizontal profile requirements.

1. Do not draw the improved soil with a vertical edge.
2. Always draw a slight slope between two soils, with the denser soil supporting the amended soil.

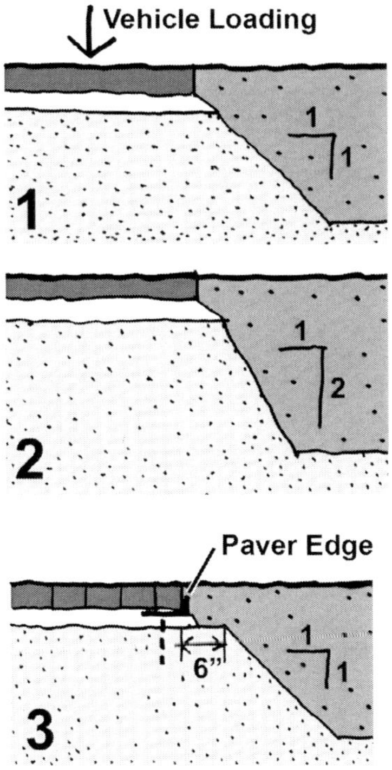

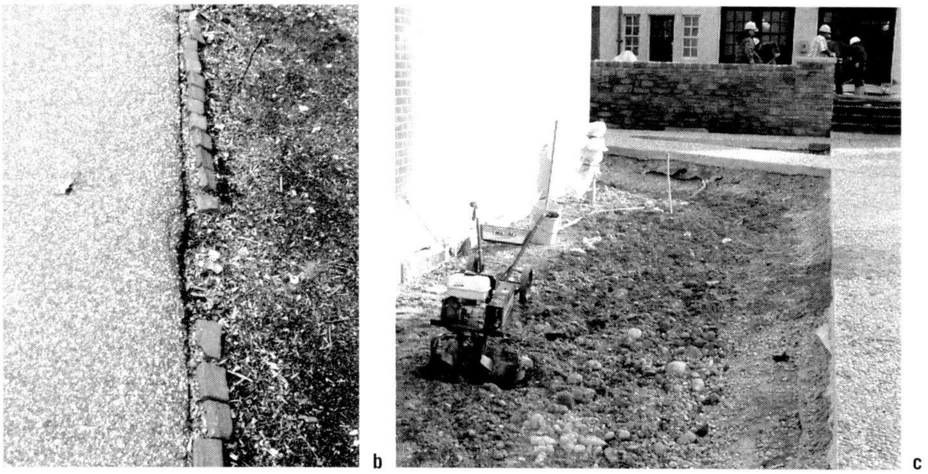

Figure 2.4.40. Soil transitions at paving edges.

a. Edge conditions change with paving type.
   1. Concrete with vehicle loading.
   2. Concrete pedestrian loading.
   3. Sand-set pavers.
b. Unsupported paver edge sinking into planting area.
c. Correctly prepared subgrade with sloped subgrade to support walks and tilled subgrade surface to receive B horizon soil.

Soil Installation Depth

Soil should be as deep as practical. There is always pressure to design minimum soil depths to save cost or weight. Minimum depth is dependent on many factors, including soil type, plant type, maintenance expectations, availability of irrigation, and microclimate factors above the root zone. Thinner soil depths and sandier soil will dry out faster, requiring more water. Sites with less maintenance require greater soil depth to hold water and nutrients between maintenance periods. Hotter, windier, more steeply sloped sites need greater soil depths than cooler, shadier, and flatter sites.

Minimum recommendations are as follows:

- Lawn: 6 to 12 inches (see sidebar, "Lawns on a Roof").
- Shrubs and perennials: 18 to 24 inches.
- Trees: 30 to 48 inches. For trees in lawn areas, install circles of tree-soil depth, 20 feet or greater in diameter, then transition to lawn soil depths. Ensure that the soil volume provided meets the amounts as specified later in this chapter.

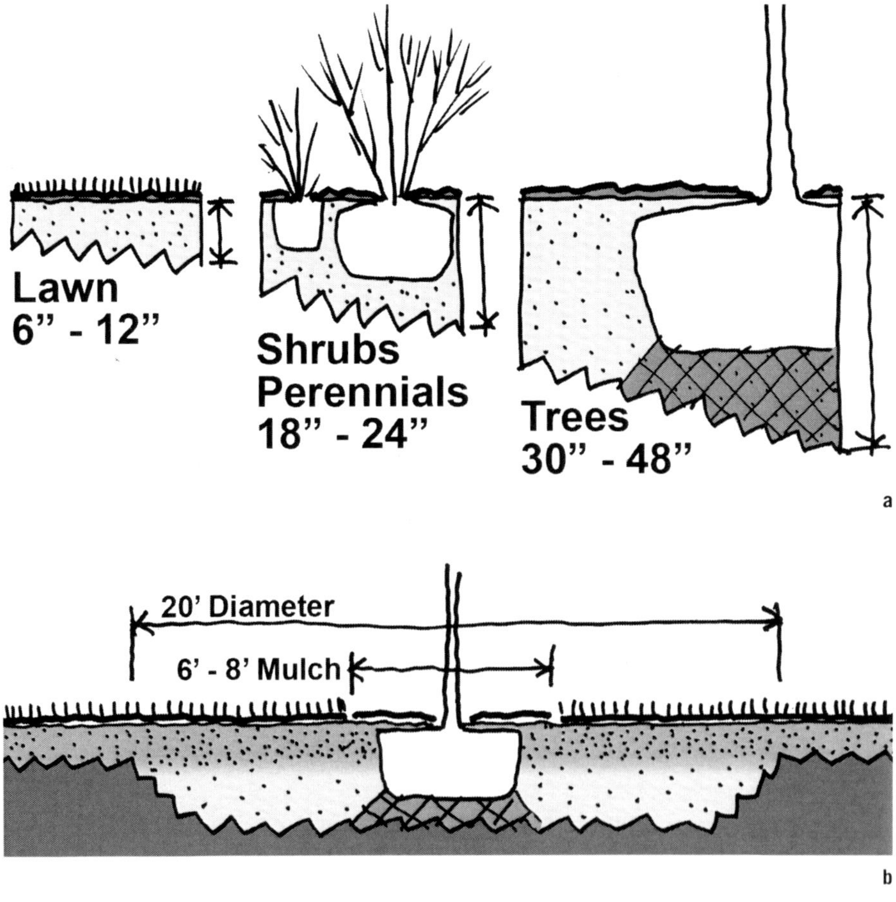

Figure 2.4.41. Minimum soil depth for combined A/B horizons.

a. Soil depth recommendations for different plant types. Soil depths do not include the O horizon and are measured to the average of the roughened C horizon interface. Thicker soil depth range is optimum while thinner depth will require more water and maintenance. Note compacted soil under tree root ball.

b. Minimum A/B horizon soil depth transition recommendation for tree planting in lawn areas.

Figure 2.4.42. Six inches of soil is not enough to support grass on south side of building but is adequate on north and east exposures. Perennials in 8-inch-deep soil also require significantly more maintenance on the south side of the building.

Lawns on a Roof

At a large office building in Washington, D.C., lawn panels were designed with 6 inches of sandy loam soil on each side of a terrace that wrapped around the entire building on the 11th floor. The lawn was irrigated, and maintenance was high. The lawns on the east and north terraces grew to expectation and were successful. The lawn on the west-facing terrace required considerably more water and other maintenance to keep it healthy. The lawn on the south face could not survive, no matter how much water was available, and required yearly replacement. Only deeper soil, up to 12 inches, would have helped.

SOIL VOLUME REQUIREMENTS

The volume of soil available for rooting must be large enough to support the intended tree size. Calculate the total usable soil volume using Table 2.4.1. The table assumes a loam soil with good drainage and no irrigation in a climate zone that receives adequate rainfall, 30 inches or more per year, to grow trees without supplemental irrigation or fertilizer. Adding irrigation or fertilizer will increase the tree size prediction for a given volume of soil. There is no data to support a specific tree size increase as a result of adding irrigation or fertilizer, but it may be as much as a 100 percent increase. These trees are then dependent on the continuation of high levels of maintenance and may go into a steep decline if maintenance practices are stopped or cut back.

Table 2.4.1. Tree size to soil volume relationships ***(Urban 1992)*****.**

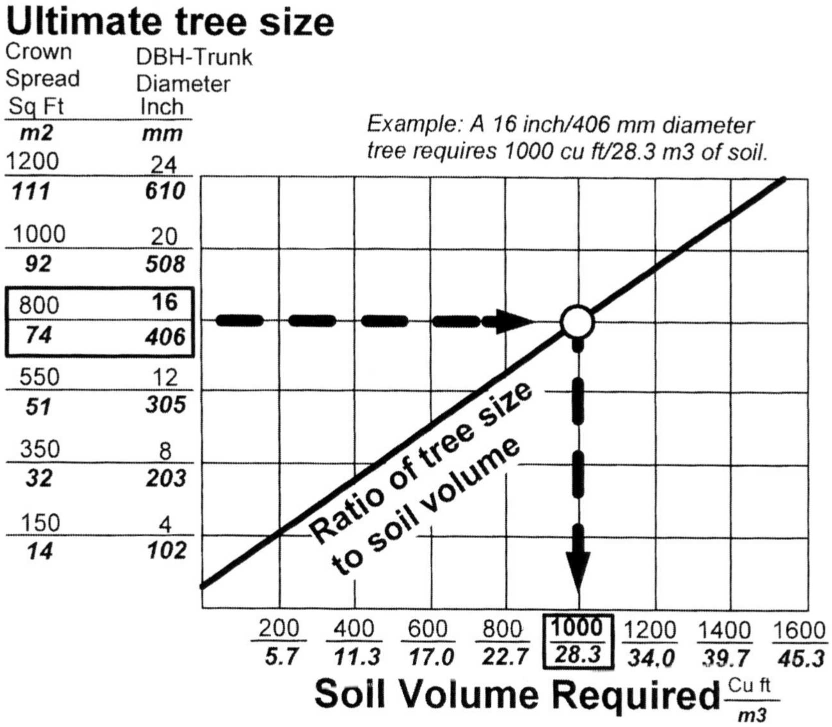

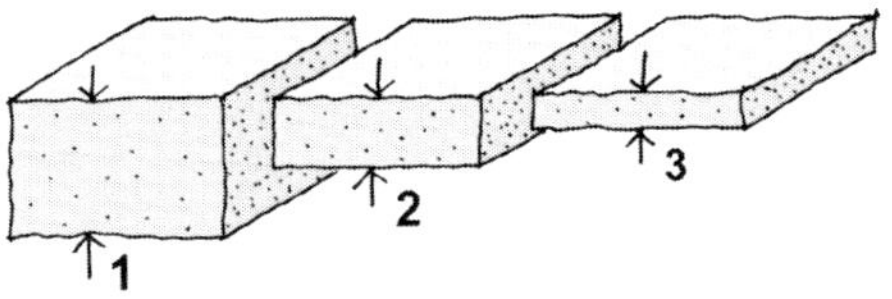

Figure 2.4.43. Estimate the value of existing soil's contribution to the available soil volume calculation.

1. 36 inches or more: Soil supporting existing plants and trees.
2. 18 inches: Soil near root-limiting bulk density.
3. 9 inches or less: Soil under pavements.

Calculating the Available Volume of Existing Soil

The existing soil should be included whenever there is reason to believe that it will support rooting. Estimate the depth of rooting as well as the soil's ability to support roots. Factors in this estimate include the amount of sand or clay, underlying soil drainage, and the compaction level in the soil.

Most roots remain in the top 24 inches of soil, more or less depending on soil type, drainage, and compaction. Deeper tree roots may only function seasonally, but are important to the yearly gathering of resources for growth. Soil below the root zone makes a contribution to the tree as a reservoir of water that wicks toward the surface during dry periods. Use a depth of 3 feet or more when calculating the availability of good-quality existing soil.

Compaction and poor drainage will reduce this depth to as little as 6 inches, while sandy soil and deep drainage conditions may increase the depth to 4 feet or greater. In urban areas, old masonry basements and deep rubble fills may increase the depth of usable soil, while compacted hardpans and soil interfaces will decrease the depth. Soil under the pavement supports some rooting, from a few inches to several feet in depth, unless severely compacted. Roots in utility trenches have been observed at 5-foot depths and greater. Trees growing near buildings built before the 1940s will often be healthier than trees near modern buildings, thanks to modern construction techniques that increase compaction.

Available volume must also be factored by the amount of compaction in the soil. As compaction approaches root-limiting bulk density, the soil efficiency must be discounted in the equation. There is no research to support actual calculations. Experience with soil and observations of rooting and plant growth suggest that for soil that has been heavily graded or compacted at levels close to root-limiting, it is reasonable to estimate a 50 percent reduction in volume, increasing to 75 percent for soil under paving.

There are many variables to consider in making these estimates. Use them only for general predictions. In dense urban areas, it is often best to assume the worst and to make only a small allowance for the value of the existing soil. However, if predevelopment conditions supported good tree growth, it is reasonable to assume that post-construction soil will have some value if not graded or heavily compacted. Streetscape projects in existing business districts often fit this assumption.

Calculating the Volume of New Soil

The final part of calculating available soil volume is determining the amount of new or improved soil required. Most installed soil types, whether open to the sky, in vaults, or under suspended sidewalks, are likely to function as indicated in the soil volume chart.

With soil that is a part of compacted structural soils, as described in Part 2, Chapter Six, the designer will need to account for the reduction in rooting capacity because of the qualities that make it able to support pavement. Tree growth in soil/aggregate structural soils is limited by the amount of soil within the volume of aggregate. The amount of actual soil is only about 20 percent, suggesting that only 20 percent of the volume should be considered as contributing to the tree's growth. Other types of structural soil have not been evaluated sufficiently to make specific recommendations, but a significant decrease in root performance should be anticipated.

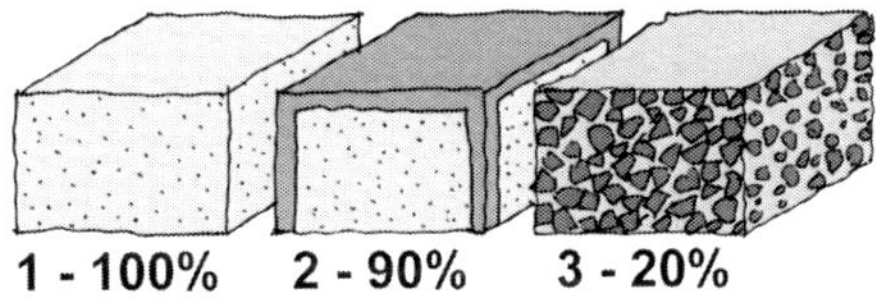

Figure 2.4.44. Soil volume value of different soil systems.

1. Loam soils: 100 percent.
2. Suspended structure filled with loam soil: 90 percent or greater.
3. Rock-based structural soil: 20 percent.

Connectivity: Designing to Enhance Soil Volume

Soil volumes can be designed to enhance limited opportunities. Construct soil "windows" through wall foundations to connect adjoining soil volume. Add drain mats such as Miradrain or Enka to the vertical and horizontal surface of walls, vaults, and foundations to improve airflow into the soil and increase root growth at lower levels in the soil profile.

In the most intense urban spaces, soil volumes can only be enhanced by increasing volumes under paved areas. Interconnect soil volumes from tree to tree where possible. Cluster trees and use linear trenches or root paths. Multiple strategies to increase soil volume under paving are presented in Part 2, Chapter Six.

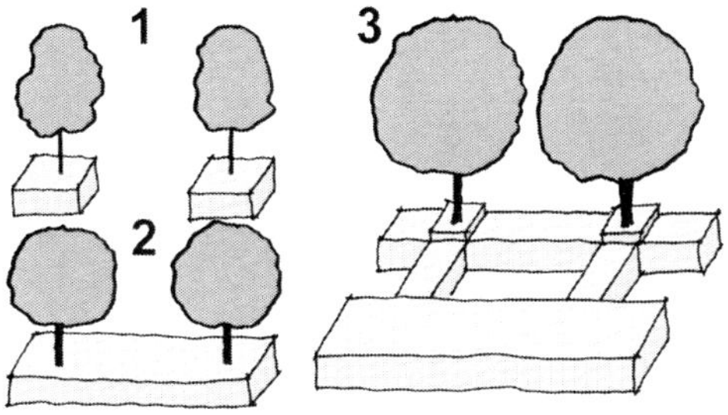

Figure 2.4.45. Increasing effective soil volumes in urban areas.

1. Separate soil volumes limit tree root potential.
2. Connected soil volumes allow for shared root space.
3. Connections under pavements and to adjacent soil volumes provide the greatest rooting potential.

Utility Conflicts and Soil Volume

Utilities compete for space with needed soil volumes. This must be understood and negotiated throughout the design and construction process. Conflicts are direct and indirect.

Direct conflicts for space occur where the utility line runs through or close to a soil area. The utility takes up space and limits the options to modify the soil. Subsoiling is often impossible near shallow utility lines. Excavation near pipes and wires must be more careful. Damage has expensive repercussions, especially when fiber optic lines are cut. Lines must be surveyed and marked in the field. Often, exact locations and depths or even lines' existence are unknown.

Indirect conflicts include future problems between the utility and the roots of the trees growing in the soil. Utility managers may not want roots growing near utility lines, fearing the roots will damage the lines. Future maintenance may have to cut roots or be limited by structures designed to support pavements over roots. Finally, leaks in the lines may harm the trees. Gas line leaks will quickly kill trees. Steam lines, even when operating properly, emit heat that can limit rooting if soil temperatures exceed 95°F. Steam line breaks can kill large existing trees.

Figure 2.4.46. Underground utilities compete for space to install additional soil volume.

Figure 2.4.47. Tree killed by gas main leak.

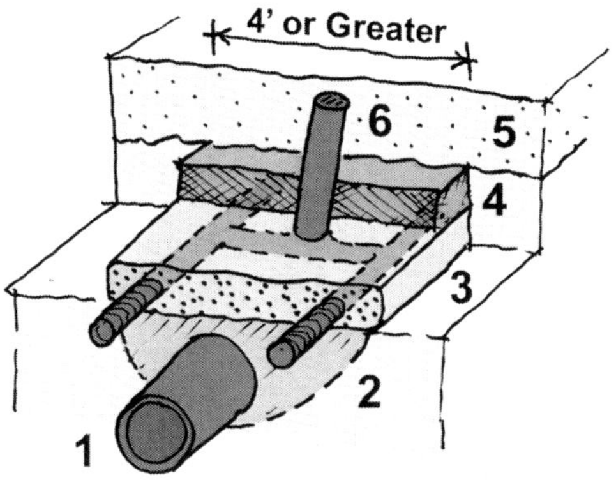

Figure 2.4.48. Solutions to conflicts between roots and utilities. Steam or gas line intercept to collect and divert heat or gas from the root zone.

1. Utility line.
2. Drainage fill pipe bedding.
3. Washed gravel wrapped in filter cloth. Two perforated drain lines are connected to riser.
4. Compacted clay loam fill.
5. Root zone.
6. Four-inch pipe riser fitted with slotted drain cover spaced 50 to 100 feet along line.

Most of these conflicts can be solved by negotiation among the competing interests. Most political jurisdictions will recognize that these conflicts are an unavoidable facet of design in urban areas. Declaring that they will go away by prohibiting trees near utilities would be similar to saying that pedestrian/auto conflicts can be solved by eliminating crosswalks. In both situations, management with some acceptance of risk is the solution.

A heat intercept zone can be added between the tree soil and steam lines if the line is deep enough. Root barriers can be added over the top of utility lines to separate them from soil zones.

SOIL BIOLOGY MODIFICATIONS

Adding organic amendment to the soil and restoring the organic cycle can reactivate damaged soil biology. Apply 4 to 6 inches of compost to the surface and till it into the top 4 to 6 inches of the soil after the soil is rough-graded. Using locally composted yard waste injects the soil with significant soil organisms as well as being a carbon source to support them. All compost should be mature, with a carbon to nitrogen (C/N) ratio lower than 25:1. This creates an organic A horizon in the soil and permits fairly poor-quality soil to be used as planting soil.

Figure 2.4.49. Creating an organic A horizon.

a. Compost applied to the soil.
b. Compost tilled into the surface 6 inches of the soil.
c. Tilled A horizon on top of existing soil B horizon.

a b

Figure 2.4.50. Mulch.
a. Properly mulched tree.
b. Mulch volcano, the calling card of a poor maintenance company.

Bark mulch placed on top of the soil provides the horizons below with an additional carbon source. Mulch should be replenished periodically, but never at rates that exceed those that the previously installed mulch breaks down. Avoid placing mulch against the bark at the base of trees, creating "mulch volcanoes," which can start bark rot and girdling roots.

To further enhance soil biology, apply compost teas and composted yard waste as a part of the maintenance program. Biological soil testing is needed to guide compost tea application. Soil samples are assayed to determine levels of important segments of the soil food web. Delay soil biology testing for several months after installation to allow the organic material to stabilize. Compost teas are normally applied at least three times a year and brewed to specified requirements based on the soil biology assay. With a commitment from knowledgeable management, it is possible to maintain successful landscapes at large commercial sites using entirely organic procedures.

Inoculations of mycorrhizal fungi and additions of other organic material such as kelp and humic acids make limited improvements to soil biology. Most of the improvement occurs with the application of organic amendments. Mycorrhizal inoculants are more effective if used in conjunction with fertilizer. There are many types of mycorrhizae, and many are specific to particular trees. Inoculating the soil around newly planted trees with leaf litter, duff, or topsoil taken from the ground around healthy, mature trees of the same genus will improve the soil biology specific to that tree. Obtaining this material is not easy, and sources must be identified during the preparation of soil specifications.

SOIL CHEMISTRY MODIFICATIONS

Soil chemistry modifications should reflect the results of soil testing. (See Part 1, Chapter Four for detailed information on various chemical requirements and Part 1, Chapter Seven for chemical testing discussion.)

Proper attention to the soil's organic properties, as mentioned before, normally corrects many chemical problems, but the soil may still benefit from chemical treatments. The amount of chemicals available to the plant is related to a soil's cation exchange capacity, or the ability of the soil to hold onto chemicals. Cation exchange increases in finer-grained soil and soil with greater organic content.

Newly planted trees do not appear to benefit from the addition of fertilizers during the first year unless soil testing indicates specific deficiencies. Fertilizer during the second growing season does improve the establishment of the plant. However, the application of compost can have similar results.

Phosphorus is not water-soluble and must be tilled into the soil before planting to be effective. Phosphorus is sometimes over applied and can reach toxic levels. It will remain in the soil for many years. Agricultural soils and soil from landscapes that have been over fertilized may have elevated phosphorus content.

SOIL pH

Soil pH may be the most important soil chemical component to understand. Soil pH is difficult to change, particularly to make it more acidic. pH can be lowered, but only temporarily. Match plants to the pH of the available soil. Do not depend on changing the soil pH to match the plants.

Increasingly, hydrated lime is used to stabilize clay soils at construction sites. These soils will have a pH over 8 and create problems for many plants.

Irrigation water can change soil pH and salt content. Confirm the pH and sodium levels of the water being used to irrigate.

IMPORTED TOPSOIL AND SOIL MIXES

When new soil must be brought onto the site, it may come from fields or from development sites that are in an earlier phase of construction. Imported topsoil should be considered the same as existing site soils that are stripped and stockpiled. These soils may have to be amended. As amendments become an increasingly larger proportion of the total soil, the soil is more properly classified as a soil mix. There is no industry standard for where simple amending of soil becomes soil mixing, but a reasonable point would be if the amendments need to be incorporated before the soil is spread. By this definition, if the amendment needs to be incorporated throughout the soil profile or deeper than can be achieved by tilling (about 6 inches), it becomes a soil mix. If the designer wants a soil mix, the specifications should clearly state this.

Topsoil

Where budget is an issue, using an imported loam, sandy loam, or sandy clay loam topsoil is a cost-effective alternative to soil mixes, but good-quality loam topsoil is increasingly difficult to obtain. As the available topsoil texture becomes finer-grained, particularly soils high in silt and/or fine sand, soil compaction and drainage in the installation become increasingly critical. Soil with large amounts of silt is the most difficult to work with.

Compaction rates during installation of fine-grained soils have a narrow tolerance range. Fine-grained topsoil left under compacted will shrink and erode. Over compaction during installation will reduce drainage and root penetration. The less coarse to medium sand in the soil or the more soil's structure and soil peds have been crushed, the easier it is to over compact the soil during installation. Silt soil often has weak structure and fragile peds, while clay soil has stronger structure and its soil peds are more forgiving to movement and compaction forces.

If available, unmixed topsoil of reasonable quality may be preferable to soil mixes. In addition to the cost difference, it is easy to make mistakes in the types and ratio of amendments, and the resulting mix may not be an improvement. If the design fee does not include time to monitor mix testing and installation, an amended topsoil may be the preferred alternative. Unmixed topsoil may be more sustainable than soil mixes if it is harvested from a site that is already in the development cycle and if that site is close to the project site.

Soil Mixes

In many large metropolitan markets, good quality, A-horizon topsoil has become difficult to find and expensive to purchase. Poor-quality soils that are marketed as "topsoil" will be just that: cheap, poor-quality soil. The additional cost of a soil, sand, and compost soil mix may be worth its benefits. Soil mixes have the advantage of offering control of drainage and compaction resistance that cannot be found in native soil. Quality control may be greater, and the soil may be easier to install in a wider range of weather. Where there is intensive urban activity creating compaction, soil mixes can be a superior growing medium to topsoil.

Figure 2.4.51. Many factors including project schedule and available space to work will affect the decision whether to use natural topsoil or a soil mix.

Factors That Influence the Design and Use of Soil Mixes

When starting to design a soil mix, six critical elements must be considered:

- plant cultural requirements
- the size and location of the project
- availability of soils, products, and equipment
- budget
- maintenance capability
- sustainability goals

Plant Cultural Requirements

Soil mixes can be custom-tailored to meet the cultural requirements of the plants, within certain limitations. It will be difficult to make an acidic soil mix in a region such as Chicago, which has limestone-based soils. However, it is still possible to develop a low-pH soil in this area with sufficient time, money, and control.

It is difficult to install different types of soil mix in the same beds. Do not mix plants requiring high pH with plants that require low pH, or plants that need damp soils with ones that benefit from dry soils. While these requirements should be normal for all landscapes, there is a tendency for designers to think that soil mixes allow greater design flexibility. It may seem easy to change the soil to match the plant; however, there are limits to how complex one can make the soil installation plan.

Figure 2.4.52. Many plants, such as these *Pieris japonica*, grow better in natural soil with pH and soil biology suited to their cultural requirements.

Figure 2.4.53. Size, complexity, and location of the project influence the type of soil to be specified.

Use of On-Site Soil in Soil Mixes

There are several factors to determine if use of on-site soil resources makes sense. Large trucks, soil blenders, and loaders require access and maneuvering space. An on-site soil-blending operation may require up to 5,000 square feet of space, plus room for soil storage. The minimum cost-effective on-site soil mixing operation is about 2,000 to 5,000 cubic yards of soil. This soil-mixing threshold requirement limits the use of existing soils as a component in the soil mix. For most urban projects, soil mixing will be off-site, using a soil source other than the existing soil from the site.

Simple soil mixes, such as adding organic amendment to soil before spreading, can be prepared on-site, using a loader to turn the mix components. If a loader-mixing method is used, a soil screen may be required to break up large clumps and remove roots and plant debris. With the loader-mixing method, soil mixing may be incomplete but still acceptable.

Preparing soil mixes requires considerable testing and oversight by the designer. Small projects may not have the budgets to allow sufficient quality control.

The further the site is from the soil source and mixing facility, the greater the cost. Trucking of soil mixes may quickly become more expensive than the actual soil cost. The further the site is from the designer's office, the less time the designer can spend on-site to monitor quality.

Availability of Soils, Products, and Equipment

All parts of a soil mix are bulk products. To make a soil mix, all the products must be shipped to a common point, mixed, and reshipped. This factor increases cost and restricts the material options to those readily available near the project.

The products in soil mixes are mostly natural materials, and the soil industry is small. Supply and demand, weather, and the nuances of running a small business will change the availability of products from year to year. Designers must be aware of the local supply of products research availability of products before specifying. Attending yearly regional nursery industry trade shows is a good place to become familiar with soil suppliers who often have booths to explain their products.

Budget

In many markets soil mixes can double the cost of soil over using imported topsoil. Manufactured additives such as ESCS or calcine clays can drive costs even higher. Work with a local soil supplier to prepare accurate cost-estimates. Designers should be sure the added cost of the soil mix is adding appropriate value to the project.

a

b

Figure 2.4.54. Soil mixing equipment.

a. Soil blending machines are not available in all markets.

b. Soil mixing using a loader can substitute for a blending machine.

Maintenance Capability

Soil mixes can reduce or increase the amount of maintenance required over the life of the project compared to using imported topsoil. Soil mix designs try to balance compaction resistance and drainage capability with water- and nutrient-holding capacity. As soil becomes coarse enough to drain well and resist compaction, the soil holds less water and fewer nutrients, which may add to maintenance costs. On the other hand, if the only topsoil available is a silty or fine-grained sandy loam, maintenance costs of using a coarse-grained sandy loam soil mix with moderate compaction resistance may reduce maintenance in areas where compaction is expected.

Sustainability Goals

The design profession is a long way away from understanding, which soil solutions are more environmentally sustainable than others. Few agree on the definition of sustainability or how to measure the concept.

Reuse of existing soil resources at the site is clearly the most sustainable approach. Adding fewer amendments to the soil may be more sustainable than more amendments. Organic amendments are likely to be more sustainable than processed products such as sand. Sand may be more sustainable than calcine clays or ESCS. Yet there are no studies to support any of these assumptions. For example ESCS, which may increase infiltration and improve compaction resistance, requires significant energy to process, ship, and mine. A rural landscape is destroyed at the site of a shale quarry and processing plant. These costs and impacts must be

Figure 2.4.55. Natural soil might be a better choice for meeting project goals for sustainability.

balanced with the value that another, more urban site may be healed. Research is needed to determine how to calculate relative amounts of environmental harm and benefit.

Soil Mix Components

Various products are brought together to create a soil mix. The products specified for the soil mix should reflect the performance characteristics desired. For a detailed description of these products, see the section on soil amendments at the beginning of this chapter.

Topsoil for Soil Mixes

Most soil mixes start with a natural soil. It is the cheapest and often the best component for rooting space. True topsoil is harvested from the O and A soil horizons and has the organic and soil biology component needed to support plants. The organic content of most natural topsoil is only about 2 to 5 percent. Topsoil is normally black-brown to light brown, or brown with hues of black, red, tan, or yellow. The brown to black color is organic staining that indicates past soil food web activity.

If the intent is to mix sand or other aggregates to increase drainage and compaction resistance, a clay loam or sandy clay loam is the best soil. Such soil is between 30 and 35 percent clay and between 40 and 50 percent sand. Ideally, the topsoil would have a low percentage of silt and fine sand.

If only organic amendment is being added, a coarse sandy loam with between 15 and 20 percent clay is likely the best choice.

Avoid topsoil that contains more than 35 percent clay. Soil high in clay or silt will be difficult to blend and may form a mix of "soil balls" surrounded by the other mix components. Avoid a topsoil that contains more than 45 percent silt or 25 percent fine sand. Soil high in silt or fine sand will contribute to a self-compacting soil mix, especially if the other component in the mix is coarse sand. Avoid topsoil that contains more than 6 percent organic matter. If the clay in the soil is an expansive clay type (see Part 1, Chapter Two), the amount of sand added to the mix should be increased to ensure adequate drainage.

a

b

Figure 2.4.56. Topsoil.

pH

The pH of each mix component, including the soil, makes a contribution to the overall pH of the soil mix. Select a soil source with a pH close to the desired pH of the final mix based on the proposed plant requirements.

Soil Mix Design Development

Soil mixes are a combination of sand or other aggregates with topsoil and organic amendment. The goal is to develop a soil that has good drainage capability, while providing adequate moisture- and nutrient-holding capacity for the plants.

When sand is added to a soil, be sure that the final coarse to medium size sand content exceeds 50 percent. At lower amounts of sand, drainage rates are not increased.

As the sand or aggregate content increases above 55 percent, the water- and nutrient-holding capacity goes down and the drainage rate goes up. High-sand soils are reliably drained and more tolerant to a wide range of compaction rates. These soils are less likely to become over compacted, but require a continuous supply of water and nutrients, which increases maintenance. Mixes that substitute fine-grained ESCS for coarse-grained sands have a higher water- and nutrient-holding capacity but will still require supplemental water and fertilizer. Using ESCS adds significantly to the cost of the soil.

As the sand is reduced in the mix, close to the 55 percent threshold, compaction rates become critical. Too much compaction, and the drainage rates in finer-grained soil slow to unacceptable levels. Too little compaction in finer-grained soil and soil settlement can become unacceptable. The window between too much and too little compaction is narrow and hard to manage during construction.

Soil mix design is a multi-step process and does not end with the publication of specifications. The specifications should set performance standards and the types of mix components to be used. At the time of the writing of the specifications, the designer cannot know the actual source of the soil or organic amendment. Minor variations in these materials will change the mix proportions. Only after the soil, sand, and organic amendment sources are submitted by the contractor, with their test results, can soil mix proportions be estimated and tested. Testing of the soil to be used in the mix must include the measuring of the different sizes of sand particles, known as sand fractions.

Infiltration Rates

A good measure to evaluate the performance of a soil mix is its infiltration rate when compacted to a known level. A developing standard is to test infiltration at 80 and 85 percent of maximum dry density as measured by the Proctor test. Table 2.4.2 shows recommended minimum infiltration rate ranges for various soil mixes.

Drainage rates will vary widely with different materials, particularly organic amendments. Do not be surprised by much higher rates than expected. Infiltration rates in soils always go down after installation as

Table 2.4.2. Recommended minimum infiltration rates for various soil mixes.

Soil mix type	Application	Minimum infiltration rate target range at between 80% to 85% compaction
Topsoil/organic matter	Trees/shrub	0.5–2 inches per hour
	Low-use lawn	1–2 inches per hour
Topsoil/sand or ESCS/ organic matter	Trees/shrub	1–3 inches per hour
	Lawn	2–3 inches per hour
Sand or ESCS/topsoil/ organic matter	Trees/shrub	2–4 inches per hour
	Lawn	3–6 inches per hour
	High-use lawn	5–10 inches per hour
ECSC/soil/organic matter and ESCS soilless mixes		Check with ESCS manufacturers

roots fill the pores and fines settle through the soil. When in doubt, specify a higher rate limit rather than one that might be too low, especially when using a natural topsoil.

Mix ratios should be estimated to obtain the desired proportion of coarse and medium sand fractions in the soil. The larger sand particles control the drainage rate. For example, if the total coarse and medium sand in the soil is approximately 25 percent and the goal is to have them be 50 percent of the soil mix, a ratio of soil to coarse sand to organic amendment of 4:4:1 to 4:6:1 will likely result in the correct mix. Coarse concrete sand still contains some amount of fine sand, which must be factored into the calculation. Labs specializing in soil mix testing will recommend component proportions to the designer based on supplied component testing and soil goals.

Soil Mix Design Refinement

An important part of the design process is the mixing of sample batches of soil in the office to confirm basic assumptions on infiltration rates. This happens after the contractor has been chosen and exact sources of mix components identified.

The soil submittal process should include a minimum of 2 gallons of each type of material to be used in the mixing trial. These samples not only represent a physical record of the submittal, but also offer the designer the opportunity to refine the mix design. The only equipment needed is a large bowl or bucket, a measuring cup, a large spoon, and a wire mesh colander.

Make up about 2 quarts of the proposed soil mix, carefully measuring the different components. If needed, add small amounts of water so that the soil is damp but not saturated before combining. The finer the soil is pulverized, the slower the drainage. Do not over pulverize or over mix the sample; leave some small pea- to nickel-size peds.

Place the mix in the colander, and using your fist, compact the soil stiffly and evenly, leaving a bowl-shaped depression with a minimum of 2 inches of soil between the soil surface and the wire mesh. Slowly pour water to fill the depression and continue until water starts dripping out the bottom of the mesh. Time how long

Figure 2.4.57. In-office soil mix development.

1. Equipment required.
2. Measure mix by volume ratio.
3. Mix soil. Do not overmix. Leave most of the soil peds intact.
4. Slowly compress soil in screen colander with fist, making a depression to hold water.
5. Slowly pour in water.
6. Observe drainage rate.

the water takes to stop dripping out the bottom and how long it takes all the water to soak into the soil. Use this information to compare to other mixes.

Prepare several different mix ratios to gradually increase the topsoil content. Make records of each mix. Find the mix ratio where the soil drains out of the depression into the soil very slowly. This mix has too many fine particles for lawn soil, but might be acceptable for a garden bed where future over compaction is less likely. Next, find the mix where the water drains out of the bottom almost as fast as it is poured in the top. This mix has too much coarse sand for planting beds, but is about right for a high-sand, compaction-resistant lawn mix. It will require irrigation and frequent fertilization and will not be suitable for low-maintenance lawn situations.

Somewhere in between is a mix that satisfies the compromise between too many fine particles and too much coarse sand. This mix will be a balance between the project's need for compaction resistance and the cost and availability of regular maintenance. Develop several mix proportions that fit between these two points, and ask the contractor to start testing these proportions for infiltration rates under lab conditions. Be cautious about any soil mix near the two extremes. Each requires significant knowledge of soil and plant relationships.

By comparing the results of the office samples with the resulting lab analysis, a designer can become skilled in predicting the right mix with the types of soil and sand available in the region. The scientific soul may desire a more objective soil mix design method, but given all the variables of soils, plants and design goals, this more subjective method is both suitable and practical.

Mix Design Variations

The following are the most common soil mixes. These are designed to be compacted to levels that are less than root-limiting for the particular soil's classification. The upper limit of compaction should generally be between 1.4 and 1.65 Mg/m^3, depending on the soil classification. Mixes with a predominance of sand (80 percent or more) may be compacted up to 1.7 Mg/m^3. See the soil compaction discussion later in this chapter. For soil mixes to be used below paved areas that can be compacted to engineering standards of 90 to 95 percent dry density and still support roots, see Part 2, Chapter Six.

Soil mixes with sand as the dominant component, as previously described, will have low organic content. To obtain an adequate organic content in the soil for planting beds and tree soils, till 3 to 4 inches of yard waste compost into the top of the soil profile, as described earlier in this chapter. This surface organic layer is important for bed areas but not necessarily recommended for lawns. Too much organic amendment in the top layer of a lawn soil will make for an unstable surface and gradually compact into a poorly draining interface layer.

Topsoil-Based Soil Mixes

These mixes are the least expensive of the soil mix designs. The intent is to enhance the base topsoil component to increase drainage or its organic component. Topsoil-based mixes are excellent for planting beds, but less efficient for rooftop applications where drainage is important, or for high-impact lawn applications where compaction resistance is important.

Topsoil and Organic Amendment

Add stable, high-lignin compost at a rate of between 10 and 15 percent by volume to improve drainage and broaden the compaction tolerance of the soil during installation. Remember that the greater the amount of organic amendment, the greater the amount of soil settlement. Maintaining low compaction rates and good drainage is critical in soil mixes that are mostly topsoil.

For these soil mixes, use a sandy loam topsoil. For topsoil higher in silt or clay, greater amounts of organic amendment may be needed but never more than 15 to 20 percent by volume. With higher levels of clay or silt, the soil mix may fail the infiltration test when compacted. Avoid these soils. These fine-grained soils will normally have low infiltration rates, close to half an inch per hour when compacted. To compensate for the low infiltration or anticipated settlement, increase surface slopes in the bed to greater than 10 percent.

Topsoil/organic soil mixes are the most sustainable and least costly soil mix option. The typical mix ratio of topsoil to high-lignin compost is 10:1 to 7:1. Adjust the mix ratio to obtain the desired infiltration rate (see Table 2.4.2).

Topsoil, Sand, and Organic Amendment

When incorporating coarse sand into topsoil, the medium to coarse sand content in the final mix should never be less than 50 percent. A good level for planting mixes for perennials, shrubs, and trees is 55 to 60 percent medium to coarse sand. If the sand proportion is too low, the soil may become self-compacting and can develop the consistency of concrete. The greater the content of medium to coarse sand, the greater the compaction resistance. Ideally, topsoil that has a significant portion of medium and coarse sands present in the base soil should be selected, but these types of soils are rare. If clay or silt loam topsoil is used, the added sand will likely exceed the topsoil volume, and then the soil mix is better described as a mineral-based soil mix. (We'll learn more about mineral-based soil mixes later in this chapter.) Add high-lignin organic amendment from between 5 and 10 percent by volume — lower in turf areas, higher in shrub and perennial beds.

For trees and shrubs, a typical mix ratio of topsoil to sand to high-lignin compost is 6:4:1 to 5:5:1. Adjust the mix ratio to obtain the desired infiltration rate (see Table 2.4.2). The variation in the amount of sand in the topsoil is a big factor in why these mix ratio ranges are so large.

Topsoil, ESCS, and Organic Amendment

ESCS products can be added to topsoil to increase drainage. Because of the interconnected pore space within the material, the material itself can make channels through the soil for the movement of air and water. Incorporate coarse (3/8-inch) ESCS material at a rate of between 25 and 30 percent by volume. Unlike sand additives, it is not necessary to have ESCS levels of more than 50 percent of the mix to increase drainage. ESCS can be added to the soil in greater amounts to dramatically improve drainage and compaction resistance. Adding a maximum of 5 to 10 percent high-lignin organic amendment will also improve the organic and drainage capability of the soil. This mix is particularly effective where clay loam and silt loam topsoil is the base soil. Adding ESCS to a soil mix adds to the cost, but provides a superior product.

A typical ratio of topsoil to ESCS to high-lignin compost is 7:2:1 to 6:2:1. Higher amounts of ESCS are required to improve compaction resistance. Adjust the mix ratio to obtain the desired infiltration rate (see Table 2.4.2). Regional ESCS manufacturers can assist in designing these soil mixes to reflect their product characteristics.

Mineral-Based Soil Mixes

Soil mixes that start with a majority of mineral material, such as sand or ESCS products, will have high drainage rates and good compaction resistance compared to topsoil-based mixes. These soils will be easier to compact to a consistent level and will settle less over time. However, mineral soil mixes with less than 10 percent clay will be very dry and require supplemental watering and fertilization. High-sand soil mixes have been successfully used in organically maintained landscapes where regular application of compost and compost tea replaces fertilizer.

Soil textures for lawns that are expected to receive high compaction forces require high ratios, up to 90 percent, of sand or ESCS. The textural design of soil for athletic and golf green turf is beyond the scope of this book. Consult *Sports Fields—A Manual for Design, Construction and Maintenance*, by Puhalla, Krans, and Goatley, or a sports turf specialist.

Too Much Organic Matter

Adding more organic matter to soil sounds like an easy way to improve the drainage rate, and such soil will grow very nice plants. But, if the soil is being installed deeper than 8 to 12 inches, problems will develop.

If the organic matter added is greater than 10 or 15 percent by volume, the soil will be too rich. It will continue to compost and shrink in volume, and it may be too soft and not able to support maturing trees. If such soil becomes too wet, it could become anaerobic.

Sand, Soil, and Organic Amendment

This is a subtle variation on the soil, sand, and organic amendment previously described. The soil/sand mix contains more soil, while the sand/soil mix contains much more sand to achieve much faster drainage. Faster-draining mixes are often used for rooftop applications.

Mix concrete sand with a clay loam to sandy clay loam topsoil. High-lignin organic amendment is added at approximately 5 to 10 percent by volume. Sand to soil ratio is dependent on the amount of coarse to medium sand in the soil, the size of the sand, and the desired infiltration rates. The design goal is to achieve a minimum amount of coarse to medium sand in the mix of 55 percent or greater for shrub and tree soil, and approximately 70 percent or greater for lawn soil. Clay should be a minimum of 10 to 15 percent for shrub and tree soil and a minimum of 5 to 10 percent for lawn soil. The intent here is to create a gap between graded or poorly graded soil with significant amounts of clay and coarse sand and only small amounts of silt and fine sand. This is only possible if the soil has the maximum amount of clay possible and the sand is as coarse as possible. This mix is compaction-resistant for lawn applications while still maintaining reasonable water-holding capacity. Intermittent irrigation will still be required for lawns.

A typical mix ratio of sand to clay loam topsoil to high-lignin compost is 5:5:1 to 10:5:1.5. Adjust the mix ratio to obtain the desired infiltration rate (see Table 2.4.2).

ESCS, Soil, and Organic Amendment

Use mixes with higher sand content. These mixes are very compaction-resistant but will require irrigation. The manufacturers of ESCS products are a good source of information on mix ratios (see www.escsi.org). Product porosity and gradation vary from source to source. Most producers have a horticultural products division that researches different applications and soil mixes. Soil mixes that are almost entirely ESCS and organic amendment have been developed. At these rates, the soil is entirely dependent on frequent irrigation and fertilization.

For a typical mix ratio, consult an ESCS manufacturer.

Soilless Mixes

There are many versions of planting mixes that contain no soil at all, which are referred to as soilless mixes. These include ESCS mixes with only organic amendment, all-sand mixes, and all-organic-matter mixes. Each mix has advantages and disadvantages. As organic amendment increases above 10 percent by volume, soil settlement may increase to unacceptable levels. For most applications that include large trees, soil mixes are preferred over soilless mixes.

Consult ESCS manufacturers and local commercial nursery potting medium suppliers for typical mix ratios.

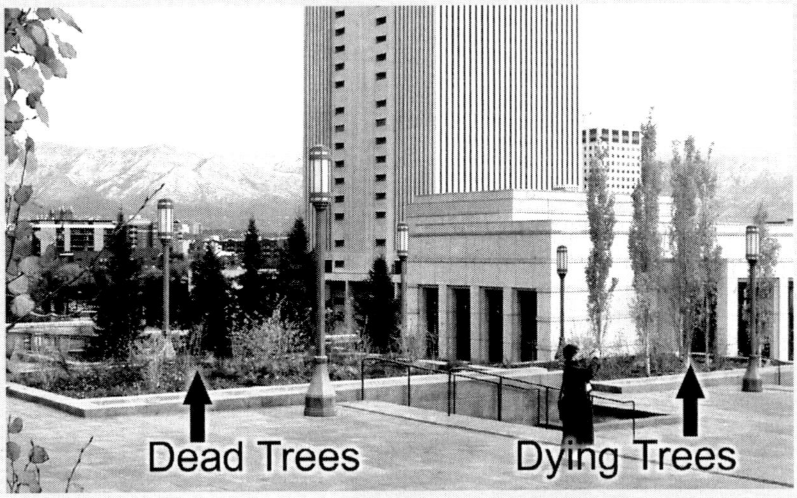

Figure 2.4.58.

a. These Mormon Temple planters were filled with ESCS soil and planted with aspen trees. Only a few have survived.

b. Soil settlement of several inches.

Temple Square, Salt Lake City

Much of the soil in the roof gardens of Temple Square is a soilless growing medium of ESCS and organic compost. The ESCS material was specified as size 3/8 inch minus with 40 percent fines. Compost was added to the top 6 to 12 inches of the planting beds at a rate of about 20 percent by volume. There were problems maintaining plant moisture during the establishment period, tree loss has been high, and soil settlement was observed within a few years after installation due to the depths of the soil and the high organic content in the surface soil.

Roof Plantings

Soil mixes for roof plantings must have better drainage than other plantings. Roof soils are much more reliant on irrigation since they are cut off from groundwater recharge. These soils are more sensitive to over watering, from both bad management and the perched water table that develops at the filter cloth interface. Moving water horizontally is critical in these soils. To overcome too-moist conditions, excess water must move laterally to exit out the vertical drain board at the planter edge. (See the discussion on rooftop drainage later in this chapter.) Typically, mineral-based soil mixes are used, with infiltration rates of at least 2 to 3 inches per hour.

Lightweight Soil Mixes

Often it is necessary to design lightweight soil for rooftop applications to respond to structural limitations. ESCS-based soils are normally specified to reduce soil loading. Lightweight soils are much dryer and hold fewer nutrients than loam soil. These soils also are not as strongly aggregated and do not hold to roots as well as soil-based mediums. Larger trees will not be as stable in these soils as in sand/topsoil-based soil mixes, and leaning trees may be the result in windy locations as the trees mature. Use the heaviest soil possible. (See further discussion on roof plantings later in this chapter.)

SOIL MIX TESTING

Soil Testing and Submittal Scheduling

Allow ample time for multiple testing of different soils and mixes. Each round of testing can take several weeks. Proactively work with the contractor to start soil testing several months before soil installation is scheduled. Do not wait for the contractor to initiate the process. If the mix has not been approved by the date the soil is needed, the owner is not likely to allow a delay just because the landscape architect is not happy. It may be the testing protocol that is compromised.

Testing of Mix Components

Test all mix components, sand, soil, and organic amendments, separately before developing the soil mix design. A slight difference in sand shape and soil textures can make a big difference in drainage rates. Require that a minimum of 2 gallons of each component, including the soil, sand, and organic amendment, be delivered along with each product's testing data. Use the samples to compare color, texture, and consistency with the delivered product.

Test the soil to be used in the mix for texture, including sand fractions, and chemical analysis, including pH. Test organic amendment for completeness of composting and pH. Review manufacturer's sand analysis testing, including sand fraction distribution and Fines Modulus Index. Ensure that sand is free of limestone-based rock. Organic amendment from a low-lignin source such as yard waste compost or material that is not fully composted will create an inferior soil mix.

The tests allow for control of each component and ensure that the several components in the mix, when combined, can meet the requirements. The sand fraction testing of the soil is required to calculate the effect of adding more sand to the soil. In any geographic area, there are wide ranges of soil, sand, and organic amendment. Encourage the contractor to find sources that meet the design requirements. Soils with high levels of silt and/or fine sand will require higher levels of coarse sand to be added, causing the clay content in the mix may drop to unacceptably low levels.

Determining pH of the various mix components is critical. The pH of the final mix will be approximately the proportional average of the pH of the various components. pH is hard to lower, and soil, sand, or organic material with high pH may create long-term problems for the selected plants.

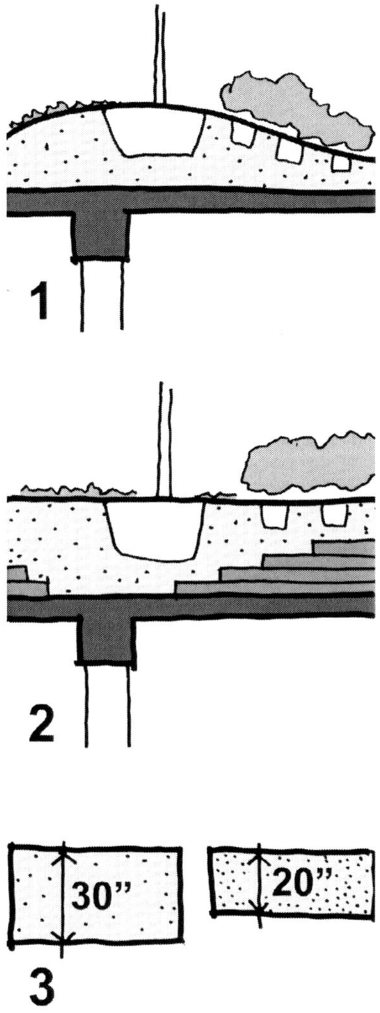

Figure 2.4.59. Alternatives to lightweight soil.

1. Contour soil depths. Move heaviest loads to strongest places.
2. Use EPS foam to contour soil depths from below.
3. Use thinner but heavier soil mixes. Twenty inches of sandy loam will weigh the same as 30 inches of lightweight soil and may grow better plants.

Testing the Soil Mix

Test for infiltration rates with the sample compacted to 80 and 85 percent of dry density. Record the bulk density for the soil at 100, 80, and 85 percent dry density. There are only a few labs in the United States that test landscape soil for infiltration at designated Proctor compaction testing and also provide bulk density measurements at a designated Proctor rate. Having the mix tested for bulk density and Proctor allows the horticulture levels of bulk density to be compared with the engineering data of Proctor.

Infiltration rates determined at 80 and 85 percent of dry density should fall within levels indicated in Table 2.4.2. The bulk density determination will provide a guideline for the upper limit of compaction when preparing the

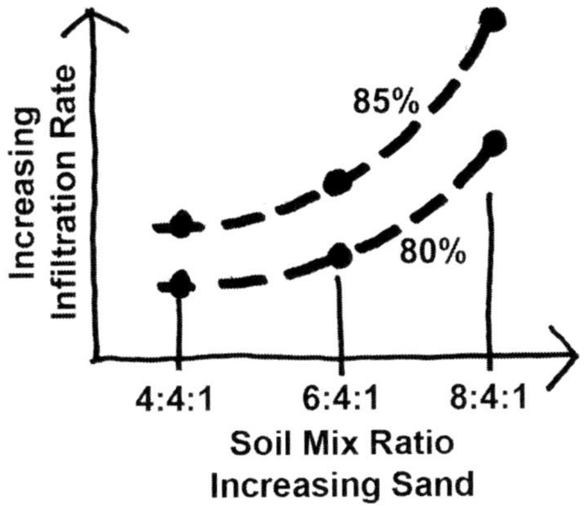

Figure 2.4.60. Soil mix test progression at 80 and 85 percent compaction.

compaction mock-up at the construction site. The Proctor report will also include the optimum moisture for the soil when compacting. This information will help in the evaluation of soil conditions during installation.

Note that for this test, Proctor, not bulk density, is used during the test for infiltration. Proctor can be easily determined in the lab on samples. The developer of this rationale for measuring infiltration, Norm Hummel, owner of one of the nation's premier soil labs, chose Proctor because it allows a consistent measuring point for all soils.

Test the soil mix for chemical composition, including pH, and texture, including sand fractions. These tests record the levels of critical components and can alert the designer to potential problems created by the combination of mix components or to changes in the component sources. Be prepared to determine why pH may be higher or lower than predicted, or to change the mix if the percentage of fine sands is too high. It is not uncommon for mix component sources to change from the first submission to the final mix testing. This may reflect an unavoidable change in supply availability or an intentional switch to a less expensive source.

Soil mix testing is a trial-and-error process. There are too many variables to precisely predict the performance of different sand and soil proportions. Two or more rounds of soil mix testing may be required. The first set of tests determines the infiltration rates with the soil compacted to 80 and 85percent for three different mix ratios. For a hypothetical sand, topsoil, and high-lignin compost soil mix, three sample mixes will need to be tested for example: 4:4:1, 6:4:1, and 8:4:1. If none of the infiltration rates of these ratios is acceptable, the information gained should permit the estimation of a final mix, which must also be tested. Note the logical progression of the mix ratio change in the first series of tests. Using a consistent progression makes estimating the final mix easier.

Table 2.4.3. Soil testing critical path.

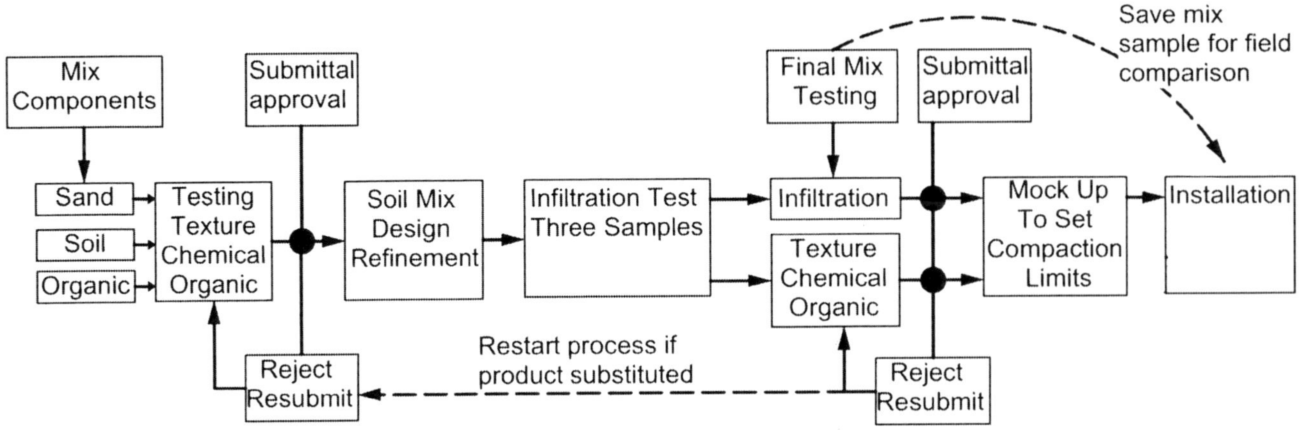

Range of Acceptable Results

The second mix test may be a more precise soil mix to attain specific infiltration results. However, do not burden the contractor with precision that is not relevant or attainable at the construction site. The final mix design should be expressed in whole units, stated simply so that the loader operator can easily remember the number of buckets placed in the mix hopper. Fractional units, except for the organic amendment, may complicate the mixing operation, and rounding sand and soil to whole units reduces the chance of operator error. The mix design recommendations should have a broad range of tolerance and not be so close to the point of failure (too low or too high an infiltration rate) that a little difference in the mix caused by rounding will cause a problem.

Soil mix design is an inexact science. Actual source stockpiles will vary widely from the sample. Infiltration and compaction performance varies with particle shape, size, and other qualities of the parent material. Slight changes in the amount of clay in a mix can cause significant variations in drainage rates. Soil and organic amendment can form isolated balls in the mix and change the mix consistency.

Soil-blending machines are more precise than bucket loaders, but these do not exist in all markets, nor are they available to all contractors. Blending machines should be required where available, but market capability should be checked before they are included in the specification.

The designer should not rely too much on laboratory testing as the sole basis for soil approval. Recognizing the color and texture of the materials by feel will be indispensable in assessing whether a mix design is going to work and whether the product delivered is close to the mix tested. This knowledge is only gained by hands-on experience. Designers must get out in the field, visit the mixing yards, and plunge their hands into soils. They need to be at the site when the soil is being installed to check quality. They must be able to make quick and reasonable assessments in the field as to the quality of the product being delivered. On most projects, there is not sufficient time for the designer to enjoy the luxury of lab testing to make decisions about a mix being installed.

A SAMPLE TESTING SPECIFICATION

The following is a typical specification section for product and soil mix testing.

Submittals—Product Samples And Testing

A. Product Data: Submit manufacturer product data and literature describing all products required by this section to the landscape architect for approval. Provide submittal 12 weeks before the installation of planting mix.

B. Material Certificates: Submit material certificates for all natural and bulk material, indicating that the material meets the requirements of the specification, to the landscape architect for approval. Provide submittal 12 weeks before the installation of planting mix.

C. Samples: Submit samples of each product and material where required by the specification to the landscape architect for approval. Label samples to indicate product, specification number, characteristics, and locations in the Work. Samples will be reviewed for appearance only. Compliance with all other requirements is the exclusive responsibility of the contractor. Delivered materials shall closely match the samples.

1. Submit 2-gallon samples of all topsoil, sand, compost, organic amendment, and soil mix. Submit multiple 2-gallon samples of each topsoil and planting mix that represents the range of quality expected within the source stockpile.

    a. Samples should be labeled to include the type of material and specification number, name, address, and telephone number of manufacturer or supplier, and address of the location of source of the material or material stockpile.

b. Samples of all topsoil, sand, and planting mix shall be submitted at the same time as the particle size and physical analysis of that material.

c. Soil mixes shall be labeled as to the percentage of each component in the mix.

d. Samples of all products and planting mix components shall be submitted 12 weeks before the installation of planting mix. Planting mixes shall be submitted no less than two weeks after the approval of the mix component.

D. Testing Submittals: Submit soil test analysis report for each sample of topsoil and planting mix from an approved soil testing laboratory.

1. The soil testing laboratory shall be approved by the landscape architect in advance and have a minimum of five years experience with the test protocols of the United States Golf Association — Green Section.

2. Testing shall be performed in accordance with the most current edition of *Methods of Soil Analysis* published by the Soil Science Society of America, Inc.

3. Provide a particle size analysis, including the following gradient of mineral content (*Methods of Soil Analysis*, Part 1, Hydrometer Method):

USDA designation	Size in mm
Gravel	+2 mm
Very coarse sand	1–2 mm
Coarse sand	0.5–1 mm
Medium sand	0.25–0.5 mm
Fine sand	0.1–0.25 mm
Very fine sand	0.05–0.1 mm
Silt	0.002–0.05 mm
Clay	<0.002 mm

All soil mixes shall be tested for particle size and organic content after passing through a 1/4-inch sieve rather than the standard 2-mm sieve to include larger pieces of organic material.

4. Provide a chemical analysis (*Methods of Soil Analysis*, Part 3), including the following:

a. pH

b. Percent organic content by oven-dried weight

c. Chemical levels by parts per million, including:

Macronutrients	Micronutrients
Phosphorus (P)	Boron (B)
Potassium (K)	Chlorine (Cl)
Calcium (Ca)	Cobalt (Co)
Magnesium (Mg)	Copper (Cu)
Sulfur (S)	Iron (Fe)
	Manganese (Mn)
	Molybdenum (Mo)
	Nickel (Ni)
	Zinc (Zn)

Nutrient tests shall include the testing laboratory recommendations for supplemental additions to the soil mix for the plants specified and notice of when chemical levels are excessive.

d. Soluble salt by electrical conductivity of a 1:2 soil water sample measured in milliohms per centimeter

e. Cation exchange capacity (CEC)

5. Provide a physical analysis of each planting mix to include the following test results:

   Provide a water permeability analysis of each sample of soil mix ASTM F 1815-97 with sample compacted to 80 and 85 percent of maximum dry density using the standard Proctor method, ASTM D698. Each test shall include the calculation of the bulk density, measured in units of Mg/m^3, for each sample when compacted to 80 and 85 percent maximum Proctor density.

6. All testing will be at the expense of the contractor. The landscape architect may request additional planting mix test on different mix component ratios to attain results that more closely meet the mix requirements.

E. Submit the manufacturer's particle size analysis for all sand and gravel to the landscape architect for approval. Provide the manufacturer's Fines Modulus Index for each sand source.

F. Submit the manufacturer's particle size analysis, pH, and certificate of length of composting period for all compost, organic amendment, and other organic materials. Submit results of the Solvita compost maturity test.

Submit results of all compaction testing required by the specifications including the bulk density test of the mock-up and installed soil, and the compaction testing log of penetrometer and moisture meter readings to the landscape architect for approval.

TESTING DURING MIXING AND INSTALLATION

While it is prudent to randomly test soil mixes during the actual mixing and installation process, the practical reality for most small- to medium-size projects is that there isn't time for this testing. Most of the physical tests require a week or more. There is the additional practical problem that unless a very precise soil-blending machine is used, there will be wide ranges in soil textures as measured by a soil test, even if a reputable contractor is making a good-faith effort to blend with equal consistency. Specifications must accommodate ranges in textures due to this imprecision. Table 2.44 is a list of recommended ranges of acceptable variations from the approved sample.

The best quality control is to have several gallons of the approved mix at the site to check color, consistency, and texture by feel. Someone on the design team should be able to make comparisons with this known sample, as this skill does not take a great deal of training. The requirement for an installation mock-up can also serve as a large-scale quality control sample. (See the discussion on installation mock-up later in this chapter.)

Table 2.4.4. Recommended range of acceptable testing tolerances above or below the approved sample.

Test requirement	Tolerance
Infiltration rate	
0.5–1.5 inches per hour	+/– 0.2 inch per hour
1.5–3 inches per hour	+/– 0.5 inch per hour
3–6 inches per hour	+/– 1 inch per hour
6 inches per hour or more	+/– 2 inch per hour
Bulk density	+/– 0.5 g/cm^3
Proctor density	+/– 2.5%
pH	+/– 0.25 pH units

Figure 2.4.61. Clods of parent soil that did not get mixed with the amendments.

Soil Clods in the Mix

Under normal mixing conditions, some clods or peds of soil and organic amendment will always emerge intact from the mixing process. Small amounts of clods are desirable, and indicate that the soil was not over mixed. Over mixed soil tends to break down the small soil peds, and may be more self-compacting.

Large clods tend to remain when the soil mix is too wet or too dry. Require that mixing occur at optimum soil moisture conditions. Table 2.4.5 is a recommendation for clods in a sand/soil/organic soil mix. Testing for clods is not standard; the designer should use these recommendations as a guide for visual inspection. This limitation of clods only applies to soil mixes. For harvested topsoil that is not amended or only amended on the surface after installation, clods of all sizes are important to maintain.

Table 2.4.5. Maximum clod inclusion in soil mixes.

Clod size (largest dimension)	Percentage of the soil mix volume
Less than 1 inch	Unlimited
1 to 3 inches	20%
3 to 6 inches	5%
> 6 inches	Less than 2%

SOIL MIXING PROCEDURES

Topsoil used in sand/soil mixes must be screened or shredded before mixing in sands. While this breaks down most of the large soil peds, it is necessary to avoid leaving too many topsoil clods within a sand matrix. Large roots, stones, and clumps of plant remains are also removed this way.

Proper levels of mixing and mix design proportions are best obtained using a soil-blending machine that automatically adjusts the mix proportion. For small projects and in locations where blending machines are not available, mixing using a bucket loader with a skilled operator can achieve satisfactory results. When this mixing technique is employed, a mix ratio with a wider range of tolerance is needed. This wider range is achieved in a sand/topsoil mix by increasing the proportion of sand and enforcing the requirement to mix only when the soil is dry enough to allow the soil peds to crumble.

Soil source stockpiles must be protected from rain and groundwater wicking. Covering the stockpile with filter cloth instead of plastic will permit the pile to evaporate water wicking from the ground below, while shedding excess rainwater during hard rain. When mixing with a loader, having the soil shredded or screened improves the consistency of the mix. Soil screens and shredders are readily available.

Once mixed, the soil must again be protected from too much water. The soil mix stockpile will be porous and absorb water rapidly. Cover the final stockpile with filter cloth or store in a covered space.

SOIL INSTALLATION

The following recommendations apply to any type of soil including topsoil stripped from the site and specialty soil mixes.

Work only during periods when soil and subgrade soil are friable. Excavate soil replacement areas with care not to undermine the supporting soil for walks and structures. Maintain a sloped surface of undisturbed subsoil away from these structures.

Relieve compaction in the subgrade soil. (See the discussion on compaction earlier in this chapter.) Sculpt subsoil grades to slope toward drain lines and low points. Water will follow interface gradients and may become trapped in sumps and depressions. Install subsurface drainage lines along low points. Assume that drainage in the subsoil at the end of the project will be slower than the original drainage rates. (See the section on drainage design later in this chapter.)

Prepare the subgrade by roughening the top layer of the subsoil by dragging the teeth of a backhoe bucket across the surface. This process will help break down the interface between the two soil types and disturb subsoil crusting. Begin installing soil as soon as the subgrade is prepared.

Use low-impact equipment with track belts, large tires, or low tire pressure to lower compaction and soil damage. All equipment should be rated for ground pressure of 4 psi or lowere. But low impact does not mean no impact and excess soil compaction will occur in all installations. Use conveyors and cranes to move soil from the stockpile if available. Often, limited site access will require the soil to be dumped in one location and moved by small machines over previously installed soil. Repeated passes in the same location by even a small vehicle will compact the soil to greater than root-limiting levels. Check the compaction in these work areas and be prepared to enforce requirements to loosen soils compacted by the installation equipment.

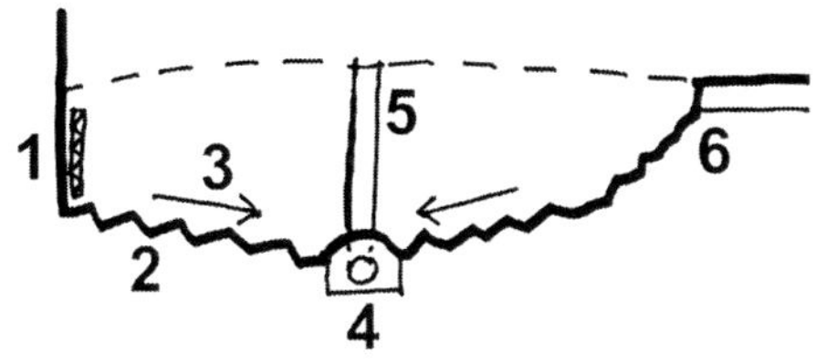

Figure 2.4.62. Subgrade preparation.

1. Drain board against vertical walls, if required.
2. Roughen or till subgrade.
3. Slope subgrade toward drain lines.
4. Drain lines, if required.
5. Drain line inspection riser.
6. Supporting slope for paving.

a

b

c

Figure 2.4.63. Low-impact soil installation.

a. Low-impact soil loader. Despite its small size and track treads, this machine easily overcompacted the soil in places where it made repeated passes and turns.
b. Soil conveyor. *(Photo courtesy Soil Foodweb, Inc.)*
c. Crane delivery. *(Photo courtesy Carolina Staylite Corp.)*

Figure 2.4.64. Soil blowers are not suitable for fine-grained, natural topsoil installation.

Soil blowers are increasingly being used for installations in difficult-to-reach urban sites. The soil must run through a pump that breaks it down into very fine particles. Almost no soil peds remain. There is no research into the impact of this installation method, but it is reasonable to assume that in a topsoil-based material, all structure will be lost. If the soil is a high-sand mix, this method may not be a problem. Soil blowers are a slow way to install soil and thus more expensive than other methods.

Install all soil in layers, called lifts, with each lift between 12 and 18 inches thick. Compact each lift to the density developed during the soil installation mock-up before installing the next layer. (See the compaction mock-up description later in this chapter.) Repeat until the desired soil depth is reached.

In large soil installations where blowers or conveyers are not practical, track loaders must bring in soil. These machines will over compact the soil as they travel over previously installed lifts. Several techniques will help remediate this damage. Use a tooth bucket and always back-drag the bucket over the previous tracks of the machine each time it backs out of the work space. This is effective but time-consuming. The contactor can also till the top of each lift after it is installed, however, the depth of over compaction may exceed the depth of the tiller blades.

A third technique is to install soil, not in lifts, but in bands at full depth, with each band equal to the reach of the loader bucket. This may result in inconsistent soil density and uneven settlement. However, these results may be preferable to over compaction. A hybrid of the two techniques may be the most favorable method for such installations.

If soil is added over the roots of existing trees, see the discussion on soil modification under trees earlier in this chapter.

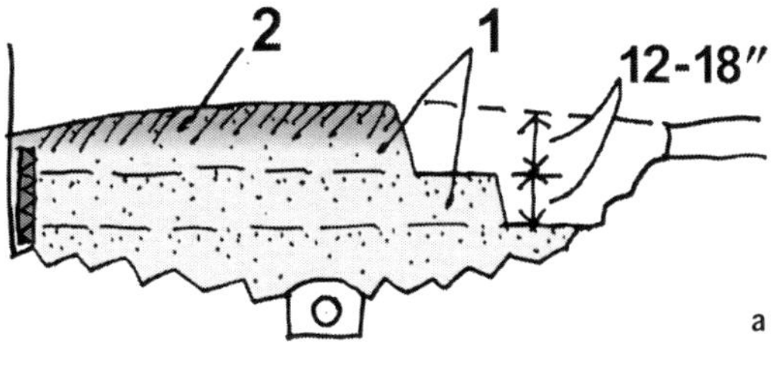

a

b

Figure 2.4.65. Soil Installation.
a. Soil installation
1. B horizon soil lifts
2. Organic A horizon till layer
b. First lift installed and compacted.

Installation of Planting Soil on Steep Slopes

Installation of planting soil on slopes steeper than 3:1 requires steps to protect the stability of the slope. Subgrades on slopes are normally compacted for stability. The sheet of loosely compacted planting soil will absorb and hold water, lubricating the interface between the two different soil types. The wet planting soil can begin to slide along this interface. This risk of failure increases with thicker installed planting soil, larger drainage areas above the slope, and steeper slopes. Slope failure risk also rises in areas of intense rainfall.

Plant roots will eventually bind the soil in place. Slippage of planting soils is most likely to occur shortly after installation, when the soil is still unconsolidated and easily saturated, and before roots have time to become established.

For large slopes greater than 10 feet high, work with the project geotechnical engineer to develop solutions. Local codes may govern slope stabilization requirements. Factors of budgets, soil type, climate, and slope height and angle will impact the options.

Several techniques are available to reduce the risk of slope failure. Several options may need to be used in concert to achieve a workable solution:

- Step the subgrade profile to create a rougher surface. This can be accomplished with the tracks of a dozer for shorter slopes and may require contouring the subgrades for slopes with large elevation changes.
- Reduce the amount of water that reaches the slope by intercepting it with a swale at the top of the slope and a mid slope bench.
- Add soil stabilizer grids to reinforce the soil structure. Consult with the grid manufacturer for sizes and application rates. Soils with stabilizer grids must still have some mechanism to keep the sheet of soil locked into the subgrades. Geogrid layers that bind the subsoil and planting soil together function well, but may be difficult to install. Geoweb cells improve the stability of the slope. They can be stacked to form nearly vertical faces which when planted form living walls or laid parallel to the slope.
- Surface-applied matting designed to reduce erosion does not necessarily reduce the problem of slippage of the soil.

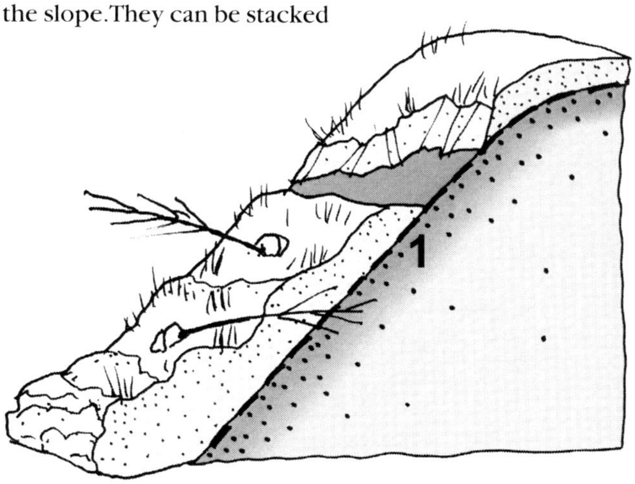

a

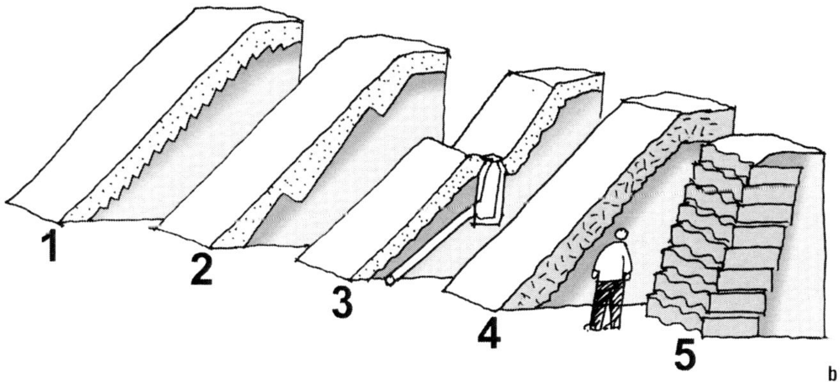

b

Figure 2.4.66. Slope failure and stabilization.

a. Slope failure.
   1. Failure plane between two soil types.
b. Slope stabilization strategies. Different strategies and combinations are more or less applicable as soil types and conditions change.
   1. Track-mark subsoil with dozer to roughen surface.
   2. Step-contour subgrade.
   3. Contour top and mid-slope bench to intercept water.
   4. Add stabilizer grids to soil to improve cohesiveness of soil mass.
   5. Use geoweb cells or geogrids to stabilize extremely steep slopes.

a b

Figure 2.4.67. Compaction equipment.

a. Plate vibrator compactor. One or two passes per lift are usually sufficient to attain compaction in sandy loam soil mixes.
b. Small vibratory roller is too aggressive for landscape soil applications.

Compaction Specification

While existing soil must be treated to prevent or reduce compaction, soil must be compacted during installation. The fact that some compaction is needed is often not addressed in details and specifications. Without it, the soil will not attain the necessary consolidation and support landscape elements. Long-term settlement may be unacceptable. Yet care must still be taken not to over compact the soil. Note that soils compacted to the correct level will still continue to settle due to organic decomposition and natural settlement within the soil section.

The effect of force applied to compact soil spreads out as the force moves through the soil. This reduces the amount of compaction that can be attained at a lower depth. At a depth of 12 inches, the level of compaction is about 10 to 15 percent of the level applied at the surface. Lightweight compaction devices do not cause significant compaction below about 10 inches, and heavy machines will over compact the surface layer if adequate compaction is achieved at deep levels in the soil. This is why the soil must be installed in layers and each layer compacted before the next one is added.

The compaction rate created by certain numbers of passes of a standard machine will vary based on soil type and moisture. In damp, coarse sandy loam, one to three passes by a 20-inch impact-plate vibrating compactor will compact a 12-inch layer to approximately the correct level for planting soil. The exact number of passes will change with soil type, moisture, and speed of the machine. Vibrating machines cause more compaction per weight and pass than drum rollers.

There is little research into the correct compaction rates for installed and graded planting soil. Agronomic soil scientists use bulk density as a common measuring standard. Bulk density is the soil's dry weight divided by its volume, most often expressed as mega grams per cubic meter (Mg/m^3) or grams per cubic centimeter (g/c^3). Note that in metric nomenclature, these two designations give the same unit value for equal compaction: 1.5 Mg/m^3 equals 1.5 g/c^3. There is considerable data on the relationship of bulk density and root penetration of various natural soils. Natural soil compaction rates are discussed in Part 1, Chapter Two. These rates should not be used for soil mixes that contain organic amendments or lightweight aggregates.

Specifying Compaction for Soil Mixes

Compaction rates in soil mixes with organic amendments or lightweight aggregates are not well understood. These amendments change the measured bulk density of the soil without necessarily changing the density of the other parts of the mix. Standard soil testing results cannot factor for these changes. Organic amendments occupy significant space in the soil at installation, but will decay and shrink over time. New research and testing protocols are needed. In the meantime, we must interpret bulk density results and make compaction specifications based on limited knowledge.

Organic amendments have very low bulk density, and most of their volume will dissipate with time. One suggestion for calculating the correct bulk density is to assume that half of the volume of the added organic amendment will be lost, so that the soil bulk density will increase by at least half of whatever amount, by volume of amendment is added. Thus if the organic amendment is 10 percent of the total mix, it would be reasonable to assume that the target bulk density of the installed soil should be the correct bulk density for the natural soil of similar texture less 5 percent. A sandy loam soil, which might be specified to be compacted to 1.55 to 1.60 Mg/m^3, would then be specified at between 1.48 and 1.52 Mg/m^3. The problem of determining acceptable compaction rates in organic soil mixes is easier if organic amendment added does not exceed 10 percent by volume and is high in lignin.

Lightweight aggregates have known bulk densities that do not change with time. It is a relatively linear calculation to determine the drop in specified bulk density of soil after a known percentage of material is added.

An alternate method is to have the mix tested for its drainage rates at 80 to 90 percent Proctor compaction. This test will also provide a bulk density figure to use to set compaction levels.

Measuring Compaction

There are few tools to quickly measure the field compaction rates being attained by contractors during their work. The following are the three most common methods of determining compaction levels and the problems with each method. See the discussion on soil compaction measurements in Part 1, Chapter Seven. Each method if used in concert with the others may offer meaningful ways to check compaction at the installation site.

Proctor tests are difficult to undertake, requiring specialized equipment and analysis of the soil before testing. This protocol is designed for engineers, and planting soils have not been researched to determine acceptable Proctor rates. Nuclear densiometers give unreliable results in soil with organic matter greater than 5 percent. They generally show the soil compacted to a density between 5 and 15 percent higher that the actual density. Densiometers also can only look at the density between 6 and 12 inches below the surface. To get deeper readings, one must dig a pit to operate the equipment.

Penetrometers, which measure resistance to a probe, are useful for determining relative compaction differences of similar soils. These devices allow rapid compaction testing as the contractor works, but the measurement data is sensitive to changes in soil moisture and soil type. A penetrometer can examine soil compaction to depths of approximately 24 inches.

Bulk density is the standard for arboricultural data on compaction. However, the test protocol using an undisturbed core sample takes a minimum of 24 hours to complete and only a few samples per work area are practical to extract. Bulk density tests to look at the results of different lifts and different locations would be time-consuming and require multiple days of testing.

Compaction and Soil Installation Mock-Up

A solution to the compaction specification dilemma is to build a soil installation mock-up for each type of soil. The contractor, in the presence of the designer, installs a small area of the required soil, say 100 square feet, at a compaction level that the designer determines is adequate to reduce settlement but still allow root penetration. Methods used in this small installation, including lift depth and number of passes by the selected compacting device, are recorded and made the standard for the project.

Undisturbed bulk density samples of the mock-up soil are tested. To save time, the designer can do this testing with a small investment in equipment, as described earlier. Measuring bulk density in the office will allow a one-day turnaround of results.

The mock-up must be in an area that will not receive any construction traffic during the period of soil installation. Areas that might receive significantly more or less moisture during a rain should be avoided. Once the bulk density of the mock-up is verified and correct, a penetrometer can be used to verify that the soil being installed in other locations is a close enough match to the mock-up. Assuming that moisture levels in the mock-up and the installed soil are similar, penetrometer readings made in the mock-up and the soil should be similar. This allows the contractor or designer to monitor the compaction rate during the work.

If a mock-up is not possible or a penetrometer not available, a less precise compaction specification may be appropriate. Instruct the contractor to compact each lift sufficiently to reduce settlement, but not to the point where the soil resists root penetration. Several functions of soil compaction can be observed. The soil at the top of each lift should imprint only shallow heel marks. Soil should drain at a minimum of 1 inch per hour when compacted, although sandy soil mixes will drain at a relatively rapid rate even when over compacted. A tube soil probe inserted into the soil should meet moderate resistance. When inserting the probe, the slightly higher compaction at the top of each lift should be felt, and each lift should get progressively stiffer. A sudden and significant increase or reduction in soil resistance is an indication that the contractor has over or under compacted a lower lift.

On a large project where densiometers are already available, they may be used if the readings are calibrated to the mock-up soil.

SAMPLE COMPACTION MOCK-UP SPECIFICATION

A. Prior to the installation of soil mixes, construct a mock-up of each soil type at the site. The installation of the mock-up shall be in the presence of the landscape architect.

B. In an area of one of the site planters that can be protected from disturbance and further compaction, install an area of soil 10 feet × 10 feet × 30 inches deep, using the requirements of these specifications, including the installation of the organic amendments tilled into the top of the soil column. Compaction methods, including the type of compaction equipment and number of passes required to achieve the required compaction rates, shall be evaluated and results measured. Compaction results shall be tested in a soil testing lab for bulk density, calculated by determining the oven dry weight to volume of undisturbed samples taken by a 2-inch-diameter × 6-inch-long core tube sampling tool. A minimum of four samples shall be taken and the results averaged. The mock-up shall also be tested using a nuclear densiometer per standard Proctor method ASTM D698.

The results of the bulk density by sample and the densiometer shall be compared. The landscape architect shall resolve differences in the two measuring systems and set values for final compaction levels based on the data obtained from the mock-up. The intent of these specifications is to reconcile the differences between the readings of the densiometer and results of bulk density by sampling in organic soils.

C. The mock-up shall be tested with a cone penetrometer and a soil moisture meter. A series of four readings shall be made at the same time as the core samples are taken. The percentage of water in the soil shall be determined at the time of bulk density testing. The results of all test sites shall be averaged.

D. In the event that laboratory testing does not confirm the required level of compaction, the mock-up shall be reconstructed, adding to or subtracting from the level of compaction force applied, until satisfactory results are achieved.

E. Submit a report of the successful compaction methods and the results of all compaction testing to the landscape architect as a record of the approved compaction methods.

F. The mock-up shall be protected during installation of the remaining soil and used to calibrate penetrometer readings. The mock-up area may remain as part of the installed work at the end of the project provided that it has not become overly compacted or the soil contaminated.

Figure 2.4.68. Extreme soil settlement in a planter with too much organic matter.

Soil Settlement

It is impossible to compact organic soil enough to eliminate soil settlement without over compacting the soil. The exception to this is high sand soil mixes. Organic amendment decays, gravity and water fill pore spaces with fine sediment, and erosion washes away soil from the surface. The greater the amount of clay, silt, or organic amendment, the greater the amount of expected settlement. If there is very little settlement, the initial compaction was too high.

Soil mixes often contain too much organic amendment. Adding more than 10 percent by volume to a soil will increase settlement as the organic amendment decomposes. Note that organic amendment by volume is not the same as organic matter content in a soil test. A rough rule of thumb is 10 percent by volume of well-composted organic amendment increases soil organic matter by about 1 percent by dry weight when tested. This is because the soil test is only looking at the dry weight carbon after ignition. Also, the protocol for testing soil begins by screening the soil to eliminate gravel fragments and any compost fragments larger than 2-millmeters. This eliminates much of the compost volume from the sample. When a soil mix is tested, request that the sample be screened with a 1/4-inch screen, not a 2-millmeter screen, to increase the amount of compost included in the test.

Settlement of installed planting soil is a serious problem that is often ignored. Surface drains cease to function, while foundations and rough surfaces that were originally covered with earth become exposed. Building waterproofing is exposed to sunlight, lawns shrink below the adjacent paving to create tripping hazards, and lights, trees, paving, and other objects in the landscape tilt out of plumb and level. Settlement of six to nine inches is not uncommon. At Dan Kiley's famous North Carolina National Bank Plaza in Tampa, Florida, soil settlement contributed to the need to demolish the design.

Figure 2.4.69. Soil settlement was a significant factor in the demise of this Tampa landscape icon.

Make clear on the drawings at what point in time the soil depth and grades are being depicted. Set final grades of installed soil higher than the desired design grades to allow for future settlement according to the following schedule:

- Turf with high sand/low organic amendment soil mixes: almost no settlement
- Turf with loamy sand soil: less than half an inch per foot of installed soil depth
- Sandy loam soil: half an inch per foot of installed soil depth
- Sandy clay loam and loam soil: 1- to 1-1/2-inch per foot of installed soil depth
- Clay loam soil and any soil where greater than 10 percent by volume of organic amendment has been added: 2 inches or more per foot of installed soil depth

Designers have two options for depicting future grades. The first is to show the depth at installation and then design the grading plan to reflect the finished grades as higher than the desired grades based on expected soil settlement. This option places a burden on the designer to anticipate the correct amount of settlement. If the soil specification changes, the grading plan must be redrawn. The second option is to draw the grade contours to reflect the grades after settlement and then require the actual installed grades to be higher than the design grades, based on soil type and compaction desired. This option allows a relatively easy change in instructions if contract conditions change, but requires much more diligence on the part of the designer during the field inspection phase. If this option is used, sections should show two finished grades, pre- and post-settlement.

Regardless of the way final grades are set, predicting soil settlement is very unreliable. Soil will continue to settle and erode over time. It is almost always better to have a bit more soil, with planting and lawn areas slightly more mounded above adjacent walls and pavement, than to have them sink too low.

New approaches to rain water management using bifiltration areas are dependant on precise grades to make the hydrology work. Soil settlement can change the hydrologic function of the system and must be accounted in the design.

Organic A Horizon Layer

Add organic amendment and any chemical amendments recommended by the soil test to the surface layer after placing the soil. Lightly till amendments into the top 4 to 6 inches. Avoid extreme cultivation that breaks down the soil into very fine particles. Adding local leaf and yard waste compost to the top of the soil profile, especially in non-lawn areas, creates the functional A horizon in a soil mix.

Hard-to-establish trees and shrubs may benefit from the introduction of specific soil organisms. Adding small amounts of leaf duff or soil taken from successful plantings of similar species will improve the plant specific species of the soil food web in the organic layer. Obtaining the source material for this practice takes planning and dedication on the part of the designer and contractor. It is an easy practice to discuss but difficult to implement, and more research is needed in this area.

Final grades of soil tilled with leaf compost will rapidly settle to the pre-tilling grade. Set the tilled grades higher than desired to allow for settlement. Use these recommended depths of organic amendment as a rough guide to creating an A horizon layer in several soil types:

- For non-lawn areas, 4 inches of leaf compost.
- For lawn areas, 2 inches of a high-lignin organic amendment.
- For high sand mixes in turf areas designed to experience compaction, do not add organic amendment. Use washed sod to reduce the clay content in the A horizon. Be aware that this will require constant watering and fertilizer after installation.

Post-Installation Soil Biology and Chemical Testing and Adjustment

Several months after the soil installation, test it again for chemical properties, including pH to determine if further adjustments are needed.

Develop a chemical and/or compost tea and organic-matter additive program to bring pH and nutrient levels into balance, based on the test results and the plant types in the soil. Appropriate organic amendment and compost teas, rather than processed chemicals, can modify some imbalances.

pH cannot be permanently lowered. If pH needs to be adjusted downward, several applications of sulfur based-chemicals will be required each year for the life of the project. Continuous application of chemicals to lower pH will have negative side effects including increases in the soil of aluminum to plant toxic levels. Where possible, change the plant types rather than the soil pH.

Test soil chemistry and biology parameters on a regular basis as part of maintenance to ensure that the soil is balanced with the plant needs.

Specialized soil labs, such as Soil Foodweb, Inc., can determine the levels of the four critical soil biological indicators of bacteria, fungi, protozoa, and nematodes. These labs will make recommendations for soil additives that can restore the balance using compost teas and organic amendment. Compost teas to increase biological processes should be applied during the first year after soil installation. The initial testing and use of compost teas should be required by the soil installation specifications. Repeated soil testing and applications of compost tea and organic amendment should be required as a part of site maintenance.

Testing and adjusting soil biology to improve plant performance is a relatively new practice in commercial maintenance. It requires commitment by the property manager for success. Results of organic adjustments may take longer than chemical additives, but with fewer environmental side effects. In large commercial landscapes, such as Battery Park City in New York City, organic maintenance practices have been demonstrated to be cost and results competitive with chemically-based maintenance.

Protection

Once the soil is installed protect it from compaction, erosion, and contamination after installation. Use mulch, mats, temporary seeding, and access restrictions as you would with the soil preservation requirements discussed in the previous chapter.

SOIL DRAINAGE

Drainage is critical to successful soil improvement. Poor drainage can cancel all the previous hard work to improve other aspects of the soil.

Evaluate and Estimate Changes to Soil Drainage

Make a thorough evaluation of existing surface and subsurface drainage patterns, as indicated in Part 1, Chapter Seven. Note rates of wetting and drying in existing soils, and predict changes to drainage patterns and rates caused by construction.

Figure 2.4.70. Saturated soil at the curb line within the tree planting area. If drainage is not added, these trees cannot survive.

The steeper the slope, the more the soil will dry out. South-facing slopes greater than 15 percent, north-facing slopes greater than 20 percent, and all slopes in sandy soils will dry out sooner. Areas flatter than 2 percent will stay wetter longer. Areas where subgrades have been subjected to compaction will drain more slowly.

Check for soil crusting caused by silt and lime-based material on the surface of the subgrades. Areas used for storage, mortar mixing, stonecutting, and concrete truck washouts during construction are vulnerable to poor drainage. Crusting on the surface of subgrades will slow or stop the percolation of water out of the planting mix. Remove or break up the crusting layer immediately before adding planting mix.

New walls, pipe installations, and fills can modify subsurface flows, making areas wetter or drier than conditions were prior to construction. Expect seepage from the bottom of deep-cut slopes.

Watch drainage patterns during construction. Visit the site when the foundations have been excavated to observe subsurface soil and drainage conditions. Observations made several days after a heavy rain can reveal problem areas. Notice which areas the contractor has used for access and storage, meaning they are likely to be compacted. Contractors rarely follow predictable patterns when establishing means and methods to build a project. Confirm compaction assumptions, and modify soil and drainage plans during construction.

Prepare drainage plans based on worst-case assumptions. It is fairly easy and cost-effective to add a drainage system in the design phase and take parts of it out at the end of construction if the site appears to drain well. If drainage assumptions are wrong, it is almost impossible to add a drainage system to a project once most of it is built. A specification requirement that says merely "The contractor shall notify the landscape architect in the event that soil drainage is not adequate" is an unacceptable approach to drainage design.

Surface Drainage: Modify Rates of Wetting and Drying

Drainage begins with water infiltrating the soil at the surface. Modifying soil wetting and drying properties is the most cost-effective way to improve drainage. Design grades to reflect the soil type, its underlying drainage situation, solar orientation, and types of plants to be grown.

Too Much Water

Large areas of newly installed or cultivated soil will absorb water more rapidly after installation and become saturated during periods of wet weather, while the adjacent soil remains relatively dry. The absorption rate will drop as the soil consolidates and roots fill the upper layers. Where excess water may be a problem, slope paved areas away from planting soils and

Figure 2.4.71. Water seeping out of a slope predicts soil drainage issues for this site.

mound the surfaces to reduce the amount of water that infiltrates the soil. Use curbs on the edges of planting beds to reduce the inflow of water. Established plants can dry out soils rapidly, and are of great value in reducing moisture in silty and clay soil.

If drainage is slow, use water-tolerant plants. However, there are limits to how effective plant choice can be at overcoming poor drainage. Just because a plant may grow in wet soil does not mean it can be removed from a well-drained nursery bed and planted into a hole surrounded by saturated soils. If drainage is poor, plant the tree on a slight mound so that it can grow roots over the wet soil as it becomes established. Once a tree is established, seasonal differences in groundwater, combined with the tree's ability to dry out the soil, may be enough to permit growth.

Most of the plants that are considered wet-tolerant are river-bottom species. In their native environment, the soil may be moist for a portion of the year and even flooded periodically for several weeks or even months. In many naturally wet areas, soil moisture and floodwaters may contain significant amounts of oxygen. Poorly drained urban soil may be saturated for long periods of time with stagnant water that is anaerobic (devoid of oxygen). Few river-bottom species can tolerate anaerobic conditions. It is critical for the designer to recognize potentially anaerobic conditions.

Sloping the soil in any planting space is the best assurance of good drainage at the surface and promotes rapid plant establishment. The greater the clay content in the soil and the more slowly the subsoil drains, the steeper the grades need to be. The greater the sand content in the soil, the flatter the grades can be. Table 2.4.6 indicates slope recommendations for adequate drainage in different soils.

Surface drainage inlets. Use surface strip drains in swale bottoms of poorly draining soil to improve plant growth, especially near inlets. Connect the strip drain into the inlet

Figure 2.4.72. Mounding to create soil volume and improve drainage results in mature trees. Note lean responding to prevailing wind, indicating that soil was not cohesive enough to provide support.

Table 2.4.6. Minimum slope recommendations to improve drainage.

Soil type	Use	Minimum slope
Soil with greater than 30% clay content	Swale flow line	2%
	Lawn	3%
	Planted beds	10%
Soil with less than 10% clay content	Swale flow line	1%
	Lawn	1.5% (soils with less than 5% clay can be flatter if there is sufficient subsurface drainage)
	Planted beds	5%

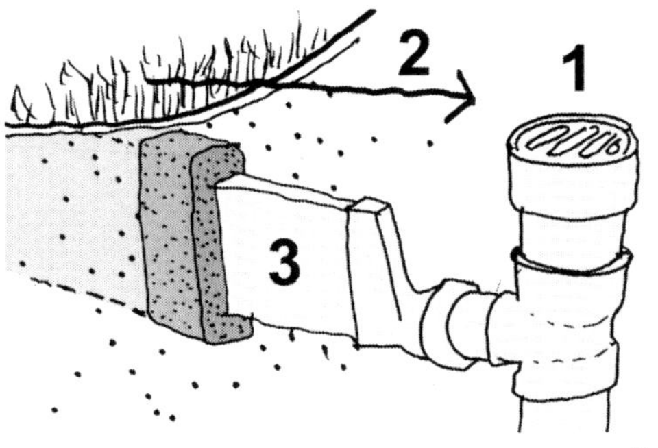

a

b

Figure 2.4.73. Improvement to slowly draining soil where water collects.
a. Add strip drains in swale bottoms.
1. Inlet.
2. Swale flow line.
3. Strip drain in sand or gravel bed.
b. Strip drain by American Wick Drain Inc.

at an elevation below the plant root zone. Soil saturation can occur around inlets when they are located at the low points in flat drainage areas. The soil around the inlet receives water at very low flows during almost all rains. This water tends to seep into the soil, especially in areas where soil has been installed and not adequately compacted. Large areas can become saturated before the drain begins to function. The inlet rim should be set low enough to direct water into the drain and account for soil settlement.

Sand is often added to the soil to improve drainage. This will not work unless there is enough coarse sand to bring the coarse- and medium-sand content to more than half the soil volume. These requirements are almost impossible to meet without removing the soil. (See the discussion on mineral soil mixes earlier in this chapter.) Incorporating ESCS products at a rate of 25 percent by volume, or high-lignin organic amendment at a rate of 10 to 15 percent by volume, are better ways to improve surface drainage in heavy soils.

Rainwater Management

Rainwater designs that attempt to recharge or filter storm water may deliberately bring more water to the planting soil than can be tolerated. Designers of these features must have a thorough understanding of planting soil infiltration and subsoil percolation rates. Subsoil will normally drain more slowly after construction, and newly installed planting soil will drain more slowly after it has settled or become filled with roots. On the other hand, as plants become larger, they will draw more water out of the soil in the spring and summer.

Trees can be an important part of any rainwater management system, but should not be located in the wettest part of the system. Plant trees on the edges of depressions or on slight mounds so they can adapt to the wetter conditions.

Rainwater features, particularly in urban areas, generally try to push the maximum volume of water through the soil. The soils in these features are often on the edge of becoming anaerobic. Always provide the largest soil volume possible as the best defense against overwhelming the system. Because subsurface drainage rates are likely to be slow, it is best to design a subsurface drainage system. If a drain system is provided and the soil is not overly compacted, the planting soil can be reasonably well-draining sandy loam soil. Over compaction may be the primary cause of failure of these features.

If a subsurface drain system is provided, the system will only provide quality control (retention) but not quantity control (detention). This is because the subsurface drain pulls too much water out of the macropores during the first 24 hours after the rain event. A hybrid system would provide the subsurface drain system at the midpoint in the soil section. Soil water below the drain lines would be considered as detention while the water above the line is retention. The upper soil will dry down soon enough to permit the tree to become established. As the tree matures it will be able to utilize the lower soil volume as its transpiration functions dry out the slower draining soil below the subsurface drain lines, improving the efficiency of the system.

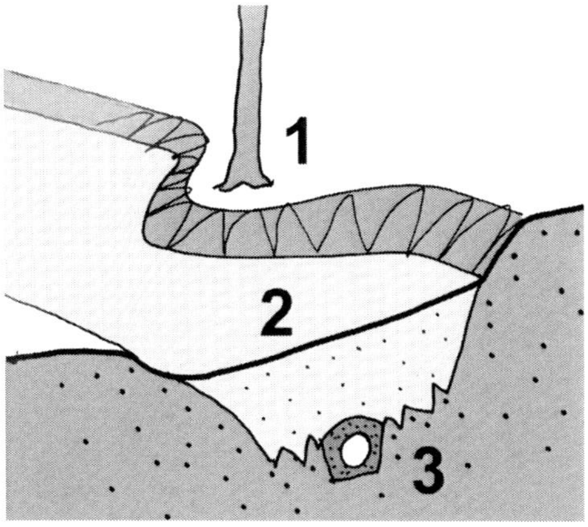

Figure 2.4.74. Tree soil and rainwater management features.

1. Locate trees on edges, slopes, or mounds.
2. Use large volumes of low-compacted soil.
3. Provide a subsurface drainage system.

Too Little Water

Dry climates or sites with sandy soil may need more water in the planting soil. To improve soil water levels, slope paving toward planting areas. Flatten grades, and set planting areas in low points. Increase the soil-wetting and water-holding capacity by adding organic amendment to the soil surface, and use mulch on top of the soil to reduce evaporation. Polymer gels can be mixed into the soil to reduce the frequency of irrigation. Check the polymer manufacturer for the amount to be added and the projected longevity of the gels.

When the design requires steep south-facing slopes, utilize particularly drought-resistant plants, reduce the slope angle, and improve soil-wetting and water-holding capability in the slope area with compost.

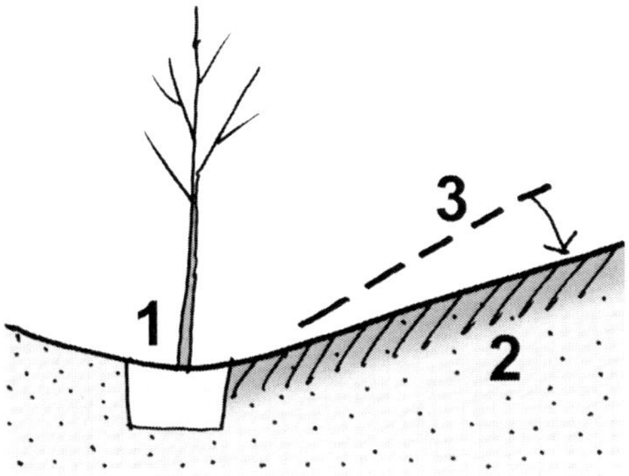

Figure 2.4.75. Dry sites and too little water.

1. Plant in low spots.
2. Improve water-absorbing and water-holding capacity of the soil.
3. Flatten slopes.

Subsurface Drainage

Subgrade drainage must be assured. If the design team assumed at the beginning of construction that subgrade soil would have adequate drainage, they must check this assumption before installing any planting soil. Observe how the subgrade drains during construction. Any subgrade areas that are wet for more than a day after a large rain event should be assumed not to have adequate drainage. If unsure, dig a hole 12 inches deep and 10 inches in diameter at the low point in the subgrade. Pour water into the hole and let it drain down. Then refill the hole and measure the rate of fall in the water in the hole. If it drains at less than 1/2 inch per hour, consider changing your drainage assumptions. Where possible, install drain lines that have a positive flow outfall either to a storm drain or to a lower grade.

Dry Wells

There will be situations where the subsoil does not percolate fast enough and it is not possible to find a gravity drain outfall for a perforated line. Drainage improvement may only be needed temporarily until a newly installed soil area consolidates, plants become established, and soil surface infiltration rates slow. Dry wells may be the only option for improving drainage in situations where the topography is flat or the site lacks storm sewer outfall options. As soil conditions approach critical percolation levels, predicting whether they may or

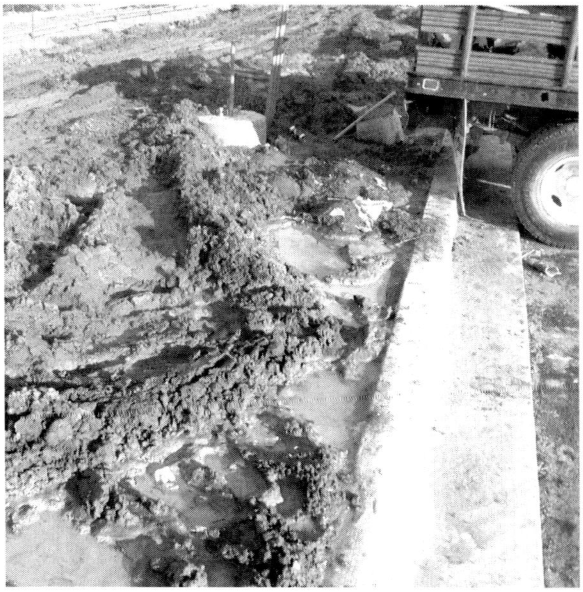

Figure 2.4.76. A site that drained well before construction now is fully compacted and holding water.

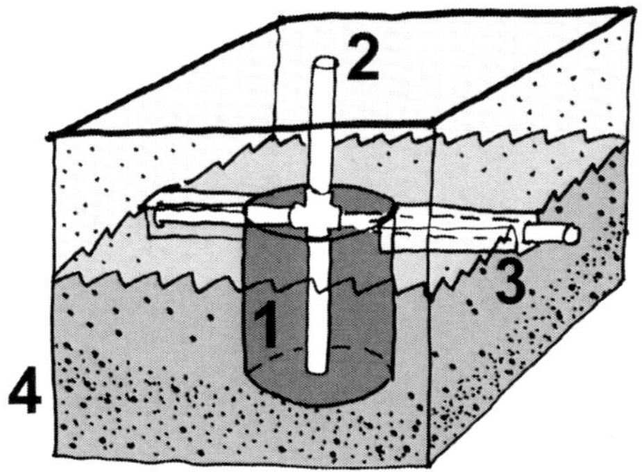

Figure 2.4.77. Dry well to drain planting soil. One per tree.

1. Gravel-filled dry well as deep and large as possible. Three feet in diameter by 4 feet below planting soil is a reasonable minimum.
2. Vented riser to surface.
3. Connect dry wells together with drain lines.
4. Dry wells are most effective if they extend to a more pervious layer.

may not drain well is difficult. Dry wells are relatively inexpensive, compared to other drainage strategies, and may be a cheap solution or the option of last resort to improve marginal conditions.

In urban areas, especially cities with combined storm and sanitary sewers, there may be prohibitions on connecting subsurface drains to storm sewers. This issue sometimes can be negotiated by explaining how these systems function. Healthy, well-drained planting beds slow the flow of surface runoff and even out the peaks in the runoff. The planting soil must become saturated before the drainage system begins to slowly release the water. Plant stems and foliage absorb the first portion of the rain event, up to the first tenth of an inch. Organic amendment on the surface and in the soil will absorb chemicals in the runoff. There may be a concern that excess nitrogen may leach out of the soil. Healthy soil and plants should require less fertilizer, and more of that nitrogen will stay in the soil if it has a healthy soil biology.

Three factors will determine the effectiveness of a dry well: subsurface soil percolation rate, volume of the drywell, and its depth. The percolation rate of the soil is set by the soil type and compaction rate. In urban areas, the percolation rate may increase with depth, because either the compaction rate decreases or a relatively more pervious soil type lies below a less pervious subgrade.

Larger dry wells have a greater surface interface area with the surrounding soil than small ones, allowing more water to pass into the soil. Dry wells with greater storage volume can hold more water at lower elevations between rain events, reducing the time that the planting soil remains saturated. As the dry well increases in depth, the pressure on the water at the bottom of the well increases, increasing the rate of water flow into the soil.

Under optimum conditions, increased porosity of the lower soil level, combined with the added water pressure and expanded water-to-soil interface area, is enough to drain the collecting water from the planting soil above.

Thus, it will be helpful to make the dry well as large in diameter and as deep as possible. Consider constructability issues—how deep and close to objects can excavations go? Dry wells 3 feet in diameter and 4 feet below the level of the lowest drain line are the minimum size to have an effect. Deeper, narrower designs can function well if site information reveals porous layers at significant depth and equipment to make the hole is able to access the site. Multiple small dry wells can be more effective than one large one. Two 3-foot diameter dry wells have 60 percent greater surface percolation area than one 4-foot well of equal depth. In compacted urban soil, a minimum of one dry well per tree may be required.

Include ridged, perforated schedule 40 inspection riser pipes from the bottom of the dry well to the surface. This allows inspection of groundwater elevations, and in marginal situations permits the well to be pumped during periods of seasonal high water.

Pumping out excess seasonal water may be a useful measure during the first few years while the tree is becoming established, but is not a sustainable option in locations where permanent soil water may be expected.

Dig dry wells with a backhoe or by hand, and ensure that the sides of the hole are irregular in shape and not glazed. Dry wells in clay soil dug with a power auger may not function if the auger glazes the side of the hole. Avoid using augers in fine-grained soil. Dry wells can be any shape and function better if they are irregularly shaped. Fill dry wells with large, even-size stone or gravel; #57 stone or larger is preferred. A layer of coarse sand or small pea gravel at the top of the dry well can be an effective filter for the soil above. Do not use filter cloth between the stone and the soil around the sides of the dry well, as it slows percolation. If really large stones are used to fill the hole, a transition layer of smaller-size gravel between the large stones and the filtering medium may be needed on the top of the well.

Connect subsurface drain lines to the dry well to collect water from the planting soil. Where possible, interconnect dry wells with the drainpipe. If one well fails to percolate, the others may be able to pick up some of the water.

Improving Drainage Without Drain Lines

Subsoiling will improve the impact of poor drainage on the success of the tree. A series of sand, stone or compost-filled trenches in the subgrade will increase the surface area of the excavation available to percolate water between the planting soil and the subsoil. An outfall for the drain line may be accessed by employing a directional boring machine to reach a lower point otherwise blocked by topography, paving, or distance. Limiting the area that can drain into the bed and increasing the runoff from the bed by mounding or grading can reduce the amount of water entering the soil. Trees can be planted on mounds and water-tolerant trees can be specified.

Normally, any one of these options will not provide sufficient change in the drainage balance to make the difference. However, employing many techniques together can make the difference between success and failure. Note how many of the options involve changing fundamental design decisions. Drainage is a design constraint and implies that the designer considers existing and proposed drainage conditions at the concept design phase.

Newly placed, unconsolidated planting soils have very high drainage rates. This can be an advantage unless the soil is in an excavated depression that does not drain. If lack of drainage is or may be an issue, disturbing the soil to incorporate amendments or to improve the soil quality may not outweigh the increase in water absorption that is a by-product of soil improvement. Reusing the excavated soil may be the best approach to poorly draining soil where some excavation is required to break compaction. The existing excavated soil will be similar in texture to the surrounding soil, and water drains more rapidly between soils of similar texture.

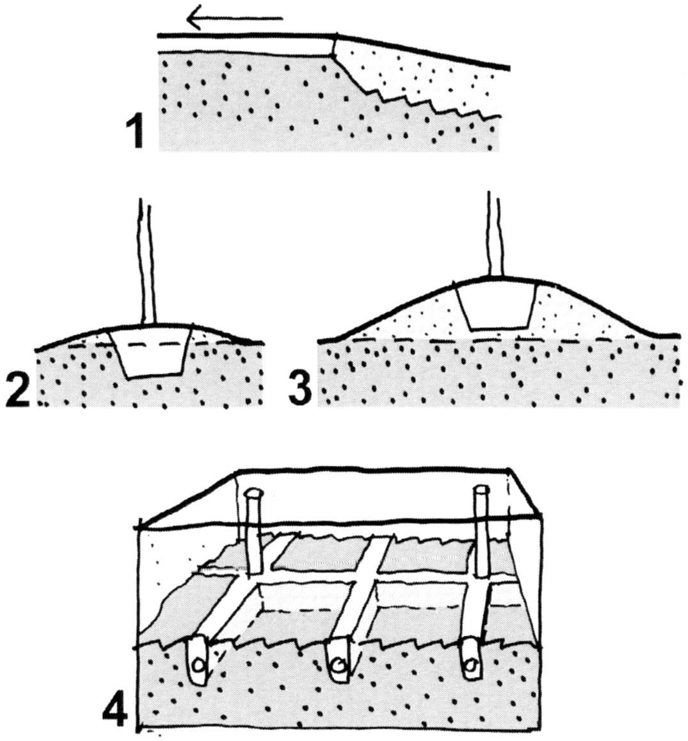

Figure 2.4.78. Improving drainage situations where drain lines with positive outfall are not possible.

1. Slope paving away from planting areas.
2. Slight mounding of tree planting in marginal situations.
3. Large mounding of tree planting in difficult situations.
4. A series of sand-filled percolation trenches 4 to 6 feet on center with vented risers can be more effective than dry wells, but are more expensive.

Subsurface Drainage Lines

Perforated drain lines remain the most reliable method to remove water from planting soils. They must be designed with an understanding of soil hydrology.

It is far cheaper to include a drainage system in the initial bid drawings that to have to add it at the end of the project. By the time an observer recognizes that a drainage problem exists, most of the walls and paving may already be in place, making it impossible or expensive to connect drains to logical outfalls. If drainage is found not to be a problem, removing the system and requesting a credit from the contractor is relatively painless.

Drain lines only remove water that drains by gravity from the soil. Gravitational water is that portion of the water that is in macropores and channels large enough that capillary action cannot resist the weight of the water. In fine-grained clay loam and silt loam soil, where these soils have lost their structure or become compacted, there may be little gravitational water and just adding drain lines may not significantly improve drainage. Drain lines also depend on horizontal flow in the soil to move water to the line location. Spacing of drain lines must be closer in fine-grained soil than in coarse-grained soil. The movement of water from soil into a drainage system is slow under the best of circumstances. Even in sandy soils, water will not cross the interface into the pipe until the soil above is entirely saturated. Water will move horizontally to saturate soil for great distances before it will cross this interface. (See the discussion on water movement in soil in Part 1, Chapter Two.) Once the water pressure in the soil is sufficient to push water across the interface, the surface area of the interface still restricts the flow. In the case of drain lines, the surface area is only a small percentage of the soil perimeter.

Filtering systems at drain lines. Current drainage design standards typically use perforated, corrugated, plastic lines in a gravel bed wrapped in a filtering fabric, also known as a geotextile. In some specifications, the pipe is wrapped in a geotextile. These designs may not be the most effective, since geotextiles can clog. Once this happens, the system stops working and cannot be fixed without digging up the line.

Geotextiles act as an additional soil interface, slowing down the percolation of water from the soil into the drainage system. With the exception of rooftop applications where sheet drain boards are necessary, the use of geotextiles in soil drainage systems is discouraged in favor of sand-based filtering mediums around the pipes. (Drain board systems are discussed later in this chapter.)

Until about the mid-1970s, drainage systems used a filtering sand material to keep soil fines from entering the drainage system. This way, when the pipe clogs, it can be cleaned without digging up the entire system, provided the designer has remembered to add cleanout risers to the system. The interface between the soil and the filtering medium is less distinct than that of a geotextile, so water moves out of the soil faster. Sand-filtering materials allow water to percolate through without bringing excessive silts into the pipe. Coarse sandy gravel and concrete sand filters are effective in most soil types.

Whatever the filtering material, the contact surface area, with the soil and the percolation rate across this interface, controls the rate at which water will move out of the soil. Wider filter beds, especially in fine-grained soil, improve the drainage rate.

Specify pipes with holes or slots only on the bottom. Slotted perforations are more compatible with sand bedding material. If cheaper, corrugated pipe that has perforation on all sides is used, taping a strip of plastic sheeting on top of the pipe will reduce sedimentation buildup in the pipe. Pipe should then be bedded in a coarse concrete sand trench 12 inches wide and 10 inches deep. Note that no filter cloth is included in this detail, nor is gravel used around the pipe. Both of these form strong interfaces between the soil and the drain, slowing the drainage rate. Filter cloth can become clogged, stopping drainage.

Drain line specifications. A crushed pipe is the most common failure in a drainage system. The typical single-walled plastic pipe is relatively weak. Urban construction sites require higher-strength pipes because of the potential for damage during installation. Commercially available perforated pipe comes in a variety of strengths. Double-walled corrugated pipes offer a combination of strength and flexibility, allowing for alignment changes to avoid the many obstructions in an urban landscape. Ridged, perforated schedule 40 pipe is the strongest available, but it is expensive to install, requiring glued joints and turns made with elbow fittings.

Drainage pipes are available with slits or holes, with slits being preferable. Slit size should be small enough to stop the filtering medium from entering the pipe. Pipes with openings only on the bottom are preferred to pipes with openings on all sides. This way, water can only enter from the bottom of the pipe, and more likely to be held in suspension and flow out of the pipe provided it has enough slope.

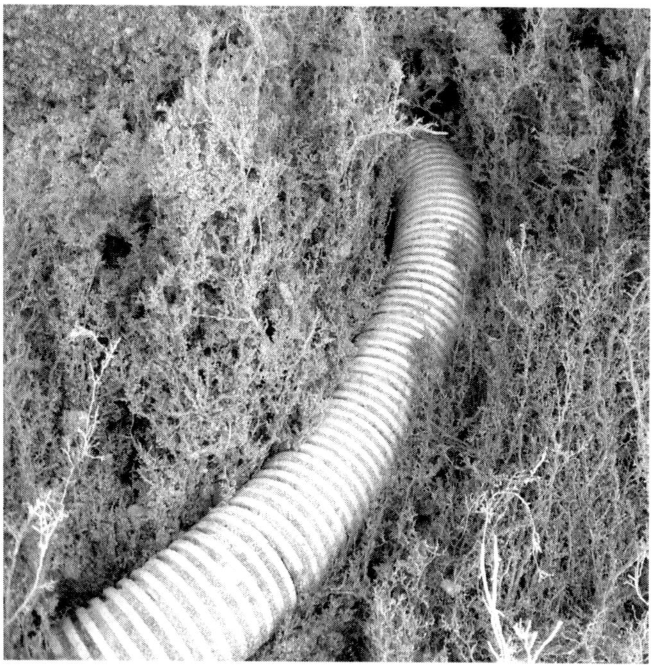

Figure 2.4.79. Drain line in sandy loam planting soil completely engulfed in roots. There was limited silt and root penetration into the pipe, despite the absence of filter cloth.

Besides being less likely to be crushed during construction, double-walled pipe is smooth on the inside, which reduces clogging. Smooth-walled pipes can be set flatter than pipes with a corrugated interior. When pipes are specified with holes only on the bottom, inspect frequently to be sure the pipe is laid correctly.

Whichever pipe is used, require that all joints be solid. Require taped, reinforced joints for corrugated pipe and glued joints for PVC pipe. Drain lines should be bedded in filtering material to support the pipe bottom.

If the drain line passes under a walk, the pipe should be changed to a solid line with no perforations. If water can exit the pipe in these areas, it can undermine the pavement's subgrade material. Also specify solid plastic sleeves when lines must pass through walls. They are also a good addition when drain lines pass under walks. Sleeves should be one pipe size larger than the through pipe. Sleeve locations need to be indicated on the design drawings.

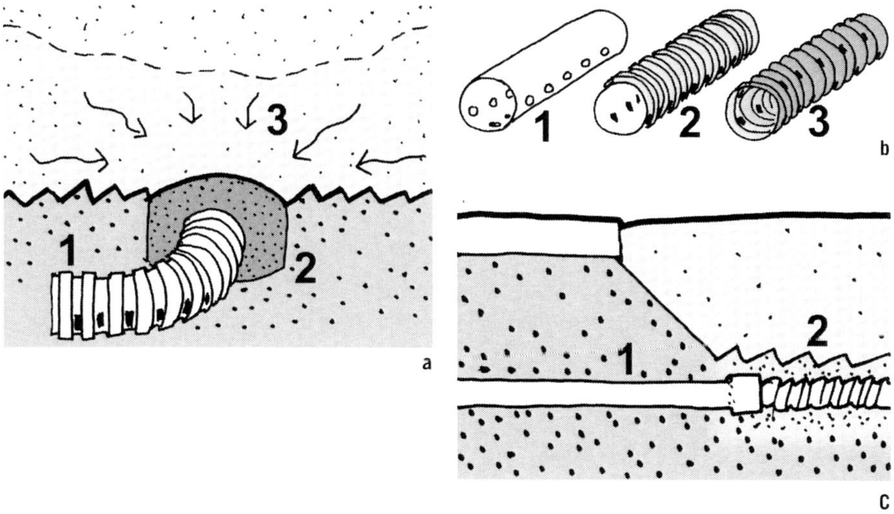

Figure 2.4.80. Drain lines.

a. Drain line detail.
   1. Perforated drain line with holes on the bottom.
   2. Coarse sand filter a minimum of 12 inches wide and 10 inches deep.
   3. Only gravity water flows into the drain line, and only once the soil above and beside the line is saturated.

b. Drain line options.
   1. Rigid smooth wall PVC pipe (strongest but also most expensive).
   2. Corrugated double-walled PVC pipe (preferred).
   3. Corrugated single-wall pipe (too weak for most urban uses).

c. Drain line under walk
   1. Solid PVC pipe in compacted soil bedding under walk.
   2. Drain line in sand bedding.

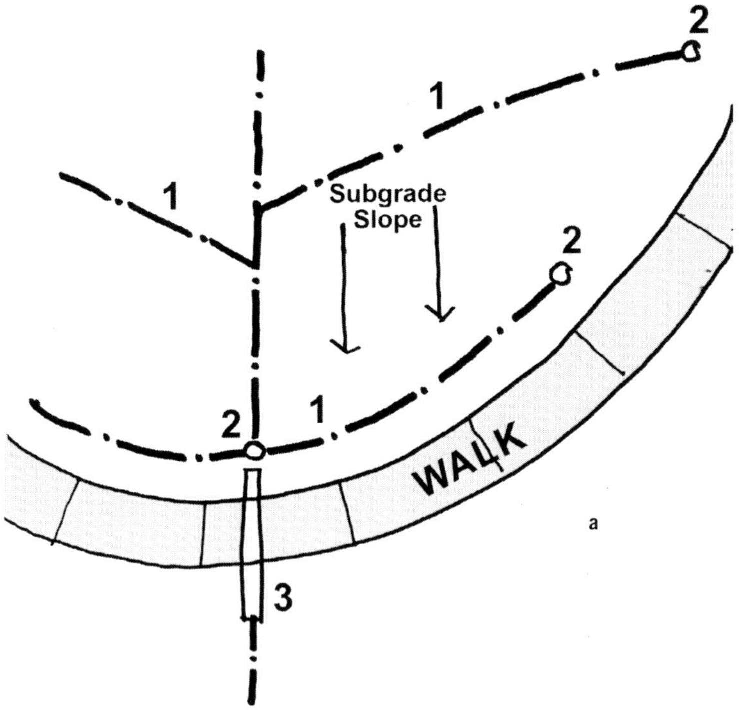

a

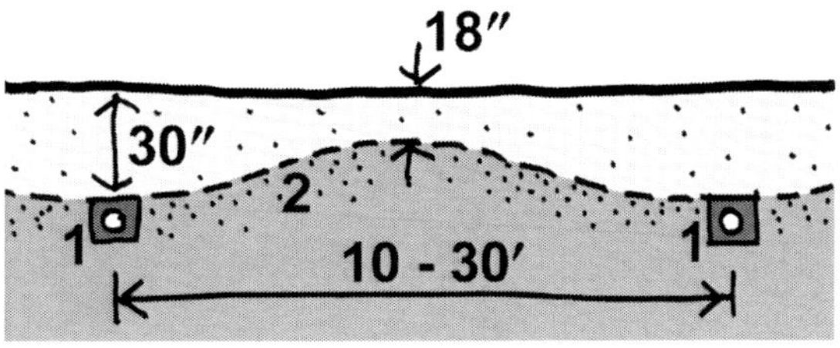

b

Figure 2.4.81. Drain line layout

a. Drain plan.
   1. Drain line slope at 1.5 percent.
   2. Cleanout risers.
   3. Soil pipe under walk.

b. Section.
   1. Drain lines.
   2. Mound of saturated soil after initial drain-down.

Drain pipe layout. The standards for layout and spacing of drain lines are largely derived from agriculture, where large areas of land must be drained for crops with relatively shallow root systems. Spacing is based on balancing the cost of pipe installed to the crop yield expected.

At urban sites, drainage becomes more critical, and buildings, paving, and walls disrupt the soil horizons. Urban soils are likely to have highly compacted subgrades and perched water tables. Irrigation is common, and over irrigation is a threat on every project. Design standards should emphasize positive soil drainage and redundancy of drain lines to the point of over draining the soil. Too much drainage will never remove more water than the soil's field capacity.

Start drainage layouts with a line that runs parallel to any obstruction to the water flow along the subgrade planting soil interface. Intermediate drain lines in large areas should branch off this line, spacing the lines to quickly remove water from the top 18 to 24 inches of the soil. The line of removed gravity water will mound between the drain lines after the initial drain-down. Over time, this water mound will dissipate. The mound is higher and steeper in fine-grained soil than coarse-grained soil. To obtain a meaningful lowering of saturated conditions in fine-grained soils, drain pipes may need to be placed as close as 10 feet on center. In coarse-grained soil, drain line spacing may be up to 30 feet on center.

Set pipes just below the interface of the installed soil and the subgrade. For areas where only the surface soil is being modified, set the tops of drain lines about 30 inches deep. Shallower pipe depths will require closer pipe spacing. Align pipes to be roughly parallel with the contours of the subgrade-planting soil interface, so that the pipe is sloped downhill at slightly more than the minimum slope for the type of pipe being used. In areas of installed soil, drain lines must be set below the bottom of the installed soil.

Slope pipes at a minimum of 1 percent toward the outfall. Pipes can be laid almost flat, but will tend to silt-in faster. Rigid, smooth-walled pipes, while more expensive, can carry water at flatter slopes and tighter tolerances. Flexible, corrugated pipe is less expensive to purchase and install, but should not be installed at slopes less than 1.5 to 2 percent.

Connections to storm water systems. Drain line connections to a storm water system are best made at an inlet or manhole. Cut a hole in the structure and secure and seal the pipe with mortar. The pipe invert should be set above the elevation of the top of the storm drain lines connected to the manhole to keep water from back-flowing into the drainage system during storm events. "Field connections" can sometimes be made directly into the storm pipe. Engineers are less likely to approve field connections. The drainpipe must always be connected on the top of the pipe. The requirement to connect into the inlet or pipe at an elevation higher than the main pipe may mean that the invert of the drain line is too high to function adequately.

Design and calculate precise pipe inverts and slopes for all subsurface drain lines and inlet connections. This is a critical engineering task that is part of the soil designer's responsibility, not the civil engineer's. It should not be the installing contractor's job to calculate slopes and inverts. Do not show just a typical detail section to indicate that drain lines are added to the project. Urban drainage systems are too complex and too much is at stake to assume that the contractor will get it right in the field.

Drain line information gets lost when included on the same drawing as the planting plan. Draw a soil and drainage installation plan that is separate from the planting plan. Show drain lines, inverts, connection points, risers, and outfalls. When drain lines transition from a deeper planting bed soil to a thinner lawn soil, ensure that the details show the transition and the proper elevation.

Cleanouts and inspection risers. Install drain line cleanout and inspection riser pipes at the uphill ends of each drainage line and periodically along the pipe. An inspection riser at the low point in the soil subgrade is useful for troubleshooting. Inspection risers should be a solid schedule-40 pipe tied into the drain line, with an elbow connection at the line end or a Y-connection at a midline connection. Require metal or plastic screw caps on all cleanouts and inspection risers. A small amount of grease applied to the threads of the cleanout will permit easy removal after installation. The cleanouts will be visible and their location, particularly in lawn or paved areas, must be considered in the design.

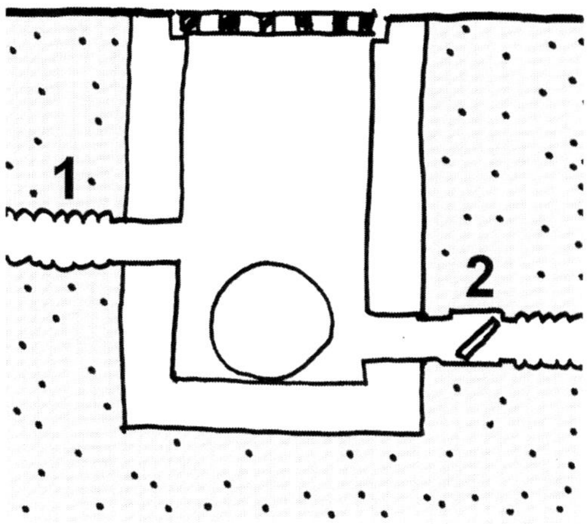

Figure 2.4.82. Drain line connections at inlets.

1. Inverts of drain lines are normally above the top of the pipe in an inlet.
2. If the drain line must be below the top of the pipe, a backflow preventer may be required.

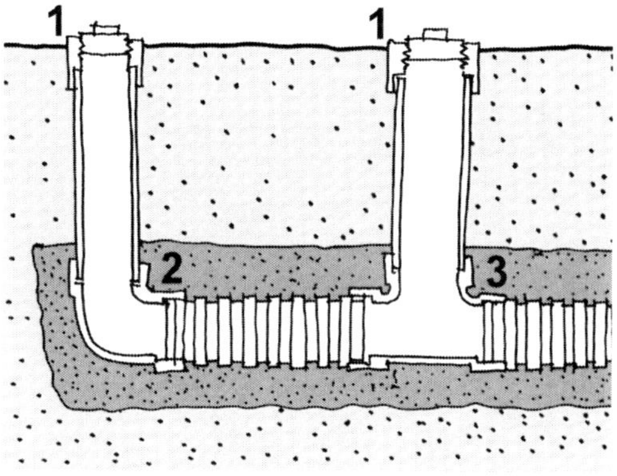

Figure 2.4.83. Drain line cleanouts and inspection risers.

1. Screw caps.
2. Elbow fittings at line ends.
3. T fittings at midline.

ROOFTOP PLANTING

In dense urban spaces, the only place to put plants may often be on top of buildings and other structures. Small planting areas enclosed by walls and footings may have no connection to subsurface soils and drainage patterns should be considered similar to rooftop planters. These conditions require constructing a positive method to remove soil water. In these landscapes, failure of the drainage system is almost always fatal to the planting and expensive to repair.

Prevent these problems by engineering effective drainage systems. Specialized soil mixes must be designed to be compatible with the drainage design and allow for long-term water management. In

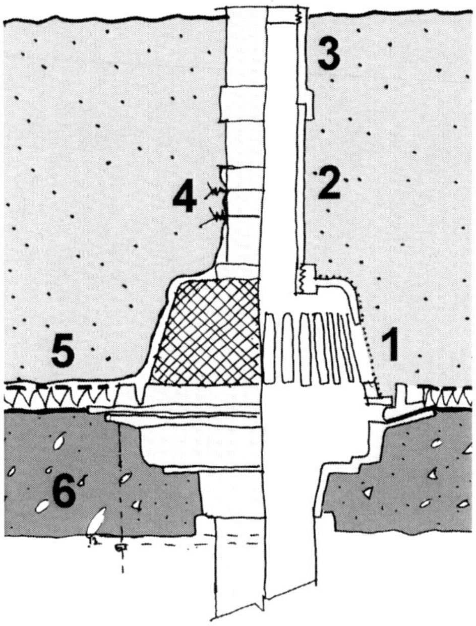

Figure 2.4.84. Planter drain (SQ-2-2490 by Jay R. Smith Co.) collects roof water, is compatible with most major waterproofing systems, and has inspection and cleanout capability from above. Surface drain systems can be connected to the 4-inch riser.

1. Drain body.
2. Inspection riser.
3. Cleanout cap or drain grate.
4. Geotextile connection to riser.
5. Geotextile and drain board.
6. Concrete structure.

most cases, the soil provided is the only soil the tree can access, which requires careful calculations of soil volumes. Finally, the roof must be able to support the weight of the soil and the anticipated weight of mature plantings.

Rooftop soil and drainage design requires close collaboration with the rest of the design team. Establish clear boundaries of responsibility with regard to liability. A reasonable division of responsibility is for the architect to design and document the structure up to and including the waterproofing, protection board, and the drains in the bottom of the planter through the waterproofing. The planting designer should design and document the planter drain board, filter cloth, soil, and grading including any surface drains. If surface drains connect into the lower planter drains, coordination is required to ensure that the transfer of responsibility is clear.

Rooftop Drains Below the Soil

Rooftop drains should have rims that tighten down on the waterproofing material. Often these drains terminate under the soil with a domed grate. This leaves the drain concealed under the soil, inaccessible for inspection or repair. Figure 2.4.84 shows a type of planter drain that permits a riser pipe up through the soil to allow inspection and cleanout of the drain. Note the way the drain board and the filter cloth meet the drain.

Drainage and Ponding on the Roof Surface

The building architect may accept more water to pond over the membrane than is acceptable to the designer of the planting soil. Coordination with other design team members is critical.

Roofs to be covered by planters are often designed by the architect with minimum or even no slope. Roof structures under planting areas should slope at a minimum of 1 percent toward the roof drains. Planters that drain to the edge of the foundation wall are acceptable. Overlaps in the waterproofing and protection board, pipes and objects on the surface of the roof can create small dams. Upturned beams can create bathtubs and the architect may not provide a drain in each one. Each drain requires a penetration of the membrane, a potential leak point, so the architectural team will try to reduce the number of drains. Careful study of architect's drawings is needed to find potential drainage issues. Water deeper than 1/2 inch may create saturated area within the planter soil. Specify tolerance for maximum allowable water depth at 1/4 inch.

Weep holes may be provided by the architect through obstructions that are adequate to drain most but not all of the water. Weep holes are almost never set flush to the bottom of the roof deck, creating shallow ponds in the planters. A series of larger drainage openings rather than weep holes are needed to let water drain under a wall. Design these spaces 4 inches or more wide by 4 inches high, with the bottom of the opening flush with the top of the adjacent structure. The large size is needed to allow application of waterproofing material inside the space.

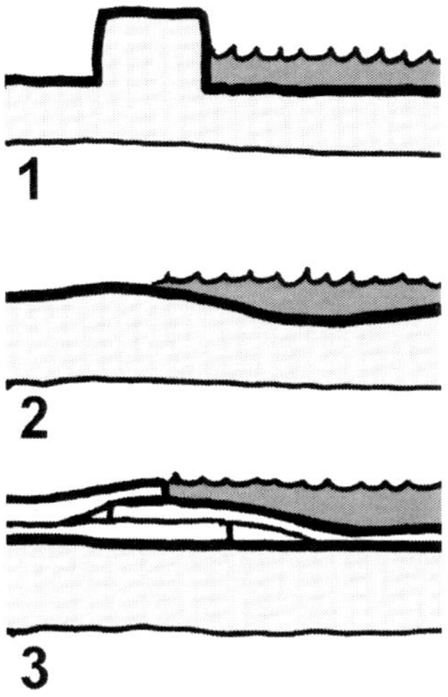

a

b

Figure 2.4.85. Drainage problems on rooftop planters.

a. Water ponding within planters is often not critical to the building design, but will create drainage problems for the plants. Allow no more than 1/4 inch of standing water.
   1. Upturned beams.
   2. Flat roof slabs with uneven surfaces.
   3. Overlapping waterproofing and protection board layers.

b. Standing water in a planter, the result of failed planter drainage conditions. All plants in the planter eventually died from too much water.

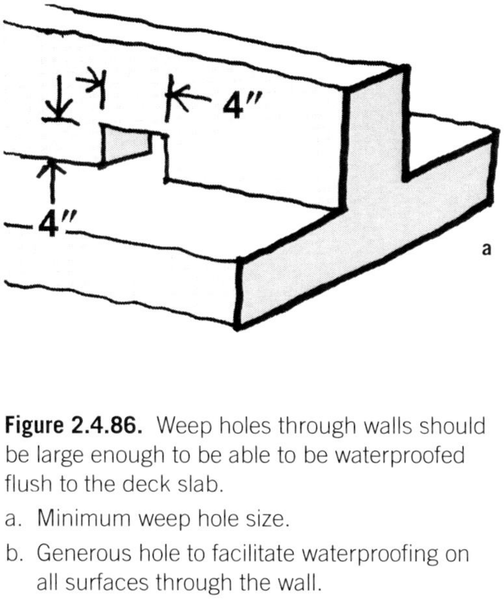

a

b

Figure 2.4.86. Weep holes through walls should be large enough to be able to be waterproofed flush to the deck slab.

a. Minimum weep hole size.

b. Generous hole to facilitate waterproofing on all surfaces through the wall.

Minor ponding, while not critical to the roof designer, can be fatal to the plants. Finding and fixing these minor water problems often falls to the planter designer.The planting soil designer must review architectural drawings to determine that the plans accommodate positive drainage from the roof surface. Request changes in the design drawings where needed to solve problems. Roof work inside planted areas usually is not built to the same tolerances as the parts of the structure that are more visible. Even though the drawings may suggest positive drainage, ponds may still occur.

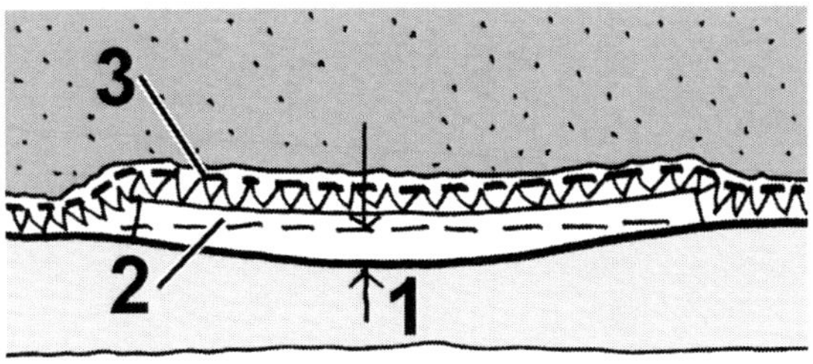

Figure 2.4.87. EPS to lift drain board out of water.

1. Water depth greater than 1/4 inch.
2. EPS foam board.
3. Drain board and geotextile.

Require a water test of the roof slope to ensure that no puddles were inadvertently formed during construction. The tolerance for the depth of standing water above the roof should be half the thickness of the drainage board or 1/4 inch. In any areas of the roof where there is unacceptable standing water, apply a layer of EPS foam under the drainage board to lift it above the water.

a

b

Figure 2.4.88. Determining whether water is trapped within planters.

a. Water testing slab. When the drains are opened, the site designer can use this test period to check for trapped water.
b. Trapped water, the result of an improperly constructed weep hole.

Waterproofing Systems

There are two common systems suitable for waterproofing a planter: a hot, fluid-applied, rubberized system and sheet membrane system. Each system has advantages and disadvantages. Asphalt, cement paints, and spray-on applications are not adequate for use with a planting soil system. The building architect should make all decisions regarding the waterproofing selections.

Hot, fluid-applied, rubberized systems are applied in place and are better for unusually shaped spaces. The fumes from installation may make them inappropriate for application over occupied buildings. The rubber is considered to have some amount of self-healing properties as the subsurface cracks or the material is damaged. Leaks are more likely to be expressed near the location of the problem and may be easier to locate. Fluid-applied systems terminate easily at the top of the planting soil and may be stopped just below the planting soil level. These systems are dependent on the quality of workmanship for their integrity.

Sheet membrane systems are made of large sheets of impervious, flexible material, fitted with the seams sealed in place. Membranes require a secure termination onto the wall. This termination system is often a metal bar bolted through the membrane into the wall. The termination bar is best placed below the soil line. The location of the termination bar must be carefully coordinated with the planter grades.

If a leak develops in the membrane, water may enter the building in a location far from the actual leak. The integrity of the system is dependent on the skill of the person sealing the joints, and how well the membrane is protected after installation.

Ensure that the design of the waterproofing and roof drains is compatible with the drainage system. Some roof membrane suppliers require proprietary drain boards, which may be adequate for the roof system but too thin for planting soil drainage. As a choice of last resort, install a second drain board layer over the required roof drainage system.

Soil installation can damage the membrane if not protected. Assure that the waterproofing system includes protection board over all vertical and horizontal surfaces. The protection board is an integral part of the waterproofing system and must appear in the waterproofing documentation. If not included in the system, the soil designer should make a case for its inclusion. Root barrier membranes have been added to some waterproofing system to keep roots from damaging the waterproofing. The waterproofing company may require these additional membranes.

Drain Board Installation

Plastic core drainage boards, a minimum of 1/2 inch thick, such as Miradrain G series (www.mirafi.com) or Enka drain (www.colbond-usa.com), are the standard method of draining planting mixes over roof areas. Enka drain material is very flexible and is the better choice for small and curved planters. It comes in several thicknesses, and it is important to use the thicker 0.8-inch material. Install drain boards over all vertical and horizontal surfaces within the planter. Adding drainage to the vertical surfaces has been shown to improve root penetration within the soil and provides redundancy for the horizontal drain board in the event of a clog in the filter cloth. Maintain the top of the drain board between 3 and 6 inches below the soil line.

Apply drain board to all walls, whether or not the soil is over structures. The drain board boosts the rooting value of the planting soil volume behind the wall by creating an airspace along the wall surface. Significant root growth will follow this airspace.

Preventing Soil and Root Penetration of Drain Board

Install an additional layer of woven filtering geotextile over the drain board in rooftop applications to prevent soil and roots from penetrating into the board. Most drain boards come with a geotextile already attached. However, drain boards are only about 36 inches wide, and the attached geotextile overlap is only about 3 inches wide. The overlap has been shown to be inadequate to stop small amounts of soil and roots from entering the drainage core. This can be fatal to the drainage capability of the roof. The extra layer of woven geotextile prevents this problem.

Woven geotextiles normally come in rolls 12 feet wide. The wider material allows for fewer joints with greater overlap. A 12- to 18-inch overlap is recommended between sheets of geotextile. Secure overlaps with tape during soil installation. The geotextile should also be folded over the top of the vertical drain board to reduce the amount of soil that enters the drainage system.

Woven geotextiles are recommended. They resist clogging, the most common cause of drainage failure. Selection of the geotextile must be made with the knowledge of soil type and the manufacturer's recommendations. Reputable manufacturers will provide technical assistance to make the correct fabric selection.

Figure 2.4.89. Drain board and geotextile installation.

a. Apply drain board to the bottom and sides of planters.
   1. Drain board. Stop drain board 3 inches below soil surface.
   2. Woven geotextile to cover joints in drain board.
   3. Fold geotextile over top and down backside of drain board.
   4. Overlap pieces of geotextile 12 to 18 inches.

b. Drain board and geotextile applied with correct overlaps.

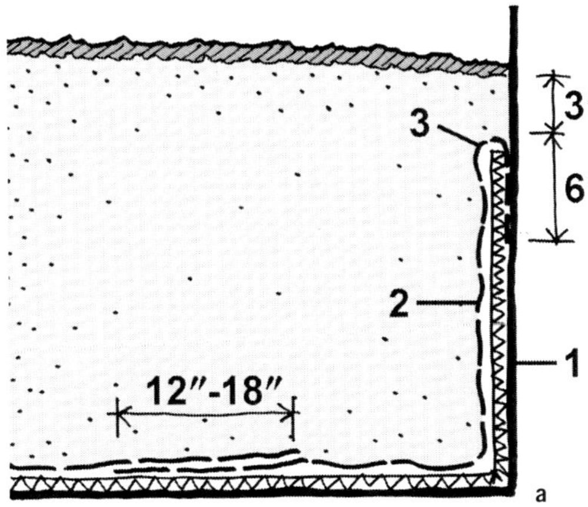

a

b

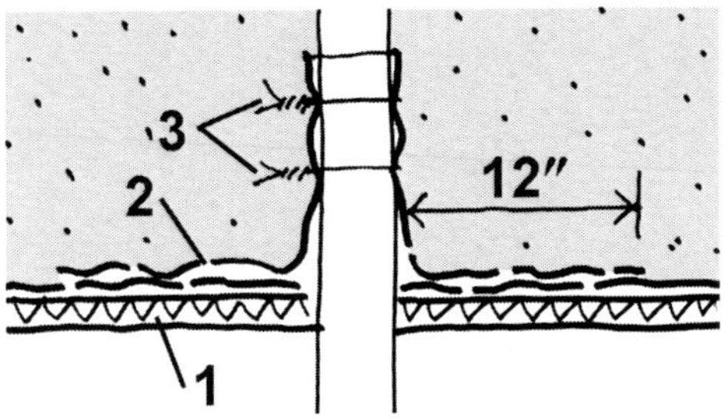

Figure 2.4.90. Extend geotextile collars around all pipe penetrations through the drain board.

1. Drain board and geotextile.
2. Geotextile collar.
3. Secure collar to pipe with two wire ties.

Pipe Penetration of Drain Board

Soil movement into the drain board can block drainage. Seal all penetrations in the drain board and geotextile. Roofs will have many pipes, conduits, and other interruptions of the drain board. Make collars of geotextile and secure them to the pipe with copper wire or plastic ties. Overlap any openings in the cloth by a minimum of 18 inches. Extend the woven geotextile over the top of the drain board and tuck it into the backside of the exposed vertical face to keep soil from washing into the drain board.

Soil for Rooftop Planters

The preferred soil for rooftop applications is a sand/soil/organic soil mix described earlier. Adjust the sand in the mix to achieve an infiltration rate of 2 to 3 inches per hour. Use a higher rate for lawns and lower for planting beds. The greater the soil depth, the lower the acceptable infiltration rate may be as gravity will pull water from the upper soil levels. Avoid soils with an infiltration rate of less than 1 inch per hour.

It is often assumed that a rooftop application must use lightweight soil. This is not always the case, and designers should request that the heaviest soil possible be specified. (See discussion on soil type earlier in this chapter.) In a building still in the design phase, it may be reasonable to simply make the structure a little stronger to accommodate the additional weight of good soil, which normally is 110 - 120 pounds per cubic foot when saturated. Products that lighten soils can be too well drained, require more much irrigation and fertilizer, or fail to have enough cohesion to support large trees.

Figure 2.4.91. Roots that grew through a 6-inch-deep section of soil. This soil later eroded away, revealing the waterproofing below. The roots are still viable.

Soil Depth

The soil depth requirements for rooftop plantings are similar to the minimum soil depth requirements for other installations discussed earlier in this chapter. Set the depth by determining the soil volume needed to grow the desired trees, then divide that over the area available for soil. Theoretically, a large tree can grow in a thin soil section provided that there is adequate irrigation, soil volume and enough soil right at the tree to install the root ball and get the tree established. Soil depths away from the root ball location can change, and the tree will respond to the change in soil shape. The absolute minimum depth to expect tree roots to transverse is likely about 6 inches if there is additional rooting volume beyond the thin soil area.

Varying Soil Depths and Subsurface Conditions

Often soil depths will vary dramatically as the below-grade structure elevation responds to the architectural program and above-grade elevations respond to site design requirements.

Soils of different depths will be reflected in the growth rates of plants over time. Soil depth changes will appear as lines of growth difference. This is particularly evident in lawn and ground-cover beds, where difference can be seen in just a few years after planting. Trees will take longer to change, but the long term effect will be more dramatic and harder to mitigate.

Where possible, try to incorporate these changing conditions into the design as a change in surface treatments to mask the difference. One of the most difficult situations is where an underground building may end in existing soil that will remain in place. Making the transition point dissimilar to the building footprint helps. Carrying the rooftop mix as far into the landscape as possible and tapering the depth of the mix can diffuse the line. If the rooftop mix is a lightweight ESCS-based soil, make a transitional mix in part of this area by increasing the topsoil ratio in the soil between the roof and the natural soil beyond.

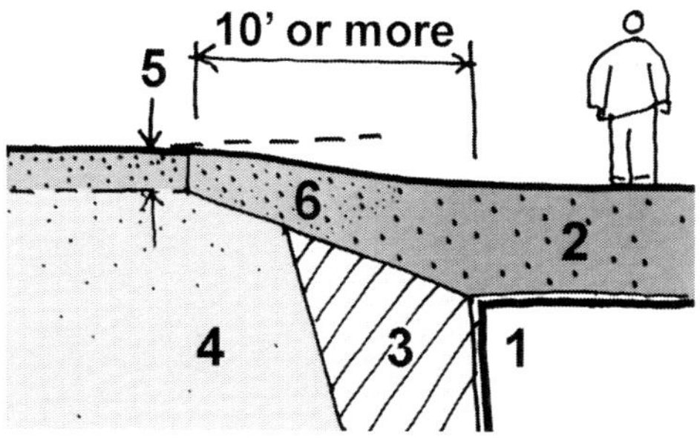

Figure 2.4.92. Soil transitions.
Provide gradual soil transitions at underground building edges to conceal the impact from the building below.

1. Underground building edge. Ensure that drain board extends down along the wall of the foundation.
2. Planting soil.
3. Backfill compacted to 90 to 95 percent.
4. Undisturbed soil.
5. Remaining or improved A horizon.
6. Transitional blended soil mix.

Soil and Tree Weight Considerations

In any roof planter, weight will be an important issue. Weight includes soil, paving, walls, live loads, and increase in tree weight over time. Most often, the soil designer is requested to reduce the weight of the landscape soil in order to work within structural constraints or to reduce the cost of the structure. Both soil and tree weight can be manipulated to reduce the overall weight on the structure. Soil can be made lighter or its depth reduced. Different trees have different weights. Selecting a lighter-weight tree or one that grows slowly, or requiring pruning or removal at a predetermined size, can allow fairly large species of trees to be grown in a rooftop planter.

The locations of these elements in the design can also be modified to reduce their impact. Roof structures are designed to meet a particular load requirement, which implies that the entire roof can be loaded evenly with this amount. This means that the stated design load is what occurs at the weakest point in the structure and the structure will have significant areas that are much stronger. The allowable loading on top of a column or at a beam is much higher than the allowable average load and the allowable load will slowly decrease with distance from the column or beam. The structural engineer should be able to inform the soil designer where the minimum and maximum loadings will be located.

To take advantage of these load variations, a designer can concentrate soil on the areas over columns or near beams, and can gradually thin out over the center of structural spans. Tree roots will respond to the soil volume regardless of the change in soil configuration.

Roof areas will also have live loads to accommodate snow or, in many cases, people and activity on the roof. The live load for people is quite substantial. Areas of shrub and perennial planting can be demonstrated to have a much lower live load, since crowds of people would not be able to gather in these spaces. Depending on the structure and the structural engineer, responses will vary, but the designer of the rooftop landscape must ask appropriate questions to get the most flexibility in the design.

a

b

We Did Not Use Trees Because of Weight Limitations

Often, designers justify the exclusion of trees in the design of a rooftop landscape because of weight limitations. While there may be a few cases where weight is a legitimate factor, it is more likely that the designers did not want to include trees or that trees would have not allowed the design flexibility desired. Analysis of many types of existing modern commercial structures indicates that there is almost never a situation that cannot provide enough soil for trees if the designer understands the structure, the requirements of trees and soils, and is willing to allow those factors to influence the design.

Figure 2.4.93. Two renovations of buildings of similar age, neither of which was originally designed for gardens. At the HUD headquarters, the designers justified a lack of trees based on lack of structure to support the weight. At the Hirshhorn Museum, the design team worked with the existing building structure to create significant soil volumes for trees.

a. Hirshhorn Museum.

b. HUD headquarters.

Soil Weight

Soil weight varies and is always calculated at its saturated weight, which assumes that the drainage system has clogged and water is backing up into the soil. Saturated weights vary from about 60 to 80 pounds per cubic foot for soil made from lightweight aggregates to a maximum of about 120 pounds per cubic foot for loam soil compacted to a point that is not root-limiting.

Soil can be made lighter with any of the lightweight aggregate materials, such as ESCS, perlite, or ground EPS, as discussed earlier in this chapter (see Figure 2.4.59 on page 221). However, lighter-weight soil has a reduced water-holding and cation exchange capacity.These soils will need more irrigation and fertilizer. In extreme situations, the soil looses its cohesiveness, or the ability to bind together and secure roots. Large trees may become unstable. Adding large amounts of organic amendment, greater than 15 percent by volume, will also lighten soil weight, but soil settlement will be significant and these soils will contribute to unstable trees.

If soil must be lightened and canopy tree species are to be planted in this soil, do not make the soil any lighter than 80 pounds per cubic foot to accommodate minimum structural attachments of roots.

The best soil for rooftop applications is a coarse sandy loam soil mix, with about 10 to 15 percent clay and a maximum of 10 percent by volume of high-lignin organic amendment.Adjust soil weight by reducing depth. If the structural requirements limit sandy loam soil to less than 24 inches deep, consider using a small proportion of lightweight aggregate in the mix to increase the depth. The balancing act of depth to weight requires consideration of many factors, including climate, location, maintenance, project design goals, tree types selected, soil source availability, and careful study of the structural design. Collaboration with the architect, structural designer, and a soil expert is needed.

In areas where the distance between the design finish grade and the structure elevation is deeper than the allowable soil weight, EPS foam can be placed under the soil to raise it upward. Use EPS with molded drainage channels on the bottom to ensure proper roof drainage. However, soil should still reach the minimum depth for the types of trees being planted. It is often better to make a well-drained, 120-pound-per-cubic-foot soil a little thinner using EPS foam than it is to solve the weight problem by using a lighter-weight, but deeper, soil.

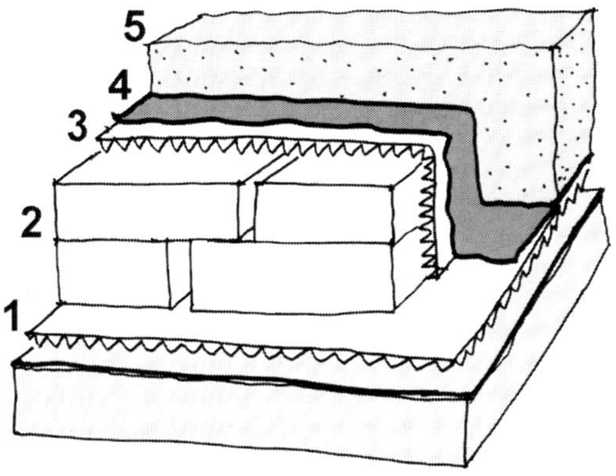

Figure 2.4.94. EPS foam to reduce soil depth.

1. Drain board under EPS.
2. EPS foam blocks. Space blocks 1 inch apart and stagger joints.
3. Drain board on top of EPS.
4. Geotextile over drain board.
5. Planting soil.

Tree Weight

Tree weight can increase considerably with growth. The rate of increase varies depending on the species of tree. Ultimate tree size and tree weight are limited by soil volume. In confined soil volumes, it is possible to calculate the probable size of a tree in the future and thus its future weight.

Here is a methodology to calculate future tree weight: Use the prediction for the tree's ultimate trunk diameter at 4 feet above ground (dbh), as determined by the soil volume to tree size table presented earlier in this chapter (Table 2.4.1). Convert the diameter from inches to tenths of a foot, to simplify the final calculation, as the table of wood weights is in cubic feet. Calculate the area of the trunk diameter in square feet (area = πR^2). Estimate the tree height in feet at the predicted trunk diameter by observing the tree heights of the same species with similar size trunks in the same growing conditions. Multiply the area of the trunk in square feet times the estimated tree height. The resulting figure is the approximate cubic feet of wood in the tree.

Note that trees in soils over structures are often irrigated and heavily fertilized. Such maintenance practices may permit the tree to exceed the soil volume growth predictions. If high maintenance is anticipated, observe growth rates of similar trees under similar maintenance practices, and modify the prediction. No research has been done on the impact of maintenance to the soil volume to tree size table.

This methodology yields an approximate number that will be conservatively high for the average tree, probably overly conservative for columnar trees such as bald cypress. The author, in collaboration with other arborists, concludes that this method would always produce an overestimate of tree weight. Overestimation is an implied safety factor consistent with good engineering practices. More research is needed to refine the projection.

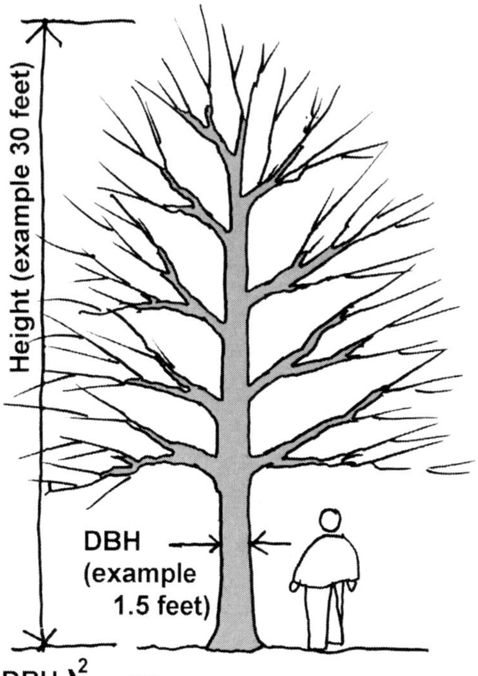

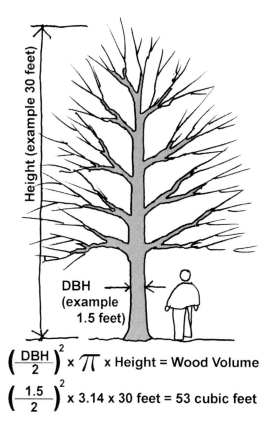

$$\left(\frac{\text{DBH}}{2}\right)^2 \times \pi \times \text{Height} = \text{Wood Volume}$$

$$\left(\frac{1.5}{2}\right)^2 \times 3.14 \times 30 \text{ feet} = 53 \text{ cubic feet}$$

Figure 2.4.95. Calculating the wood volume of a mature tree.

Once the volume of wood is known, multiply the volume by the green wood weight, shown in Table 2.4.7. For tree species not included in the table, make a conservative prediction based on species that are of similar habit or tree type.

Assuming the example tree is a red oak, with 63 pounds per cubic foot, the example tree's 61 cubic feet of wood weighs 3,843 pounds.

The final part of the equation is to determine the impact of the tree's weight on the loading of the structure. The structural engineer will want to know what the area is over which the majority of the weight will be distributed into the soil, which is determined by the area of the trunk flare and zone of rapid taper of the tree. These two structures become larger from the stress of wind and tree weight loading. It is reasonable to assume that within this area, the majority of the force of the weight of the tree is transferred into the soil. For a 24- to 30-inch-trunk diameter tree, the plate of roots is approximately 10 to 12 feet in diameter, or approximately five times the trunk diameter. Using a root plate of five times the trunk diameter is a reasonable basis to determine the distribution of the tree weight into the soil. This estimate method will produce a conservative prediction and was developed from discussion with experienced arborists. More research is needed to develop a more precise estimate.

The final calculation for the example red oak is to divide the tree's 3,843-pound weight over the 44 square feet of bearing surface. This equals 87 pounds per square feet of loading. Compared to the 330 pounds per square feet of loading contributed by the three feet of soil, the tree's weight is proportionally and of reasonably limited impact to the structure.

Table 2.4.7. Green wood weight of trees (Source: ANSI Z133.1-2006)

Scientific name	Common name	Weight, lb per ft^3
Abies concolor	white fir	47
Abies procera	noble fir	29
Acer rubrum	red maple	50
Acer saccharinum	silver maple	45
Acer saccharum	sugar maple	56
Aesculus hippocastanum	horsechestnut	41
Alnus rubra	red alder	46
Betula papyrifera	paper birch	50
Calocedrus decurrens	incense-cedar	45
Carya illinoensis	pecan	61
Carya ovata	shagbark hickory	64
Celtis occidentalis	hackberry	50
Diospyros virginiana	persimmon	63
Eucalyptus camaldulensis	red gum	50
Fagus spp.	beech	54
Fraxinus americana	white ash	48
Fraxinus latifolia	Oregon ash	48
Fraxinus pennsylvanica	green ash	47
black walnut	58	
Larix spp.	larch	51
Liquidambar styraciflua	sweetgum	55
Liriodendron tulipifera	yellow poplar, tuliptree	38
Melia azedarach	Chinaberry	50
Nyssa sylvatica	black gum	45
Picea rubens	red spruce	34
Picea sitchensis	Sitka spruce	32
Pinus contorta	lodgepole pine	39
Pinus lambertiana	sugar pine	52
Pinus monticola	western white pine	36
Pinus palustris	longleaf pine	55
Pinus ponderosa	ponderosa pine	46
Pinus strobus	eastern white pine	36
Pinus taeda	loblolly pine	53
Platanus occidentalis	sycamore	52
Populus spp.	cottonwood	49
Populus tremuloides	quaking aspen	43
Prunus serotina	black cherry	45
Pseudotsuga menziesii	Douglas-fir	39
Quercus alba	white oak	62
Quercus coccinea	scarlet oak	64
Quercus kelloggii	California black oak	66
Quercus palustris	pin oak	64
Quercus robur	English oak	52
Quercus rubra	red oak	63
Quercus stellata	post oak	63
Quercus virginiana	live oak	76
Robinia pseudoacacia	black locust	58
Salix spp.	willow	32
Sequoia sempervirens	coast redwood	50
Taxodium distichum	baldcypress	51
Thuja plicata	western red cedar	28
Tilia americana	basswood	42
Tsuga canadensis	eastern hemlock	49
Tsuga heterophylla	western hemlock	41

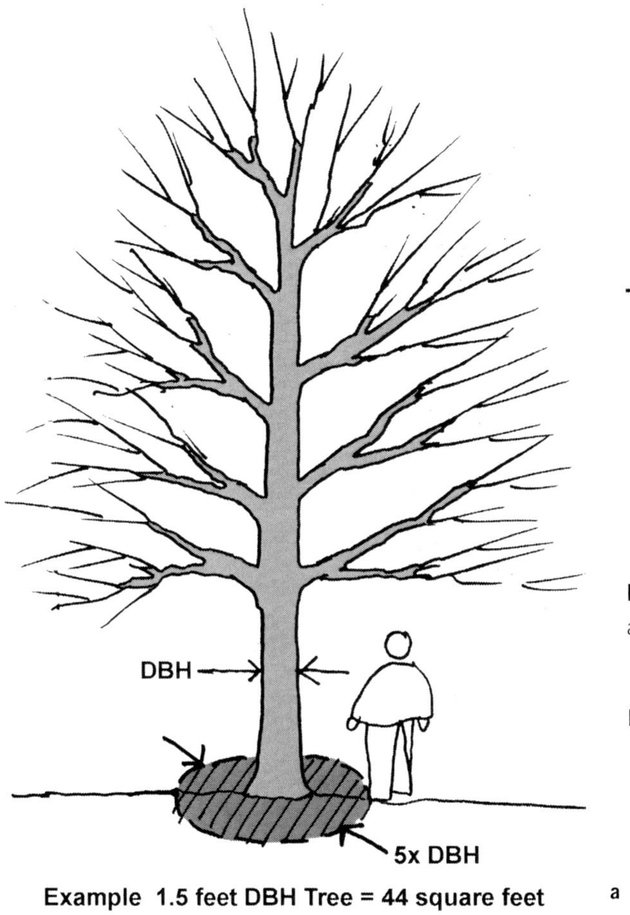

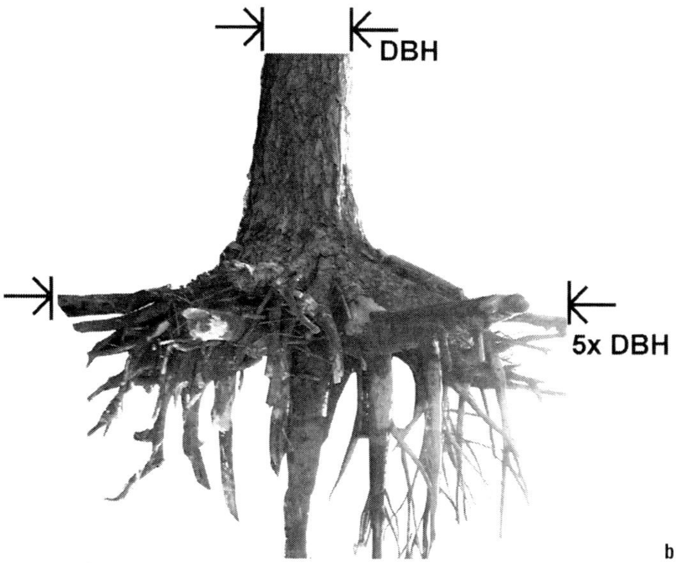

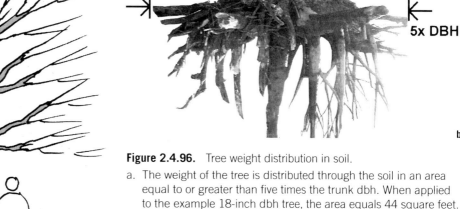

Figure 2.4.96. Tree weight distribution in soil.

a. The weight of the tree is distributed through the soil in an area equal to or greater than five times the trunk dbh. When applied to the example 18-inch dbh tree, the area equals 44 square feet.

b. Tree and root system five times the trunk dbh. *(Photo credit: Miles Barnard)*

At each step of the computation, conservative estimates allow for a large safety factor in the equation, which is desirable in making these kinds of predictions since no significant research has been done to refine this methodology. If a more refined estimate is needed, a trained arborist can measure the actual mature tree to determine its weight. For structures where the weight is critical, it is advisable to have the tree weight calculated on a regular basis to determine if it is exceeding the allowable trunk diameter limits.

Root Ball and Root Weight

This prediction model ignores the weight of the root ball and the accumulation of root weight in the soil over time. The weight of the root ball has little to no impact on the weight of the overall planter. If the tree is being planted into standard-weight planting soil, the weight of the root ball at planting simply displaces the soil already calculated in the planter, and, therefore, no additional weight is added. If the tree is to be planted in lightweight soil, the difference in the saturated weight of the root ball soil of 120 pounds per cubic foot and the saturated weight of the lightweight soil must be added. The volume of the soil in the root ball can be calculated from the ANSI Z60.1 standards.

As the tree grows, it produces roots. These roots weigh less than water and would float if the soil became saturated. Since the roots displace the open spaces within the soil, less water will be in the soil when it is saturated. This has the net effect of

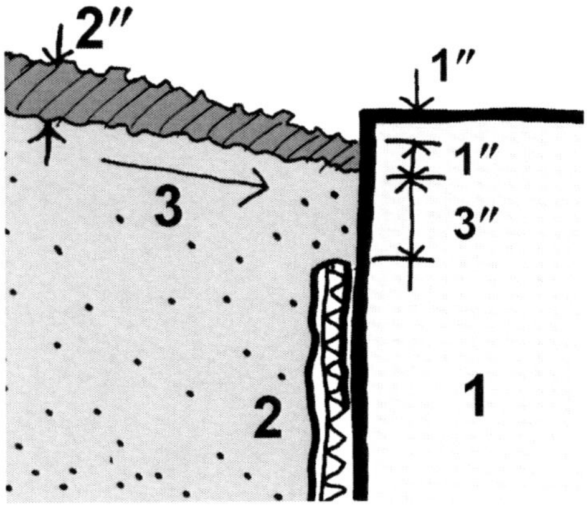

Figure 2.4.97. Soil grades in planters: Covering waterproofing and top of drain board is important. Slight mounding of soil anticipates soil settlement.

1. Planter edge.
2. Drain board.
3. Slope soil grades at 5 to 10 percent and thin mulch along the edge of the planter.

reducing the overall planter weight when in a saturated state. Because the structural engineer is concerned with saturated soil, it is not necessary to factor in the weight of root growth as a part of the overall soil weight equation.

Soil Grades in Planters

Final grades of planting soil should always be several inches higher than the building waterproofing material. The top layer of soil is normally quite dry due to the drain board directly below, and standing water does not accumulate against the wall. The drain board and waterproofing need protection from the sun, and the soil will settle along the wall over time. Having the soil against building stone may require negotiation with the building designer. Some architects will request that the soil be below the waterproofing, arguing that portions of the wall would be unprotected from water intrusion. Another consideration is that limestone will wick soil up along its face, staining the stone.

If the drainage board is correctly installed, the small amount of soil above the waterproofing should never become saturated, a condition that is required to allow water to move into the wall material. If the soil at the top of the planter is saturated for any length of time, much bigger problems exist than the small amount of water that could penetrate the wall.

Mound the soil in the planter to anticipate planting soil settlement. See the section on planting mix compaction earlier in this chapter.

Extensive Green Roof Applications

Traditional rooftop planters generally have soil deep enough to support large shrubs and trees but are not a "green roof" in the contemporary use of the word. The term "green roof" is used primarily for roof areas that filter and store storm water.

With the advent of the term "green roof," two different designations of rooftop plantings are being used. "Extensive green roofs" are shallow (±3 inches of soil depth) and have specialized plant, soil, and drainage requirements. The design of extensive green roof soil and drainage is beyond the scope of this book.

"Intensive green roofs" are roof gardens with soil thick enough to support large ornamental plantings, including trees. The soil types depth needed for intensive applications are similar to soils discussed in this chapter.

SUMMARY

- Understand the key factors of soil and drainage improvement, including compaction, texture, drainage, biology, and chemistry. The presence of existing trees limits the options for improvement.
- Other considerations such as budgets, construction schedules, and commitment to sustainability are important when evaluating soil for amendment or replacement.
- Prepare soil and drainage plans.
- Understand the different types of soil amendments and how they may impact soil performance and budgets.
- Measure existing soil and subsoil compaction, and anticipate further compaction during construction. Ensure that plans require compaction reduction.
- Compaction reduction and soil improvement near existing trees must preserve roots.
- Organic amendments are the best approach to modifying existing surface soil texture.
- When designing deep soil installations, design the new soil profile to reflect natural soil profile conditions.
- Design soil installation depths and volumes to provide adequate growing conditions.
- Add organic and biological amendments to the soil to improve and support the soil food web.
- Make adjustments to soil chemistry only when indicated by a soil test and when making the necessary changes with organic amendment is not feasible.
- Reuse of existing soil resources is more sustainable and often produces better results that importing soil.
- Existing soil often only requires increases in organic matter and reduction in compaction to make it a good planting medium.
- Imported topsoil can be a significant savings over soil mixes if suitable soil resources are available.
- Soil mixes require care in their design and implementation. Soil mixes can be superior growing mediums over imported soils for some applications.
- Ensure that there is good soil drainage out of installed soil and subsoil. Design drainage systems whenever construction is likely to damage existing drainage patterns.
- Drainage on roof plantings and spaces enclosed by walls and deep footings requires the inclusion of physical drainage systems.

REFERENCES

Key References

Craul, Phillip J. 1992. *Urban Soil in Landscape Design*. John Wiley & Sons, Inc., New York, NY. 396 pp.

Craul, Phillip J. 1999. *Urban Soils: Applications and Practices*. John Wiley & Sons, Inc., New York, NY. 366 pp.

Craul, Timothy A., and Phillip J. Craul. 2006. *Soil Design Protocols: For Landscape Architects and Contractors*. John Wiley & Sons, Inc., New York, NY. 339 pp.

Ferguson, Bruce K. 2005. *Porous Pavements*. CRC Press, Boca Raton, FL. 577 pp.

Harris, Richard W., James R. Clark, and Nelda P. Matheny. 2004. *Arboriculture: Integrated Management of Landscape Trees, Shrubs, and Vines*. 4th ed. Pearson Education, Inc., Upper Saddle River, NJ. 578 pp.

Trowbridge, Peter J., and Nina L. Bassuk. 2004. *Trees in the Urban Landscape: Site Assessment Design and Installation*. John Wiley & Sons, Inc., Hoboken, NJ. 205 pp.

Urban, J. 1992. Bringing order to the technical dysfunction within the urban forest. *Journal of Arboriculture* 18(2):85–90.

Urban, James. 2000. *Ramsey/Sleeper Architectural Graphic Standards*. 10th ed. John Ray Hoke, Jr., ed. John Wiley & Sons, Inc., New York, NY.

Other Resources

Brady, Nyle C. and Ray R. Weil. 1999. *The Nature and Properties of Soils*. 12th ed. Prentice Hall, Inc. Upper Saddle River, NJ. 881 pp.

Brinton, William F. 2002. *Earth Plant and Compost*. The BIO-Dynamic Farming and Gardening Association, Inc., San Francisco, CA. 73 pp.

Burns, Russell M., and Barbara H. Honkala, tech coords. 1990. *Silvics of North America: Volume 2. Hardwoods*. Agricultural Handbook 654. U.S. Department of Agriculture, Forest Service, Washington, DC. vol. 2, 877 pp.

Costello, Laurence R., et al. 2003. *Abiotic Disorders of Landscape Plants*. University of California, Division of Agriculture and Natural Resources, Oakland, CA. 242 pp.

Dirr, Michael A. 1998. *Manual of Woody Landscape Plants*. Stipes Publishing, Champaign, IL. 1,187 pp.

Plaster, Edward J. 2003. *Soil Science & Management*. 4th ed. Delmar Learning, a division of Thomson Learning, Inc. Clifton Park, NY. 384 pp.

Puhalla, Jim, Jeff Krans, and Mike Goatley. 1999. *Sports Fields: A Manual for Design Construction and Maintenance*. John Wiley & Sons, Inc., Hoboken, NJ. 464 pp.

Singer, Michael J., and Donald N. Munns. 2002. *Soils: An Introduction*. 5th ed. Pearson Education, Inc., Upper Saddle River, NJ. 429 pp.

Urban, James. 1992. Bringing order to the technical dysfunction within the urban forest. *Journal of Arboriculture* 18(2):85–90.

Watson, Gary W., and Dan Neely, eds. 1994. *The Landscape Below Ground*. International Society of Arboriculture, Savoy, IL. 222 pp.

Watson, Gary W., and Dan Neely, eds. 1998. *The Landscape Below Ground II*. International Society of Arboriculture, Champaign, IL. 265 pp.

Watson, Gary W., and E. B. Himelick. 1997. *Principles and Practice of Planting Trees and Shrubs*. International Society of Arboriculture, Savoy, IL. 199 pp.

Whitcomb, Carl E. 1987. *Establishment and Maintenance of Landscape Plants*. Lacebark Publications, Stillwater, OK. 618 pp.

Information Resources

Natural Resource Conservation Service: www.nrcs.usda.gov
Expanded Shale, Clay, and Slate Institute, ESCSI: www.escsi.org

Soil Testing Labs

These are examples of typical soil testing labs around the United States. Check with your local soil expert for recommended labs in your region.

General Soil Testing
CLC Labs (soil physical and chemical testing, sand fractions and soil mix evaluations)
325 Venture Drive
Westerville, OH 43081
614-888-1663

Hummel & Co., Inc. (performs specialty Proctor and bulk density/infiltration rate testing)
35 King Street
Trumansburg, NY 14886
607-387-5694

A&L Analytical Laboratories, Inc.
2790 Whitten Road
Memphis, TN 38133
800-264-4522

Organic Testing
Woods End Research Laboratory, Inc.
P.O. Box 297
Mt. Vernon, ME 04352
207-293-2457

Soil Food Web Testing
Soil Foodweb, Inc.
728 S.W. Wake Robin Avenue
Corvallis, OR 97333
541-752-5066

Soil Foodweb New York, Inc.
555-7 Hallock Ave.
Port Jefferson Station, NY 11776
631-474-8848

Toxic Chemical Testing
Phase Separation Science, Inc.
6630 Baltimore National Pike
Baltimore, MD 21228
410-747-8770

INTRODUCTION
Tree-Based Strategies

A detailed explanation of the ten design principles continues with tree-based strategies, Principles 5, 6, and 7. Designers need a thorough understanding of tree biology to effectively place trees in urban landscapes. Read Part 1, Chapter Five for an introduction to this biology, so critical to the successful implementation of tree-based strategies.

Urban landscapes are primarily used by humans. The needs of the program, the budget, and the aesthetic goals are often in direct conflict with tree requirements. The more designers understand the principles defining tree growth, the more likely that they can make and influence informed decisions that can be defended when other project requirements or engineering considerations pose challenges to successful tree growth.

Figure 2.TS.1. Designers must balance trees' needs with the requirements of cities.

Over the next three chapters, we'll discuss design principles that reflect the needs of the tree. These include the following:

Principle 5: Respect the Base of a Tree

Discusses the impact of the large base structure of trees on paving design.

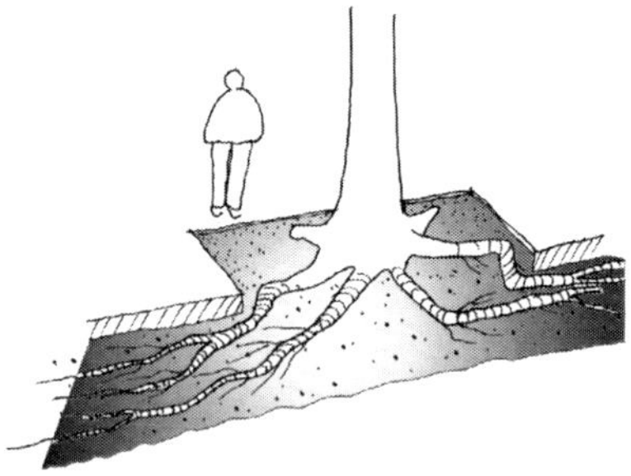

Principle 6: Make Space for Roots

Explains how to design space for roots beneath pavement when there is insufficient good-quality soil for roots within the available planting space.

Principle 7: Select the Right Tree

Examines the process of species selection and the placement of trees in the urban landscape.

A Word About Tree Preservation

While the preservation of existing trees is important, its complexity is outside the scope of this book. Preserving large trees during the design and construction of an urban landscape requires different techniques and skills than those required to plant new trees. However, many of the scientific principles of trees and soil discussed here are relevant to tree preservation. An excellent reference on the topic of tree preservation during construction is Trees and Development by Matheny and Clark.

PART TWO

5

Principle 5—Respect the Base of the Tree

The base of a tree is the critical junction between the trunk and roots and is called the root crown. In urban areas where people and trees compete for space, designers tend to pave as close to the base of the tree as possible. Often, solid paving comes within inches of newly planted tree trunks—trunks expected to grow to several feet in diameter. The tree may decline or die due to strangulation. Or the tree may damage the pavement, and roots cutoff during subsequent pavement repair may damage or kill the tree. All of these outcomes are unacceptable.

Failing to provide for the root crown of the tree is a significant error in many landscape architectural designs. This part of the tree is discussed at length in Part 1, Chapter Five. Because this issue is so important to the long-term success of the tree, we'll give a quick review here.

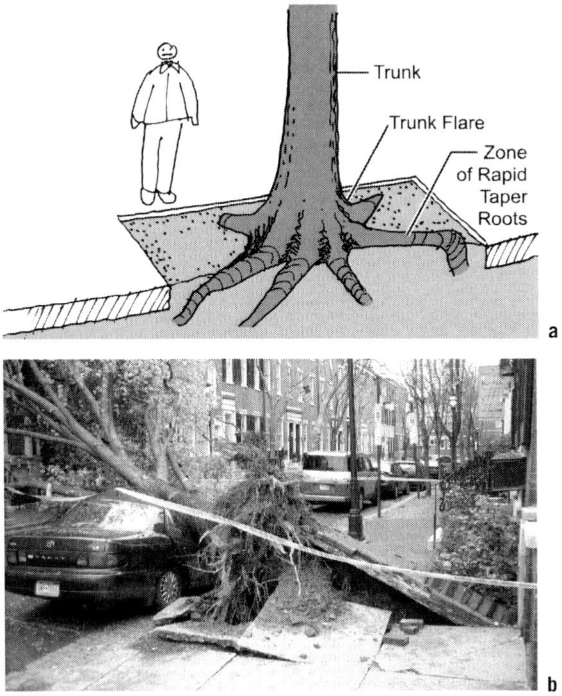

Figure 2.5.1. Designers must incorporate the requirements of the root crown in the design of all paving near the tree.

a. Root crown.

b. Inadequate respect of the root crown requirements. *(Photo credit: Dennis McGlade)*

Figure 2.5.2. Large trees and tight urban spaces can coexist.

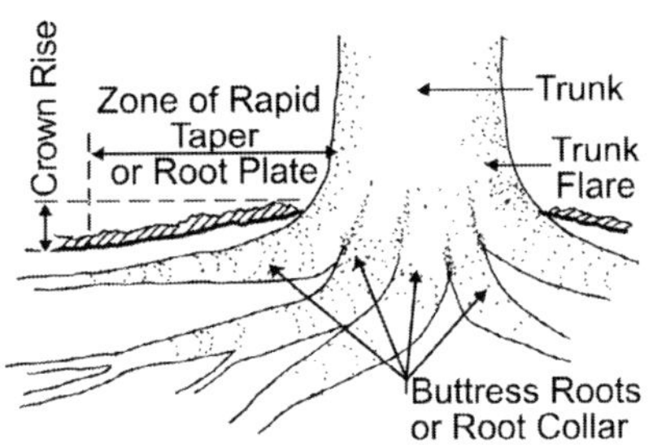

Figure 2.5.3. Diagram of the base of the tree. See Part 1, Chapter Five.

ROOT CROWN

The root crown or root collar of a tree includes the flare at the base of the trunk and the initial roots that develop below the trunk. These roots generally taper and subdivide rapidly to form the root system of the tree.

Trunk Flare

A tree is structurally a vertical trunk and branches supported by a horizontal root system. At the point where the trunk joins the roots, a transition area transfers wind and crown loads in the trunk to the roots. The tree puts on more wood in this area to resist this force. The extra wood swells the base of the tree, and this zone is called the trunk flare or root collar. The trunk flare diameter at the ground line can be 1.5 to 3 times the diameter of the trunk at 4.5 feet above ground. This ratio varies with tree age, species, soil conditions, and the presence of girdling roots.

Figure 2.5.4. This tree was planted on level ground. The developing root crown has made the tree appear to be on a mound. This is not to be confused with a mound of mulch at the base of the tree.

a

b

c

d

Figure 2.5.5. Trunk flare conflicts.

a. Trunk flares will become large even in limited space.
b. Conflicts between the trunk flare and the tree's own girdling roots.
c. Working with the tree. A steel angle was substituted for the concrete curb.
d. Working against the tree. Designer's dream becomes a tree's nightmare.

Figure 2.5.6. Zone-of-rapid-taper conflicts.

a. A single tapering root pushes the curb and paving aside.
b. Tapering roots molding to the space allotted and rising more than a foot as wood piles on wood.
c. The zone of rapid taper becomes damaging at an early age and its expansion does not stop. Several years after the first repair, the sidewalk is lifted more than an inch.
d. Fingers of tapering roots rippling the pavement.

Zone-of-Rapid-Taper Roots

Below the flare, the trunk divides into many roots that are quite large at the trunk and then quickly taper as the forces within the root lessen. This segment of root is called the zone of rapid taper. In a mature tree, these roots typically taper from 10 to 12 inches in diameter or greater at the trunk to about 3 to 4 inches in diameter, 6 to 8 feet from the trunk. Tapering roots cause the greatest conflict with paving.

Tapering large roots can withstand compaction and exert significant lifting force. Zone-of-rapid-taper roots add more wood along the topside of the root as it responds to stress within. As the wood expands, the soil at the base of the tree will lift at a rate of 2 to 3 inches every 10 years. This process is what makes zone-of-rapid-taper roots so damaging to paving.

Trunk Flare Conflicts

When the trunk flare or side of a root comes in contact with an object, the tree adds wood in that location in response to the restriction. The stress in the tree causes significant wood to be added to give the tree stability. This increase in wood causes significant damage to urban structures.

Figure 2.5.7. Trunk-flare wood mounding over the sidewalk. This wood is cut away or the paving removed at great risk to the stability and health of the tree.

Figure 2.5.8. This understory tree will never cause a conflict with paving, but will also never shade the street or contribute to the city's canopy.

DESIGNING FOR THE FUTURE ROOT CROWN

The design of paving around each tree must anticipate the growth of the root crown. Planting smaller species of trees may appear to be an easy solution. Yet large trees such as oaks and maples contribute to the urban environment in ways that small trees such as hawthorns or crape myrtles cannot. Larger tree canopies are needed to cool cities, reduce energy consumption, improve water and air quality, and make livable communities. The closer the tree canopy is to human activity, the greater its benefit.

Providing space for the ultimate size of a large trunk flare might make it seem impractical to use large trees in dense urban places. However, this is not necessarily the case. Large-canopy trees can be grown in urban areas if a balance is struck between paving design, tree requirements, and other urban requirements.

Tree Openings: Space Between the Tree and the Edge of Paving

The space between the trunk and paving is an active transition zone that is mostly soil at the time of planting and becomes mostly roots as the tree matures. Increasing the distance from the paving to the base of the tree will reduce conflicts. This space is not a good location for a tree grate or any other material that competes with the development of a large trunk flare and zone-of-rapid-taper roots.

Changing the nomenclature used to describe this space may help in understanding its role and the need to make changes in the culture of its design. Terms like "tree pit" and "tree box" connote a limited role and a diminished respect for the importance of this space in the landscape. A term such as "tree opening" suggests that this space is more important to the tree.

Figure 2.5.9. Woody roots replacing soil in the tree opening.

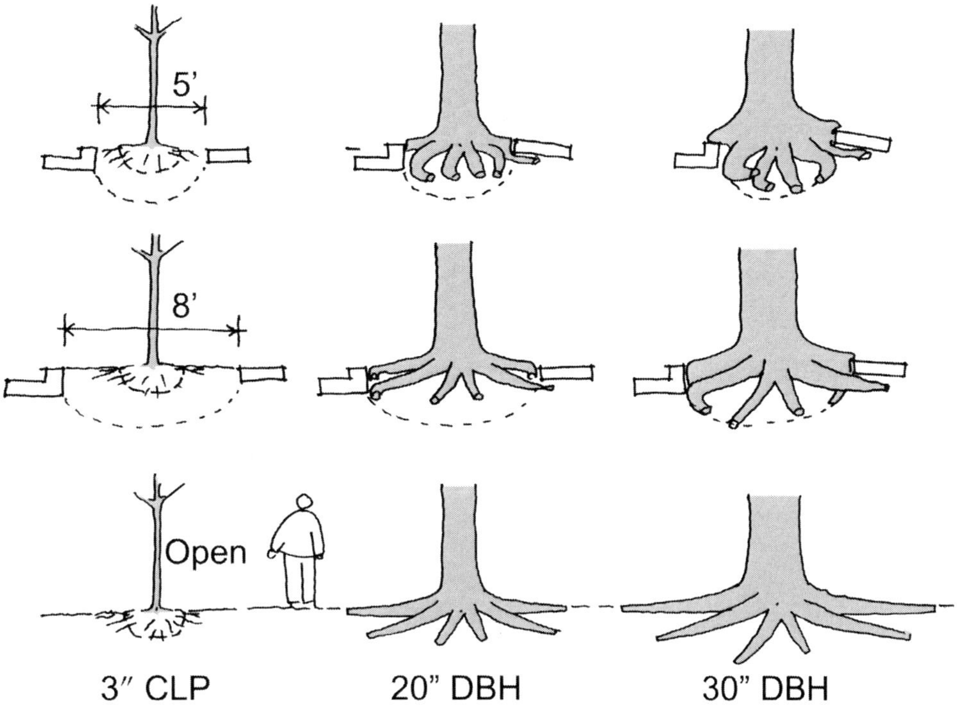

Figure 2.5.10. Root crown predictions for open-grown trees and the same tree planted in a 5-foot- and 8-foot-wide tree opening.

Drawing Root Crown Sections

Reducing paving around trees will change the design of urban projects. Designers should draw paving sections, to scale, that depict a tree at the largest size expected, given the soil conditions and species. These drawings will reveal conflicts between the tree's future structure and paving, and will allow owners to evaluate the ratio of paving to tree opening size and determine if the future risk of pavement failure is acceptable. Figure 2.5.10 shows a tree at several stages of its life in different-sized tree openings. Use these kinds of sketches to communicate the importance of a larger opening.

The book *Reducing Infrastructure Damage by Tree Roots*, by Costello and Jones, developed a procedure for determining the trunk diameter to trunk flare diameter ratio. A table of data for trees in California found that the trunk diameter-to-flare diameter ratio ranges from 1:2 to 1:3, with typical trees having trunk flares twice the trunk diameter measured at 4.5 feet above the ground. Local lists for other species and regions can be developed by averaging 15 or more open-grown, mature trees of a given species. Figure 2.5.11 summarizes this data and other information generated from arborists' observations of different trees. This information, combined with the designer's own observations of mature local trees, should allow the accurate portrayal of trees in project design sketches.

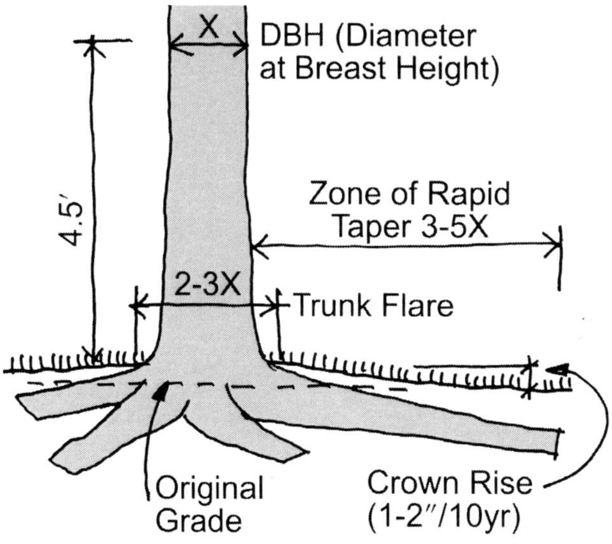

Figure 2.5.11. Dimensional relationships of the base of mature trees.

DESIGNING TREE OPENINGS

Making Compromises on Size

We will never eliminate, but only reduce, the conflict between trees and paving in dense urban spaces. At the same time, we need trees in our cities and accept as a society that trees come with assumed levels of risk. What is reasonable practice and who is responsible when either a tree fails or someone trips on an uneven paver? Has the designer done due diligence to make a maintainable landscape for his or her client? The community must decide that the risk of having trees is worth the damage and injury that result from placing trees and paving in close proximity. Designing the urban environment to respect the needs of trees can reduce those risks.

Tree opening sizes are not the only part of the equation. The type of paving and paving sub-base; soil type, compaction, and drainage; types of edge details; use of root-deflecting devices; tree species; expected maintenance; and the performance expectation of the client all influence decisions as to what is reasonable practice.

The following are options to reduce the conflicts between paving and roots. Individually, these recommendations will not prevent conflicts. When used together, the designer demonstrates due diligence through a best effort to reduce root-paving conflicts.

Opening Size: Length vs. Width

In tight urban spaces, the width of a tree opening will be limited by the required pedestrian flow rate. Making the tree opening even a few inches wider will help reduce conflicts between roots and paving. When designing the tree opening, ask what would be the minimum size of the paving instead of the minimum size of the tree opening. Go back to Principle 2!

Note that it is not a requirement that all tree openings be the same size. When designers try to impose such a standard the result is the tree opening is made small enough to fit the most restrictive space. Good designers can develop solutions to vary the size of the openings while still accomplishing well designed urban spaces. Good urban design standards allow flexible dimensions on the size of the tree opening. The use of tree grates also forces the tree opening to become regular and smaller. Good designers will argue against the use of tree grates even when they are in an existing standard.

Often, the length of the tree opening can be much larger, even becoming a completely unpaved space from tree to tree. If there is no parking along the curb or parking is long-term, the space can be lawn or a tough ground cover. This zone does not have to meet disability access requirements, except at parking spaces designated for disabled people. Loose-laid pavers on planting soil may be appropriate. A

Figure 2.5.12. Long, narrow tree openings provide the greatest amount of open soil with the least intrusion into walking spaces. Note the 16-inch-wide band of pavers against the curb to move in and out of parked vehicles.

narrow walking band 16 to 18 inches wide, including the top dimension of the curb, can solve the problem of getting out of and into cars.

The root crown in a longer, narrow opening will adapt to the space to some degree, although there are limits to how much the trunk flare can be expected to change. If the root can be deflected along the long axis of the tree opening or downward into suitable soil under the pavement, it will take longer for conflicts to become a problem. On the other hand, if soil and drainage conditions are such that roots remain on the surface, it is likely that even very wide tree openings will have conflicts with paving. Root-paving conflicts in poor soil have been observed even when the tree opening is 10 feet wide or more.

Figure 2.5.13. Bowed tree openings allow the largest space at the trunk location and let pedestrian traffic flow.

Paving Around the Tree Opening

The types of paving and subgrade modifications next to the tree opening influence strategies for managing conflicts between paving and tree roots.

Flexible Pavement

Different types of flexible pavements, from brick and pre-cast concrete to asphalt and gravel, can adapt to the dynamic movement of the surface caused by root expansion.

Brick and other loose-set pavers can be reset as the flare lifts the surface. This is expensive and the paving will need to be reworked many times. Adding a layer of woven geotextile or geogrids under the paving can make the pavers rise in smoother lines, reducing tripping hazards. The smaller the paver size, the smoother the transitions between pavers. The larger the paver size, greater than 4 inches by 8 inches, the more likely the lifted paver will create a tripping hazard. Where larger pavers must be used, design greater distance between the tree and the paving edge.

Pavers can be removed to enlarge the tree opening as the tree grows.

Figure 2.5.14. Brick pavers re-set several times to roll over expanding roots.

Figure 2.5.15. Gravel and asphalt pavement are forgiving of root conflicts.
a. Gravel paving with hard-paved walks on either side of the gravel surface to meet accessibility requirements.
b. Asphalt paving can meet the aesthetic needs of important landscapes such as these walks at Harvard University.

Asphalt, gravel, and stone dust have many of the same beneficial qualities as unit pavers and require fewer repairs. Reinforcing the underside of the asphalt with geotextile or geogrids may result in smoother surfaces in the lifted asphalt. Asphalt can be placed quite close to the tree, and gravel paving or stone dust can be installed right up to the trunk. These paving options are relatively cheap but may not be appropriate for all applications.

Rubber Sidewalks

Rubber bricks and pads have been tried as paving material near trees to reduce root lifting conflicts. The theory with rubber is not to stop the lifting, but to accommodate it in a way that reduces trip-and-fall issues by allowing the pavement to roll. It will be some years before we know if this rolling is gentle enough to be acceptable.

These materials are expensive. Rubber sidewalks require the subgrade to be compacted to 95 percent of maximum dry density. This compaction is the cause of most tree failures in cities, and results in roots that grow directly under the pavers. In testing conducted by the sidewalk maker, the rubber pavers were removed every couple of years and roots that had accumulated under the walk removed. The advantage seemed to be that it was easy to remove and reinstall the pavers. No research has examined the results if the pavers are left in place and the roots allowed to grow. More research is needed, although this seems to be a promising product for building sidewalks under large existing trees.

Figure 2.5.16. Rubber sidewalks. *(Photo courtesy Rubber Sidewalks Inc.)*

Concrete Paving

Concrete has limited ability to move and it shears at joints or cracks, leaving sharp changes in paving elevations. This is the primary conflict between trees and paving in cities. The typical 4 inches of un-reinforced concrete sidewalk is no match for tree roots. The concrete can be made thicker and reinforced, but this increases cost and makes repairs more difficult.

Enough concrete and steel can withstand the pressure of a tree root. Reinforced concrete, 6 inches thick or greater, may be required. Research is under way to determine the minimum strength of concrete necessary to withstand root pressures.

Concrete has two significant advantages over other paving surfaces. While it may appear to seal off water from reaching the soil, it also stops evaporation from the ground and groundwater condensates on the underside of the paving. This pulls water up from deeper in the soil. During drought, trees surrounded by concrete are often less stressed than trees in lawn. The second advantage of concrete is its strength, which allows a wider set of options to improve soil for trees under the pavement. We'll go further into this in the next chapter.

Figure 2.5.17. When concrete paving moves, it shears into large plates, creating tripping hazards.

Suspended Paving

Suspended paving options that impose an air space between the underside of the paving and the soil are the best way to eliminate paving conflicts and reliably grow large trees. This paving support system is described in Part 2, Chapter Six. Suspended paving systems will not solve the trunk flare conflict, and tree openings must still be large enough to accommodate the expected flare. Removal of a portion of the paving in the future may still be required if the tree opening is not designed large enough.

Figure 2.5.18. Concrete spans over soil trenches, providing rooting space for these trees.

Which Came First, the Crack or the Root?

The root may be growing in an area where the sidewalk cracked first. The root is exploiting a crack, not causing the crack. As concrete cures, it shrinks, making many small fissures. Control joints and expansion joints are also perfect root spaces. Air and water penetrate these cracks and small roots then grow. Researchers found that sidewalk cracking was similar in areas with and without trees. Tree roots do increase paving movement, but may not start the problem. Better sidewalk construction may be part of the answer.

Figure 2.5.19. Suspended paving systems support many paving types while providing significant soil volume for trees. *(Photo courtesy DeepRoot Partners)*

Figure 2.5.20. Thicker concrete and a gravel sub-base will reduce paving damage by roots.

Aggregate Base Courses Under Paving

The type and thickness of aggregate base course material can influence the incidence of root conflicts. Paving sub-base material made of aggregates with limited size range and no fine particles, such as AASHTO #57 stone designation, can decrease root penetration under the pavement. The aggregate sub-base material creates a dry space under the pavement and distributes the load of root pressure on the paving surface. Combining 5 to 6 inches of gravel under 6 inches of reinforced concrete will reduce root-paving conflicts. This is a more expensive sidewalk to build than a standard 4-inch walk. While root damage is reduced, the success of the tree is still dependent on the availability of sufficient soil volume, and a better sidewalk does not increase soil volume.

Improved Soil Conditions Under Pavement

Soil conditions under the paved area will affect where roots grow. If the subsoil is root-limiting, the roots may try to grow on top of the subsoil directly under the pavement, causing damage. Improvements to the sub-pavement soil that encourage deeper rooting often reduce paving damage. Various options to provide rooting soil under the pavement are described in Part 2, Chapter Six, "Make room for roots."

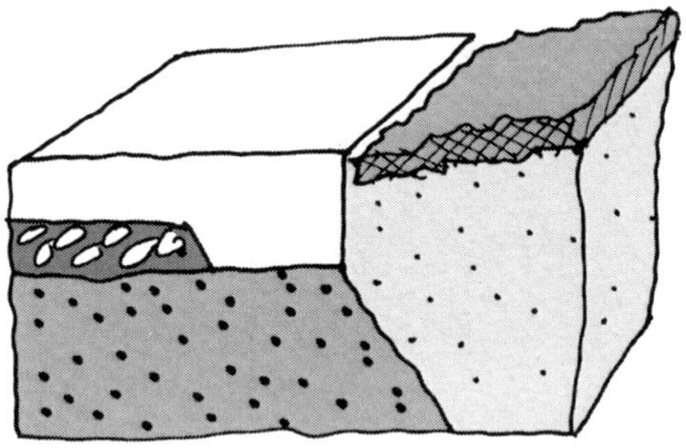

Figure 2.5.21. Thickening concrete edges around the tree opening further reduces root damage when combined with a thick gravel layer below the paving.

Edge Details and Root-Deflecting Devices

Thickening the edge of the concrete around a tree opening or adding root barriers will reduce root damage. A thicker concrete edge also serves to reduce damage from the occasional vehicle that mounts the sidewalk. Root barriers that have vertical ribs will deflect roots down into deeper soil.

Root barriers should be placed directly adjacent to the paving and must always be installed with the top edge of the barrier above the soil and mulch line. Roots can easily grow over the top of a barrier installed flush to the grade.

Know where the roots are going after they reach the bottom or end of a root barrier. Stopping the root from damaging the sidewalk does not relieve the designer of the responsibility to provide for the long-term growth of the tree. Root barriers in compacted soil may either buy time until there is a conflict or simply ensure that the tree never gets large enough to cause a conflict.

When using sand-set pavers, root intrusion into the setting bed and joint filler of the paver is common and difficult to stop. Mortar-set pavers along the edge of loose-set pavers will reduce this intrusion, but will not stop it. The roots will eventually make the pavers hazardous.

Figure 2.5.22. Root barrier deflecting roots downward and horizontally.

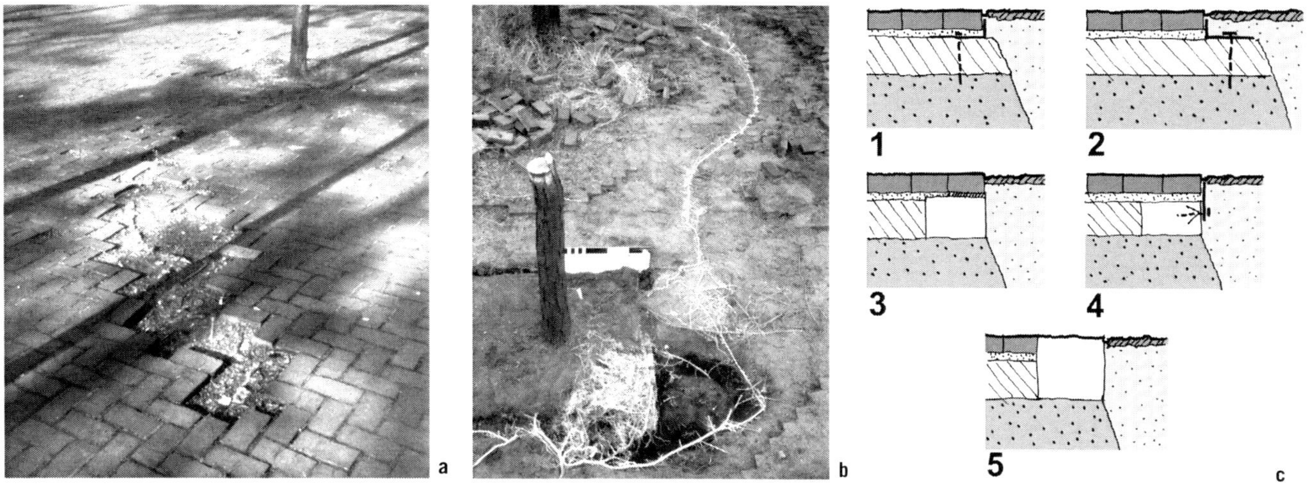

Figure 2.5.23. Loose-set pavers.

a. Loose-set pavers damaged by relatively small roots growing in the sand setting bed.

b. Excavation of sand-set pavers. This tree had an 18-inch-deep root barrier around the 4-foot-square tree opening. Roots grew under the barrier and into the sand setting bed.

c. Alternative edging for loose-set pavers.
   1. Plastic paver edge set under last paver. This detail is harder to build but has less impact on soil volume.
   2. Plastic paver edge set in the typical configuration, with significant impact on soil volume. Not recommended.
   3. Concrete base at edge of tree opening with last row of pavers mortar-set.
   4. Concrete base at edge of tree opening with steel edge restraint bolted to base.
   5. Concrete base as solid curbing around tree opening. Preferred configuration with the least root-paving conflicts. Curb can be raised slightly to divert salt-laden water in cold climates.

d. Failed paving from inadequate edge support.

Sand-set precast or brick pavers require an edge detail to keep the pavers from migrating into the planting soil. This detail normally requires a compacted subgrade to extend into the planting area, significantly reducing soil volume in a narrow tree opening. Use of a concrete edge around the tree opening secures the paver while permitting larger soil volume for the tree.

MITIGATION OF PAVING CONFLICTS

Maintenance

Greater maintenance can overcome root-paving conflicts by repairing damage as it occurs. Lifted paving can be ground down or the adjacent paving depression filled. Unit pavers can be reset higher or simply removed. Concrete paving can be lifted to even out elevations by a process known as mud-jacking, where fluid concrete is pumped under the paving slab. At some point, the entire sidewalk will need to be reconstructed.

a

b

c

Figure 2.5.24. Paving maintenance.
a. Tree in conflict with pavers.
b. Re-set pavers to resolve conflict.
c. Grinding concrete (light-colored areas) to temporarily remove tripping hazard.

Maintenance as a solution to root-paving conflicts is always temporary and should not be the crutch to support lower standards for paving. It is better to buy stronger pavement and design soil for rooting under the pavement. Stronger pavement will reduce conflicts but not necessarily help the tree. Only by designing adequate rooting space will we improve the condition of the tree.

Tree Species Selection

Different tree species typically develop more or less aggressive trunk flares and zone-of-rapid-taper roots. See *Reducing Infrastructure Damage by Tree Roots* for a reference on the differences between trees. The list of trees was created for California, and designers in other areas must do their own research. Fortunately, this book discusses a way to evaluate trees in other areas.

Trees that produce large canopies and are the most valuable for the future of the urban forest, also produce large root crowns. This should not be surprising, as the crown is there to resist forces within the

a

b

Figure 2.5.25. Aggressive and less aggressive species.
a. Most oaks have a large root crown.
b. Plane tree often has a less aggressive root crown.

canopy. The larger the canopy, the larger the root crown. For example, the tunnel that passes through the base of the Wawona redwood tree in Mariposa, California, actually goes through the tree's trunk flare.

Figure 2.5.26. The Wawona redwood's trunk flare.

Client Expectation

If asked, would a city or client say, "Yes, I am willing to accept the risk of stressed trees, damaged sidewalks, and injured pedestrians?" Probably not. At an early stage, designers should start a discussion of the client's risk tolerance, making clients aware of the compromises that are being made. Make every effort to resolve these compromises satisfactorily for both the health of the tree and the safety of the pavement.

SURFACE TREATMENTS WITHIN TREE OPENINGS

The surface of tree openings changes over time, from bare soil and nursery root ball to a space full of woody surface roots. This process takes 30 to 40 years, depending on the species and the size of the opening.

To support the roots during establishment, the soil within the tree opening needs access to water and air. At the same time, tree roots must quickly break out of the tree opening and into the soil underneath the pavement to find room to grow. Assuming the designer has provided for this breakout, the roots that remain in the tree opening will become large structures to support the tree and the movement of water and chemicals. Few absorbing roots will remain in the opening as the tree matures.

Mulch

The best management practice for young trees is to cover the surface of the soil in the tree opening with organic mulch. Organic mulch cushions the soil from compaction, holds water, moderates soil temperature, and provides a small amount of organic matter to the soil food web. These mulch functions will become less valuable as the absorbing roots become transport and structural roots. The mulch will need to be replenished every several years, but should never exceed 2 to 3 inches in depth of organic matter, including the previously installed mulch.

Do not allow mulch to build up around trees. Deep layers of mulch around the trunk can result in girdling roots, bark rot, and rodent damage. After about 10 years, a healthy tree in a small opening should no longer need to be mulched. Bark should be forming on the roots that are pushing out of the ground.

Figure 2.5.27. Lightly mulched tree. Note that ground-cover plants have not been planted around the base of the tree.

Figure 2.5.28. Too much mulch.

The King of Tree Grates

In Florida, a massive 14-foot-diameter, rubber-coated steel tree grate was installed. The strands of twinkle lights around the trunk and the permanent electric box installed at the base of the trunk indicate the owner's attitude toward the tree as an object of ornament instead of a living organism. Nothing about this design except the large planting hole respects the base of this tree. Fortunately, the rubber coating on the grate is starting to peel off the steel, and the grate may be removed for aesthetic reasons before the grate or its steel support beams strangle the tree.

Mounded mulch makes it difficult to water the tree, and the mulch absorbs much of the water, keeping it from penetrating into the soil. The top of the mulch should always be a little below the paving.

Tree Grates?

In intense urban spaces, the traditional approach has been to cover the tree opening with a tree grate. This is not a good solution and is one of the biggest causes of structural damage to urban trees. They do nothing positive for the tree. Recently, the City of New York Parks Department banned the use of tree grates.

Tree grates are expensive and rob project funds that could be better spent on soil improvement. The tree opening is made smaller than necessary because larger grates are expensive, and smaller grates are selected to save money. These smaller grates establish a standard that makes the space for all trees the same size, even where there is the opportunity to make a larger planting space (see Principle 2, "Make bigger holes").

Roots lift the grates and create a trip hazard. Since the grate is supposed to be a walkable surface that invites the pedestrian, a tree grate with a lifted edge may be considered an attractive nuisance in a trip-and-fall lawsuit.

The center hole in the grate must be enlarged as the tree grows, or else it will girdle the trunk. Few communities have the budget to enlarge the grates as recommended. In the design of many cast-iron grates, the innermost ring of metal is thicker than the remaining rings. Cutting this ring compromises the structural integrity of the grate.

Grates require that the elevation of the tree root ball be below the paving grade. In poorly drained soil, this may kill the tree. The space between the grate and the root ball collects trash,

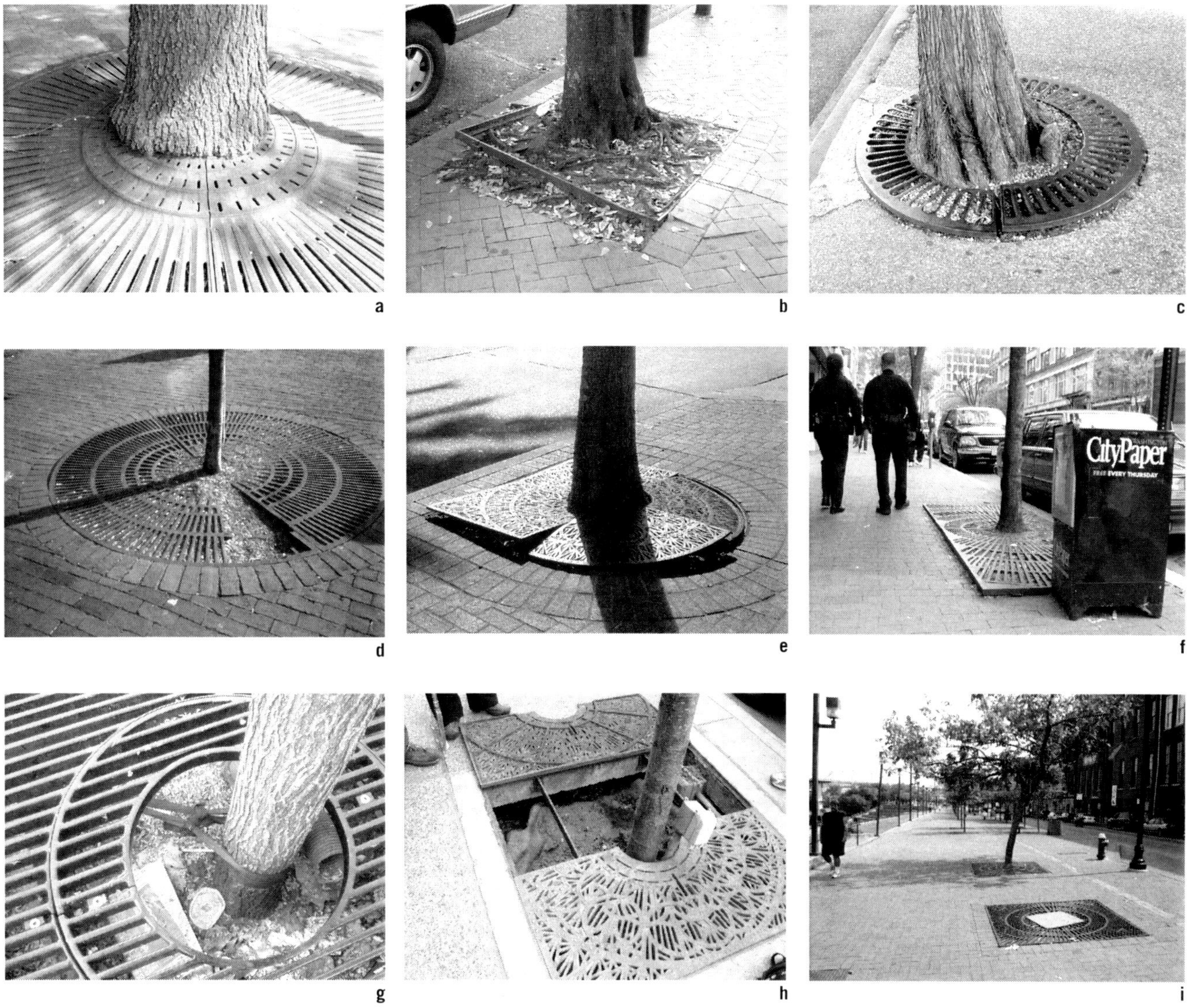

Figure 2.5.29. Tree grate images. Show these to anyone considering buying grates.

a. Girdling tree grate.
b. Grate and frame pushed out of the way by aggressive roots.
c. Roots pushing grate. Note roots along backside of curb.
d. Broken grates, all too common on city streets.
e. Tripping hazard and girdling the trunk.
f. Tripping hazard, a public menace ignored by the law and press.
g. Trash pit, aka tree opening.
h. Tree planted 12 inches below the paving. There is no way to "fix" this situation.
i. The final "fix" for many tree grates.

which is difficult to remove. Once the grate is removed, the trunk flare may be at too low an elevation to be able to fill the depression without burying the trunk.

Tree grates are fabricated out of cast iron, steel, plastic, and concrete. No matter what material is used, they are bad for trees and should always be avoided.

Tree experts have spent 25 years trying to get the word out about the need to ban tree grates but they still continue to be used. Designers who insist on using tree grates should at least use a model that has a very large trunk hole, a minimum of 24 inches in diameter. Locate the root ball as close to the elevation of the pavement as possible. This may allow the roots to push the grate up and cause its removal before the grate begins to strangle the tree. Once removed, if the tree was not planted too deeply, the remaining space can be filled with mulch, gravel, or stone dust.

Grated trees might have a better chance if tree grates were beveled on their bottom edges. This would let the tree push the grate up and out of the way as it grows, avoiding strangulation. This would

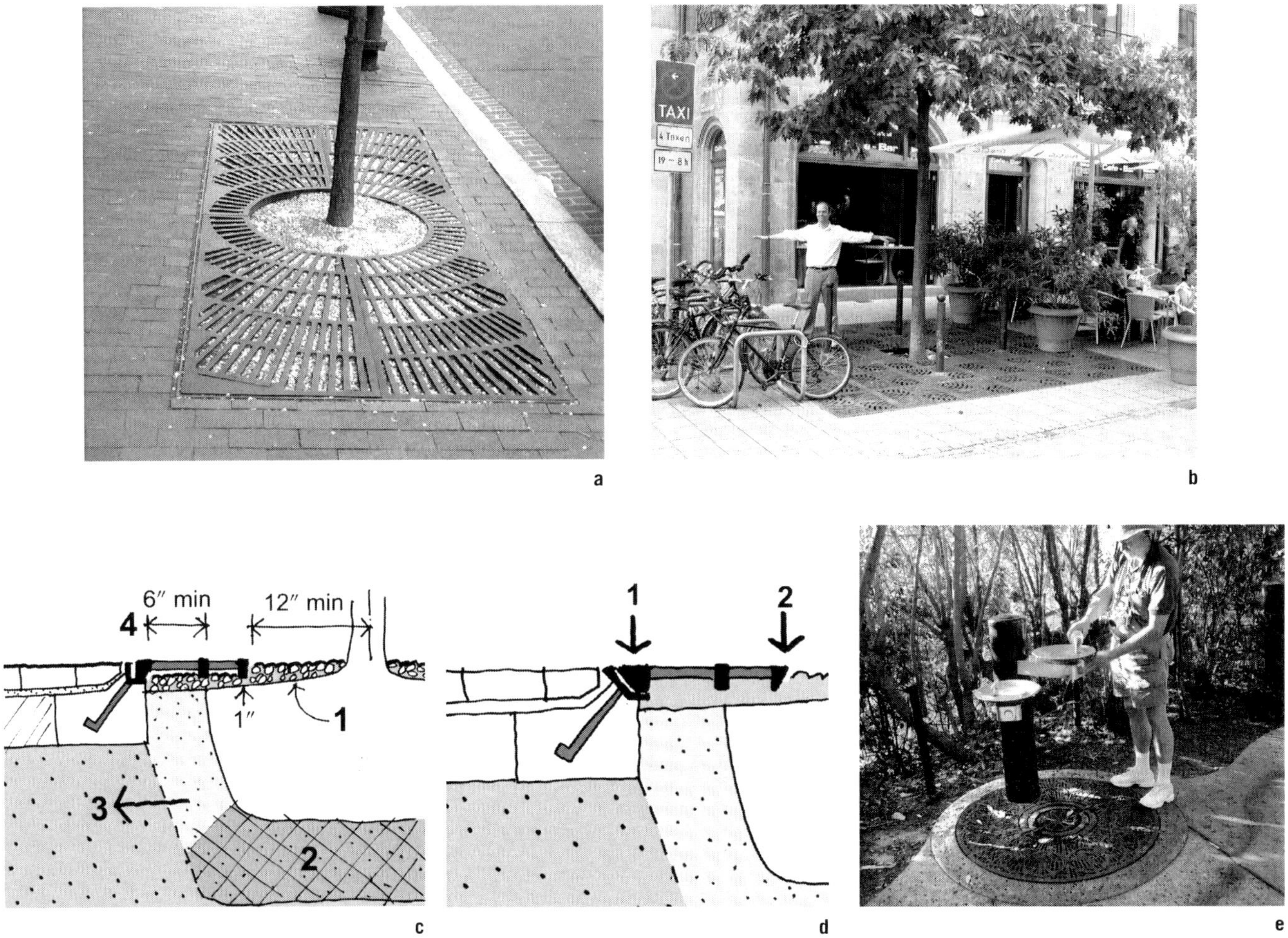

Figure 2.5.30. Tree grate details.

a. If tree grates must be used, select one with a large center hole.
b. If tree grates must be used, select the biggest one available. Change the size to fit space available within the design.
c. Installation detail:
   1. 24-inch- or greater diameter opening. Fill space with gravel.
   2. Compact soil under root ball.
   3. Rooting soil under sidewalk. See Part 2, Chapter Six.
   4. 6-inch minimum space between paving edge and root ball. Specify correctly sized tree to fit in tree opening.
d. Proposal for improved grate design to reduce tree damage.
e. Reasonable reuse of grates no longer needed for trees. *(Photo credit: Jocelyn Ball)*

obviously make the grate a tripping hazard, but that is precisely the intent to force the removal of the grate as quickly as possible. Once the grate starts to move, it is time to get rid of it and let the tree take over the space.

The following are details for better installations for grates. The inclusion of these details is not an endorsement of tree grates, only a recognition of the unfortunate reality of their continued use.

Alternatives to Tree Grates

Mulch! One More Time, Mulch

Again, organic mulch is the best covering for tree openings.

If organic mulch is not acceptable, designers should propose alternatives that are the least restrictive for the intensity of use of the space. How many pedestrians are expected in the area, and how frequently are they likely to walk in the tree opening? Is it a problem if an occasional person walks on mulch? Are different types of surfaces acceptable as conditions change?

Gravel and Synthetic Mulches

Natural gravel, expanded shale (ESCS) gravel, crumb rubber, and other synthetic materials have been used to mulch trees. These materials may still require sweeping and replenishment, and do not contribute to the organic layer of the soil.

The Emperor Tree Grate

Florida, the Dutch have outdone you. This massive tree grate in Maastricht, Netherlands, is not only nearly 16 feet square but is more than 10 feet above the root crown, which lives in the parking garage below! Unlike many smaller grates, the design for this tree better reflects the compromise between the needs of trees and people.

All mulches help reduce soil compaction and water evaporation out of the soil. These mulches may be difficult to clear of small debris such as cigarette butts and bits of paper. Organic matter will accumulate in these materials, which is good for the tree but may not be appreciated if a tidy appearance is important. Weeds will eventually take hold in the organic accumulation.

In wet climates, gravel can hold significant moisture against the trunk. Do not make gravel more than a few inches deep.

Limestone gravel will raise soil pH in the tree opening. Rubber mulch becomes quite hot, which affects surface rooting in newly planted trees. There are differing opinions on the toxicity of rubber mulch. The primary offensive chemical in rubber mulch is zinc, which can build up in the soil and may kill plants. Avoid these mulches.

Gravel can be secured with resin binders. An advantage of resin-bonded material is its ability to drain freely, allowing air and water to reach the soil within the tree opening. If installed correctly, the material will break apart as the tree grows and should be considered temporary, expected to last less than 10 years. If installed too close to a small tree (closer than 4 or 5 inches), or installed too thickly (more than a couple of inches thick), the material can begin to girdle the tree just like a tree grate.

a

b

c

Figure 2.5.31. Gravel and synthetic mulches

a. ESCS gravel used as a mulch. Note light and utility box kept outside the tree opening.

b. Resln-bonded gravel installed too close, but thin enough to crack as the tree grows.

c. Resin-bonded gravel installed incorrectly (too close and too thick) girdling the tree only one year after installation.

Figure 2.5.32. Stone dust. In this case, a tree grate was removed and the space filled with stone dust. Note wires wrapping the tree trunk, which should be removed.

Figure 2.5.33. Plants as a ground cover under trees in a crowded urban area. Note curb and low fence barrier needed to protect the ground-cover plants.

Stone Dust and Decomposed Granite

Fine-grained aggregates can be flexible but also relatively stable surfaces. Finer aggregates are more stable to movement than larger-sized stone mulch. Avoid these surfaces on slopes greater than 5 percent, as material will wash out of the tree opening.

Limestone dust will increase soil pH and may compact to the point where water will not infiltrate. Other types of stone dust may have less impact on pH and better infiltration rates. Check locally available materials.

Plants

Plants will be in competition with the tree, with groundcover plants typically dominating at first. If the tree survives, it will slowly control the light and available rooting space. The tree will eventually kill off most plantings, but by that time, these plants will have fulfilled their intended function.

Understory plantings are normally watered more frequently than trees, because they show drought stress sooner. People are more likely to respond with water for the smaller plants before the tree becomes water-stressed. The tree usually will be able to use some of this water. In some cases, well-meaning people or malfunctioning irrigation systems can overwater the tree, keeping the root ball saturated. The author had a client who killed a newly planted tree in less than two months with too much water. The client lamented, "How could the tree have died? I watered it every day!"

Understory plantings should be considered temporary, to be removed or replaced with different plants that can tolerate the conditions under a mature tree. Property managers should not attempt to replant and "restore" the original plantings.

Lawn. Mowed grass is an acceptable surface, but has several drawbacks. Lawn requires relatively frequent maintenance, invites potential damage to the tree base from mowers, and competes with the tree for resources. Its watering cycles are different from the tree's. As the tree matures, the lawn is not shade-tolerant. Some grass species produce chemicals that harm trees, while some trees produce chemicals that harm lawns. Accepting a mulched area between the lawn and the tree can reduce mower damage and resource competition. The size of the mulched area should be larger than the original root ball of the tree. Mulch rings of between 6 and 10 feet in diameter, maintained for at lease 5 to 10 years, have been demonstrated to improve tree recovery from transplant shock.

Extreme Ground Cover

Even good ideas can be taken too far. This bubble of ground cover placed on a metal frame is an ingenious and expensive attempt to make design trump nature. Yet nature always laughs last. The trees did not live very long and had to be replaced.

When designing understory plantings, no plant (lawn, annuals, ground covers, or shrubs) should ever be placed on top of or into the tree's root ball. Digging into or adding soil over the root ball stresses the tree at the critical point of transplant recovery. Always draw the root ball of each tree on the plan, and place no plants, lights, electric boxes, pavers, or tree grates within this space.

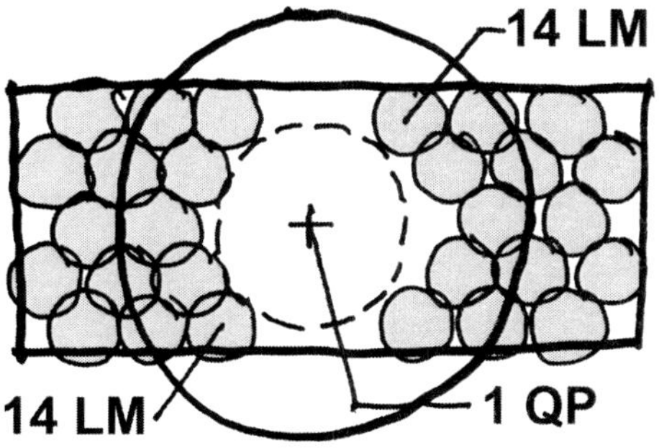

Figure 2.5.34. Typical plant layout in a tree opening. Never draw plants within the root ball of the tree. Note dashed line representing root ball. Draw this line on every tree to scale on planting plans.

As the tree develops a large trunk flare, it can defend against mower damage. The maturing tree root system and enlarging canopy will overshadow the lawn, slowly converting the ground near the tree to an area of roots, sparse grass, and organic accumulation. This is ideal for the tree unless the tree owner mounts a vigorous campaign to improve lawn quality.

Annuals. Flowering annuals and bulbs make an attractive surface, but come with the price of constant tree root disturbance. If annuals are included in the initial planting year and continued every season, the tree roots may develop at a deeper level. Adding annuals or any planting under an established tree causes greater problems by damaging absorbing roots and cutting larger roots. Use a pneumatic digging tool to prepare soil around large existing trees. This allows the installation of plantings with little damage to the trees. Pneumatic soil preparation is commonly available from arborists.

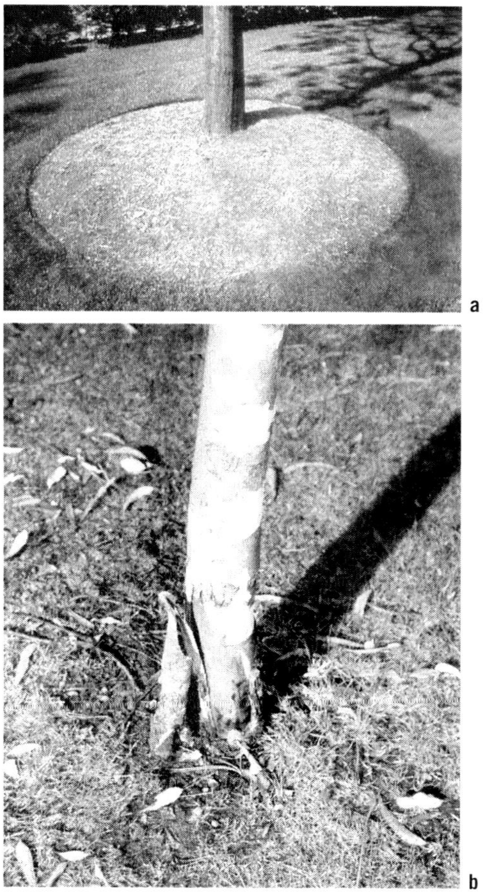

Figure 2.5.35. Trees and lawn.

a. Large mulch rings around trees help the tree recover from transplant shock and protect the trunk.

b. Lawn too close to the trunk subjects the trunk to "lawnmower disease."

Figure 2.5.36. Annual planting in the tree opening.

Figure 2.5.37. Maintain annual plantings under mature trees by separating the rooting space of the tree and the ground cover.

Annuals need lots of water, and their wilting can serve to announce that it is time to water the tree. Do not plant annuals within the root ball area of a newly planted tree. Over time, it will become impossible to maintain annual plantings. Introduce containers set on the paving to keep annual color in an urban space as the trees mature.

Small shrubs, ground covers, and perennials. Low plantings may be the best alternative to mulch around trees. The smaller plants invite additional watering during establishment. A few species, such as the old standbys of liriope and English ivy, can tolerate the conditions of almost full sun at planting and deep shade as the tree matures. Other species will gracefully fade away as the tree matures. The native plant design community will gasp at the mention of the word "ivy," but in an intense, inner-city tree planting, ivy remains one of the most reliable ground covers. Successful cities are compromises with nature and small uses of ivy to solve difficult urban planting situations may be reasonable.

Understory plantings will compete with trees for available soil nutrients. Compost, compost teas, and even organic fertilizer may be needed. Soil testing should be undertaken before adding any chemicals to the soil. In intensely developed areas, plantings may need a protective barrier to keep pedestrians out of the tree opening. A low fence, curb, or rail can serve this purpose. See more discussion on barriers later in this chapter.

As with all types of treatments within the tree opening, plantings should never be installed within the root ball of the tree. Instead, allow understory plants to creep over the top of the root ball.

Figure 2.5.38. Permanent shrub planting in the tree opening will at some point become difficult to maintain.

Paving

Sometimes, a paved surface is required, either because the intensity of use requires that the tree opening be used as an occasional walking surface, or because the designer was not successful in convincing the client or him- or herself of the merits of using the previously described alternatives.

Rubber. Poured-in-place or molded brick-shaped rubber, often seen as a playground surface, has been used as a covering for tree openings. This material may be flexible as the tree grows, but it is unclear whether it is soft enough not to girdle the tree. More research is needed on the suitability of this material and its impact on trees. For reasons of heat buildup alone, avoid this material within the tree opening of a newly planted tree, at least until new information can be researched. Rubber sidewalks, discussed earlier in this chapter, have similar issues.

Figure 2.5.39. Poured-in-place rubber surface within the tree opening. It would have been better to leave a space around the base of the tree.

Loose-laid pavers. Various types of pavers, from stone to pre-cast and brick, can serve to cover the tree opening. These pavers can be placed on sand or stone dust with sand joints. The smaller the paver size and the larger the joint, the more air and water connectivity there is between

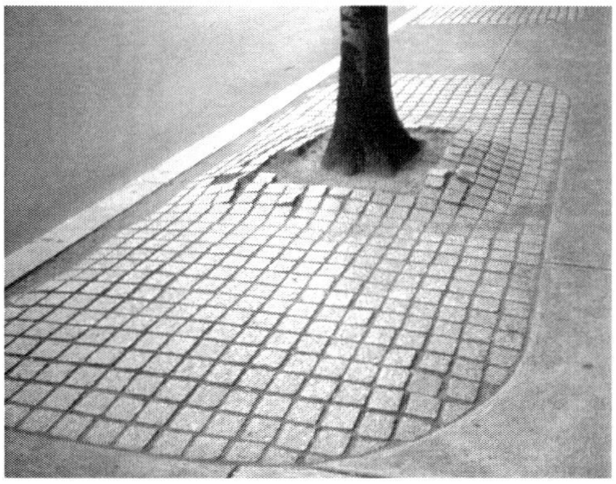

a

b

c

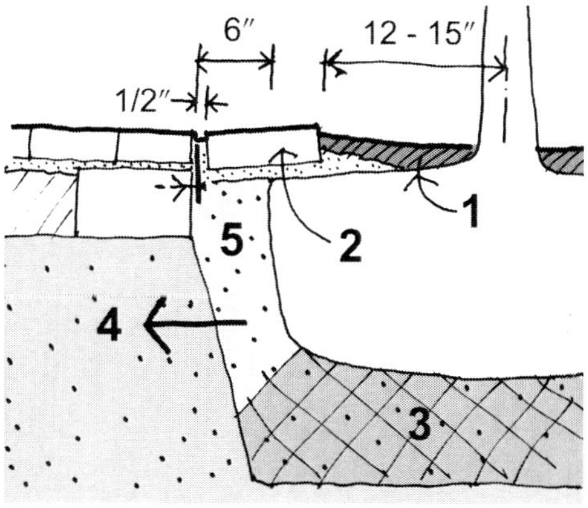

d

Figure 2.5.40. Loose-laid pavers in the tree opening.

a. Pavers originally laid flat, rising in the center as the root crown expands.
b. Pavers retrofitted around crown.
c. Pavers with a plastic edge embedded under the sand around the tree. This is as deadly as a tree grate. *Never use a paver edge on the tree side within the tree opening!*
d. Detail for paver installation within the tree opening.
    1. 24-inch- or greater square opening. Fill space with mulch, gravel, or sand. Do not fill material over trunk.
    2. Pavers set in sand bed with 1/2-inch sand joints.
    3. Compact soil under root ball.
    4. Rooting soil under sidewalk. See Part 2, Chapter Six.
    5. Six-inch minimum space between paving edge and root ball. Specify correctly sized tree to fit in tree opening.

the surface and the soil below. Four-inch square pavers with 1/2-inch sand-filled joints on a 1-inch sand setting bed are the optimum dimensions. Number 8-size stone as a setting bed and joint filler allows better air—water exchange. Adding a layer of geotextile under the setting bed will help the pavers bridge over compaction irregularities in the planting soil and allow them to rise in a smooth mound as the tree roots and trunk flare expand. Clients should be advised that the pavers will have to be gradually removed and/or reset as the tree matures.

If the pavers are set too close to the tree, girdling may occur. Do not use plastic brick edge reinforcement between the trunk and the paver. Girdling of the tree is assured with this detail, as the damage is concealed and the edge does not allow individual pavers to move. A good rule of thumb is to never place pavers over the root ball of the tree, or at a minimum no closer than 18 inches from the trunk, to provide sufficient room for the root crown to move pavers up before the trunk flare reaches the paver face.

Avoid mortar joints and cement sub-base material. The tree cannot move these pavers, which may constrict trunk development. Water and air do not move through the joints. Modifying mortar set pavers is more difficult once a tree/paver conflict develops.

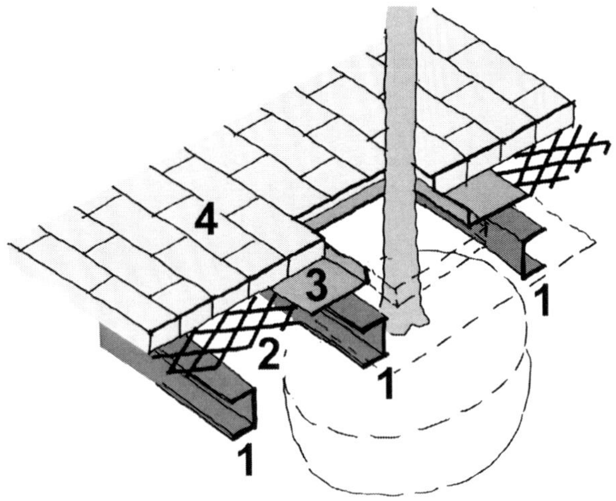

Figure 2.5.41. Suspended pavers are similar to tree grates. *Don't use them!*

1. Support beams.
2. Grating.
3. Retainer edge.
4. Pavers.

Suspended pavers on metal grates within the tree opening. Metal systems are available that support pavers over the top of the tree opening. These are tree grates in disguise. These metal gratings have all the drawbacks of a tree grate and may actually be more harmful. The structure of the grate is hidden, and early detection of trunk conflicts is not readily noticeable. Making the hole for the trunk larger as the tree grows is harder with these systems than with other grate options. The tree root ball must be set lower than with tree grates to allow the support beams to pass over the ball. Always avoid these systems.

CURBS AND BARRIERS AROUND TREE OPENINGS

Often curbs and/or fence barriers are placed at the edge of the tree opening to help keep people and vehicles out of the tree opening. Fenced barriers are often required if plants are the covering material for the opening.

Curbs

Curbs help keep people out of the tree opening. If high enough, they can add to the overall soil volume and improve drainage.

Curbs keep water running across the paving from entering the tree opening. In warm climates, getting this additional water into the tree opening may be beneficial. In cold, moist climates, water on the sidewalk may contain significant salt content, and the curbs may therefore be beneficial. However, in the summer, these same trees may need the extra water that would be blocked by the curb. Tree openings with access to large soil volumes under the pavement should experience little impact from deicing salt. The salt becomes diluted in the large soil volume and flushed away by spring rains. In small tree openings with confined soil volumes, sidewalk salt can add significant stress. A drain system needs to be developed that allows storm water to access the soil volume below the pavement during the growing season, but diverts salt-laden water in the winter. Assuring adequate drainage in the soil and sufficient soil volume often eliminates the waterborne salt problem.

Where possible, design curbs to be part of or rest on the sidewalk paving base to preserve soil volume. Avoid foundations under curbs.

a

b

c

d

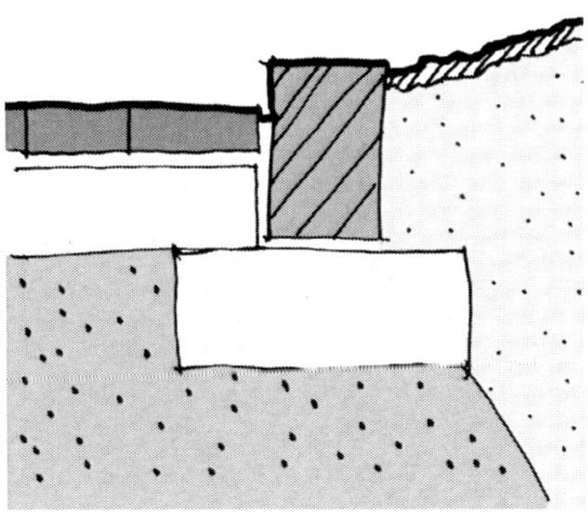
e1

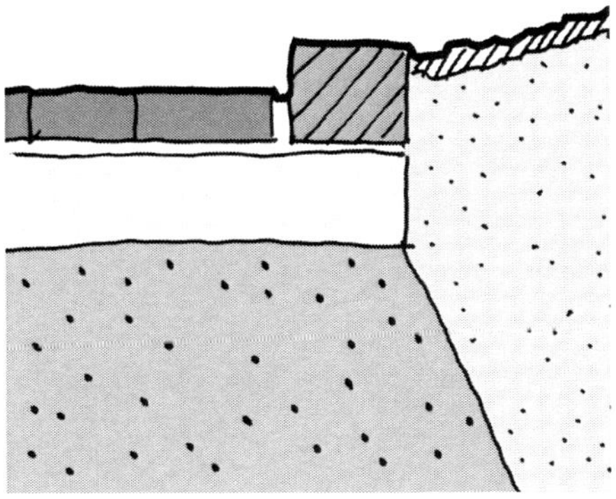
e2

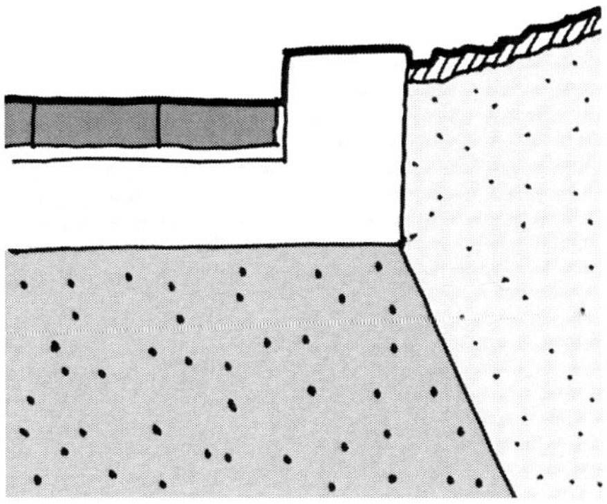
e3

Figure 2.5.42. Curbs.

a. Higher curbs increase soil volume.

b. A subtle bend in the concrete formwork can be sufficient to divert water and even pedestrians.

c. Nice curb design but forgot the soil.

d. These curbs were not effective to keep people out of these planters, so the city added a rail barrier.

e. Details of curbs at the edges of tree openings.

1. Traditional curb with footing that reduces the soil volume in the tree opening. *Avoid!*
2. Curb set on concrete base as integral part of the paving section. Reduces impact on soil volume.
3. Monolithic concrete curb. Reduces root-paving conflict.

a

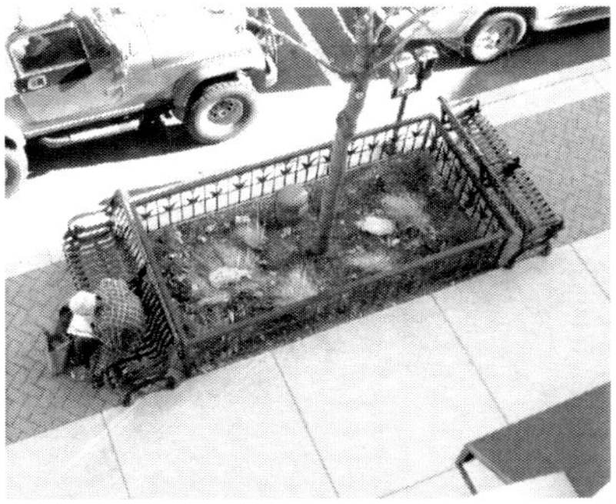
b

c

d

e

f

g

Low Fences

Low fences are an important feature whenever trees are planted in areas with high pedestrian traffic. Consider them as vertical tree grates. Fences and rails can serve as seating or places to park a bike or the dog. These barriers are expensive, roughly the same cost as a tree grate. Cost is the primary reason why more barriers are not installed.

Barriers need to be high enough to not become a tripping hazard. A minimum height of 18 to 24 inches is considered desirable, although there are plenty of lower barriers that function quite well in congested spaces. Cars and car doors bang into the barriers if placed too close to the curb. It is usually only necessary to put them on the tree opening face that is perpendicular to traffic, saving cost. Low fences are recommended, but designs must be simple, strong, and easy to repair.

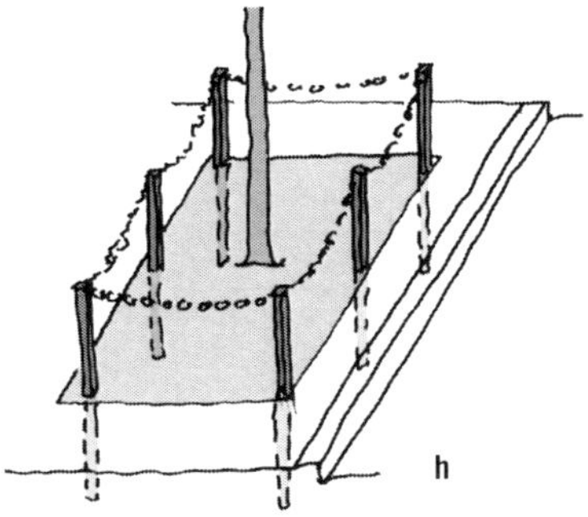
h

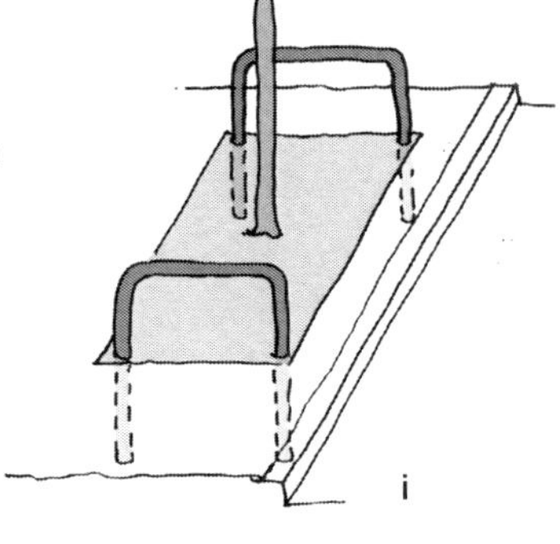
i

Figure 2.5.43. Fences and barriers.

a. Stout fence and curb at bus drop-off area.
b. Fenced tree opening in retail center. The two benches were likely sufficient to protect the tree opening. The fence is primarily decorative.
c. Low, simple barrier outside the entrance to the White House. Despite intense pedestrian activity, the tripping hazard excuse was not used here.
d. Sturdy, simple vehicle barrier in Holland. This barrier has no concrete footing, just pipe set in the earth for easy removal and replacement if damaged.
e. The minimum barrier size. See discussion on tree guards.
f. Effective temporary barrier during tree replacement: The Tuileries Gardens, Paris.
g. Barriers are needed to control bicycle parking.
h. Simple chain barrier with no footings. Barriers are temporary until the tree matures.
i. Pipe wicket design on the ends of the tree opening perpendicular to pedestrian flow. Can function as a bike rack, seat, or place to tie your dog.

TREE OR TRUNK GUARDS

Tree guards or trunk guards are closely related to tree grates and are equally damaging to trees. They are a relic of another era, developed to keep horses from nibbling at tree bark. Like tree grates, guards are expensive, robbing the budget of money needed for soil and drainage. They can damage the tree and tend to collect trash inside the frame. They provide few positive features to protect the tree, while causing great harm as the tree grows.

Most tree guards are too small in diameter and will constrict the tree. As the top of the tree sways, the trunk and lower branches cut into the top portion of the guard. This is the primary conflict with this object, and damage has been observed within a few years of installation. At the bottom of the guard, the frame constricts the developing trunk flare. If the tree opening is large enough, a guard should not be necessary. If for some reason a guard must be used, the minimum size should be the diameter of the root ball. The structure should be simple, so that trash does not collect, and the guard should be considered temporary and removed as the tree matures.

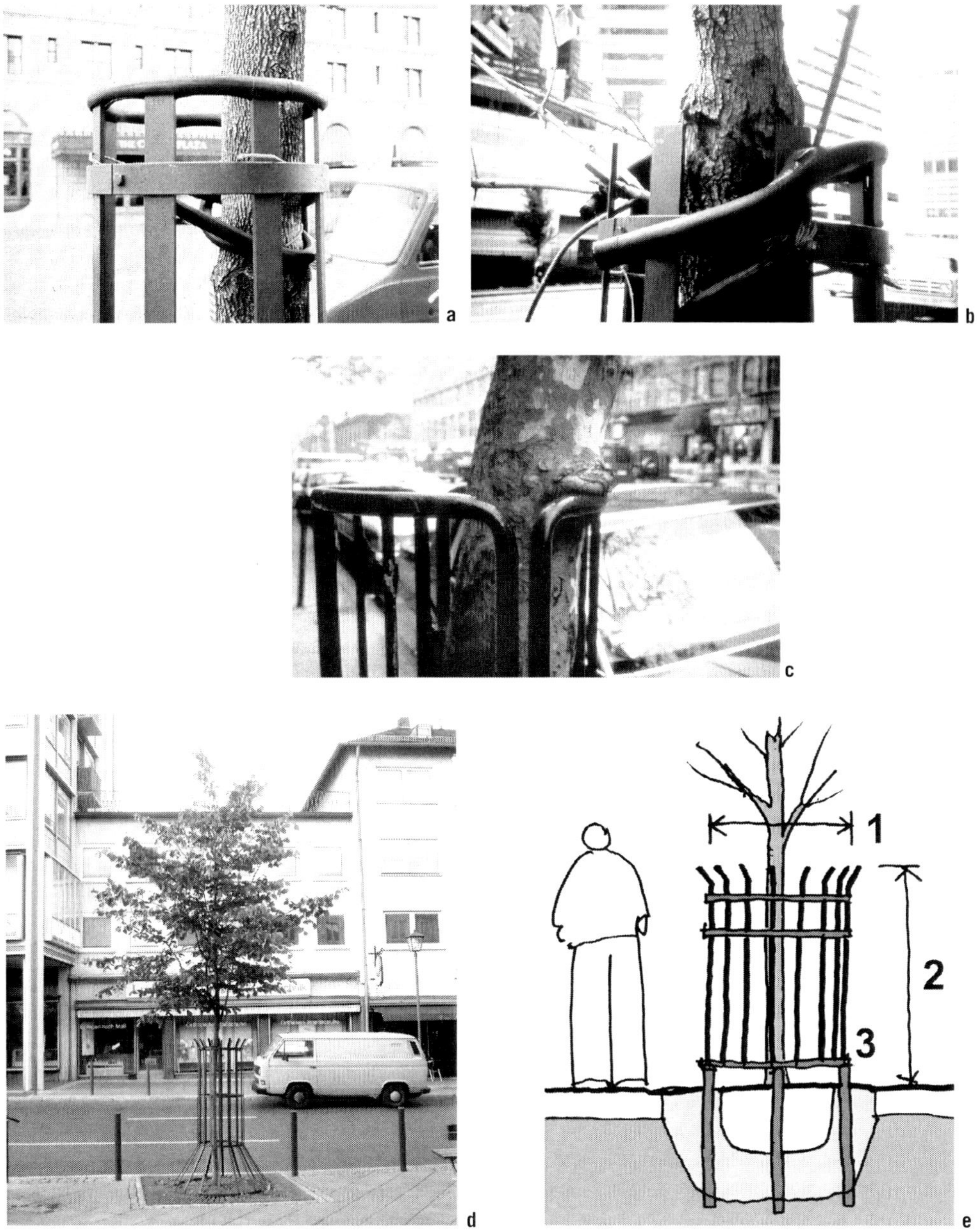

Figure 2.5.44. Tree guards.

a. Tree guard at installation—the designer's pride.
b. Tree guard after five years. The guard killed the tree and the tree killed the guard.
c. Tree guards must respect how much trees move in their space after planting.
d. Even this tree guard is not large enough. It must be removed before the tree touches the upper edge.
e. A tree-friendly guard proposal.
   1. Tree guard supports should not penetrate the root ball. A guard mounted on a tree grate should be at least 30 inches in diameter.
   2. Height at least 12 inches below the first branch.
   3. Space vertical bars and bottom horizontal bar for ample room to remove trash.

a

b

ELECTRICAL FIXTURES INSIDE TREE OPENINGS

Often, a design will call for electrical outlets within the tree opening, to be used for seasonal tree lighting, maintenance, or vendors. Seasonal lighting can harm trees if not installed with the greatest of care. Hard-wired conduits and junction boxes damage the tree as the trunk encounters the structure, and should always be located well outside the root ball. This may be impossible if a tree grate is specified (which is one more reason never to use a tree grate). Flexible cable connections can be specified and relocated as the tree grows. Do not make the wires so long that they can be wrapped around the trunk.

Up-lights are often placed at the base of the tree. These features should always be outside the limit of the root ball. Lights are also often placed in the tree canopy with wires attached to the trunk. Wires and connectors should never be wrapped around the trunk of the tree. This will not harm the tree immediately, but remember that the tree grows and the wire will eventually become enveloped within the trunk. It would be great simply to say "never attach anything to the trunk," but if wires are added, do it in a way that causes the least harm to the tree.

Lights within the canopy or at the base of the tree can be hot enough to damage the cambium. Use low-voltage lamps with cowlings that hold the lenses away from the edge of the light. Avoid putting the lamp in a location where the lens is closer than 18 inches to the bark of the tree.

c

Figure 2.5.45. Electricity and trees.

a. Avoid lights this close to the root ball.
b. Traditional but unacceptable place to locate outlet electric box. Find a location outside of the tree's trunk flare. Note wire tie already girdling the trunk
c. A flexible electrical connection is better than a rigid conduit.
d. Trees are not light posts. Designers should fight to stop this type of tree abuse.
e. Do not attach wires by straps.
f. A more acceptable way to attach wires to trees. However, the attachment strap is not long enough and will have to be replaced in a few years. Account for tree growth on any detail that attaches objects to trees.

d

e

f

a. Trees as light armatures.
b. Wires compressing trunk.
c. Wires girdling the branches of a tree.

'Tis the Season to Be Concerned?

Many cities use street trees as armatures for seasonal lighting in retail districts. This type of lighting causes several problems for the tree. Installation breaks small branches and damages buds. If the lights are left in place all year, wires wrapped around branches begin to constrict and girdle branches and the trunk.

More research is needed to understand the compatibility of trees and seasonal lighting. Limit the practice whenever possible, and assign people skilled in working with trees to handle installation and removal.

IRRIGATION AND WATER MANAGEMENT WITHIN TREE OPENINGS

In areas of the United States where rain exceeds 30 inches a year, irrigation for long-term growth is not needed. Irrigation is helpful during the establishment period of the first several years. Irrigation systems are notoriously maintenance-sensitive in urban areas. Keeping a system operational requires a high level of commitment. Once pipes, wires and valves are under the pavement, maintenance becomes more difficult and costly. Many streetscape irrigation systems are abandoned.

Hand-watering from water trucks or hose bibs is often the preferred system, and may be less expensive. In most cities, additional water is only needed during limited periods. If the design provides sufficient soil and a way to harvest natural rainwater, the only water that should be required is during establishment and periods of extreme drought.

The smaller the tree opening, the slower the rate of water application to eliminate runoff. Think about watering your house plants. It is easy and relatively quick to water the plants in the big pots where the soil is well below the lip. Plants in small containers where the soil is close to the lip require a slow and tedious effort to fill without overflowing, and the smaller soil volume dries out quickly, requiring more frequent watering. The same effect happens when trying to water a street tree. Principle 2, "Make bigger planting holes," comes into play here. The larger the area, the easier it is to hydrate the soil.

The design of pressurized irrigation systems evolved from golf and garden projects where systems are easily accessible and there is a maintenance budget to keep them in working order. Plastic heads and other features are not built to withstand intense urban use and abuse.

Spray heads are the most difficult to maintain. Drip systems are slightly better. There are reports that rat poisons commonly used in urban areas cause the rats to seek out water and chew into drip lines. A new tree bubbler system made by Toro may be the best option for hydrating soil within the tree opening when an automatic irrigation system is required.

Whatever the system, keep all lines, valve boxes, and heads out of the root ball. Keep valve boxes away from the tree opening altogether, as they will compete for needed soil-volume space.

Regardless of how large the tree opening is, in an urban streetscape it will never be large enough to provide the required water for a large tree. Soils under the pavement also will require water. The system under the pavement needs to be considered separately from the requirements within the tree opening. See Part 2, Chapter Six for discussion on water management under the pavement.

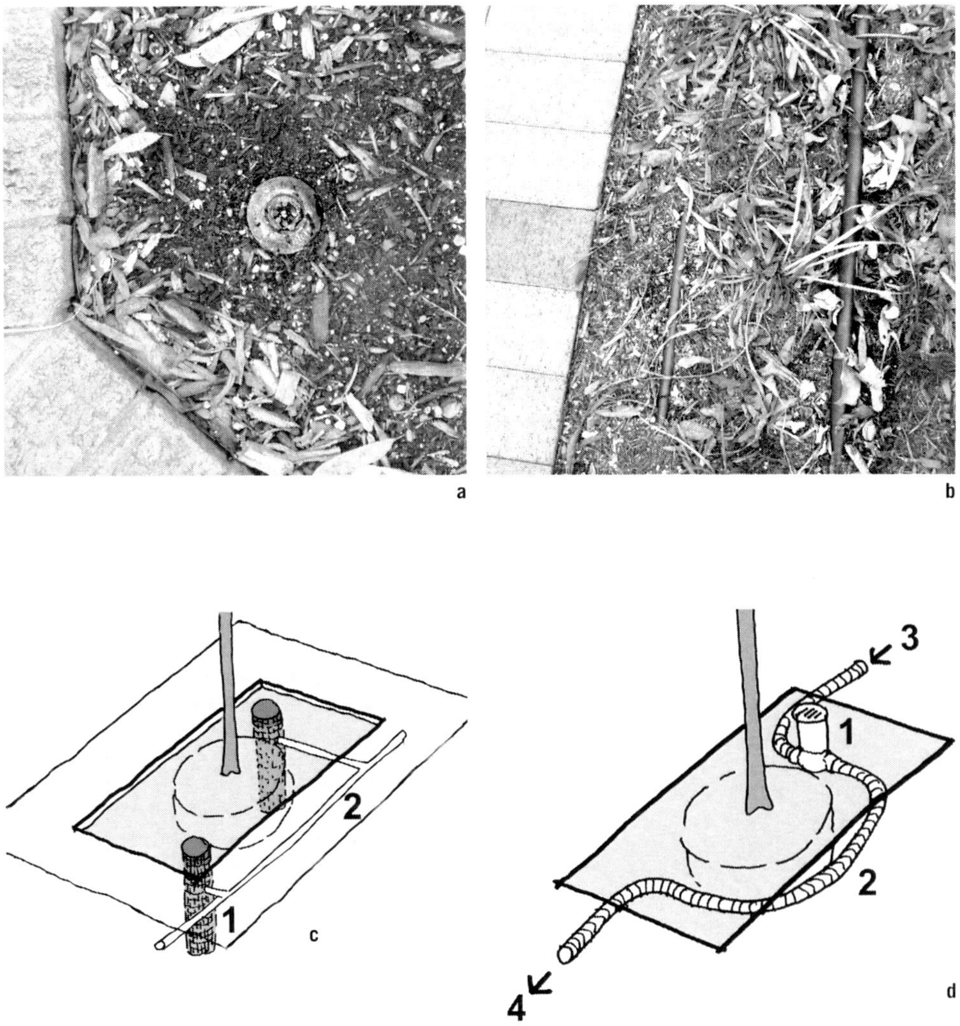

Figure 2.5.46. Irrigation within the tree opening.

a. Spray heads are difficult to maintain in urban spaces.
b. Drip lines may be easier to maintain and transition to under paving soil systems.
c. Bubbler columns, an alternative to drip, do not easily hydrate soil under paving.
   1. Perforated column with bubbler head.
   2. Pressurized water supply line.
d. Perforated pipes within the tree opening and under the pavement can be supplied by hose or pressurized bubbler head.
   1. Small grated inlet. Add water by hose or equip inlet with pressurized bubbler head.
   2. Two-inch perforated drain line set 12 to 18 inches below grade.
   3. Connect perforated line through under paving soil system from next tree higher in elevation.
   4. Connect line next to lower tree.

SUMMARY

- Respect the trunk flare and zone of rapid taper roots of the tree by designing the opening in the pavement to fit the requirements of the tree's future growth.
- The space between the tree trunk and the permanent edge of pavement is a temporary surface that changes from earth to wood over a 20- to 40-year period.
- The surface of the transition space must be a material that is flexible to change.
- Tree grates damage trees. Avoid them.
- Curbs and low barriers around the tree opening are beneficial to control salt and pedestrian intrusion into the tree opening.
- Tree guards damage trees. Avoid them.
- Keep conduit-wired electric junction boxes out of the area of the tree's future trunk flare.
- Conflicts between tree roots and paving around the tree opening cannot be eliminated, but only reduced to levels that meet the owner's tolerance of risk. Use the options presented in this chapter to reduce risk.

REFERENCES

Key References

Costello, Laurence R. and Katherine S. Jones. 2003. *Reducing Infrastructure Damage by Tree Roots: A Compendium of Strategies.* Western Chapter of the International Society of Arboriculture, Cohasset, CA. 119 pp.

Harris, Richard W., James R. Clark, and Nelda P. Matheny. 2004. *Arboriculture: Integrated Management of Landscape Trees, Shrubs, and Vines.* 4th ed. Pearson Education, Inc., Upper Saddle River, NJ. 578 pp.

Matheny, Nelda, and James R. Clark. 1998. *Trees and Development: A Technical Guide to Preservation of Trees During Land Development.* International Society of Arboriculture, Champaign, IL. 183 pp.

Urban, James. 2000. *Ramsey/Sleeper Architectural Graphic Standards.* 10th ed. John Ray Hoke, Jr., ed. John Wiley & Sons, Inc., New York, NY.

Other Resources

Costello, Laurence R., et al. 2003. *Abiotic Disorders of Landscape Plants.* University of California, Division of Agriculture and Natural Resources, Oakland, CA. 242 pp.

Dirr, Michael A. 1998. *Manual of Woody Landscape Plants.* Stipes Publishing, Champaign, IL. 1,187 pp.

Ferguson, Bruce K. 2005. *Porous Pavements.* CRC Press, Boca Raton, FL. 577 pp.

Lilly, Sharon J. 2001. *Arborists' Certification Study Guide.* International Society of Arboriculture, Champaign, IL. 222 pp.

Trowbridge, Peter J., and Nina L. Bassuk. 2004. *Trees in the Urban Landscape: Site Assessment Design and Installation.* John Wiley & Sons, Inc., Hoboken, NJ. 205 pp.

PART TWO

6

Principle 6: Make Space for Roots

Up By Roots provides the tools to improve the growing conditions of large trees in cities. In an ideal world, every tree would have enough soil, but this is almost never the case in urban areas. There will be times when not planting a tree is the best answer, and one of the purposes of this book is to help designers know when to make that choice. This book is intended, however, to advocate planting trees, which are a worthwhile environmental and aesthetic investment for landowners and communities provided they are given the conditions in which to succeed.

Trees must "break out" of confined urban planting spaces in order to mature. Absorbing roots seek out small spaces between pavement and compacted subgrade where they can find air and water for growth. When these roots find suitable growing conditions, they will enlarge, damaging the paving and thereby increasing maintenance cost and liability. It is difficult to create urban tree planting spaces large enough to support long-term growth without some roots needing to grow under the pavement. The best approach is to anticipate root breakout and control it by providing spaces where roots can grow without damage.

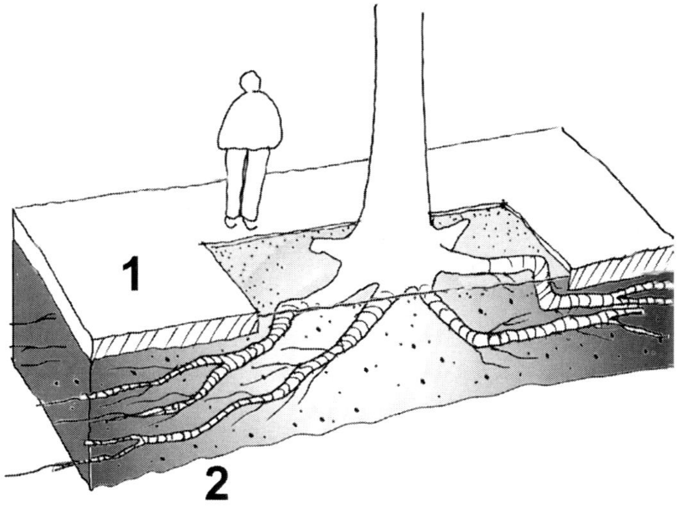

Figure 2.6.1. Make space for roots under the pavement.

1. Always make the tree opening as large as possible and respect the base of the tree. And then ...
2. ... make space for roots under the pavement.

Figure 2.6.2. Under current urban tree planting standards, trees have to "break out" of the tree openings any way they can.

Many options exist to provide for the coexistence of roots and pavement. While expensive, these options must become a standard part of the urban infrastructure.

Factors in selecting the most appropriate option include budget, type of paving and tree, existing soil conditions, and drainage conditions. In most instances, a combination of several options may be appropriate.

HOW MUCH SOIL?

The object of Principle 6 is to provide adequate soil volume or to provide the most soil volume that can be afforded within the project budget. Providing soil volume under the sidewalk is the most expensive part of planting a tree in the city. Some of the existing soil under the sidewalk may be adequate with little or no improvement. In other situations, the designer must provide all of the required soil.

Multiple options to improve soil under paving are needed because of the many conditions found in the urban environment, and they impact the need or ability to make changes. Existing soil and drainage, available space, project budget, and the client's threshold to accept failure all factor into decision-making. In most projects, several options can be combined to expand rooting options and improve trees. It is the designers' responsibility to make the recommendations that meet the goals of the project. The easiest and cheapest method to provide the greatest amount of soil volume is usually the correct choice.

Soil Volume Calculations

Calculate the soil volume required for each tree. Table 2.4.1 in Part 2, Chapter Four indicates a method to calculate approximate volumes required to grow trees of various sizes.

Calculate the soil volume that might be available to the tree. This should include the soil within the tree opening, existing or prepared soil under the pavement, and any soil in adjacent rooting spaces.

In dense urban streetscapes, it will often be difficult to provide the soil needed even with the use of all of the space under the pavement. Where lack of soil volume limits the potential of the tree, the client should be informed about how this limitation will result in slower growth, smaller trees, and shorter life expectancy.

Soil volumes under pavement that interconnect from tree to tree or connect to larger soil resources, such as garden or lawn areas near the tree, will grow larger trees than will isolated soil areas. This factor is difficult to quantify but may increase the effectiveness of the soil under the pavement by 20 to 30 percent.

Installed soil volumes should not be separated from existing soil resources by grade beams or filter cloth. Any object that isolates the soil volume from the adjacent soil not only blocks roots from exploring additional resources, but also slows the movement of groundwater into the tree's soil volume. This may be an important source of water for the tree.

Soil types designed to be compacted to 95 percent of dry density and also allow tree roots to penetrate, such as sand/soil and soil/aggregate structural soil discussed later in this chapter, will not support the same amount of tree canopy as a loam soil with much lower compaction. When these soils are specified, much more soil may be required to achieve similar tree response. This changes the cost evaluation of using these options. The required increase may be so great that there is not adequate room to provide the required soil volume.

Figure 2.6.3. Trees in expanded but limited soil volume, or approximately 400 cubic feet per tree.

a. Tree at planting.
b. Tree 12 years after planting. Healthy tree appears successful.
c. Tree 16 years after planting. Tree starts to decline as it runs out of soil volume.
d. Tree 25 years after planting. Tree is dead. Trees farther down the block with access to garden spaces survive.

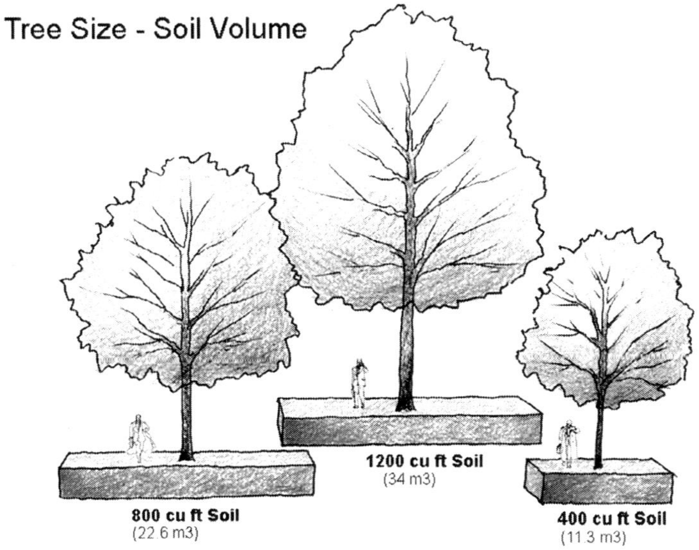

Figure 2.6.4. Tree size and life expectancy will respond proportionally to increases in soil volume.

Why Not Just Plant a Small Tree?

When soil volumes become limited, the choice is often to plant a small tree. Small trees will not perform any better in limited soil than large trees. They won't live any longer or grow any bigger. Planting a small tree only ensures that a large tree will never grow in that location. If large trees were planted only in places where it was guaranteed that they would grow with no conflicts, our cities would have far less tree canopy. In places where there is insufficient soil, continue to select large-canopy trees that can survive in restricted soil. In many situations, the tree may get lucky, break out, and grow to a large size.

Figure 2.6.5. Lucky trees planted in small holes. Note small tree species in next block.

OPTIONS TO MAKE SPACE FOR ROOTS

Become familiar with each of the following options, and select the one that is the most efficient and cost-effective for the project conditions. Using several approaches on the same project or even for the same tree may offer the most effective use of the project budget.

Each of these techniques starts with the assumption that the first five principles have been explored. None of these options will provide rooting space that is as effective as a similar volume of soil not covered with paving.

None of these options allows for the placing of rigid paving within the area of the trees' future trunk flare or the use of tree grates. Always respect the base of the tree!

Some of the techniques presented here may be proven more or less effective as research continues. Stay current on best practices by reading journals and attending conferences.

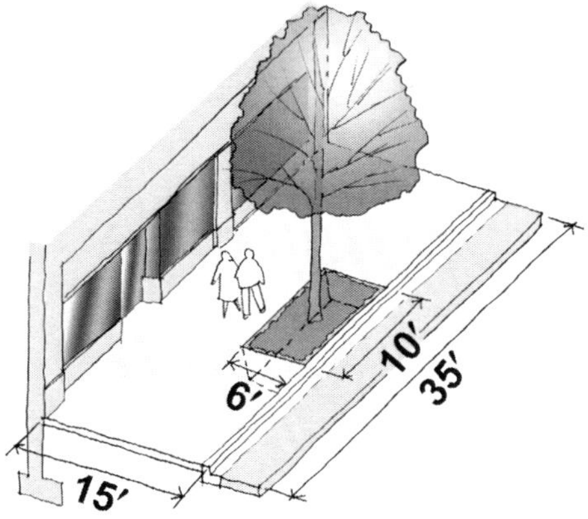

Figure 2.6.6. Soil volume comparison diagram assumptions.

In the following sections, a diagram will show how much soil can be provided by each option. This diagram shows a typical 15-foot-wide sidewalk and assumes the trees are spaced 35 feet on center. The tree opening is a generous 6 feet by 10 feet, and is excavated to an average depth of 3 feet with the excavation edges tapered to support the adjacent paving, providing 140 cubic feet of soil within the tree opening. Soil volume provided by the different soil treatments under the sidewalk will be added to the volume within the tree opening. The diagram assumes no additional soil volume contributed by the adjacent compacted soils, although there is almost always some rooting space in these areas.

Root Paths

Root paths are a low-cost way to guide roots out of confined planting spaces. Narrow 4-inch-wide by 12-inch-deep trenches are filled with strip drain board and loam topsoil. They are not intended to provide a significant volume of rooting space, but may allow roots to grow over a wide area under the pavement and better exploit available soil resources. Connecting root paths from tree to tree is important for better and more consistent tree growth within the planting.

Root paths provide aeration pathways and good soil conditions along their alignment. The non-woven geotextile around the strip drain retains water and is an excellent surface for root growth. The aeration of soil around the strip drain increases oxygen levels in the subsoil, which allows roots to grow at least 6 inches into the subsoil on either side of the trench.

Root paths are best used when there is a reasonable possibility that significant volumes of soil under the pavement or adjacent to the paved area are suitable for root growth. These conditions include the following:

- Soil that can be demonstrated to support tree rooting based on the performance of trees growing in similar conditions close to the project site.
- Existing soil will not be graded during construction.
- Coarse-grained soil.
- Remnant loam soil that has original B and C soil horizons intact.
- Clay loam soil that retains some of its structure after construction.

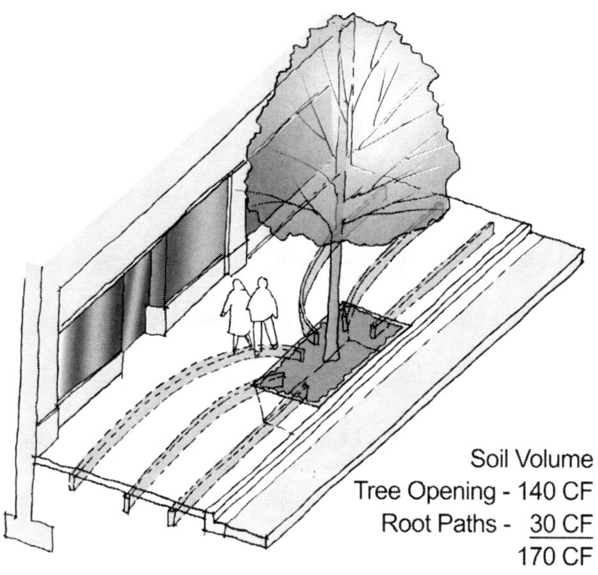

Figure 2.6.7. Root paths.

Root paths are difficult to install in sandy soil that lacks sufficient cohesiveness to retain a 1-foot-high vertical face during installation.

Root paths are an effective way to guide roots under pavement to lawn and garden areas on the opposite side of a walk. The roots that break out of the tree opening in the root path are likely to be the largest roots. As they grow along the root path, they have been observed to grow deeper under the pavement. Root paths do not create consistent and predictable rooting environments, and success is dependent on the accuracy of the pre-design soil analysis to predict the suitability of the soil described earlier in Part 1, Chapter Seven.

Space root paths approximately 4 feet on center under the pavement, which helps retain the structural integrity of the existing soil sub-base. Install as many linear feet of root paths as space and budget allow. Typical minimum installation includes three rows

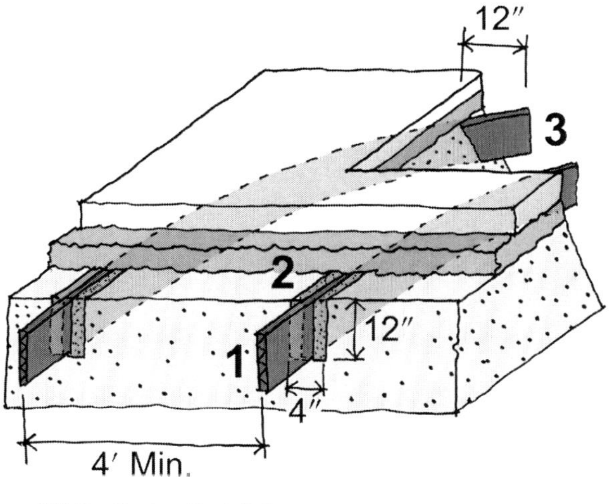

Figure 2.6.8. Root path detail.

1. Strip drain.
2. 4-inch-wide by 12-inch-deep trench backfill with loam topsoil. Compact sides of trench.
3. Extend strip drain 12 inches into tree opening.

Figure 2.6.9. Strip drain material.

Figure 2.6.10. Installation of root paths.

a. Trenching machine.
b. Installed strip drain and topsoil backfill.
c. Compacting sides of trench and topsoil backfill.
d. Strip drains extending into tree opening.

of root path trenches between each tree. Interconnect root paths from tree to tree and from trees to places beyond the pavement that can be identified as suitable rooting space.

The root path trench is dug with a standard trenching machine. Install strip drain material and loam topsoil in the trench. Use good-quality organic topsoil. All locally available quality loam topsoil is acceptable, including clay loam, sandy loam, and silt loam. The system is not sensitive to extremes of soil texture within the USDA loam categories. The soil should contain a minimum of 2 percent organic content by dry weight, and it must be friable enough to work into the narrow trench. Screening fine-grained topsoil may be required.

Figure 2.6.11. Trees in root paths after five years.

After installing the strip drain and topsoil, compact sides of the trench with two passes of a plate vibrating compactor. Add additional topsoil if the compaction process reduces the topsoil to below the top of the strip drain. The intent of the compaction is to ensure that the adjacent subsoil will not collapse into the trench. Extend root paths into the tree-planting area a minimum of 1 foot. The root path is best installed within a few inches of the proposed tree root ball.

The soil and drainage plan should show the extent of each root path line. Do not depend only on typical details. Document the installation process in detail.

Root path trenches are relatively easy to pass through the engineering approval process. The narrow trench width and shallow depth make them similar to the installation of a communication or electric wire. The shallow depth places the work above most other utility lines.

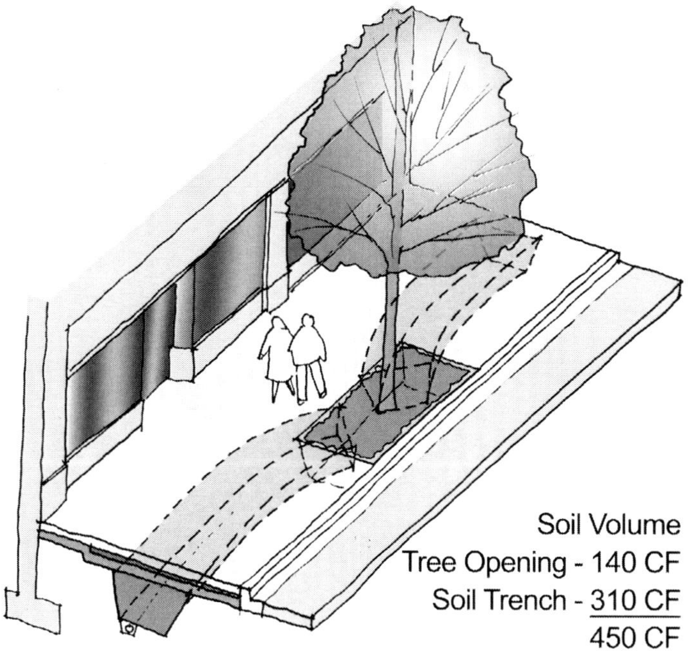

Figure 2.6.12. Soil trench.

Soil Trenches

As with root paths, these work best when connected between trees. The trench is typically dug with sloped sides to maintain the structural integrity of the compacted subgrade material. A subsurface drainage system is installed in the trench bottom. Low-compacted loam topsoil or soil mix is placed in the trench. The soil is lightly compacted to a level where it can serve as the base to pour a concrete paving slab. The compaction rate should be approximately 80 percent Proctor, or the upper level of bulk density range that is root-supporting. (See discussions of soil compaction in Part 2, Chapter Four for installation of soil and optimum bulk density rates.) The topsoil is expected to settle slightly, leaving an air gap beneath the concrete, which allows gas exchange and helps prevent roots from lifting the pavement. A gravel bed on top of the soil will enhance air and water movement, allow for irrigation, and further reduce the incidence of conflicts between pavement and roots.

The trench is typically 5 feet wide. The concrete paving must be a reinforced structural slab designed to span the trench width, resting on the compacted subgrade soil on either side of the trench. The project engineer must design the reinforcing and concrete section.

The first tree soil trench systems were built in the early 1980s and are some of the most widely used method for increasing usable soil volume beneath the pavement. The system provides soil in situations where the existing subsoil is not likely to provide for tree rooting.

Engineers may recommend footings on the street side or even on both sides of the trench. The need for these footings has been successfully challenged, and the designer should work with the project engineer to encourage their elimination. Footings add to the cost and restrict the movement of water and roots between the trench soil and adjacent subsoil. Increasing the size of the reinforced paving area over the compacted soil, moving the trench away from the curb, placing the footing only on the curb side of the walk, or flattening the side slopes on the adjacent subsoil can help the engineer feel more comfortable with a system without footings. However, each change reduces the soil volume and effectiveness of the system. Soil volumes lower than 500 cubic feet will not support a long-term functional tree.

Trenches can be used to connect trees to larger soil volumes beyond the limits of paving. If no footings are required, the adjacent compacted soil volume may become available for limited root exploration and reserve water retention. Soil trenches are a cost-effective way to enlarge soil volumes but often do not provide for sufficient soil volumes to grow large trees.

The soil type requirements within the trench are quite broad. Sandy loam or sandy clay loam soil is preferred as the growing medium within the trench. Avoid very sandy soil, heavy silts, and clay soils.

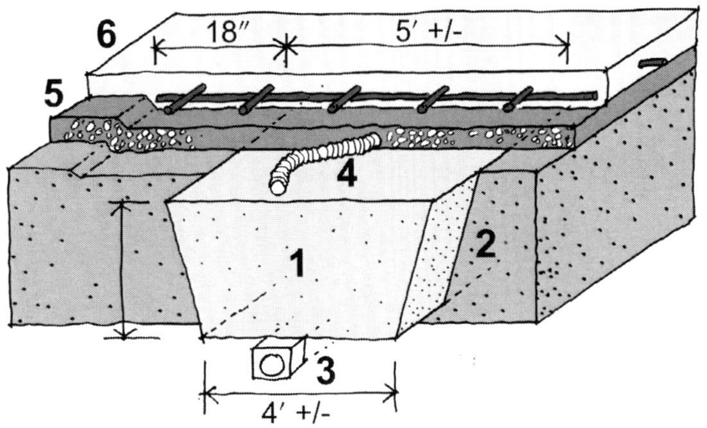

Figure 2.6.13. Soil trench detail.

1. Loam topsoil compacted to 80 percent.
2. Slope sides of trench. Assure soil beyond trench is compacted to 95 percent.
3. Drain line.
4. Perforated water line in gravel layer.
5. Gravel base course (#57 stone).
6. Concrete paving. Thicken the concrete over the trench and for a minimum of 18 inches past the edge of the trench. Concrete reinforcing per project engineer.

a

b

Figure 2.6.14. Trench under construction.

a. Prototype trench dug directly behind curb. Later designs moved the trench back several feet from curb to avoid footing requirement.

b. Details of light footings in trench must resolve problems of lower compaction of soil around footing.

Where soil drainage is poor, provide subsurface drainage lines and inspection risers as described in Part 2, Chapter Four. Provide access for water to reach the soil. Water-harvesting systems through the pavement, non-pressurized piped tree watering and fertilization systems are preferred over pressurized irrigation systems, except in dry climates with less than 30 inches of rain per year. Any irrigation system placed below the pavement is subject to failure and will be difficult to repair (see discussions on irrigation elsewhere in this chapter).

If the system can be built without footings on the sides of the trench, soil trenches are one of the most cost-effective options to provide additional soil under pavement. However, the amount of low-compaction soil volume is limited by the concrete's ability to span the distance between the two contact points. The soil within the trench may be calculated as 100 percent root-supporting soil. Trench widths of 5 to 6 feet will allow the most cost-effective structural design, and soil volumes of up to 500 cubic feet can be obtained when trees are spaced 35 feet on center. Using a stronger and wider spanning slab or increasing the distance between trees can achieve larger volumes.

The concrete slab is typically 6 inches thick and reinforced with #4 rebar spaced at 12 inches each way. The increased reinforcing should overlap the adjacent compacted subsoil by at least 18 inches. The compacted subsoil should be excavated with slopes as shown in Figure 2.6.13. Actual structural design of the reinforcing must be developed by the project engineer to reflect local conditions, codes, and the engineer's own risk tolerance.

Footings for street lights must be designed to pass through the loosely compacted soil, and conflicts with other utility lines must be resolved.

Figure 2.6.15. Trees in trenches, Bethesda, Maryland.

Linear soil trenches create narrow, linear root systems. The long-term structural ramifications for tree stability have not been studied. Trees have grown in linear trenches for 25 years without a structural failure, but there are no trees in these systems large enough to have a failure from inadequate root architecture.

Soil trenches within public rights of way have been approved by several transportation departments, including Montgomery County, Maryland. Nearly two miles of soil trenches were installed there in the late 1980s, and the trees are performing well. The existing soil in this site was conducive to rooting beyond the trench. Jurisdictional review and approval may require considerable time, so it is advisable to obtain conceptual approval prior to submission of plans.

Soil Vaults

Soil vaults are four-sided enclosures that keep roots contained and separated from other infrastructure elements. They are made from either cast-in-place or precast concrete. The top of the vault is normally precast, and the bottom of the vault area is usually an open void set directly on the subgrade. A footing is often required under the vault wall. Soil and drainage are installed within the vault. The soil volume is limited by the size of the vault, and roots have no opportunity to explore soil outside of the vault. Large vaults, especially precast vaults, can conflict with other infrastructure, such as utilities, lights, and drainage structures.

Vaults range in size from 5-foot squares, holding only 100 cubic feet of soil, to as large as 20 feet by 20 feet, holding up to 1,000 cubic feet of soil. The top of the vault is normally designed for vehicle loading. The cost of providing large soil volumes is high, thus resulting in the design of inadequately

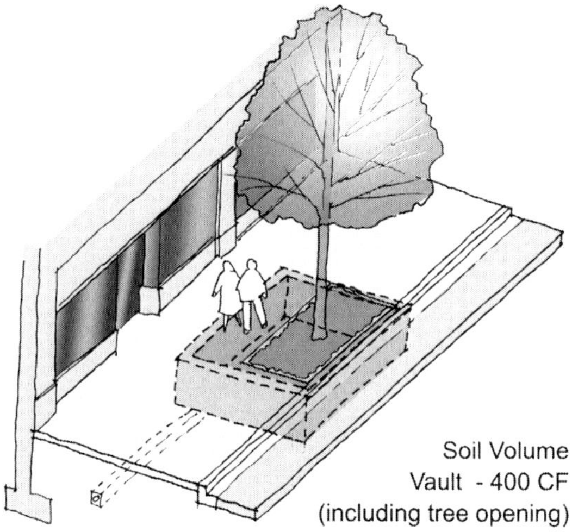

Figure 2.6.16. Soil vaults.

Figure 2.6.17.
Vault installation. As large as these vaults are, they still provide less than 1,000 cubic feet of soil per tree. *(Photos: Anton Dekker)*

a. Precast walls filled with soil.
b. Precast lid sized for vehicle loading.
c. Linear vault with soil and trees planted.
d. Linear vault completed. Tree on both sides of the water are in vaults.

small structures. Regardless of volume provided, vaults are the most costly option, per cubic foot, to improve soil. The smaller the volume, the greater the cost per cubic foot of soil.

Provide well-drained soil with high nutrient- and water-holding capacity. As soil volumes become limited, soil quality becomes more important. Almost any soil texture with a reasonable cation exchange capacity can be installed.

Provide access for water to reach the soil. Non-pressurized piped tree watering and fertilization systems are preferred over pressurized irrigation systems, except in dry climates with less than 30 inches of rain per year.

Install drain boards on all walls of the vault, similar to the drain boards required for roof planters, to provide better aeration around the soil volume. (See Principles 5 and 6.) Confirm that the bottom of the vault is above the invert of the required subsurface drain. Vaults usually require some artificial means to add water to the soil, so it is important to provide access openings to check and maintain the soil within the vault.

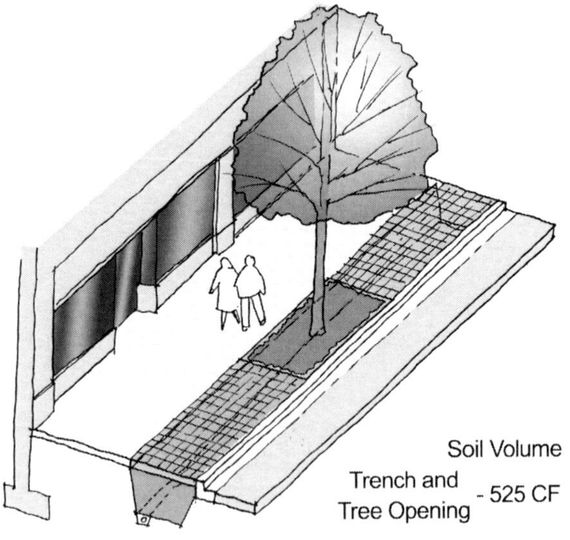

Figure 2.6.18. Sand soil. Diagram assumes that this material should not be compacted to the point of minimum soil settlement and is confined to an area of flexible pavers out of the walking zone.

Sand (Not Quite Structural) Soil

Coarse, sandy soils can be an excellent medium for tree growth if their limitations are understood. Soil nutrient-holding capacity can be improved slightly with organic matter, although these soils will always be relatively infertile. They tolerate high levels of compaction before they become root-limiting, but this level of compaction is still far below acceptable engineering standards for sidewalks. The biggest problem with coarse, sandy soil is its low water-holding capacity. These soils require a site with good rainfall during the growing season, or they must be irrigated.

Els Couenberg, in Amsterdam, Netherlands, developed a special soil mix that could be compacted to a high rate, about 80 percent of maximum dry density, and still allow roots to grow. At these compaction rates, the maximum observed soil settlement was up to 3/4 inch over three years in soil placed 48 inches deep. In the Netherlands, this amount of settlement was considered acceptable as a paving sub base. Unit pavers could be reset in areas where settlement caused tripping hazards. Amsterdam planting soil, as it came to be known, has been shown to be a good growing medium for trees when compacted to the 80 percent rate. Tests in the Netherlands have concluded that when compacted to 90 percent of dry density or greater, this soil becomes root-limiting and does not support good tree growth. The formula for Amsterdam planting soil is medium to coarse sand with 2 to 4 percent clay and 4 to 5 percent organic matter. The sand must have a median size of approximately 0.21 mm.

Amsterdam, where these soils have been most successful, sits on a high water table. The city controls the water level, with almost no seasonal fluctuation. This groundwater can wick into the soil by capillary action, providing the trees with needed replacement water. Tests of the Amsterdam planting soil in other locations in Europe without high water tables showed less promising results with overly dry soil, which required significant supplemental water.

In the United States, a product called sand structural soil, with similar mix ratios to Amsterdam planting soil, has been proposed as a compacted paving subbase intended to support tree roots. Installations have been completed, and no

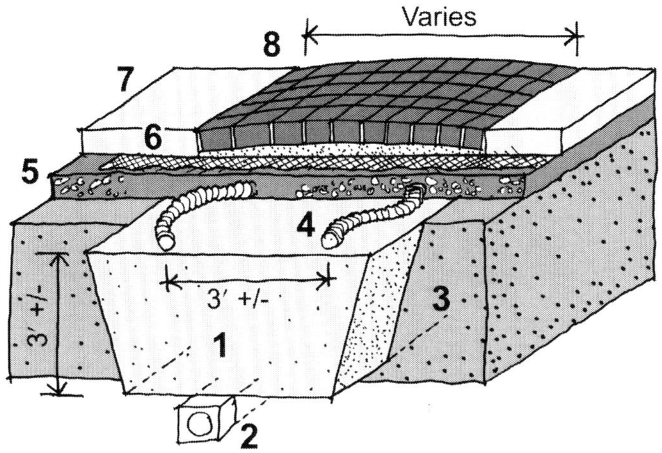

Figure 2.6.19. Sand soil detail.

1. Sand soil.
2. Drain line.
3. Compacted subgrade under adjacent paving. Provide sloped excavation.
4. Perforated water line in gravel layer.
5. Gravel base course (#57 stone).
6. Geotextile to reduce differential settlement. Extend fabric under adjacent paving.
7. Adjacent paving. Many suitable options.
8. Flexible sand-set pavers with 1/2-inch joints over sand soil. Slight crown to anticipate settlement.

controlled studies have been published on root growth at 95 percent compaction. The amount of compaction and the results of tree performance have not been verified. Claims have been made that these sand soils can be compacted to 95 percent dry density and still support roots, which is counter to the findings of Dutch and Danish researchers.

a

b

Figure 2.6.20. Sand soil installation in the Netherlands.

a. Sand soil is successful in Amsterdam because of acceptance of some settlement in pavers and proximity of water table. Tree removed from sand soil in Amsterdam with absorbing roots on bottom.
b. Trees in Amsterdam sand soil.

Figure 2.6.21. Trees on Pennsylvania Avenue, Washington, D.C., in sand soil trenches below the pavement. Trees are irrigated.

Sand soil must be mixed to tight tolerances, with between 2 and 4 percent clay content. This narrow mix tolerance is difficult to achieve, except by the most highly controlled operations. Adding clay to sand, especially in small amounts, has always proved challenging. The mix requires the use of calcium-free sand. It also requires extensive soil testing of mix design and compaction during installation, using equipment and contractors specialized for the production of golf-course mixes. During installation, compaction tolerances are very sensitive and must be tightly controlled.

Data on the value of sand structural soil, with respect to rooting volume for supporting crown area, are not available. Do not use the methodology outlined in Part 2, Chapter Four to predict tree response to soil volume. For soil that is not irrigated or fertilized, the ratio of roots to soil volume may be substantially less than that for loam soil.

It is likely that sand soils will prove useful in places where a high degree of surface compaction from foot traffic is anticipated and where it is not critical to compact the soil more than 85 percent. These applications might include lawn areas with large trees and flexible paving such as precast concrete pavers. They are best suited under gravel paving, where minor settlement is acceptable. Until the soil's ability to be compacted while continuing to support roots is documented, it should not be recommended as a paving subgrade.

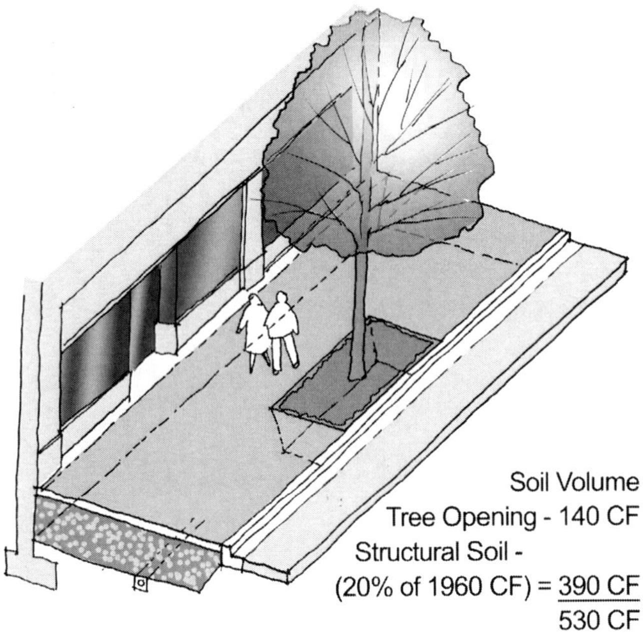

Figure 2.6.22. Soil/aggregate structural soils. Note that only the amount of soil in the structural soil mix is counted as available for tree rooting.

Soil/Aggregate Structural Soils

In the mid-1990s, Cornell University developed CU Structural Soil. This is a mixture of stone aggregate and soil, with a small amount of polymer gel to hold it together, which can be compacted to 95 percent of dry density and still support root growth. The mix takes advantage of the fact that there are about 20 to 25 percent void spaces between pieces of compacted gravel, which can be filled with soil to support root growth. The approximate formula is 20 percent clay loam soil, 80 percent 3/4-inch angular gravel with no fines, and 0.03 percent polymer gel. It is important that the aggregate be angular in shape and the stone pieces similar in size. The wider the range of the aggregate sizes and the less angular the stone, the less space for soil and roots. The clay loam soil should be approximately 25 to 35 percent clay to maximize water-holding capacity. Too much clay in the soil can cause mixing problems.

CU Structural Soil is a patented formula marketed by Amereq of New York. Designers who want to use CU Structural Soil should work with Amereq or one of its licensed suppliers to obtain the correct mix ratio. Similar products and local variations have appeared on the market. Settlement failures have been recorded in mixes that provide more soil than recommended by Cornell. Use a contractor with demonstrated experience in mixing and placing this material.

Michael Mills, in Vancouver, British Columbia, has developed a slightly different mix that he has been installing for more than 10 years. The Carolina Stalite Company markets a structural soil called Permatil, which is made with expanded shale and is in roughly the same proportions as the CU mix. Neither Mills nor Carolina Stalite uses polymer gel. The use of expanded shale makes the resulting product more expensive, but provides a higher cation exchange than crushed aggregate, which may be of benefit to the tree. A long-term experiment examining the relative effectiveness of different types of soil systems was started in 2004 by the Bartlett Lab in Charlotte, N.C. Early results indicate that structural soil does not grow trees as well as uncompacted soil. However, it may be many years before sufficient data are available to reach final conclusions.

Even with the addition of polymer gel, installations of CU soil have been observed where the soil has shaken to the bottom of the truck and formed soil balls. This renders the soil useless for the tree. Inspections during installation are important. Mix designs that do not use polymer gel rely on correct moisture content and special handling to avoid separation, or add other types of soil stabilizers.

The greatest limitation of the soil/aggregate formula is the small amount of actual soil in the mix. Only about 20 percent of the mix volume is available for use by the tree. The rest of the volume is rock, whose primary function is to support the structure above. Trees will not grow larger than the volume of soil provided. To achieve 1 cubic foot of usable soil under the sidewalk, a designer must specify 5 cubic feet of soil/aggregate structural soil. This requires significant space and large budgets to achieve required soil volumes. Normally, other options to improve soil under paved areas are more cost-effective.

Roots must grow through the small spaces between the aggregate and eventually will expand to a larger size than these openings. The roots become kinked as they expand. The long-term impact of these small openings on root strength and function has not been tested. Larger-size aggregate, approximately 1-1/2 inches, has been used to provide more space between the stones. This may increase the size of roots that can grow in the soil. Interestingly, the larger aggregate has larger spaces, but the soil volume does not increase.

In many regions of the United States, the most cost-effective crushed stone available is limestone. Limestone can raise the pH of the soil to 8.0 or higher. This requires using trees tolerant of high pH. Non-limestone aggregates are usually available, but are more expensive and harder to obtain. In the Chicago region, for example, granite railroad ballast is being used in structural soil applications as a substitute for the local limestone aggregate, which raises the cost of the product.

Soil/aggregate structural soils are well drained and much dryer than loam soil, and therefore irrigation may be needed. Installation also requires compaction of the subgrade, which may create poor drainage under the structural soil, making subsurface drainage mandatory.

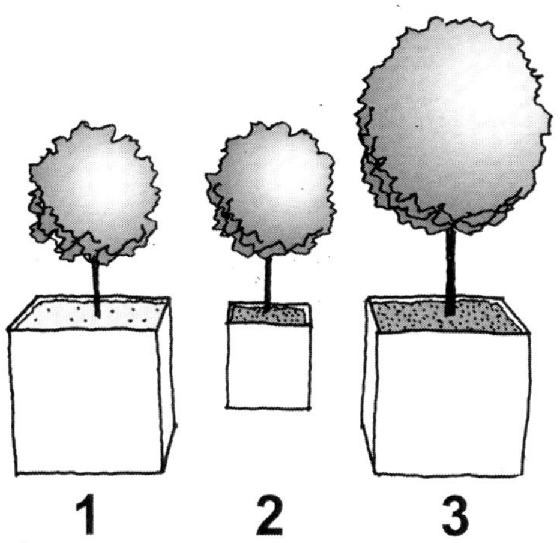

Figure 2.6.23. Tree response to soil/aggregate structural soil. Trees 1 and 2 grew to approximately the same size, while tree 3 grew in proportion to the soil volume in its container.

1. Tree growing in soil/aggregate structural soil.
2. Tree growing in the volume of loam soil without aggregate present in the structural soil of tree 1.
3. Tree growing in a container of equal size to tree 1 but filled with loam soil and no aggregate.

Figure 2.6.24. Roots growing through soil/aggregate structural soil.

Figure 2.6.25. More than five years after planting, trees on the right growing in structural soil require irrigation and are showing fall color in early August. Trees on the left are growing well in loam soil without additional water.

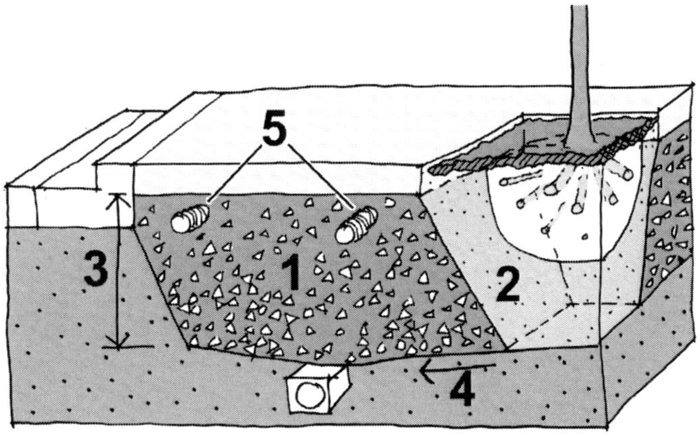

Figure 2.6.26. Soil/aggregate structural soil detail.

1. Soil aggregate structural soil. Note slopes on excavation and at edge of tree opening.
2. Planting soil—never structural soil—within the tree opening.
3. Provide soil as deep as possible. Provide 5,000 cubic feet of structural soil per tree to attain 1,000 cubic feet of actual soil.
4. Slope excavation toward drain system.
5. Watering lines spaced 3 to 4 feet on center in the top of the structural soil.

The rapid drainage in structural soil makes it necessary to irrigate not just the tree opening, but also the entire soil volume. (See discussions on irrigation elsewhere in this chapter.)

Structural soils of any kind should never be used in situations where they are not needed for structural purposes. Other soil options may work better for the soil within the tree opening not covered by paving, and for flexible paving where smooth surfaces are not required. Never use structural soil within a tree opening.This soil never needs to be compacted to 95 percent, and providing high-quality soil around the root ball of the newly planted tree will improve its recovery from transplanting. Require an angle of repose on the compacted structural soil around the tree opening to support the paving edge.

The subgrade below soil/aggregate structural soil must be compacted to 95 percent of dry density. A geotextile separator may be needed where subgrade soil conditions are plastic enough to permit gravel migration into the subgrade, which may cause settlement within the structural soil.

Before paving is installed, protect stockpiled structural soil and installed material from rain with plastic sheets. Heavy rains can wash the soil out of the aggregate.

Given the extreme inefficiency of the ratio of excavated volume to soil usable by the tree, strips of structural soil less than 20 feet wide might be better constructed as soil trenches or structural cells (see description later in this chapter), where more soil can be included for less cost. A 5-foot-wide soil trench set of structural cells, as described in this chapter, will provide more soil usable by the tree than a 20-foot-wide trench of soil/aggregate structural soil.

Soil/aggregate structural soils may have applications as a transition to other options and to add soil in places where other options may not be practical. These might include tight, contorted spaces and fills around utility lines and against foundations where full compaction is required.

Figure 2.6.27. Cover structural soil with plastic after installation to prevent erosion. *(Source: FLL)*

Sand/Aggregate Structural Soil

German researchers have been working with a structural soil that is a mixture of sand and aggregate in a very controlled particle distribution curve. Several formulas are being developed and include the use of porous aggregates such as crushed brick or pumice. Researchers claim the mixes can be compacted for sidewalks and still support root growth.

In the cool, wet climate of northern Europe, these soils have supported trees for more than 10 years. These soils are extremely well drained, and are likely to have similar problems as CU soil if they are used in hotter or dryer climates. At this time, the only available research is in German. The distribution curves for the soil developed are available from Forschungsgesellschaft Landschaftsentwicklung Landschaftsbau E.V. (Landscaping and Landscape Development Research Society), otherwise known as the FLL.

Several suppliers of expanded shale products (ESCS) in the United States have developed similar soil mixes. Most of the time, these soil mixes are not compacted for paving. One exception is the Mormon Temple project in Salt Lake City, where a large-scale application of this mix was compacted to support paving. Tree failure occurred in areas where the irrigation system failed.

Figure 2.6.28. At the Mormon Temple, ESCS soils are irrigation-dependent.

1. Trees in foreground and left, surviving but irrigation-dependent.
2. Trees on right and back suffered 100 percent loss when irrigation zone failed and were replanted. Note: None of these trees have grown large and all are stressed.

Suspended Sidewalk and Structural Cells

All the previously described options for root space under the sidewalk provide only limited soil volumes. A different approach is to suspend the sidewalk structure above the soil with columns and beams to create a grid like structure that supports a deck. The space within the post-and-beam structure is available for low-compacted soil and tree roots.

There have been a number of attempts to make suspended sidewalks. The City of Charlotte, North Carolina, has made columns of poured-in-place concrete by digging deep holes to make concrete columns in low-compacted soil and pouring a reinforced sidewalk over the tops of the columns. This system is labor-intensive and requires site-specific engineering to meet required loading standards. Arborists in the Netherlands have tried filling plastic water-storage boxes with soil. They found the boxes difficult to fill and roots being girdled as they passed through the small holes in the sides of the boxes. A plastic and concrete prefabricated system designed to store water has also been tried in the Netherlands. This system is also very labor-intensive to install, and a rebar-reinforced concrete structure must be designed to top the plastic system.

The most interesting suspended paving system is Sky Forest in Japan, designed by landscape architect Peter Walker, where an intricate post-and-beam system was installed to support paving and the resulting space filled with soil. The design is remarkable for the efficiency of its structure, and the trees appear to be thriving in the large quantity of high quality soil. While the system required significant engineering and attention to detail, it might be replicated with a prefabricated system.

Figure 2.6.29. Sky Forest, Saitama Plaza, Tokyo, Japan. *(Photos: Peter Walker + Partners)*

a. Thick layer of soil beneath a suspended paving structure has produced a successful grove of Zelkova trees.
b. Model of the structural system.

a

b

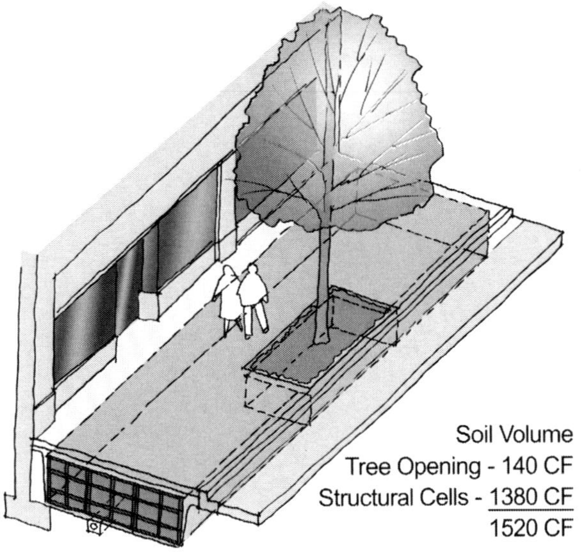

Figure 2.6.30. Structural cells are the only system that can provide sustainable soil volume within the space of a typical urban streetscape.

Structural Cells

In collaboration with DeepRoot Partners LP (www.deeproot.com), the author helped develop a modular, pre-engineered cell system to create large spaces under pavement filled with low-compacted soil to support tree roots. These structural cells support the pavement and protect it from root damage. The system's modular design fits irregular urban conditions. Size of the rooting area is limited only by the availability of space, utility conflicts, and the project budget. About 93 percent of the space within the cells is available for tree-rooting soil, a huge increase in efficiency over previous systems.

The system consists of a series of plastic columns molded onto a modular frame, which creates open-sided box cells. Cells are stacked to the designed depth, and a deck is secured on top of each stack.

An airspace under the deck allows the soil to be irrigated and fertilized, while helping to keep any roots growing in the upper soil layers from lifting the sidewalk. The air space can receive rainwater either from infiltration through pervious pavers above the cells or by channeling surface water from drains and roof leaders.

As with all below-paving soil options, structural cells function best when the tree opening is made as large as possible. Structural cells placed within the area of the future trunk flare will result in pavement failure as the trunk flare develops. The airspace under the deck accommodates the zone-of rapid-taper roots.

Where the soil within the boxes is in contact with adjacent soil volumes, roots can access any suitable soil outside the box, and ground moisture can move between the different soils.

The foundation of the system is a layer of aggregate, which rests on compacted subgrade. Subgrade compaction levels and type and thickness of base course aggregate are dependent on the soil conditions encountered and the loading requirements of the paving. Depending on subgrade soil conditions, a layer of geotextile under the base aggregate and drain lines may be needed. The aggregate should extend 6 inches beyond the edges of the cell system.

Figure 2.6.31. Structural cells.

a. Detail.
   1. Structural cells filled with soil suitable for trees. Leave air space above soil and below cell deck.
   2. Aggregate sub-base with drain line.
   3. Geogrid curtain and compacted backfill along outer perimeter of cells.
   4. Geotextile on top of cell deck.
   5. Aggregate base course and paving.

b. Structural-cell frames can be stacked up to three layers high.

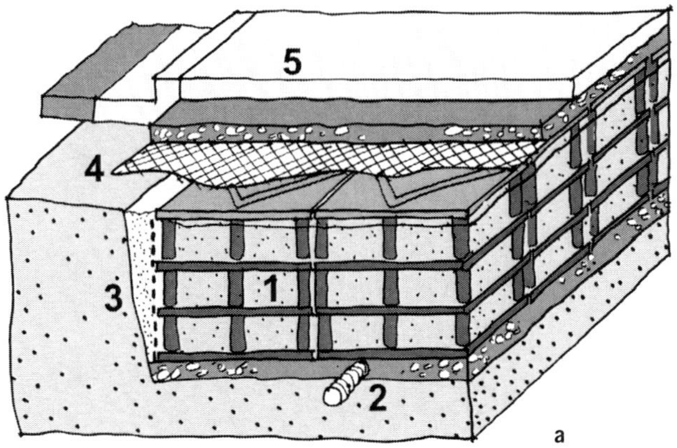

a

b

Structural cells are designed to meet AASHTO H-20 loading requirements (American Association of State Highway and Transportation Officials) when combined with the load distribution of the paving above the cells. The H-20 standard is often the required standard for structures such as electrical vaults, inlets, and grating for municipal sidewalks and parking areas. Consult the manufacturer for pavement design compatibility.

Figure 2.6.32. Structural cells are designed to meet AASHTO H-20 loading of 8,000 pounds per wheel to a maximum of 32,000 pounds per axle.

Planting Soil Within the Cell

The conventional attitude about proper soil specification in urban areas is based on providing well-drained, compaction-resistant soil and soil that will not settle too much. In most soil specifications, combined clay and silt content above 30 percent is discouraged, because sandier soil will drain better when compacted. Sandier soil also tends to settle less over time. The price for using sandier soil is lower cation exchange, water-holding capacity, and biology function.

A wide range of soil types can be used as planting soil within structural cells. Compaction can be low, allowing for much higher clay and organic content. Low-compacted clay loam soils will drain adequately. Subsoil removed from the excavation may often be used as planting soil by adding organic matter. Use of this amended backfill where practical will reduce the cost and environmental impact of the installation. Use techniques defined in Part 2, Chapter Four. Locally available topsoil and planting mixes may also be used.

Avoid soil with more than 35 percent clay, 45 percent silt, 80 percent sand, or 15 percent gravel. Loam, sandy clay loam, and medium sandy loam soils are optimum. Sandy soils can be improved by the amendment of organic matter. Because soil settlement within the structural cell is not a problem, organic matter up to 15 percent by volume can be added to the planting soil. Adding more than 15 percent organic matter may create unstable conditions for the tree due to the resulting spongy soil.

Planting Soil Compaction

Spacing of the columns allows for efficient placement of planting soil in cells. Planting soil is lightly compacted as it is being placed. Walking over the soil or using a light compaction device is sufficient. The intent of the compaction is to eliminate the larger soil voids within frames and to provide a soil that is structurally stable once the tree grows to a large size. Bulk density of between 1.1 Mg/m^3 (clay loam) and 1.4 Mg/m^3 (sandy loam) is sufficient. (See Part 2, Chapter Four for information on measuring compaction.)

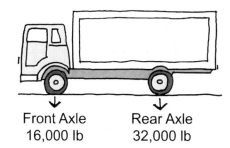

a

b

c

d

Figure 2.6.33. Installation of structural cells. *(Photos: DeepRoot Partners)*

a. Placing structural cells on compacted gravel subgrade.
b. Planting soil installed within cells in 15-inch lifts.
c. Compacting soil to eliminate large air pockets.
d. Attaching decks. Geotextile will be placed over decks at time of paving installation.

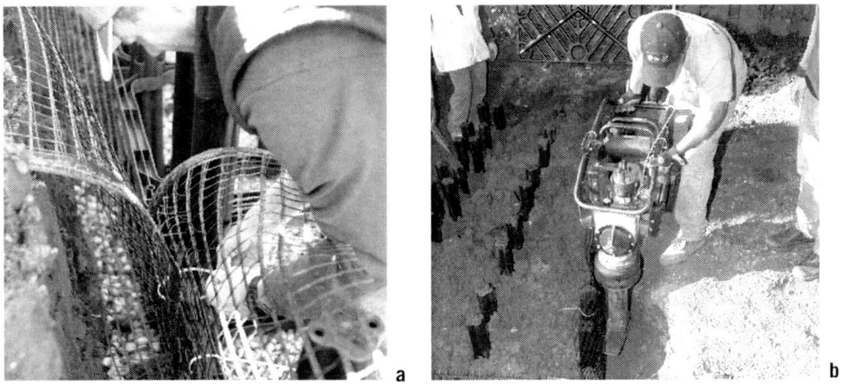

Figure 2.6.34. Geogrids and compaction adjacent to structural cells. *(Photos: DeepRoot Partners)*

a. Attaching geogrids to side of structural cells.
b. Compacting fill next to cells to 95 percent to support paving.

Geotechnical Considerations—Transition to Adjacent Soils

When the loosely compacted soil within the cells abuts the compacted soil at the edge of the cells that is supporting new or existing pavement, the designer must plan for transitional geotechnical conditions between the two soils. Type and degree of consolidation of the compacted soil, angle of repose in the soil of adjacent loading, and particle migration are the three primary areas of concern.

Vehicle weight loads on paving adjacent to the cells must be factored into the design. Loads do not spread through soil vertically, but spread out at the soil's angle of repose. This angle is approximately 1:1 to 0.5:1 in most soil. Standard civil engineering practice requires that the zone within the angle of repose be undisturbed. Maintaining the bottom of the structural cells 2 feet or greater from the backside of the curb will reasonably support the curb and vehicle loading in the street beyond. This assumption must be confirmed with the project engineer.

The soil between the backside of the curb and the edge of the structural cell excavation supports the pavement that spans between the soil cells and the curb. Coordinate other design elements, such as electrical and traffic control conduits, other utilities, and footings for lights and other structures. Conduits may be located within the cell structure. Where light-post footings are required, space the cells to allow for compaction of the soil around the footing.

Along the perimeter of the structural cells, where paving continues beyond the limit of the cells, compacted soil must be placed between the low compacted planting soil and the edge of the excavation. To transition between the soils of different compaction, a layer of geogrid fabric is placed at the perimeter of the cell structure. Geogrid is used as its open weave permits roots and water to easily cross between the two soils. Backfill material can then be compacted as the cells are filled with planting soil.

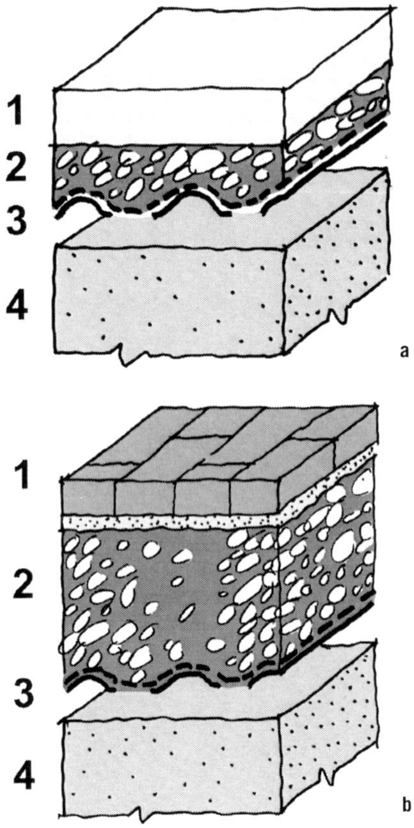

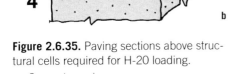

Figure 2.6.35. Paving sections above structural cells required for H-20 loading.

a. Concrete paving.
   1. 4-inch concrete.
   2. 4-inch aggregate base course.
   3. Geotextile and cell deck.
   4. Planting soil.
b. Flexible paving.
   1. Sand-set pavers.
   2. 12-inch aggregate base course.
   3. Geotextile and cell deck.
   4. Planting soil.

Paving Types and Base Course Depth

The paving type over structural cells may be any material, from poured-in-place concrete and asphalt to sand-set pavers and loose gravel paving. Each of these paving systems can achieve the H-20 loading requirement by increasing the thickness of the base course aggregate. Four inches of base course aggregate are required under 4 inches of unreinforced concrete, while 12 inches of base course are required under flexible paving systems such as sand-set pavers or gravel. The base course layer may be thinner in areas where large vehicles cannot access the paving.

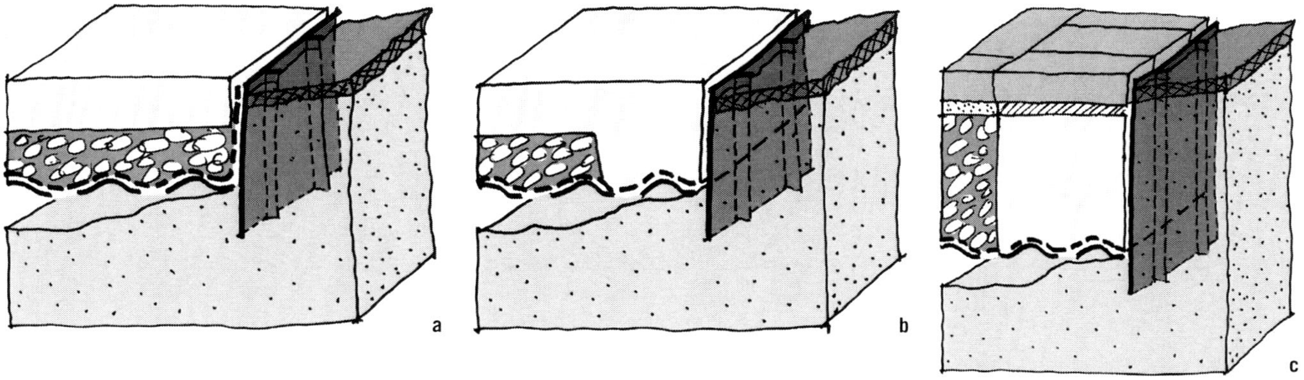

Figure 2.6.36. Paving edge details at the tree opening. Root barrier added to guide zone-of-rapid-taper roots under deck.

a. Concrete paving edge. Geotextile turned up to retain base course.
b. Concrete paving edge. Concrete turned down to cell deck to retain base course.
c. Sand-set paver edge. Concrete curb to retain base course with last row of pavers, mortar set on top of curb.

Paving at the Edge of the Tree Opening and Planting Soil

Where paving ends next to planting soil and the tree opening, place a retainer to stop gravel from migrating into the soft planting soil and undermining the paving edge. This can be accomplished by forming a concrete curb along the edge of the cell deck. Plastic paver edging systems are not recommended due to the potential to penetrate the deck with the required edging spike and the lack of consolidated base course material beyond the edge of the cell deck.

Soil Volume

Structural cells can provide each tree with sufficient soil (see Part 2, Chapter Four for how to calculate). Where budget or space conflicts restrict the volume of soil, structural cells remain the most efficient method to add soil volume under the sidewalk.

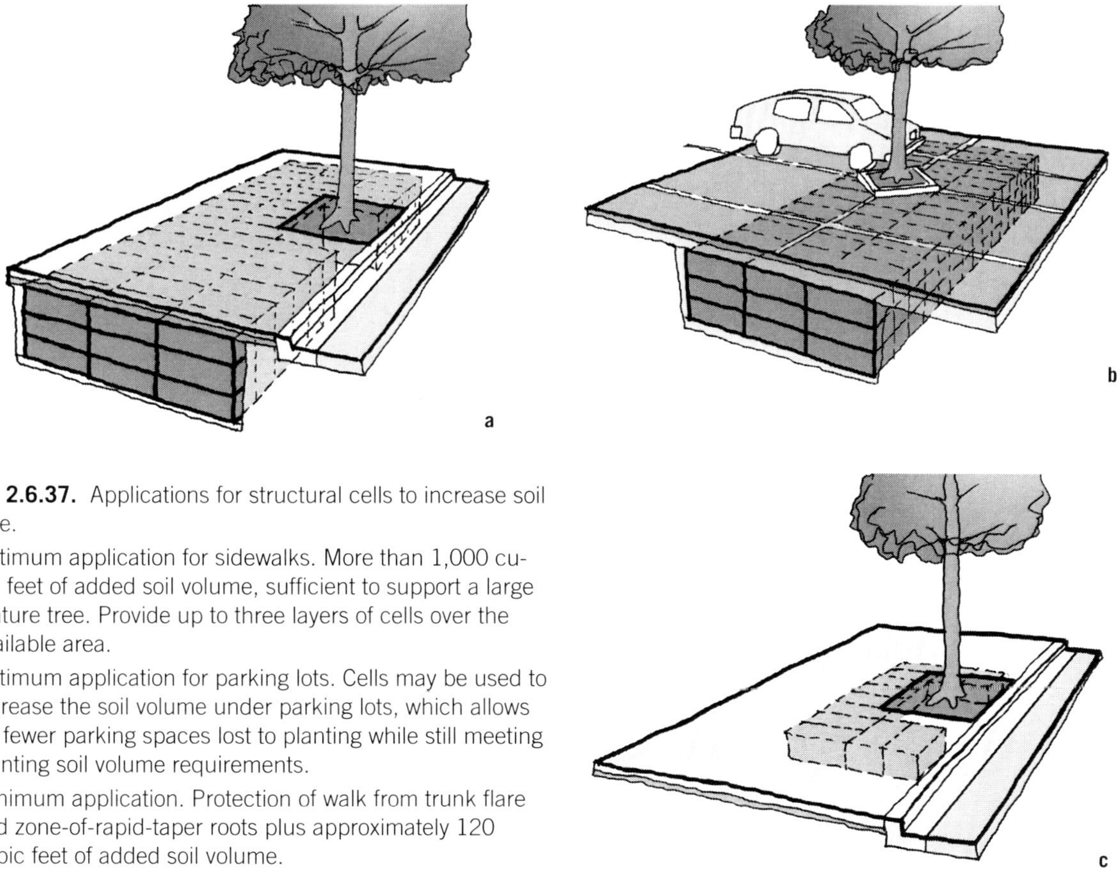

Figure 2.6.37. Applications for structural cells to increase soil volume.

a. Optimum application for sidewalks. More than 1,000 cubic feet of added soil volume, sufficient to support a large mature tree. Provide up to three layers of cells over the available area.
b. Optimum application for parking lots. Cells may be used to increase the soil volume under parking lots, which allows for fewer parking spaces lost to planting while still meeting planting soil volume requirements.
c. Minimum application. Protection of walk from trunk flare and zone-of-rapid-taper roots plus approximately 120 cubic feet of added soil volume.

IRRIGATION AND WATER MANAGEMENT UNDER PAVEMENT

Every under-paving rooting approach needs a reliable source of water to the soil under the pavement. In regions with more than 30 inches of rain a year, natural rainfall should be sufficient for this function if the paving is designed to harvest water and the soil is adequately drained.

Where does the water come from in an urban area that is completely covered in concrete or asphalt? These materials are surprisingly porous, especially as they age. Shrink cracks can be found in concrete at the time the material is poured. Expansion and construction joints open and close with temperature and humidity. Asphalt becomes cracked and degraded.

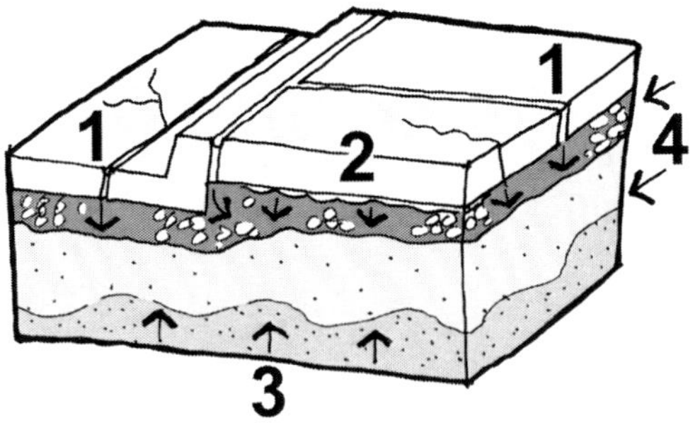

Figure 2.6.38. Water flows within an urban paving system.

1. Cracks and joints in the pavement.
2. Condensation.
3. Capillary movement from lower water resource.
4. Hydrologic conductivity from horizontal water resources.

A second source of water is the groundwater below and beside the pavement. As the pavement heats up, water will condense on its underside. Condensation causes more water to be drawn up from below by capillary action. This phenomenon can be demonstrated by placing a sheet of plastic on a dry area of soil on a hot day. Soon, you'll see droplets forming under the plastic. As tree roots remove water from the soil, capillary action draws small amounts of water up from adjacent soil. Finally, water moves horizontally through sandier soil and subbase material that has hydrologic connectivity to places where water can more easily penetrate the pavement.

The water that collects in the soil under pavement from either leaks or condensation does not evaporate as quickly as the water in soil exposed to the wind and sun. During a drought, the soil under pavements will be markedly wetter than planted soil adjacent to the pavement. Trees in paved areas often exhibit less drought stress than trees growing in open urban soil areas.

Systems to increase water to the planting soil below the pavement must cover a broad area to anticipate the long-term root growth of the tree. Small systems near the root ball may assist in the establishment of the tree, but have little value as the tree matures.

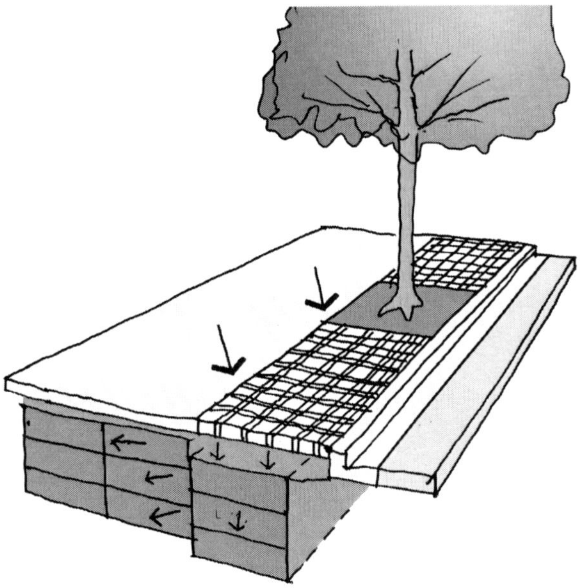

Figure 2.6.39. Porous paving.

Sustainable Water Harvesting Systems

Unfortunately, as construction techniques and products improve, these inadvertent water sources are disappearing from the urban environment. Designers must develop replacement systems that replace this important water source. To the extent that the replacement system can harvest rain that falls on the pavement as opposed to pressurized irrigation, the trees will become increasingly sustainable.

Porous Paving

Porous pavers provide additional porosity to the pavement. This is the easiest way to harvest rainwater. The paver design filters out large trash and coarse sediment. Finer sediment does silt up the joints but the pavers never completely stop draining. Even when clogged, there is still sufficient water to provide the water needed by the tree.

Porous pavers or porous concrete are not compatible with soil trenches and root paths due to their structural requirements. Other methods to add rainwater to soil trenches and root paths must be designed. Base course material 12 inches thick is needed to install porous pavers over structural cells.

Water Harvesting for Non-Porous Paving

If porous paving is not feasible, water can be provided to the soil under non-porous paving. Perforated piping can be run either through the soil or preferably through the aggregate base course under the paving. The pipes are connected to an inlet, which collects water supplied by rain, a water truck or other external water supply. Another alternative is to equip each inlet with a manually operated, frost proof hose bib or a valve-operated bubbler. When a solenoid-activated valve water source is installed, either operate it manually or put it on a separate zone from the rest of the irrigation system because the water frequency will be less frequest than with soils exposed to the sun and wind.

Flexible, perforated watering lines run from the inlet to the planting soil under the pavement. Each line should end in a second inlet or cleanout at the end of the run. Provide an inlet at every tree. The interconnection of the inlets allows the system flow to be checked. Water flows should be set such that water begins to run out of the pipes at the lower inlet to ensure that the soil has become hydrated. Watering cycles after tree establishment should only be during dry periods. Assuming that the soil volumes are large enough to support a large tree, in wet regions in the United States, watering once or twice a month during the summer should be sufficient after tree establishment.

Inlets can be designed to improve the removal of sediment and to split the water flow so large storms do not overwhelm the soil. Connecting root paths to small drains that collect surface water and bring it to the root zone can enhance the principle of root paths. For soils under suspended concrete paving such as structural cells or trenches, small inlets can be installed in the pavement that empty directly into the air space above the soil.

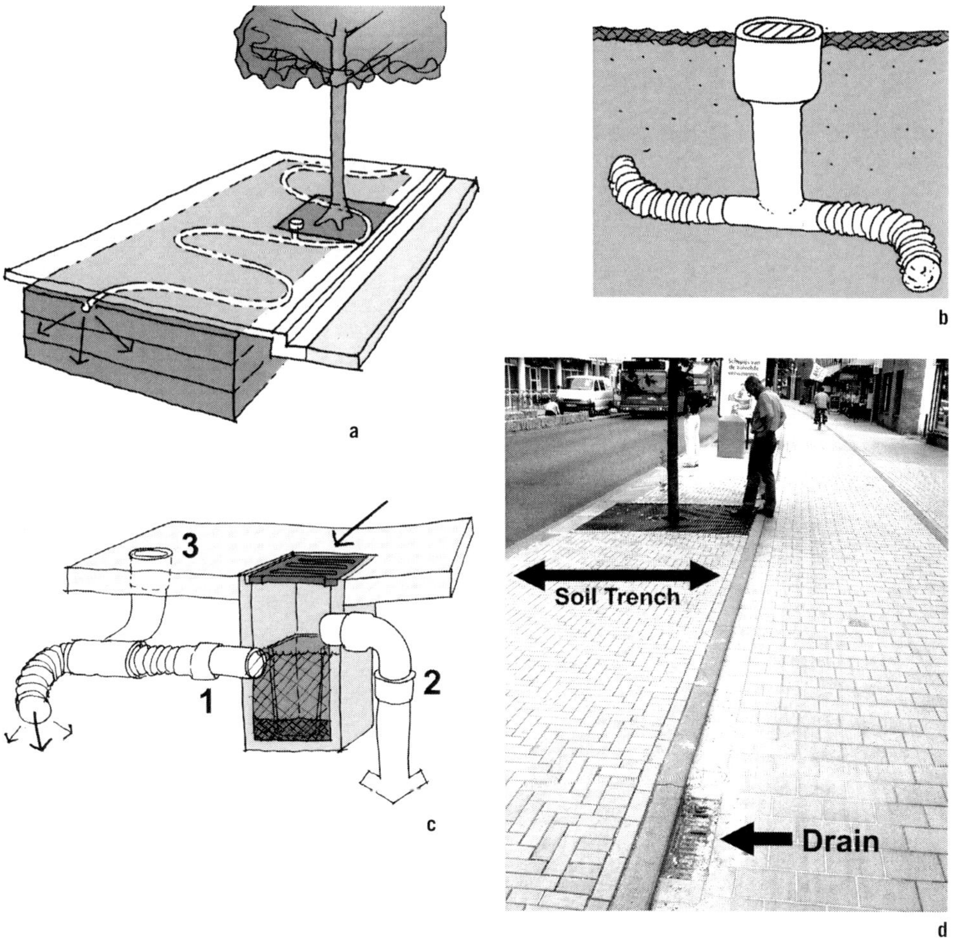

Figure 2.6.40. Inlets and perforated watering lines.

a. Perforated lines snake across the top of the below-paving soil system. Water enters the system either by a hose or pressurized bubbler within inlet. Connect perforated pipe to the next tree. Begin and end the line with a cleanout.
b. Inlets and lines can be assembled from available fittings and pipe. A small system such as this may be inadequate to supply water to the tree as it becomes quite large.
c. Inlet to harvest rain water. By setting the primary storm overflow invert above the line feeding the below-paver soil watering line invert, excess water can be diverted during large rain events. Bottom of inlet serves as primary sediment catchment.
   1. Tree soil perforated watering line.
   2. Storm overflow line.
   3. Include sufficient cleanouts, one every 50 to 100 feet, to maintain system.
d. Inlet that harvests water into a tree soil trench.

Sediment

All systems that collect surface water to be infiltrated into the soil must solve the problem of sediments clogging the inlet, pipes, and infiltration zone. The system must have a way to collect, clean, or flush collected sediments. This maintenance requirement adds to the cost and reduces the effectiveness of the system. Regions of the country that use sand for ice control experience significant clogging of filtration systems and may require cleaning several times a year.

Salt

In cold and wet regions, surface water that flows from the pavement to the tree rooting space may carry deicing salts in winter. Small amounts of salt can be flushed through the soil if the soil volume is large enough, drains fast enough, and the tree species is salt-tolerant. Ideally, in locations of high salt use, the system should be closed off during the winter and opened during the spring, summer and fall. However, the city of Toronto finds salt damage primarily in trees that are in small confined soil volumes with poor drainage. Trees with large well drained soil volumes rarely exhibit symptoms of salt damage.

Overwatering

It is critical to assure that the planting soil drains fast enough to compensated for too much water. Understand the drainage rates in the soil under and beside the tree planting soil. Provide subsurface drain lines when drainage rates are too low. Provide access openings through the pavement to inspect the soil moisture.

Planting Soil and Rainwater Management

There is an increasing interest in using the soil under the pavement as a place to filter, slow, and store excess rainwater. Trees might use this water and transpire it back into the atmosphere. In suburban sites with larger open soil areas, achieving these goals is easier. The larger the volumes of soil, the less likely the soil will become oversaturated. As development densities increase, soil-volume-to-drainage-area ratios are reduced. More water is added to less soil, and the soil will be saturated for longer periods.

There are good reasons why engineers have, for centuries, tried to keep water from remaining in the soil near structures and under pavements. Saturating soil near structures causes failures. There are equally good reasons why arborists have been trying to remove water from urban soils: Too much water kills trees. The proposed changes in tree and rainwater management may have unintended consequences if the tree to soil moisture relationships are not calculated correctly.

Trees that are expected to grow in the same soil used for rainwater management face significant obstacles. Salt and sediment accumulation must be considered. The soil must drain fast enough to not cause soil oxygen deficiencies. This drainage requirement makes it difficult to store water in the soil volume. As the soil drainage increases, the water will carry fine sediments deeper into the soil, which may result in clogging. The soil's water-holding capacity must be designed to find the balance between too much and too little drainage.

Each of these considerations makes it difficult to combine the requirements for good tree growth and rainwater under pavement. A soil that might function well under normal water flow conditions might not tolerate repeated inundation of water that is concentrated with significant head pressure. To overcome these problems, sandier soil mixes are used. The design of these soil mixes is likely beyond the capability of most site designers, and soil experts should be consulted.

Alternative rainwater designs in urban areas are still in the development phase. Designs to combine tree soil and rainwater systems are facing similar challenges as were encountered in the development of large window walls in architecture. In the early years of modern architecture, window walls were custom-constructed. Full-scale mock-ups were built of every assembly and wind-tested. There were failures, most notable the John Hancock building in Boston, where windows repeatedly fell out of this high-rise building. Eventually, there was enough data for manufacturers and architects to be comfortable with the designs to simply specify product systems. Alternative urban rainwater management needs this level of testing and research.

Pressurized Irrigation Systems for Soil Below Pavement

In dry regions and where soil volumes are limited, adding reliable irrigation water will increase the soil's ability to support a larger, healthier tree. However, that tree will become dependent on the artificial water supply. Artificial irrigation is a crutch to support inadequate soil volume design.

Irrigation systems are notoriously maintenance-intensive. They need regular inspection and replacement of parts. Pipes under the pavement are sealed away and cannot be accessed or repaired without pavement removal. Many under-pavement irrigation systems fail within 10 years and are never reactivated.

The two most common problems: Either the water stops due to a malfunctioning valve or clogged emitters and the soil becomes too dry, or a line breaks due to impact, soil settlement, or frost, and the soil becomes too wet. In both cases, there is often no way to know a problem is occurring until the tree begins to die. Access through the paving for soil and system inspection is important for long-term system maintenance.

Irrigation may be reasonable as a tool to help trees recover from transplanting and to become established. In this application, irrigation should be considered a temporary element that is phased out over the three to five years after planting. Often, irrigation is only provided within the tree opening. This may be reasonable if irrigation is only temporary or is needed to support shrubs or ground cover. If the soil design calls for the tree to be dependent on irrigation, the soil under the pavement must be irrigated by extending the system.

Automatic Irrigation Systems

In wet regions, a manually operated system may be sufficient, as the system is only needed for tree establishment and during extreme droughts. An automatic system may cause more harm than good. Overwatering can kill trees in a few months if the system malfunctions or is set to operate at too high a flow rate. See the preceding watering recommendations.

In dry regions or when using dry soil mixes such as soil/aggregate structural soil or sand structural soil, an automatic system may be appropriate or even required. Whenever an automatic system is used, ensure that the design includes subsurface drainage lines as a buffer against overwatering.

If subpaving automatic irrigation is combined with surface irrigation in the tree opening, maintain separate zones for the different water conditions. The subpaving soil system will require significantly less water.

Figure 2.6.41. Drip irrigation manifold in valve box.

Drip systems. Drip irrigation is the most common type of pressurized irrigation installed under pavement. The lines fit in the narrow space in direct contact with the soil. The water moves through the soil by capillary action. The design of the system must allow for removal and replacement of individual lines if the drip emitters become clogged or the line damaged. This can be accomplished by placing each drip line in a perforated sleeve.

A 2-inch-diameter perforated drain tube is ideal as the sleeve. The drip tubes can easily be pulled out of the sleeve. Pull boxes must be added at each end of every line run and must be large enough to work with the line ends. A standard rectangular irrigation valve box is sufficient. There can be no angles or manifolds under the pavement. Short manifolds can be created at each end of the run within the pull box to permit distribution of several lines from a single valve. Do not manifold the drip lines under the pavement. Bends in the lines must be of sufficient radius (3-foot minimum radius) to work the drip tube through the system.

Perforated sleeves can become crushed during the installation of the paving. Sleeve lines are best buried into a sand bed below a gravel layer. In structural cells, the drip lines are installed under the deck. Inspect the lines just before paving is added.

Bubbler systems. Bubbler heads can be installed under the pavement in a suspended paver system. A root watering head such as the Rain Bird Root Watering system may be applicable in structural soil types where unit pavers are installed over the soil. Each head and its connection to the main line must be accessible from the surface of the paving. This requirement makes bubblers impractical due to the number and size of paving penetrations required. The sandier the soil, the closer the spacing required. Consult with the manufacturer.

Soil Inspection and Maintenance

Once paving is in place, it will be necessary to inspect and maintain the soil. It is assumed that both soil and paving may remain undisturbed for several generations. In limited areas such as soil trenches, inserting a soil probe on an angle along the side of the tree opening may be sufficient. As the distance from the tree opening to outer limits of the soil increases to more than 20 feet, there should be small openings in the pavement to check soil moisture and chemical levels. Moisture levels can be monitored remotely by sensors inserted in the soil; however, sensors tend to fail with time. Excess moisture can be monitored through the inspection risers in drain lines and dry wells, but overly dry conditions cannot be observed except by plant health and direct soil probes. Nothing beats the observations that come from sticking one's fingers or a soil probe into the soil.

Soil/aggregate structural soils may be impossible to monitor. Inserting a soil probe into this material, once compacted and confined, is impossible. The top layer of this material is always dry, so looking at the surface will not tell much about soil moisture.

Structural cell systems should be provided with a minimum of one inspection port between each pair of trees. This inspection port should be a 4-inch-diameter pipe riser with a screw cap placed over one of the perforations in the cell deck. Designers may complain that the numerous caps interfere with the "look" of the pavement, but good designers will understand the need for inspection and develop aesthetically acceptable methods of providing for this function.

Soil Maintenance

Soil maintenance, including liquid fertilizer and chemical adjustments, is possible for soils provided with a subpaving watering system. Such treatment options are the best reason to include at least a perforated line system on the surface under the pavement.

Soil under structural cells is much more maintainable. If inspection openings are installed in the pavement, compost teas, compost slurries, and even fine mulch can be injected into the space under the pavement. Better systems to add amendments to the space under the paving will be developed as these systems come into more common use.

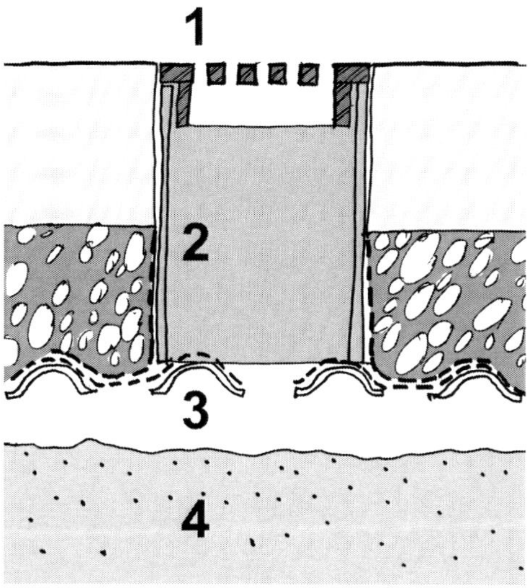

Figure 2.6.42. Soil inspection and maintenance port over structural cells allows for testing of soil qualities. Compost slurries, compost tea, and chemical elements can be sprayed into the air space above the soil if needed.

1. 6-inch grate.
2. 6-inch-diameter PVC pipe centered over slot in cell deck. Add a geotextile skirt around the pipe.
3. Cell deck. Remove geotextile covering slot.
4. Planting soil.

HYBRID SOIL SYSTEMS

No one option should be used for all projects, and designers should consider the use of several options on the same project or even a hybrid of options for the same tree. The goal is to use the most efficient, sustainable, and cost-effective option or combination of options.

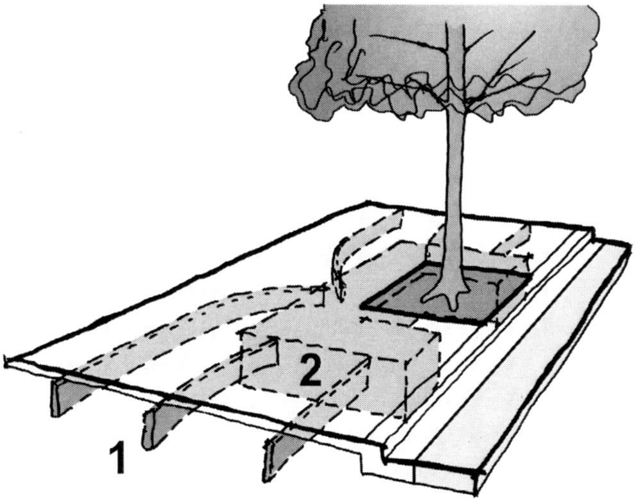

Figure 2.6.43. Hybrid soil system.

1. Three root paths connecting from tree to tree ending at the face of the structural cells.
2. Two-layer structural cell configuration around tree opening to provide an additional 240 cubic feet of soil and provide for space for the rapid-taper roots.

TREES AS A UTILITY—REVIEW AND APPROVAL IN PUBLIC SPACE

Each option changes the traditional approach to public space design. In the past, the tree box was for the tree, and the soil under the pavement held up the pavement and was a location for utilities. Intrusion of roots outside the small space dedicated to the tree was considered a "problem." Each of the rooting options in this chapter challenges that tradition.

Civil engineers often control the design of these spaces, particularly within the public right of way. If the tree soil system is presented with its environmental benefits as a utility to the city engineering departments, acceptance is more forthcoming. When the soil system also becomes a part of the rainwater management utility system, the need and acceptability of the larger under pavements soil system becomes immediately self evident. Over the last 20 years, forward-thinking civil engineers have come to accept that roots growing under the pavement are normal, and they are interested in incorporating

Figure 2.6.44. Approval of the nonstandard soil details for these trees, including the use of root paths and structural soil, required many meetings with county public works and transportation officials.

ideas that successfully grow large trees with the least conflict. Change is slow, and engineers do not like to deviate from standards even when they know there is a good reason for the proposed modifications. Few want to be the first to try something new. Having a list of places where ideas have been used successfully helps with obtaining subpaving soil option approval.

If a particular rooting space option has not been used in the project location, try scheduling a personal meeting with the engineer who controls the approval process before the plans are submitted. Come with clear drawings that show a respect and understanding of the principles of soil and drainage from an engineering perspective. Research other places where your preferred option has been used successfully or already approved. The closer the precedent city to the location where the work is being undertaken, the better. Be aware of any special conditions that might have occurred in the first approval city that may not exist in the second. These may include citizen or political support, adequate budgets, and different soils or utility configurations. Having the mayor or a member of the city council in favor of the idea helps, but be sure that there are not conflict issues between the politician and the public works staff.

Approvals may take many meetings and require persistence on the part of the designer. The city planner or urban designer may approve the approach, but the public works inspector may have the power to stop the "nonstandard work."

The designer may not be able to charge for time spent to change the standard, and his or her firm may have to show its commitment to the principles in *Up By Roots* by going this extra mile to make an improvement in the health of urban trees.

SUMMARY

- Calculate the soil volume required for the future growth of the tree, and provide needed soil under the pavement using methods that are not in conflict with the needs of the pavement.
- Avoid planting small trees to solve the problem of inadequate rooting space.
- Use root paths when budgets are low and soils under the pavements are likely to have some ability to support rooting.
- Soil trenches may be the most cost-effective way to enlarge soil volumes under the pavement but are limited as to the amount of soil that can be provided.
- Soil vaults are expensive and limit the rooting volume to the area within the vault.
- Sand structural soils have not been shown to support tree roots when compacted to 95 percent compaction.

- Soil/aggregate structural soils such as CU Soil provide very little soil volume for the amount of material purchased.
- Sand/aggregate structural soils require irrigation.
- Suspended sidewalks and structural cells offer the greatest opportunity to dramatically increase soil volumes under sidewalks.
- Providing ways to increase the flow of water and the exchange of air within the soil under pavement can improve the quality of the rooting space.
- Filter sediment and divert salt when increasing surface water flow into the soil under the pavement.
- Using tree-rooting space under sidewalks as part of the rainwater management system may cause problems that require research to resolve.
- Irrigation systems under pavements should be designed as simply as possible, be easy to maintain, and not necessary for the long-term health of the tree.
- Design access openings for inspection and maintenance of soil under the pavement.
- Use several soil options together on the same project and even at the same tree to provide the most efficient, sustainable, and cost-effective solution.
- Obtaining approval for the use of soil options below the pavement will require persistence and knowledge of other cities where engineers have approved these options.

REFERENCES

Key References

Costello, Laurence R., and Katherine S. Jones. 2003. *Reducing Infrastructure Damage by Tree Roots: A Compendium of Strategies*. Western Chapter of the International Society of Arboriculture, Cohasset, CA. 119 pp.

Craul, Timothy A., and Phillip J. Craul. 2006. *Soil Design Protocols: For Landscape Architects and Contractors.* John Wiley & Sons, Inc., New York, NY. 339 pp.

Harris, Richard W., James R. Clark, and Nelda P. Matheny. 2004. *Arboriculture: Integrated Management of Landscape Trees, Shrubs, and Vines.* 4th ed. Pearson Education, Inc., Upper Saddle River, NJ. 578 pp.

Trowbridge, Peter J., and Nina L. Bassuk. 2004. *Trees in the Urban Landscape: Site Assessment Design and Installation.* John Wiley & Sons, Inc., Hoboken, NJ. 205 pp.

Urban, James. 2000. *Ramsey/Sleeper Architectural Graphic Standards.* 10th ed. John Ray Hoke, Jr., ed. John Wiley & Sons, Inc., New York, NY.

Other Resources

Arnold, Henry F. 1993. *Trees in Urban Design.* 2nd ed. Van Nostrand Reinhold, New York, NY. 197 pp.

Craul, Phillip J. 1999. *Urban Soils: Applications and Practices.* John Wiley & Sons, Inc., New York, NY. 366 pp.

Craul, Phillip J. 1992. *Urban Soil in Landscape Design.* John Wiley & Sons, Inc., New York, NY. 396 pp.

Ferguson, Bruce K. 2005. *Porous Pavements.* CRC Press, Boca Raton, FL. 577 pp.

Gilman, Edward F. 1997. *Trees for Urban and Suburban Landscapes.* Delmar Publishers, Albany, NY. 662 pp.

International Society of Arboriculture. 2003. *Introduction to Arboriculture: Tree Biology.* DVD-ROM. International Society of Arboriculture, Champaign, IL.

Lilly, Sharon J. 2001. *Arborists' Certification Study Guide.* International Society of Arboriculture, Champaign, IL. 222 pp.

Loh, Felix C.W., Jason C. Grabosky, and Nina L. Bassuk. 2003. Growth response of *Ficus benjamina* to limited soil volume and soil dilution in a skeletal soil container study. *Urban Forestry & Urban Greening* 2(1):52–63.

Smiley, E. Thomas, Lisa Calfee, Bruce R. Fraedrich, and Emma J. Smiley. July 2006. Comparison of structural and noncompacted soils for trees surrounded by pavement. *Arboriculture & Urban Forestry* 32(4):164–169.

Watson, Gary W., and Dan Neely, eds. 1994. *The Landscape Below Ground.* International Society of Arboriculture, Champaign, IL. 222 pp.

Watson, Gary W., and Dan Neely, eds. 1998. *The Landscape Below Ground II.* International Society of Arboriculture, Champaign, IL. 265 pp.

Whitcomb, Carl E. 1987. *Establishment and Maintenance of Landscape Plants.* Lacebark Publications, Stillwater, OK. 618 pp.

PART TWO

7

Principle 7—Select the Right Tree

Selecting the right tree for the right place has been the accepted solution to urban tree problems, but in a dense urban environment, there may be few trees appropriate for such conditions.The already limited list of usable urban trees is dwindling quickly due to an ever-increasing number of invading pests and diseases. Our cities need a much longer list of usable trees.

To make this list longer, designers must first make the place right and then select the right tree for those conditions. In previous chapters of *Up By Roots*, we've learned to design landscapes that provide sufficient quantities of well-drained, quality soil. Once site conditions are improved, the list of usable urban trees will expand.

This book is not a catalog of information about the requirements of individual trees in an urban environment. Libraries are filled with texts that provide such information. Principle 7 is about how to interpret and use this information.

Figure 2.7.1. Select the right tree for the right place.

Figure 2.7.2. Multiple factors in selecting the right tree for the right place. Sometimes the right decision requires a longer view.

a. Large trees placed in a confined rooftop planter. Leaf area of these plane trees is at maximum size for the soil provided. A single small tree would have been more manageable.
b. Large tree near a power line requires frequent pruning until the crown tops over the line.
c. Small (but not small enough) tree under a power line will require constant pruning forever.
d. Large tree next to high-voltage power line. Here the tree was able to become large enough to arch over the lines and may be more successful than a small tree, although the tree presents significant conflicts and challenges as it ages.

Many landscape designers do not have proficiency in the knowledge of plants, because they have focused on other aspects of a complex profession. They may not possess the skills needed to make good plant choices. Where this knowledge is lacking, firms should hire horticultural or arboricultural consultants.

The design professional must relearn the skill of selecting and using trees and plants in the landscape. Fortunately, designers are beginning to recognize and discuss these issues and are once again embracing plant knowledge as a legitimate part of landscape architecture. Designers who include plants of any kind in their work must be competent in the knowledge of plants or work with a consultant who is knowledgeable.

TREE INFORMATION RESOURCES

It is important to use many resources when investigating a tree. Despite the availability of information from books, programs, and websites, nothing beats firsthand experience of the plants being proposed.

Books

Books by Michael Dirr and Gary Hightshoe are a good place to start to gain an understanding of plant requirements, but even as remarkable as these authors are, their work represents only a part of what is needed. Good horticulturists or gardeners constantly discuss plants, not just because they love them but also because they need a wide range of reference points from which to determine the limitations of a particular plant. Dirr gives us both his personal and academic observations on thousands of plants. However, plants can be found doing well in circumstances where they are not supposed to thrive, or doing poorly where one would expect them to do well. Subtle changes in genetics and environment can be the difference between success and failure. In his book, Dirr often debates himself or other experts on the finer points of plant attributes.

Both Dirr's and Hightshoe's perspectives were honed by hands-on experience in the central and eastern portions of the United States, with extensive travel to other regions. Horticulturists are limited by the time they can spend in a particular region and the observations that can be made during that time. Beyond that, they compile the observations of others through academic research and personal communications. Designers working outside the central and eastern areas of the country should also consult the works of horticultural authors who live and work regionally. Each climatic region has good texts on local plants and how they perform.

a

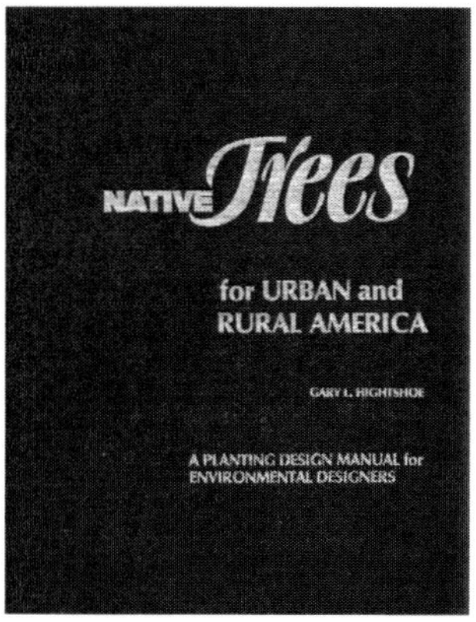

b

Figure 2.7.3. Horticultural reference books provide the first source of information on trees.

a. Dirr's *Manual of Woody Landscape Plants.*

b. Hightshoe's *Native Trees, Shrubs, and Vines for Urban and Rural America.*

Digital Plant Selection Tools

Designers have access to an increasing number of computer-based or online plant selection programs such as Horticopia or Michael Dirr's *Interactive Manual and Photo Library of Woody Landscape Plants.* They are a good place to research, but please do not solely rely on them. Search programs tend to oversimplify the criteria, leaving little room for debate or difference of opinion. For example, numeric information such as how big the plant will become relative to growing conditions and life span may not fit neatly into a program format. Much of the data on different plants is region- and climate-specific. Be sure the source of the information is based in the region of the project.

Often these digital resources are used primarily for their photo content. Never rely on a single image to make a plant choice. Find multiple images and become personally familiar with the range of actual plant forms at different levels of maturity based on field observations in the region of the project. It is unwise to select a plant that one has never actually experienced first hand.

When using Internet-based information, be mindful of the source. Online tools are useful for quick data or checking hard-to-find information. Use normal precautions to validate the source institution. The internet is just one more tool and does not replace books or personal experience.

In any research effort, use a wide range of sources for information, both digital and printed. Take into account each author's viewpoint and personal experience in the climate and soils of the region. Compare data among sources and never dismiss your own personal experience with a plant.

Figure 2.7.4. Horticopia information pages focus on the visual aspects of the plant. There are few images of the mature plant.

LOCAL KNOWLEDGE AND PLANT LIMITATIONS

The more a plant is used, the more its limitations can be identified. White pine is known to be sensitive to certain types of urban air pollution, while other pines used less often might not be classified as being pollution-sensitive. This may be because these other pines have seldom been planted in polluted areas. Fewer observations mean less discussion in the literature.

Before adding an unfamiliar plant to a design, try to find several existing specimens located in the same general area of the project and growing in similar cultural conditions. My office had a general rule that any new plant had to be supported by three successful examples growing in the area of the site with similar cultural and maintenance limitations. This is not to say that new plants could not be used, but more research was required for plants that did not meet the rule. New plants could be tested in smaller, less visually critical parts of the design.

Familiarity with the local plants of a region can be a significant hurdle for the landscape designer because the profession has become extremely mobile. Designers routinely fly into cities and start work based on a few observations, maybe from a visit to a local garden or an arboretum and possibly a discussion with a local, associated design firm. These jet-setting designers bring with them ideas and plant prejudices from their regional experience that may or may not be appropriate for the new location. Unless they are well versed in horticulture or follow the advice of their consultants, they may not select appropriate plants.

A typical safe response has been to stick to a simple palette of foolproof plants, which leads to landscapes that lack diversity. It takes years to learn the nuances of local horticulture. With this in mind, clients should be advised to hire local experts to design landscape features that involve plants.

TAXONOMIC FEATURES AND NOMENCLATURE DIFFERENCES

The particular aspects of leaf bud, bark, flower, and fruit are well documented in most species. However, there is still debate over many species and genera. Plant breeders, by exploiting species variety, contribute to the diversity of cultivars in the market but can also confuse identification by inconsistent or incorrect labeling practices.

a

b

Figure 2.7.5. Two trees in the same field, both being sold as London plane.

a. True to cultivar with greener overbark and creamier underbark.

b. Incorrectly named cultivar with tanner overbark and whiter underbark.

Buyer Beware

Purchasing plants from a quality nursery helps ensure that specified botanical cultivar arrives at the project. This is a "buyer beware" market. In the case of species that have been the subject of intensive hybridizing, different plants may be sold under similar names. When purchasing a budded or grafted cultivar, only the part of the tree above the ground is a genetically controlled product. The roots of the tree may be from a different species. Become familiar enough with the plants to be able to identify them and to know the ramifications of mistakes the nursery could make.

Propagation Impacts

Decisions made at the nursery significantly affect the potential success of plants. This includes variation of seed sources, attribution of wrong names to a species, problems with grafting and budding techniques, pruning styles, roots too deep in the root ball, and girdling roots. Any of these can result in a tree not performing as expected. Nursery quality and purchasing problems will be discussed in Part 2, Chapter Nine.

A few species, particularly oaks and certain native trees, are difficult to propagate asexually and are typically propagated from seed rather than from traditional vegetative practices. Since seed genetics vary widely, every tree will vary. This can lead to different growth rates, branch structure, time of leaf-out, and fall color. Trees that look matched in the nursery might not look matched a few years after planting. A few nurseries are now offering several species of cloned oaks to reduce this problem in this important genera. Where matched trees are important, specify asexually propagated trees, which are the trees with cultivar names.

Figure 2.7.6. Asexually propagated cypress trees exhibiting genetic diversity.

Size, Habit, and Growth Rate

Wide variations in the reported size, habit or appearance, and growth rates of plants are found in horticultural literature. Information is based on each author's observations and reports from multiple sources. There is no standard as to how dimensions are defined and under what growing conditions they should be expected. Available light, temperature, soil fertility, moisture, drainage, genetics, and competition will all influence the ultimate size, habit, and growth rate of a tree. A tree growing in a low-light, dry-soil site at the extremes of its range would respond in a dramatically different way than would the same tree planted in optimum growth conditions. Cultivars of trees (especially recent introductions less than 50 years old) have not been around long enough for us to really know how large they will grow.

Consult multiple references. Note the locations where the champion trees are growing. American Forests (www.americanforests.org) maintains an online National

Figure 2.7.7. Different cultivars of elms on the National Mall in Washington, D.C., planted with hopes of their being disease-resistant, have produced widely different canopy forms.

Register of Big Trees with links to state champion tree registers. Are the conditions at the project site dramatically different from those at the location of the champion tree? How do the sizes listed in the reference compare to the size of the champion tree? Seek out specimens in arboretums and other locations that might have optimum and not-so-optimum growing conditions. Consider the growing conditions provided in the design.

Roots

Root architecture varies by species. Trees can have a few long, coarse roots or a very fibrous root system. While their genes set a pattern for growth, roots also respond to soil type and drainage. Trees in coarse, sandy soils will tend to have coarser roots, while the same trees in clay soil will develop a finer root texture. This factor can be critical when selecting a nursery. Heavier soil should produce trees that transplant better. Roots will grow deeper in well-drained soil and closer to the surface in soil that is poorly drained, irrigated, or where the topsoil is thin. Trees with a reputation for being shallow-rooted may simply be expressing their ability to survive in poorly drained soil. In deep, well-drained soil, they will grow deeper roots.

Root architecture is one area where additional study may open new possibilities for improving urban trees. Far less work on developing better root architecture has been undertaken when compared to genetic work on the appearance of the top of the tree.

PLANT SELECTION CRITERIA

There is no perfect plant, and making selections always requires compromise of one criterion over another. While matching soil and drainage conditions to tree type is critical, the designer must consider many other issues when making a tree selection.

Temperature Hardiness

The current USDA Cold Hardiness Map was last updated in printed form in 1990. A new map that reflects climate changes and more accurate mapping technology was issued by the Arbor Day Foundation (www.arborday.org/media/zones.cfm)

in 2006. Hardiness maps in various publications vary in quality and accuracy. If information on hardiness location is critical, it is best to access the current map directly from the Arbor Day Foundation Web site.

Microclimates can significantly alter the hardiness zone of a particular location. Sites within several hundred feet of a body of water are considerably warmer in winter and cooler in summer. A rise in elevation of only a few hundred feet can reduce the average temperature by several degrees. The inner city may be more than 5°F warmer than areas immediately outside the city. South-facing slopes are much warmer than north-facing slopes. Small raised planters will have lower winter soil temperatures than the surrounding ground soil. Each of these factors affects a tree's chances of survival.

The effect of heat can be as devastating as cold. The American Horticultural Society published a Plant Heat Zone Map in 1997, which can be used to rate plants for heat tolerance. It will be some time before a large list of plants is keyed to these zones, but the map is useful to establish relative heat factors as they impact plants. Like cold microclimates, heat islands and heat microclimates can have a significant impact on a tree's ability to survive.

Heat is particularly crucial when first planting a tree, because the tree will be stressed from transplanting and not large enough to create its own microclimate. Trees planted on the south and west faces of dark buildings are often killed or stunted by the reflected heat from those surfaces.

Figure 2.7.8. A linden tree (top) that is protected from afternoon sun has larger and greener leaves than a tree in an identical planting space next to a reflective southwest-facing wall (bottom) with smaller and lighter green leaves.

Genetics, Temperature Hardiness, and Photoperiod

Genetics play a role in plant temperature hardiness. Within a given species, there will be many differences between individual plants based on where the genetic material originated. The best example is red maple, which has a native range from Canada to Florida. While all red maples are named *Acer rubrum*, those taken from the forest of Massachusetts and planted in North Carolina will not grow well and vice versa. They are different trees with the same name. Know the "provenance," or origin, of the genetic material of each cultivar, and do not use plants that are significantly out of their provenance range.

This is not just a difference between colder and warmer regions. Hardiness is strongly tied to photoperiod, or the length of day as the season changes. It is believed that one of the ways different trees respond to different locales is the time the tree is genetically programmed to harden off for winter. A western Georgia nursery that claims "we have a similar climate to Washington, D.C.," misses the point that while the winter cold extremes may be similar, they are 5 degrees of latitude, or 400 miles, farther south. The difference may be even greater if the provenance of the particular cultivar is from an even more southern location.

Typically, named cultivars fare better within specific latitudes. Use a cultivar known to perform well in the region of the project. This applies to all species.

There are two ways to better ensure that the tree being specified is appropriate for the location. Check the location of the "mother" tree from which the original clone material was taken, and pick cultivars that originated close to the project. The location of the original tree may be available from the propagation nursery. Note that the propagation nursery is often different from the grower where the tree is purchased. Ask the grower questions. A second reality check is

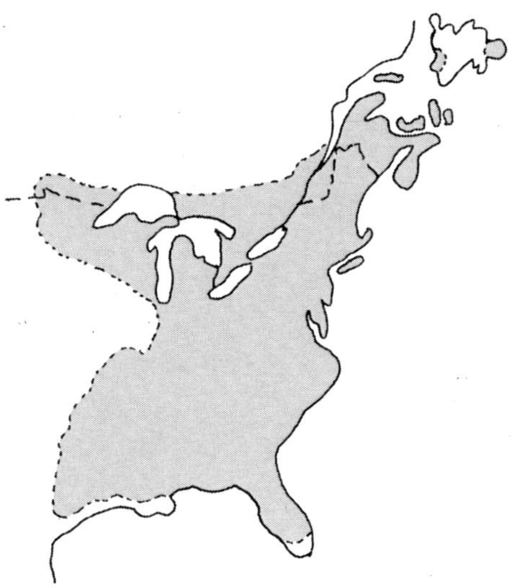

Figure 2.7.9. Native range of red maple. Though native from Florida to Newfoundland, subspecies from northern areas do not survive in the south and vice versa. Though known as a wet site species, subspecies native to dry regions do not survive in wet sites. *(Source: Textbook of Dendrology)*

to try to use only growers that are within 200 miles north or south of the project site. If there are only a few growers of this tree in the project zone, it may be that a different cultivar would be a better choice.

Cultural Requirements

Cultural requirements of a plant describe its limitations with respect to soil, drainage, wind, sun/shade, and any other factors that affect its growth and survival. A tree's ability to be transplanted is also generally described as part of its cultural requirements. Cultural requirements are closely linked to what is known as the "law of the limiting." If only one cultural requirement is deficient, such as pH, drainage, or soil volume, the tree or plant will not prosper to the extent that this one requirement is limited. Normally, all but the most extreme limitations can be mitigated.

One should never make a design dependent on maintenance to fix cultural limitations. Maintenance should only be expected to maintain the level of limitations provided in the design. Maintenance cannot improve drainage, increase rooting space, change pH, increase sunlight, modify wind, or reduce compaction. Getting these factors correct is the job of the designer.

Disease and Insects

Every tree is susceptible to some type of disease or insect, some more than others. Generally, if a tree is planted in its optimum cultural conditions, the incidence of disease and insects will be greatly reduced. Making the site right for the tree is the best defense against disease and insect problems. Plants stressed by too much or too little water, compacted soil, or other inappropriate cultural conditions are more likely to become diseased or to attract insects. On the other hand, some important insect and disease outbreaks, from Dutch elm and chestnut blight to emerald ash borer and Asian longhorned beetle, do not seem to care whether a tree is healthy or stressed. Selecting native trees is also not the answer, as most of the major disease and insect disasters of the 20th century affected native plants.

Landscapes with large numbers of similar trees are considered aesthetically comforting, but lack of diversity increases the trees' susceptibility to a disastrous infestation or infection, as well as increasing the rate at which it can move through that community once it arrives.

Some trees have pests that are simply nuisances, while others are highly susceptible to fatal attacks. It is believed that increasing the diversity of species in cities may help improve overall urban forest health; but the number of species that can reliably be planted in difficult spaces is shrinking, not expanding, due to increases in invading exotic diseases and insects. Designers must stay current on the diseases and insects that threaten trees. They can do this by joining the International Society of Arboriculture and reading its publications.

Disease and insect outbreaks are threatening many of the best urban trees. Outright bans on further planting of many species have been proposed, but such measures may be counterproductive by limiting the species selection to the point where the few remaining trees will be under even greater threat from future outbreaks. Cities should not stop planting

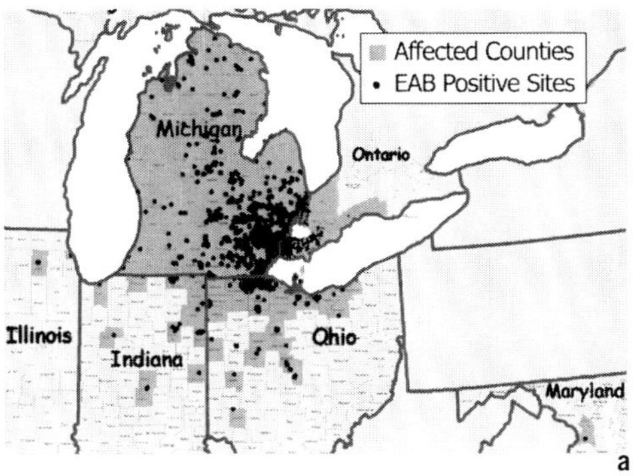

a

b

Figure 2.7.10. Spread of the emerald ash borer.

a. Identified emerald ash borer locations and affected counties as of January 2007. *(Source: USDA-APHIS)*
b. Removal of an entire street of ash. Arrows indicate removed trunk locations. This brings back bitter memories of elm loss 30 to 40 years earlier. *(Photo: USDA-APHIS)*

any species simply because it is threatened unless the outbreak of a particular pest is deemed overwhelming. The rapidly spreading attack of the emerald ash borer (EAB) on ash seems to be at that level. The slower-spreading Asian longhorned beetle (ALB) could be as devastating as the EAB, but the list of species it attacks is so large that to stop planting ALB host trees would dangerously limit the diversity of large urban trees.

While deep knowledge of diseases and insects is beyond the average designer, there are excellent resources listed at the end of this chapter that will help the designer with basic problems that come up in the daily work of designing trees in the landscape. The best way to get accurate information is to maintain a consulting relationship with a good arborist.

Figure 2.7.11. Low diversity of species will increase likelihood of insect infestation.

A rose by any other name will die the same.

—with apologies to Shakespeare

Michael Raupp Raps on Rosaceae

At the University of Maryland, Michael Raupp has been studying insects and diseases in plants at hundreds of locations in the state, with particular interest in the relationships between the choices landscape designers make and the problems that result. Two trends have emerged. First, plants in the Rosaceae family are responsible for the greatest proportion of plant problems. Second, problems with insects are greater in landscapes with a lower diversity of plant species. Think twice about planting a grove of crabapples. While a bed of a thousand azaleas might get the project on the cover of *Landscape Architecture* magazine, can it be maintained?

Light and Shade

Trees have varying abilities to tolerate low light levels, although most can tolerate full sun, even if they are shade-tolerant. As light is reduced, the tree responds with fewer leaves and flowers. Branches will "reach" toward the available light. Less photosynthesis results in thinner growth rings and fewer reserves for surviving drought, disease, and insect infestation.

There are different types of shade. Trees allow some light to filter through, and it is rare that there is total shade under a large, mature tree. In the winter and spring, there is much more sun, and understory plants often leaf out before the climax species, allowing an early start to photosynthesis. Tree roots also compete for the same resources in the soil as understory plants, which may be more significant in the decline of understory plants than the lack of sunlight.

Tall buildings create spaces that may seem shaded all day. There is no spring dose of sun. While building shade is not filtered light as is the light through trees, there is diffused light from the atmosphere, which can be quite strong on days with thin clouds or high humidity. Light may also reflect from other buildings. The actual light levels in any particular space may be significantly higher than a shadow study suggests. Trees can use this reflected or diffused light. When studying an urban space, try to observe the amount of reflected light in a space. Building shade is not accompanied by root competition in the soil, so trees and plants may actually grow with fewer limitations on the north side of a building than within the crown of a large mature tree. However, the competition for soil resources next to a building is still fierce thanks to utilities and soil compaction associated with the building construction.

Most literature uses broad terms such as "full sun" or "partial shade." Be sure to understand the author's definitions of the terms. A good source for more information about shade-tolerant trees is in the USDA handbook *Silvics of North America*. In this text, the phrase "reaction to competition" is used to describes a tree's ability to grow in low-light conditions. What they mean is how well a tree can grow from a seedling under the competing shade of existing canopy trees. The ability of a tree to survive under the canopy of larger trees makes a tree shade-tolerant.

a b c

Figure 2.7.12. Light and shade.

a. The shadow on the south side of this balustrade is created by strong reflected light.

b. Tree planted in perpetual, reflected light survives but produces a thin canopy.

c. Trees adapting to light conditions in the shade of a building are falling over in slow motion.

Artificial Light

Much is written about negative impacts of urban street lights on tree growth. However, these assertions are not supported in the scientific literature, and artificial light may actually be beneficial to the tree. See Part 1, Chapter Five for a discussion on this topic and a review of how the misinterpretation of a little science can lead to the wrong conclusion.

Wind

Trees vary in their ability to withstand wind. Wind causes desiccation of leaves, and high winds can break branches and topple trees with shallow roots. Building shapes can cause wind tunnels, which amplify wind speeds. Existing conditions can be observed, but future construction can be difficult to predict without specialized study. On very large building projects, wind tunnel studies may be available. On smaller building projects, a designer's best assessment is needed.

If the tree can survive desiccation, most trees will adapt to the wind, growing stronger roots and trunk structures. Providing sufficient deep soil improves the stability of the tree. In places where there is limited rooting space, designing larger volumes of soil on the upwind side of the tree will provide a stronger root plate. Brittle trees and trees with weak branch unions will still lose branches in higher winds. These trees should be avoided if high winds are an issue. Unfortunately, there is no good source for this information. Dirr occasionally provides notes on this topic in the "Additional Comments" section of his *Manual of Woody Landscape Plants*. Local knowledge is critical.

Wind issues become more urgent in tree preservation situations. Removing adjacent trees or buildings or cutting roots will create instability, and may result in blowdown after construction is completed. Ironically, removing branches may decrease the stability of the tree. Consult an arborist when major changes must be made to the dynamics of a tree.

a

b

Figure 2.7.13. Different pruning of silver maples.

a. Tree with lower branches retained rarely loses limbs in high wind.

b. Tree with lower branches pruned away often loses branches in high wind.

Fewer Branches, More Wind Load?

It seems counterintuitive that removing branches from a tree would increase its wind load, but time-lapse photography observation of trees in a high wind reveals the answer. A tree is not like a sail, because all the branches in a tree are not being loaded at the same time. If you watch closely, you will see that while some branches are bending with the wind, other branches are actually swaying back into the wind recovering from the previous gust. In effect, the tree is moving in many directions at the same time. This random movement dampens the overall impact of the wind load. Fewer branches mean less random movement.

Drainage

Drainage rates vary dramatically, and they may not be easy to modify, especially in heavy clay soil. A common response is to select a species that can tolerate poor drainage. Sometimes, even tolerant trees still drown.

Tolerating poor drainage is not the same as tolerating trapped water. With slow or seasonally poor drainage, the soil eventually drains and air replaces the water. Many wet soils are only wet in the spring when soil respiration is low. If soil water is stagnant, roots and microbes still respire, using the available oxygen in the water. As the oxygen is turned into carbon dioxide, the soil becomes anaerobic, with soil organisms giving off the putrid, rotting odor as described in Part 1, Chapter Three. When this state is reached, even trees that are tolerant of poor drainage will die.

In forested swamps, water flows, no matter how slowly, and replenishes oxygen. Water volumes are usually quite large, so the oxygen reduction rate is slowed. Red maple may appear to be growing in standing water, but it is still oxygenated water. A bog is an area of naturally trapped water and often has anaerobic soils. Few tree species grow in permanently wet bogs. Know whether you have a bog or swamp.

There is also a difference between a red maple that seeds itself into a swamp during a period of low water and a red maple purchased from a nursery. The nursery tree's roots are not adapted to a wet site, while the naturally seeded tree has adapted to its wet condition from the beginning. Few nursery selections of red maple are selected from wetland trees. At the same time, some red maple variations in nature are actually uniquely adapted to dry sites. Nurseries that specialize in trees for wetlands will have stock selected for wet applications, and they may have grown these trees in wet conditions to improve transplant success into wet sites—but not into bog soils.

Tree decline from too much water or too little water may look similar—the leaves wilt. But notice where the yellowing leaves are located. Trees with too much water will lose leaves from the base and interior of the tree first. Trees with not enough water will die back from the outer crown first.

Figure 2.7.14. Some trees can survive seasonal flooding as long as there is sufficient oxygen in the water. *(Photo: David Barnes)*

Air Pollution

Air pollution in cities has not been demonstrated to be a significant problem for most deciduous trees. Evergreen trees are more likely to be affected by pollution because they depend on the same set of leaves for several seasons.

Air pollution rapidly becomes diluted as distance from the source increases. Since major highways are a principal source of urban pollutants, a few hundred yards may be a sufficient buffer. Prevailing wind patterns, topography, and building configurations can increase or decrease the buffer distance. Air pollution is just one of many stress factors. A tree growing in a healthy soil environment may not be as sensitive to a pollutant as the same species of tree in a stressed soil situation. At sites where industrial air pollutants still exist, the designer must research the particular substances and try to learn whatever information is available about their effect on trees.

The one pollutant that can affect large areas is acid rain, which results in the acidification of soils. Checking the pH of the existing soil is the best indicator of how much this factor needs to be considered. *Abiotic Disorders of Landscape Plants*, by Costello et al., is a good resource on pollution impacts.

Salt

Salt pollution comes in two forms, airborne and waterborne. Airborne salt can travel greater distances, up to a hundred yards, and coat the twigs and buds of a tree. Waterborne salts stay near the application point and may travel less than 100 feet before they become too diluted to impact the plant. Work by Dirr suggests that species tolerant to waterborne salts might not be tolerant to airborne salts and vice versa. Make sure the salt source and the species tolerance is understood.

Road speed and salt application frequency are significant factors in the amount and type of salt impact. Commercial streets tend to have slower vehicle speeds, but more salt is spread on the sidewalks. Interstate highways, high-speed boulevards, and arterials are covered with salt, which is whipped up into the air by speeding traffic. Salt-laden snow along roads may be pushed onto the base of trees. Parking lots may go unsalted during the initial snow event and then be cleared of unsalted snow, while the walks near buildings will likely be salted more often.

Recognize these different conditions and use appropriate species and details to defend against the type and frequency of salt application. The greater the salt threat, the more important it is to provide for large soil volumes and rapid drainage. As growing conditions are optimized, salt problems become more a nuisance than a life-or-death issue. Stressed trees and trees with limited soil suffer the most from salt.

a

b

Figure 2.7.15. Salt damage.

a. Tale of two trees. The healthy tree on the left has a low curb around the tree opening and slightly larger space, while the dead tree on the right has a smaller opening with no curb and dies from waterborne salt damage.
b. "Witch's brooms" in the twigs of this tree indicate airborne salt damage. *(Photo: Tom Smiley)*

Small curbs can deflect water from the tree opening to keep out salt water in the winter.This also keeps out summer water, and the summer rainwater may be more critical than the lack of salt. Final decision on curbs should be region-specific. If the regional climate is dryer and warmer and the tree soil volume larger, curbs should not be used. In colder and wetter regions where soil volumes are small (less than 300 cubic feet per tree) curbs may have value to protect from salt damage.

In dry climates, salt buildup is from a combination of fertilizer and irrigation, concentrating salts at the surface. Salt buildup may be slower but is more difficult to flush away. Use of alternative chemicals to reduce the salt in the soil may have different side effects. Potassium toxicity in soil has been observed in Canada where potassium chloride is used as an alternative to sodium chloride. More research is needed on this issue.

See Part 1, Chapter Four for a more in-depth discussion on salt and remedial actions.The best reference on salt tolerance is *Abiotic Disorders of Landscape Plants*, by L. Costello et al.

Trees as Polluters—Pollen and VOCs

Trees contribute to pollution [see Part 1, Chapter Five for a discussion on pollen and volatile organic carbons (VOCs)]. Trees also reduce human VOC production and contribute favorably to other environmental systems. Eliminating trees with the highest VOC output will be very damaging to the overall environmental equation.

VOCs increase the level of ozone, but it is documented that increasing the number of trees, even those species that are high VOC producers, still reduces the amount of ozone.This is because the same trees are also powerful temperature moderators of city microclimates, and temperature is a major factor in the production of ozone. The list of trees that produce the most VOCs includes many of the most important urban trees. A single issue such as VOC emission should not be allowed to drive species determination. Do not select lower VOC-emitting trees unless they are capable of producing the same canopy benefits as a higher VOC-emitting tree.

Pollen is a more sensitive issue than VOCs.There are people whose lives are made miserable by pollen, and trees are often the biggest producers of pollen. However, eliminating pollen-producing trees is not the answer. Trees make cities livable. The list of pollen-free large trees that can survive in cities is hopelessly small, about seven species for most of the country. It has actually been proposed that city tree planting be restricted to just these few trees, a disastrous policy if implemented. See Tom Ogren's book *Allergy Free Gardening* to see a list of trees that would be banned under a pollen-free policy.

Since pollen travels long distances, most city, park, and suburban trees

Figure 2.7.16. These live oaks in New Orleans, as well as most of the trees in that city, would be removed if groups supporting reduction in pollen were to gain control of tree policy.

would have to be removed to provide relief for allergy sufferers and would make the few remaining species dangerously susceptible to attack from disease and insects. This would increase the temperature and further drive the population indoors to air-conditioned spaces, while VOC production is further increased by the use of air conditioners.

Mold and chemicals in buildings, which can cause symptoms similar to pollen allergies, may be responsible for more allergies than tree pollen. If this is true, putting more people in air-conditioned spaces will not solve the allergy problem. Fortunately, there are good allergy medications for most sufferers, making these medications a preferred alternative to cutting down the nation's forests.

There used to be cities with few trees and low pollen levels due to climate. Traditionally, severe allergy sufferers have moved to these locations. Due to a lack of understanding about the importance of native landscapes in extreme environments, so many irrigated pollen-producing plants have been added to these areas that allergy sufferers no longer find relief. In these areas, replanting native trees and reducing irrigation may be a reasonable approach, but it needs to be balanced with the cost of loss of shade and hotter temperatures that would result from the loss of tree canopy.

Wildlife

Trees attract wildlife to varying degrees. This may be a desirable feature or a nuisance, and is surely a matter of personal taste. Know your trees and their local reputations for attracting different types of wildlife, from bees and birds to squirrels and rats.

Litter

Every tree drops something at some time of the year. Like wildlife, whether this is a pleasure or a problem may be a matter of opinion. If we selected only trees that produced no litter, we would have very few trees with which to work. It is the designer's obligation to try to educate clients and the public on the aesthetic beauty of falling leaves, flakes of bark, and even the occasional branch puncturing a windshield. A city without large trees is a terrible place to live.

Figure 2.7.17. Litter from trees is a fact of life. Tree advocates must educate their neighbors to embrace the cycles of trees as a part of their value.

a b

Figure 2.7.18. Urban trees and soils from the tropics to the Arctic have more similarities than differences.
a. Singapore.
b. Anchorage.

TROPICAL TREES AND ARCTIC SOILS

There is likely to be a criticism of this book that it is another "eastern tree book" and that trees in warmer and colder climates are not considered. The reality is that urban tree and soil problems, and most of their solutions, are the same the world over. In the preparation of this book, the author has traveled from the equator to the sub-Arctic looking at trees and soil. Urban trees problems in Singapore and San Juan are incredibly similar to tree issues in Anchorage and Reykjavik. Drainage problems are less prevalent in hot, dry areas, and trunk flare and root conflict issues decrease with increasing latitude due to slower tree growth. Other than that, we all have the same basic issues to overcome.

THE FOUR BIG PLANT SELECTION QUESTIONS

The next four subprinciples of "Select the right tree for the right place" attempt to guide designers through the most contentious issues in the placing of trees in urban spaces. These issues are:

- Diversity vs. monocultures
- Natives vs. exotics
- Tree spacing
- The element of time in the design of landscapes

Each element addresses a critical aspect of the design process. Like all great debates, the current rhetoric is full of misinformation, exaggerations, and half-truths on both sides. The following examination will try not to contribute to the rhetoric. However, it is likely there are no correct answers and wide room for interpreting observations. Like any observer, I bring my own prejudices to the discussion, which will become apparent.

a. Diversity.
b. Monoculture.

Question 1—Diversity vs. Monocultures

There is a very compelling argument for planting large, continuous stands of the same tree, otherwise known as a monoculture. Whether it is a designed forest grove or a great street or plaza, a monoculture is a wonderful, almost magical experience. It sticks in people's minds and establishes a sense of place like nothing else can. Henry Arnold's masterwork *Trees in Urban Design* makes the case for this approach. There is even a compelling argument that natural models support large-scale monocultures. Forests, especially those of extreme environments, are often filled with just one or two species, a natural monoculture of trees for miles at a stretch. A single species often dominates younger, naturally regenerating landscapes. Monocultures should be considered by scale. The larger they are, the greater the chance of catastrophic failure in the event of change in disease and insect vectors. Nature has created its own monocultures that make a city with only a few species look incredibly diverse. Figure 2.7.19 depicts different sized monocultures, both natural and human-produced. Which are okay? Does it really matter?

On the other hand, there is the argument for diversity. The string of disease and insect disasters is seared into the consciousness of the design community. Chestnut blight, Dutch elm disease, gypsy moths, pine beetles, woolly adelgids,

Figure 2.7.19. Monocultures of different scales. At what size does a monoculture become a problem?

a. Small project: City Hall, San Francisco, pollarded plane trees.
b. Large project: Embarcadero, San Francisco, date palms.
c. Citywide, responding to climate conditions: Anchorage, downtown dominated by European mountain ash.
d. Citywide, responding to cultural traditions: Large portions of Berlin, dominated by linden.
e. Regional: Tulip poplar reaches monoculture status over vast areas of the mid-Atlantic region (central Maryland).
f. Global: Sub-Arctic Alaska, white spruce dominates the sub-Arctic forest in a belt completely circling the globe.

a b c d e f

Figure 2.7.20. Diversity of tree species in a diversity of places.

a. Suburban United States: Street trees of multiple species.
b. Yorkville Park, Toronto: Approximately six species.
c. Millennium Park, Chicago: More than ten species.
d. Levi Plaza, San Francisco: About six species.
e. Main Street, Greenville, South Carolina: Three species.
f. Residential streetscapes, Georgetown, D.C.: Many species.

and more recently, the Asian longhorned beetle and emerald ash borer have devastated billions of trees, both in cities and forests. Millions of acres have fallen to such assaults in the last century. It can be argued that human-planted monocultures fared poorly in each of these onslaughts, although only a handful of American chestnuts survived the blight, no matter how isolated the tree. What seems clear is the more continuous the stretch of a single species, the easier it is for disease and insects to move. When a large block of trees is lost, the damage has a greater visual impact, and it will take many years to recover.

At the management level, the argument can cut both ways. Maintenance, including dealing with disease and insects, can be made easier with large blocks of a single species, but an outbreak might spread so fast that management will not be able to keep up. The emerald ash borer outbreak in Michigan is a good example. However, the borer travels so fast that small groups of trees are just as likely to fall prey as large blocks.

Disease and insect varieties are increasing in the United States as a result of the globalized economy. Millions of uninspected products from all over the world arrive daily, bringing new diseases and insects. Often, imported insects have no competitors to keep them in check. On the other hand, exotic species may already have resistance. This leaves many native plants defenseless. (See the discussion on native and exotic tree selections later in this chapter.)

One strong point in favor of diversity is that it offers a diverse habitat for the insect and animal world. Control of insect populations depends heavily on other insects and animals. Varying the types of trees and other plants in a landscape offers a changing menu for the predator. Unfortunately, in urban landscapes, increasing the number of species from one to two, or even three, does not make for significant diversity. This requires enough different plant types, including both trees and shrubs, to support important ecological relationships. Determining the minimum number of plant species to achieve a reasonable level of diversity is a complex topic and beyond the scope of this book, but one that deserves further study.

There is no winner in this debate. Both sides have merit and a balance must be struck.

It may help to agree on a definition of a monoculture. Any set of trees that includes only one species is a monoculture. One could argue that a small space with only a dozen trees, all of the same type, is a monoculture. The better question is: At what size does a monoculture become a problem? From an urban design standpoint, a monoculture becomes a problem when the risk of the loss of large numbers of trees at a citywide scale outweighs the benefit of the original design. Monocultures are acceptable in limited places where extraordinary management practices can defend against a threat and resources are available to replace trees quickly in the event of a disaster. A couple of rows or a few continuous blocks of the same tree do not constitute a monoculture problem. A city with 30 to 40 percent of its street trees of one genus is a problem.

When monocultures are proposed, ensure optimum growing conditions for the trees. This will make the trees healthier and easier to maintain. Be aware of trees planted near new projects and avoid using the same tree types unless there is a compelling reason to do so. Government reviewers have a role in this decision, as often they are the only group with access to all of the development proposals. Select trees that are the most disease- and insect-resistant, balancing this consideration against the need for diversity.

Figure 2.7.21. National Mall, Washington, D.C.: Nearly 2 miles of American elm trees. *(Photo courtesy National Park Service Archives)*

The National Mall in Washington, D.C., is a great example of a well-fit monoculture. Thousands of American elms have survived throughout the entire cycle of the Dutch elm disease epidemic through extraordinary maintenance. The National Park Service should consider reducing elm dependence in areas immediately outside the formal axis of the Mall, but the effect within the Mall is dramatic and compelling. The biggest threat to the image of the Mall is where different elm species replacements were planted. These trees now have dramatically different forms. Dutch elm losses have had the benefit of forming broad age class distributions within the planting. This will prove useful over the future for the planting, as the trees are now able to die and be replaced in a random succession with little visual impact on the larger planting.

One of the reasons this elm monoculture has continued to be a long-term asset, even in the face of one of the most difficult disease infestations in the nation's history, is the wide spacing, 50 feet on center. This allows the replacement trees to grow in a less competitive environment, and their smaller scale looks less abrupt in this formal layout. The wider space creates less crown and root competition, making faster growing, healthier replacement trees.

Harvard Yard is an excellent example of a successful space with a diversity of tree types. Historically, this prominent landscape has always had very diverse tree species. Michael Van Valkenburgh redesigned it, maintaining the 20 to 25 different species. The project garnered design awards, and no one complains that the space would be better as a monoculture. Though Harvard has the resources to provide extraordinary maintenance, it was wise to support diversity in this planting.

Figure 2.7.22. Harvard Yard, Cambridge, Massachusetts: About 20 species

Renowned tree researcher Frank Santamour proposed an interesting recipe for diversity on a citywide scale. It is based on broadening the number of tree types to protect the landscape from disease and insects. Trees that may host the same set of insects and diseases need to be counted as one type of tree. For example, pin oak and red oak might be considered the same tree, as they generally respond to the same set of diseases. Red oak and white oak would be different tree types because they tend to be susceptible to different sets of problems. Elms that are susceptible to Dutch elm disease are one selection; those that are not, another. All plants in the Rosaceae family might be a large group to be considered as a single genus selection, even though there are many genera in this family.

With the previous information considered, Santamour's formula for any given city is:

- No more than 10 percent of trees from any one species.
- No more than 20 percent from any one genus.
- No more than 30 percent from any one family.

The theoretical minimum species number under this formula is between 10 and 12, but the actual number of species would likely be far greater. It is likely that the actual number of species in a given town would not increase dramatically, only the proportion each tree contributes to the whole. This is a far greater diversity than is found in most cities, and a high bar to reach without expanding the number of usable species through improved growing conditions.

It is hard to manage the species selection of an urban forest where the majority of trees are planted on private property. The burden of species diversity at the citywide scale must fall in large part on the designers of new landscapes. They must become aware of the population mix in the vicinity of their projects and refrain from using species that are already becoming too common. This is a monumental task to require of the profession.

Question 2—Natives, Exotics, and Invasive Species

There are assumed advantages in using native trees in an urban landscape instead of exotics. Native trees are supposed to use less water and be more resistant to local disease and insects. They are supposedly adapted to the local environment, and their stray seeds should not become invasive. On the other hand, there are assumed advantages of using exotic and cloned trees. Many exotic trees have stood the test of time in cities, taking advantage of years of breeding and testing. Exotics may have resistance to imported insects and diseases.

a b

Figure 2.7.23. Native vs. exotic trees.

a. Native willow oak: Good within its native range, but what about beyond that range?

b. Exotic London plane: Bad?

On both sides of the discussion, some of these assumptions are certainly true, but they are often exaggerated. At best, they are anecdotal and do not apply to every plant, whether native or exotic.

Using the best tree should be the best option. In urban areas, neither native nor exotic trees have a lock on the title "best."

Defining Natives and Exotics

What is the definition of a native tree? Most people assume that a native is a plant that was in an area prior to the European invasion of the Western Hemisphere, although definitions vary depending on who is speaking. I choose to assume that for a plant to be native, it must be in its pre-1492 range and growing in soil types and other cultural conditions within that range where that plant would have been found.

If a designer is selecting a native because it is likely to be the best genetic choice, be sure that it is native to or will match both the local environment and the conditions at the planting site. The greatest determinant of tree selection is its suitability to a particular soil and drainage situation. Few native soils mimic urban soils. Is a plant that is native to a particular region's well-drained organic soil still considered "native" when planted in a compacted, poorly drained urban soil? Any plant that is not growing in the soil and drainage conditions found in its typical range should be considered an exotic plant to other soil conditions. Within that definition, all trees are exotic to urban conditions. Once a tree is planted in an urban environment, it ceases to be in its native environment. Under these conditions, what makes a native any better than a tree imported from Asia?

Figure 2.7.24. *Acer* x *freemanii*. Native or an artificially bred exotic? *(Photo courtesy Frank Schmidt Nursery)*

How much genetic breeding can a native tree tolerate and still be classified as such? If a tree is grafted onto the rootstock of a different plant, which part of the tree is native? Is a Marshall's seedless green ash native if it is grafted onto a seed-propagated white ash root? Is an *Acer* × *freemanii*, a cross between red and silver maples, both of which might be considered native, still a native tree? Is a red maple grown from a genetic line that originated in a dry site still a native if planted in a wet site? The question of native vs. exotic is far more complex than those two choices indicate.

Eco-Regions

How far out of its region can a plant be before it is no longer a native? Not very far. For example: The state of Maryland's motto is "America in miniature." The landscape ranges from sea-level beaches to silty coastal plain soil and piedmont clay loams to stony mountain soil. While generalizations can be made about regional soils, small areas of sandy, dry soil and heavy clay soil are found in every subregion. The climate within each of these eco-regions also varies. Within this diverse set of landscapes are huge numbers of native tree species, most of which will not grow in every zone of the state. Yet plant lists exist that are simply titled "Native Maryland Plants," and designers are encouraged to use plants from this list in all urban

Figure 2.7.25. The urban eco-region needs its own set of "native" plants, which might include plants taken from the native habitats of the peoples living in this ecotype, including plants from Europe and Asia.

areas. This approach makes no sense, and highlights the need for a much greater understanding of plants.

Perhaps there is a need for a new eco-region type called "urban eco-regions." Here the issues of native vs. exotic can be expanded to include humans and human influences on soil, water, and air as they may impact plant choices.

Insects and Diseases

Most of the plant disasters of the last 100 years resulted from imported pests attacking native plants. This trend is likely to continue. Is a defense against pests really acquired by using natives?

Figure 2.7.26. Nursery-induced girdling roots in container plants are a huge limitation to using native plants, which are primarily produced in containers.

Nursery Production and Natives

Most native nurseries produce trees in containers to ease production and transplant problems. Many of these container-grown trees have been found to have serious circling and girdling roots embedded deep within the root mass of the container, the result of propagation in smaller containers. Fixing the girdling root problem is not easy. In many instances, a native tree is specified but the tree dies of girdling roots just when it was supposed to hit its prime. Until the nursery industry solves this problem, designers would be wise not to allow container-grown trees. This policy would eliminate the use of native trees available only in containers until the industry solves the problems of girdling roots. See further discussion on issues with container plants in Part 2, Chapter Nine.

For many species, current nursery stock is not large enough to survive either urban conditions or commercial expectations. The genetic breeding work related to many of these species lags behind other trees. Many native trees have been overlooked in the past because of difficulty in transplanting, and this problem has not been solved.

All the above challenges can be met, but it will take considerable time. Changes to nursery practices can increase the reliability of transplanting. Breeding can produce trees better suited to urban conditions. Demand for native selections will encourage growers to increase stock. Tree Introductions Inc. in Georgia finally cracked the code to clone oaks. European nurseries have developed a way to reliably transplant ailanthus. In the meantime, using the best tree, native or exotic, suited to the conditions of the site and the aesthetic needs of the project remains the best answer.

Invasive Plants

Some imported trees, such as ailanthus and Norway maple, are quite invasive and easily escape into the wild. Clearly, these trees have demonstrated the ability to dramatically alter the forest ecology. What about trees that are actually native to the United States, but are also invasive? Black locust, sweetgum, red maple, and eastern red cedar, for example, are all native to parts of the United States but also quite invasive, taking over old fields and forming temporary monocultures as a part of the natural succession of a forest. Natural systems need some level of invasive plants for quick repair after fire, flood, landslide, volcano, or even human activity that strips a piece of land from the original and more diverse forest.

Why is a field of invading Callery pear significantly different from a field of invading sweetgum? Eventually, both will evolve into a different type of forest made up of climax trees. What if some or even all of those trees are exotics? Is that a problem? More science is needed on these questions before we arbitrarily further reduce the diversity in our urban forest by eliminating exotics and trees that may be considered invasive in a natural system.

Can we breed to eliminate the invasive tendency of a plant? Because ailanthus is dioecious (meaning that there are male and female ailanthus trees), it is possible to clone male ailanthus, allowing designers to make use of the tree's exquisite ability to grow in difficult urban soils without having to accept its invasive characteristics.

Part of the problem may be that the native/exotic issue is being viewed over too short a time perspective. The northern part of North America was devoid of all plants at the end of the Ice Age, just a few short millennia ago. Every plant species currently in this region was, in a sense, invasive and exotic at one point. Long before the Vikings first landed on the shores of Newfoundland, aboriginal North Americans assisted plant migration by moving plants in trade, thereby changing the native ecology. Supporters of native plants are now classifying some early European plant introductions as native, although this is accompanied with a little wink of the eye. Will kudzu eventually find its place in the North American ecological order after a few hundred or thousand years?

On the other hand, exotic plants, which look harmless, can take up to 30 or 40 years to reveal themselves as invasive. This is especially true with trees, which may need to mature before building up sufficient numbers to become a problem. Perhaps we also need to wait a few generations to see if they are really harmful after they escape into less human-influenced environments. By now, very little land in the eastern United States is without human influence. Save for a few small patches of uncut land, all our "natural forest" is actually re-growth of logged areas. Much of the eastern American forest was once dominated by chestnuts, which were replaced by tulip poplar. Are all the trees growing in our forest in a sense invading plants?

Invasive exotic plants change the look of a particular natural landscape. Scientists are generally unwilling to accept this change as part of the natural order or to see humans and the changes they bring as part of the natural system. Why are humans excluded from the natural order when discussing environmental change?

Figure 2.7.27. Black locust as a street tree.

Figure 2.7.28. Male ailanthus as a great street tree?

Figure 2.7.29. Monoculture of tulip poplar invading land disturbed by human activity. Why is this not considered an invasive plant?

Scientific Basis for the Use of Native Plants

There is very little scientific study to support advantages of using natives over exotics in urban areas. Peter Del Tredici of Harvard's Arnold Arboretum, in an address to the American Society of Landscape Architects, has described the trend of using natives as a "faith-based" movement. His research into the scientific literature finds few studies to validate a positive impact from the use of natives. It is incredible that so many professionals have embraced a thesis that is not backed by scientific study. Unfortunately, the politics of environmental discourse makes it difficult to consider alternative views. A spirited discussion on exotic plants is needed within the design profession.

Question 3—Tree Spacing

There is a tendency for designers to plant trees very close to each other, while arborists and urban forest managers tend to place them farther apart. From each discipline's perspective, a reasonable argument can be made for either practice.

Designers look at how trees create space. Trunks define a space better than the softer canopy. Trunks are at eye level, and in smaller urban spaces, are the most visible part of the tree. There are many examples of closely spaced trees successfully maintained over long periods of time. This supports the rationale that spacing trees 25 feet on center and tighter can work. Arnold's *Trees in Urban Design* makes a compelling case for tightly spaced trees in closely observed geometry. Arnold does not observe problems with these landscapes, although some of the places cited by him have exhibited significant tree loss and have been totally redesigned or replanted. On the other hand, the National Mall in Washington, D.C., where three rows of elms are spaced 50 feet on center, a very large-scale, compelling, and memorable image, has been successfully maintained.

Trees do grow in closely spaced groves in natural forest, but it is dangerous to use the forest as an analogy for the city. City soils, even those that are improved, are not forest soils. Forests growing in poor soils tend to have trees spaced wider to use scarce resources wisely. If trees are planted in plazas with individually confined rooting space, it probably does not matter how close they are planted, as they will never grow to a size large enough for spacing to make a difference.

Forest groves are not static. The spacing is constantly changing as competition kills weaker trees and stronger canopies fill voids. A forest may appear to thrive with 20- or 25-foot spacing, but careful and repeated observations over time will reveal a subtle but constant reduction in the number of trees. The tighter the

Figure 2.7.30. Tightly spaced trees in poor growing conditions. Soil, not spacing, is the limiting factor. Note that the second pair of trees in this image has already been replaced.

spacing, the more rapid the change. City plazas are not generally designed to be thinned over time. There are examples of plazas being thinned, but the thinning is often accompanied by an outcry from those who rush in to defend the original designer's work, in spite of the fact that that work may be failing.

When two trees grow together, they cause each other to self-prune along the plane of their intersecting crowns. Smaller crowns support fewer leaves, reducing carbohydrate production. Over time, one tree may gain a slight advantage over its neighbor, shading the adjacent tree. The trees on the edges of a grove have more branches and leaves and get more light than trees in the middle. The more rows of trees and the tighter the spacing, the greater the impact of competition.

Figure 2.7.31. Do not use forest tree spacing to justify urban plaza spacing.

a. Forest trees are spaced closely together; however, only a few mature. In a forest, trees are constantly dying and new ones emerging. This is not a stable landscape.
b. Urban plaza trees at a constant 15-foot spacing to emulate a forest. Every tree has been replaced at least once.

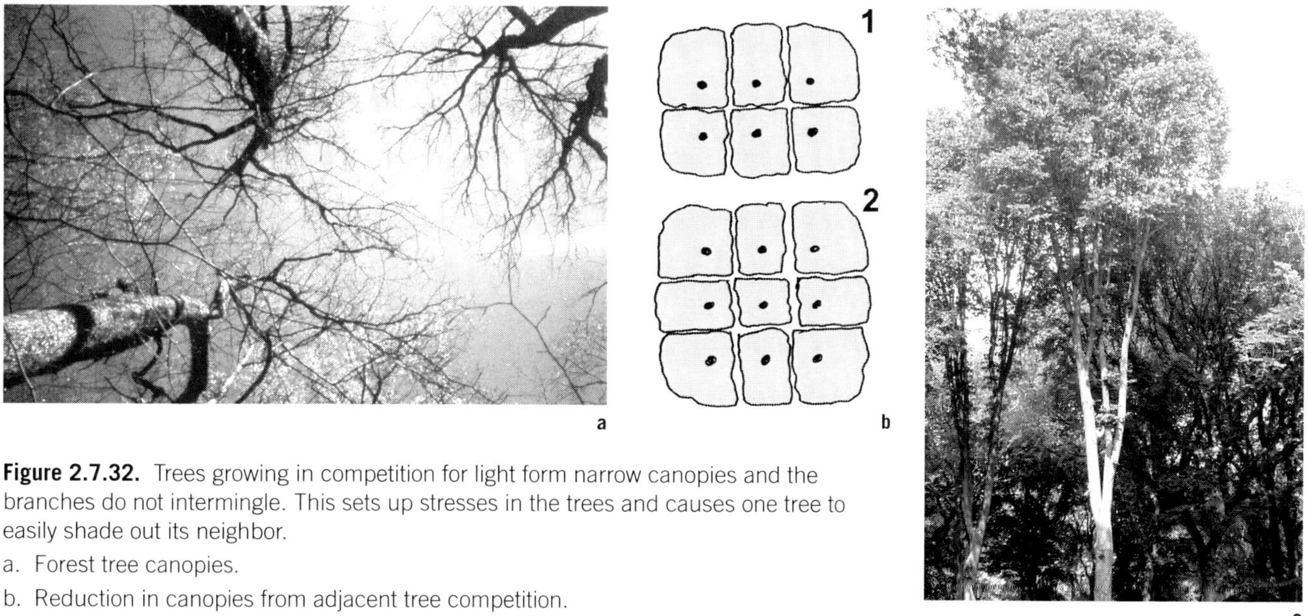

Figure 2.7.32. Trees growing in competition for light form narrow canopies and the branches do not intermingle. This sets up stresses in the trees and causes one tree to easily shade out its neighbor.

a. Forest tree canopies.
b. Reduction in canopies from adjacent tree competition.
   1. Double rows: End trees are advantaged over the middle trees.
   2. Three rows or more: Corner trees are advantaged over the outer middle trees. The interior row trees have very small canopies and struggle to compete.
c. Small, high canopy of this tree was the result of light competition with an older, adjacent tree, which has now been removed.

Figure 2.7.33. Plane trees in a large grid space 25 feet on center at Bryant Park, New York. Interior rows within the grid have required the greatest rate of replacement.

The plane tree, more than any other, demonstrates a remarkable ability to adapt to competition in tight spacing. It can succeed in poor soils, and its open crown structure adapts to a restricted space. Most of the examples in Arnold's book depicting successful old plantings of tightly spaced trees in northeastern cities are plane or sycamore trees. Because of these attributes, they have reached monoculture status in many eastern cities. Unfortunately, *Platanus* is a host tree for the Asian longhorned beetle, which will challenge its dominance.

In other areas of the United States, one or two species also dominate the successful tightly spaced plaza planting: willow oak in the southeast and honey locust in the dryer interior states. Each of these trees has broad, open branch structures, which let light penetrate the interior of the tree. This branch structure may be critical to the tree's ability to survive in the competition for light when tightly spaced.

Note that all of these trees are large, wide-spreading canopy trees. There is a trend to use small trees or columnar trees when planting in small spaces or on tight spacing. This is often justified on horticultural grounds. "There is no room for a larger tree" is the refrain. The preceding examples support the notion that one can plant large trees with tight spacing as well as small trees. One simply must understand how the tree will adapt. (See the discussion on large trees versus small trees at the beginning of the last chapter.) Please do not take this as an endorsement for planting large trees on very close spacing. The plea of this book is to plant a few large-canopy trees that will thrive rather than many smaller trees on tight spacing.

Trees with access to light on only one side will grow more branches on that side. Eventually the additional weight may cause the trunk of the tree to start leaning in the direction of the light. Many texts call this trunk lean a phototropic effect, meaning that the tree is growing toward the light. This may be true for the branches, but is usually not the case for the lower trunk. When the lower trunk is leaning, as shown in Figure 2.7.34, it indicates that the tree is simply falling over in slow motion. This lean is accentuated if there is inadequate rooting space. Providing larger rooting volumes will reduce this problem.

Figure 2.7.34. Plane trees leaning due to the extra weight of more branches on the outside of the row. Note the loss of trees in the left row (north) due to less light. Spacing approximately 12 feet on center.

Closely spaced groves or bosques of trees create very dark landscapes below, often too dark and with too much competition for soil resources to support additional plantings. Considerable horticultural effort is needed to maintain the lower-level plants. Getting replacement trees established beneath competing tree canopies is more difficult in tight spacing. Many award-winning landscapes had to be redesigned once the trees reached closed canopy, due to excessive shade.

A closely spaced row of trees can also make visibility more difficult. Being able to see through a row of trees is critical to the success of urban spaces. Pedestrians feel safer when they can see other people in the space. Retail shops located on the edge of a planting may depend on good sight lines through the trees for commercial success.

Modern designers do not have the patience to wait for their trees to mature. In 1976, Dan Kiley proposed replanting the National Mall in Washington, D.C., at 25 feet on center, later revising his recommendation to planting the elms on 12-foot, 6-inch centers, or about the same spacing he later specified for crepe myrtles at the North Carolina National Bank Plaza in Tampa, Florida. The bank plaza was demolished less than 15 years after construction, due in part to the tight spacing of the trees.

Figure 2.7.35. Tampa plaza with trees spaced 12 feet on center shortly after installation. Spaces soon became so dark that nothing would grow under the canopy and people did not feel safe due to poor sight lines.

Kiley based his recommendations on the spacing of the trees in the Tuileries Gardens in Paris, which served as one of the models for the design of the Mall by the McMillan Commission in the 1920s. While there are some areas in the Tuileries where pleached horsechestnuts are planted 12 feet apart, the majority of trees in this garden are more widely spaced. In areas of tight tree spacing, the French are smart enough not to try to grow anything under the trees, while Kiley, at Tampa Bank Plaza, installed lawns and ground covers, most of which died due to competition with the trees. The crepe myrtles were in fine shape. The death of the understory planting, the unusable nature of the park due to poor sight lines, its dark character from over-planting and the significant soil settlement forced the redesign.

Figure 2.7.36. The Tuileries, Paris. Tight spacing of trees in this garden has influenced landscape architects for generations. The trees in this garden are constantly pruned and replaced. Nothing is planted below the trees.

Spacing is dependent on many factors, from the need to create quick urban images to the need to grow understory planting. If planting is proposed below the canopy, a wide spacing, greater than 25 feet, is required—wider if the planting is to be perennials or shrubs, and even wider, up to 50 feet, if lawn is to be established. A shade-resistant ground cover may withstand tighter spacing. The number of rows is critical to the spacing discussion.

One Row

A single row of trees can be tightly spaced if there is good sunlight and space for roots and branches on one or more sides. Old beeches planted on 6-foot centers have been observed in England under ideal estate garden conditions. Assuming one does not need to see through the wall of trunks, spacing of large trees at 15 feet on center is reasonable, again given plenty of light and space for roots.

Figure 2.7.37. If there is good soil and light on both sides, there is almost no minimum spacing between trees, save the diameter of the root ball.

Figure 2.7.38. Palais Royale, Paris. *(Photos: Signe Nielsen)*

a. Trees spaced on 15-foot centers.

b. Double rows are 15 feet apart. However, the rows are pleached to maintain adequate light to support leaves on the interior branches.

Figure 2.7.39. Street trees spaced 25 feet apart. The average tree in this street is in decline. Wider spacing is recommended as blocks are refurbished.

As the space becomes more urban, trees need to spread apart. At the Palais Royale Garden in Paris, lindens are spaced less than 15 feet on center within the row, but each row is pleached such that there are leaves on both sides of each row. Even though these trees are in multiple rows, the pleaching makes them functionally single rows. The long-term tree health impact would have been dramatically different if the tree crowns had been allowed to grow together in competition. (See the discussion following on multiple rows of trees.)

Street Trees

A reasonable minimum spacing for a single row of street trees is 30 to 35 feet. This spacing provides more soil per tree and allows sight lines through the wall of trunks. This recommended spacing works with the other aspects of the street, from driveways and street lights, to signs and the need to see and move through the space filled with mature trees. Street tree spacing of 20 to 25 feet, to accommodate the spacing requirements of parking spaces and to allow parking meters to align symmetrically between trunks, is a designer conceit that will create tree conflicts. If the parking meters and the trees do not line up, the damage to aesthetics is small. Better trees are worth the price.

Figure 2.7.40. Double row tree spacing.

a. 20-foot spacing: Canopy closes quickly. If trees fail to prosper, the canopy stays low and the walk dark. As trees mature, each tree canopy becomes heavier on one side.
b. 30-foot spacing: Light still penetrates center to support interior branches as tree matures. Expect higher center space and asymmetrical canopy if trees have adequate soil for long-term growth.
c. 40-foot spacing: As this canopy matures, it will close but have adequate light, with structural balance in each tree.
d. 60-foot spacing: Plenty of room for canopy and soil to produce mature trees for 100-plus years with balanced branching and dappled sunlight. This is the work of the master, Frederick Law Olmsted, in New York City's Central Park. We should all take lessons from his foresight.

Two Rows

When a second row is added, the spacing dynamics change with the increased canopy competition. Tight spacing that works in a single row may not work in a double row. There either must be wider spacing from tree to tree or between the rows. Triangular geometry works better than grid geometry. Again, if the area below the trees is expected to support ground-level plants, the spacing should be still wider. For large-canopy trees in double rows, significant tree problems can be observed with spacing less than 25 feet. If a double row of trees is adjacent to a building taller than two stories, the building should be considered as a third row of trees. (See the discussion on three rows of trees following.) Still more spacing is needed for long-term growth and light, airy spaces. Wider spacing makes replacement trees easier to establish as stand ages and new trees are required.

Three or More Rows

With three or more rows of trees, the center trees are now confined on all sides. The center trees will always grow more slowly and will not be able to compete for sunlight with the canopies of the outer rows. At some point, the inner tree canopies will become suppressed (shaded out) by

Figure 2.7.41. Spacing of three rows or more.

a. National Mall, Washington, D.C.: Four rows 50 feet on center. *(Photo: Kay Fanning)*

b. Portland, Oregon, Parks Blocks: Four rows approximately 40 feet on center.

c. Tuileries, Paris: Multiple rows of varying spacing. Trees sheared.

d. Third block of Independence Mall, Philadelphia: Multiple rows 24 feet on center. Trees were not provided with adequate soil and the park was later demolished.

the adjacent trees and decline. Spacing in these designs must be much larger than a two-row scheme. Minimum spacing of 40 feet or more may be needed to avoid canopy suppression for large canopy trees. Triangular spacing of the center row should be required if spacing is tighter than 40 feet.

Significant Places

For a memorial or building and spaces of national significance, spacing of 40 to 50 feet for large-canopy trees is appropriate and preferred. Frederick Law Olmsted, Jr. and the McMillan Commission got it right on the Mall with the four rows of elms at 50 feet on center in both directions. This design has been sustainable, in spite of compacted fill soil and Dutch elm disease. The two rows of elms along the reflecting pool to the Lincoln Memorial, planted at 35 feet on center with 50 feet between the rows, has been more difficult to sustain, and wider spacing is evolving as trees die.

Clusters and Irregular Spacing

Small clusters of trees where there is no center tree will respond to competition with limited interior branches similarly to rows or grids of trees. Assuming that the trees are spaced at distances similar to the requirements of two rows of trees, the cluster should be stable to the forces of competition. Developing irregular spacing of large plantings may provide a hedge

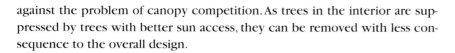

Figure 2.7.42. Clusters and irregular spacing.

a. Cedar clustered on tight spacing to look like a single tree.
b. The interior of the cedar reveals some instability and lost limbs from competition with the neighboring trunks.
c. Clump of trees planted closely together to form a multi-stemmed tree.
d. Multi-stem trees in a tight cluster will gradually lose the interior stems.
e. Irregular spacing adapts well to trees that have been lost due to competition. This design can age more gracefully, mimicking the gradual thinning of the natural forest.

against the problem of canopy competition. As trees in the interior are suppressed by trees with better sun access, they can be removed with less consequence to the overall design.

Solar Orientation and Spacing

The solar orientation of the rows will affect the growth of the crowns and the resulting canopy competition. North-south rows will respond symmetrically and be more forgiving to crown suppression. Tighter spacing between rows may be allowed, but larger spacing between trees within the row will be beneficial. East-west rows will likely grow faster and more vigorous crowns on the south side, while trees on the north side are more likely to become suppressed. Wider spacing between rows and triangular spacing will be beneficial. Building shade can have both positive and negative effects on crown growth rates. Shade and reflected light and heat all impact the equation.

Predicting Canopy Response

Designers can draw plan and section views of predicted mature canopy structures based on the branching habit of similar trees and growth impacts previously described. This should be a required activity for all designs where mature canopies are anticipated.

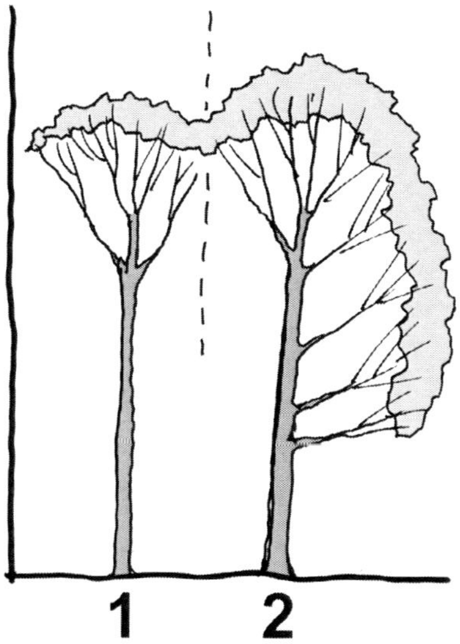

Figure 2.7.43. Sketching canopy competition response.

1. Suppressed row of trees between another row of trees and a building face has small amounts of canopy foliage and thinner trunks.
2. Outer row of trees has larger trunks and foliage extending to the ground.

Question 4—Time and Trees

Designers must understand the time it takes for landscapes to mature and how they change over time. Time is the most wonderful aspect of a landscape. Unlike other artistic endeavors, the landscape looks dramatically different after a decade or two. A building can be maintained to look much the way it looked immediately after construction. With effort, a symphony can be played to sound very much like its original performance. However, even the most careful maintenance of a landscape cannot prevent it from changing as it grows and matures. It is expected to grow, age, die, and be replanted. In a well-designed landscape, the cycle takes more than one lifetime, and no designer should ever experience all the aspects of his or her creation.

Contemporary designers and their clients do not seem to be satisfied with this arrangement and work diligently to create landscapes that are instantly completed with little regard for the future. This attitude has a significant impact on the type of trees that are specified and how they are spaced.

Creating "instant" landscapes forces the planting of larger trees. Only a limited selection of tree species can be specified in large sizes. This is partially market-driven and partially due to the difficulty of transplanting many species at large size. With limited options, landscapes become limited in their diversity. Designer and/or owner impatience with the time it takes to grow a larger tree often leads to the use of too many trees spaced too closely together.

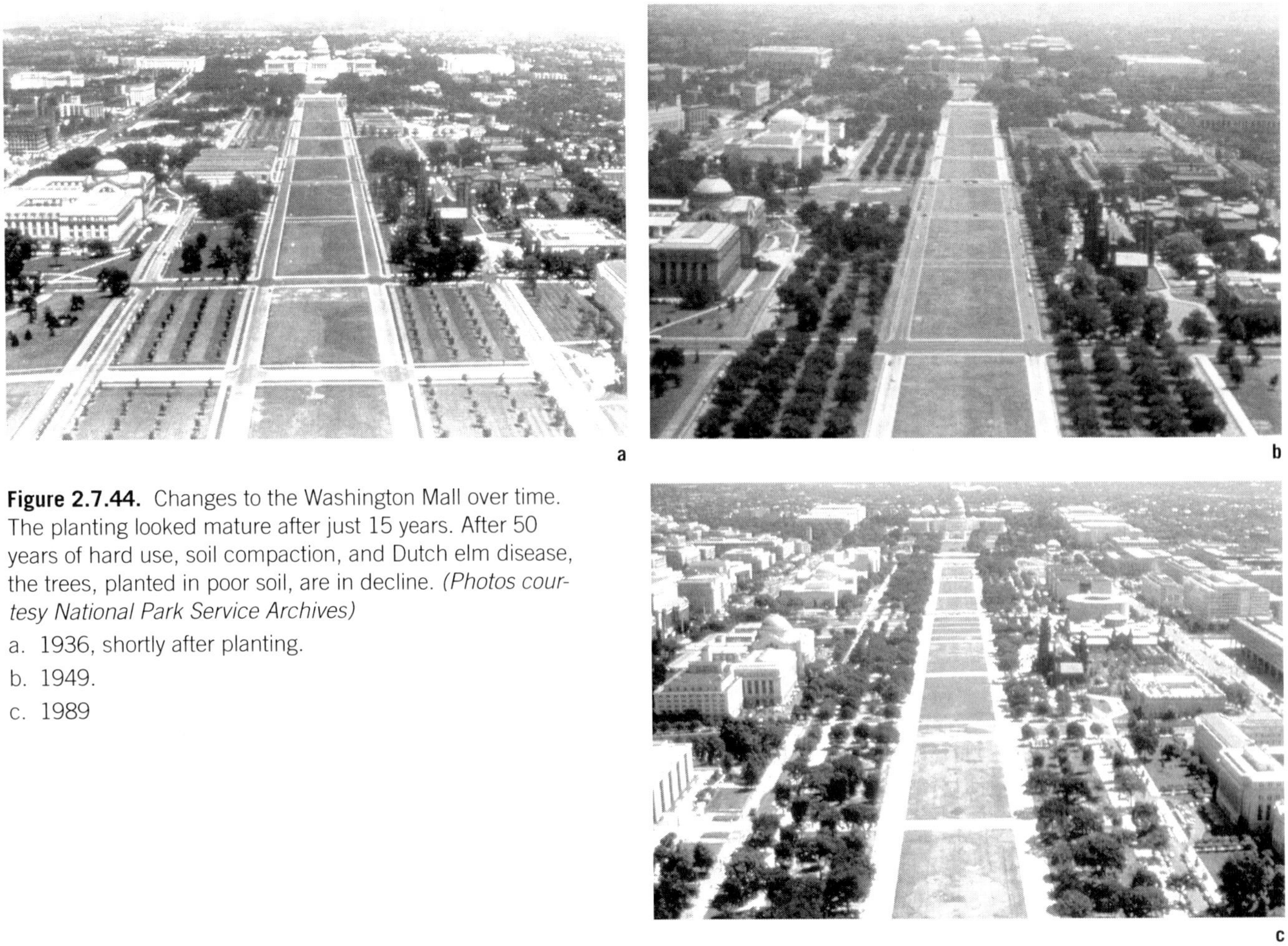

a b c

Figure 2.7.44. Changes to the Washington Mall over time. The planting looked mature after just 15 years. After 50 years of hard use, soil compaction, and Dutch elm disease, the trees, planted in poor soil, are in decline. *(Photos courtesy National Park Service Archives)*

a. 1936, shortly after planting.

b. 1949.

c. 1989

Figure 2.7.45. All of these trees were planted in 1983. The red oak was 5 inches in caliper at planting. The London plane and pin oak were planted as 1-inch whips.

a. London plane 10 years after planting.
b. London plane 20 years after planting.
c. Pin oak 10 years after planting.
d. Pin oak 20 years after planting.
e. Red oak 10 years after planting.
f. Red oak 20 years after planting.

a

b

Figure 2.7.46. What size tree to plant.

a. Three-inch-caliper tree at planting. If soil conditions are good, this size tree will recover from transplant fast and have a good chance of becoming a great tree.

b. Three-and-a-half-inch caliper elm, planted in good soil, five years later.

What Size Tree to Plant

The larger a tree is at the time of planting, the longer it will take to recover from transplant shock. It is estimated that the time to recover from transplanting is between 6 and 12 months per inch of caliper, depending on the latitude of the project—6 months per inch in north Florida versus 12 months in Chicago. During recovery, the tree needs more water and intensive monitoring for disease and insects. Bigger root balls remove more soil from the nursery and take more energy to dig, move, and install, with resulting environmental disturbance. The longer maintenance period uses greater amounts of energy, chemicals, and water to stabilize the tree. Moving large trees may make the owner and the designer feel like they have improved the environment, but it is actually not a sustainable procedure. The smaller the tree caliper, the less environmental damage is created by the act of planting and the greater the environmental benefit over time.

A 3- to 4-inch tree is the optimum size to plant in an urban landscape. It is large enough to survive urban abuse, has a reasonable presence in the landscape, and will easily recover after planting. Reserve very large trees, over 6 inches in caliper, for exceptional places, where there is sufficient maintenance to keep the tree healthy during a longer recovery period, and where the environmental cost of the installation is justified by other considerations. There should be a maximum size tree (3-inch caliper?) that can be permitted for projects that try to qualify for LEED's designation.

Planting larger trees requires greater resources. If the project does not have a large budget, the cost of planting a larger tree may rob the budget for the soil and drainage work to support the tree into the future. The project may look great at opening and then decline, never reaching the point where the tree has become a large mature specimen.

Trees grow much more rapidly than may be expected. A tree needs only a few years before it begins to quickly increase branch extension and trunk diameter. Michael Dirr's *Manual of Woody Landscape Plants* is a very good reference on growth rates. All these assumptions are based on providing well-drained soil in large quantities. Adequately watering the root ball appears to do the most to speed up the initial process of recovery. Data suggest that a smaller tree will grow larger and pass the size of a tree planted at a larger size, but I have not observed this effect in my own work with deciduous trees.

Sleep, Creep, Leap

There is a saying among arborists about the recovery of newly planted trees. The first year they sleep, the second year they creep, and the third year they leap. This growth pattern seems consistent and a reasonable measuring point to see if the tree was well planted and maintained. It reinforces the notion that the standard one- or two-year guarantee does not help an owner to know whether the tree will recover.

When Trees Grow Too Large

If provided with good growing conditions, trees will grow to very large sizes. Trunk flare, trunk diameter, crown spread, and height may conflict with any object in the tree's path, including other trees, if not considered in the design.

Pruning to control growth. It is possible to introduce pruning practices to slow or control canopy competition. Pleaching, pollarding, and crown reduction pruning are time-honored techniques to make trees grow at slower and controlled rates.

Continuous removal of branches slows down the growth of the trunk, trunk flare and root spread. In confined urban areas, this type of pruning may actually increase the life expectancy of the tree. A limited number of species of trees appear to be able to be managed by continual pruning. The cuts must be made in specific places by a qualified arborist. Just cutting the tree back to an arbitrary location is not pleaching or pollarding.

These pruning techniques increase maintenance costs significantly. Pleaching and pollarding, once started, require continuous effort for the life of the tree. A trained arborist should perform all pruning. *An Illustrated Guide to Pruning*, by Ed Gilman, is an excellent resource for pruning information.

Figure 2.7.47. Pruning to control growth.

a. Crown reduction pruning to guide branches under utility wires.
b. Pollarding where the stem is cut in the same place every year, creating a "fist" enlargement at the branch end.
c. Shearing and pollarding result in multiple sprouts that must be removed.
d. Pruning every year to maintain a tree in balance with its soil volume.
e. Shearing a double row of plane trees against a building. Eventually the inner row will thin out and become suppressed by the outer row.
f. When shearing a double row of trees, leave a space between them to allow light to reach leaves on both sides of each tree.

Pleaching or Shearing?

The term "pleaching," as defined in most arboricultural texts, includes the practice of interweaving part of the structural branches together to make a structural frame, often forming a tunnel. The term when used by landscape architects means to shear the tree like a hedge, where branches are cut each year in an architectural form. This difference in definition may cause communication problems between the two professions.

A pruning technique referred to as "topping" is the removal of the top portion of the tree, leaving stubs of branches to regenerate. This is not considered an acceptable pruning practice, and a qualified arborist will not top a tree.

Figure 2.7.48. Topping is not a good pruning practice.

Chemically controlled growth. A chemical growth regulator called paclobutrazol, marketed as Cambistat, by Rainbow Treecare (www.rainbowscivance.com), reduces tree growth and minimizes the need for pruning. This chemical must be reapplied every three or four years. It changes the appearance of the tree, making the leaves slightly smaller and darker green, and they tend to bunch together. Paclobutrazol can also be used to improve the health of declining trees, make trees better able to survive some types of construction damage, and make them more drought-resistant.

It is possible to overdose a tree with growth regulators, which can produce extremely small leaves, and not all trees are candidates for treatment. Check the manufacturer's Web site for a list of trees that can be effectively managed. Growth regulators should only be applied by a qualified arborist with experience in the use of the product.

a b

Figure 2.7.49. Overdosing trees with paclobutrazol will result in much smaller leaves.

a. Untreated live oak.

b. Live oak overdosed with paclobutrazol.

Using trees that grow slowly. With more patience on the part of designers and clients, smaller trees and very slow-growing trees can be included in the urban landscape. This opens the palette to interesting trees, such as camperdown elm, blackhaw viburnum, or the many species of Japanese maples. Large, slow-growing trees such as weeping beech could be incorporated into large-scale landscapes if owners were educated about the trees' long-term prospects.

Figure 2.7.50. Camperdown elm, an extremely slow-growing small tree.

Removing trees. Spacing can be designed such that trees are removed as the canopies enlarge. The geometric possibilities are limited, and the chances of someone, 10 years in the future, removing healthy trees to avoid canopy suppression is negligible. It would be much better to convince the client and the designer to wait for the trees to fill in at a wider spacing than to expect some trees to be removed in the future as they grow.

Conclusions on Questions of Design

The tree design process requires that designers become more knowledgeable on the science of arboriculture and ecology. Designers need a greater degree of honesty relative to deficiencies in individual and collective knowledge. More research should stimulate open discussions. But until designers embrace the existing science into their design principles it is difficult to believe that significant progress in improving urban forest can occur.

EXPANDING THE TREE PALETTE

Diversity is critical to the health and future of the urban forest. Improving soil conditions will allow the use of a larger number of species. Including new trees requires research on the part of the designers. They must learn the limitations of a tree and research growers to ensure that trees can be purchased in the sizes and quantities their project requires.

The Nursery Industry and New Introductions

Bringing a new type of tree to market is a risky venture for a nursery. The owners must believe that sufficient stock can be sold before they will risk growing quantities of plants that are not currently being sold. Designers do not want to specify a plant that is not available. Designers continue to follow plant fads or to use reliable, easy-to-sell standbys rather than explore the edges of new palettes. Given the four to ten years of lead time necessary to grow trees, and the two to five years of lead time necessary from the design phase to the construction phase of a large project, it is not surprising that growers are reluctant to introduce new species.

New urban tree varieties come from several sources. The first is from existing species not typically used as urban trees. River birch, katsura, European hornbeam, and other garden trees will make fine street trees if they are grown with a single stem and a tall clear trunk. Tulip poplar, beech, hickory, and even pine trees can be used as street trees once soil is made suitable to their requirements. Old standards such as silver maple and pear may be good candidates for cloning to forms that eliminate or reduce the problems that caused them to fall out of favor.

There are many new trees for designers to explore at the cutting edge of plant breeding activity. Examples include "Chicago Blues" black locust; a seedless, thornless Osage orange; or cloned oaks. European nurseries have also been hard at work breeding new urban trees, including varieties of Sorbus, Robinia, Acer, Ailanthus, and many others. An American designer or breeder might take inspiration for genetic diversity from a visit to a European nursery.

An important factor in the introduction of new species is trade magazines. Nursery and arboriculture trade magazines are doing a good job of including "tree of the month" articles. *Landscape Architecture* magazine, the most influential news for landscape architects, is still a bit shy at promoting new plants, although they have made improvements over the last decade.

Figure 2.7.51. Expanding the palette: Thinking out of the box will be required to build the diversity to respond to globalization.

a. *Fagus* spp., beech.

b. *Robinia cultivars,* black locust.

c. *Carpinus* spp., hornbeam.

d. *Ailanthus male cultivar,* ailanthus.

e. *Sorbus aucuparia,* European mountain ash.

f. *Catalpa* spp., catalpa.

The following is a list of possible trees to expand the palette of urban street trees. Not all trees work in all regions. The list assumes that the site has been made right for the tree.

Acer spp.	Maple, multiple species other than red and sugar maple
Aesculus spp.	Horsechestnut cultivars
Ailanthus altissima	Tree of heaven (male cultivars)
Alnus cordata	Italian alder
Betula nigra	River birch (single stem)
Carpinus betulus	European hornbeam
Carya glabra	Pignut hickory
Carya ovata	Shagbark hickory
Catalpa spp.	Catalpa
Cercidiphyllum japonicum	Katsura
Cladrastis kentukea	American yellowwood
Fagus spp.	Beech
Gymnocladus dioicus	Kentucky coffeetree
Koelreuteria paniculata	Goldenraintree
Liriodendron tulipifera	Tulip poplar
Maclura pomifera	Osage orange (fruitless cultivars)
Magnolia spp.	Magnolia, multiple species (tall, clear trunk)
Metasequoia glyptostroboides	Dawn redwood
Nyssa sylvatica	Black gum
Ostrya virginiana	American hophornbeam
Phellodendron amurense	Amur cork
Pinus spp.	Pine, multiple species (tall, clear trunk)
Prunus spp.	Cherry, multiple species (tall, clear trunk)
Quercus spp.	Species beyond the old standbys, including new cloned cultivars
Robinia pseudoacacia	Black locust cultivars
Sophora japonica	Japanese pagoda tree
Sorbus aria	Whitebeam mountainash
Sorbus aucuparia	European mountainash
Taxodium spp.	Cypress cultivars (tall, clear trunk)

False Starts and Missteps with New Introductions

As with any change, there will be missteps. Problems with new tree introductions often take years to show up. Designers must research each new tree to predict its problems. For example, poplar and black locust looks great as street trees in many European cities, but their tendency to send out sucker branching from the root system has created maintenance problems in loose-laid pavers. The problem with weak junctions in Bradford pear took a generation before its use was curtailed. Problems with one cultivar can cause marketing problems for another. The Bradford pear disaster of the 1980s and 1990s makes it hard to market other types of pear species that may not have the weak branch problem.

a

b

Figure 2.7.52. Be aware of issues with new introductions.

a. Root suckers from poplar trees damaging pavers.
b. Bradford pear's weak junctions have been a nightmare for cities.

Something Good About the Pear?

The Bradford pear was wildly popular not only because it was the perfectly shaped tree (at least until it falls apart) but because it also survived, even thrived, in poor soil. I suspect the roots that tree grows in this process may be quite beneficial to the future prospects of any tree that replaces a removed pear. All those roots add significant amounts of carbon to the soil, and the decaying roots of removed trees make channels that conduct water and air into the soil. If a less vigorous tree is planted in the space previously occupied by a pear, would it grow better, longer? If this is true, maybe the weak junctions of the pear are actually a gift to cities, offering a beautiful and low-cost way to improve difficult urban soil. This thesis would be an interesting bit of work for a researcher.

Designers and growers must work together to expand the palette. The movement in the industry toward native plants sheds some light on the difficulty of this task. Even though the use of native trees has been promoted for more than a decade, caliper-sized specimens 3 inches or larger are still hard to find in all but a few species. Designers have taken to specifying smaller-caliper trees until supply catches up with demand. Designers can improve the chances of being able to use new varieties by limiting the number of replicates of any given plant in their designs. This will have the added advantage of making the landscape more diverse.

Education and Expanding the Palette

Designers should request that professional journals carry information on new tree varieties and include more technical information on the trees featured in articles that are project oriented. *Landscape Architecture* magazine should have a tree-of-the-month article. These articles must always include the problems with a given tree as well as its advantages. More plant-related education sessions are needed at landscape architectural conferences. Universities must admit that plants and soil are an important part of landscape architectural practice, and include more course work in curricula.

Designers must take responsibility for their own level of knowledge about trees, plants, and soil. Information and arboretums are available where self-study can enrich their knowledge base. Designers must become passionate about this area of the craft of landscape architecture. In any artistic endeavor attention to craft is required to execute good design.

Figure 2.7.53. Tree-of-the-month articles such as this feature in *City Trees* should become a part of other professional journals such as *Landscape Architecture*.

Season of Planting

Modern construction schedules do not allow for flexibility in the season that trees must be installed. Only certain trees are easy to move in summer or fall, which limits the selection process. Many of the most commonly used trees are on the list of trees easy to move in a wide range of seasons. Designers need to request as much flexibility as possible in the timing of the planting sequence to broaden the tree palette.

Improvement in transplanting techniques such as larger root-ball-to-caliper ratios and use of biostimulants and antidesiccants may help broaden the planting season. Specifying smaller size trees may make the planting season less critical. Harvesting hard-to-transplant trees in the spring and holding them in irrigated yards extends the season in which they can be transplanted. New work is widening the period when bare-root trees may be successfully transplanted, but more research is needed. (See further discussion on transplanting in Part 2, Chapter Nine.)

Figure 2.7.54. Nursery stock dug early in the season for summer planting. Note plastic covering over root ball and drip emitters inserted in root ball.

Nursery Availability

The nursery industry has at any point in time a fixed number of trees available. It takes many years for a 4-inch-caliper tree to move from propagation to installation. At the point in time where the design is being conceived, the entire sphere of possible tree choices already exists and will not increase in number. The larger the size tree specified, the smaller the options of available quality trees. Over the period of time that the project moves through the design and construction process, the supply of available trees will shrink. This market reality affects designs, and designers are required to specify an available product.

Human Influences on Tree Selection and Location

Human activity influences the trees to be selected and where they can be placed. This activity includes power lines and other utilities above and below the ground, paving and structures near the tree, urban abuses such as dogs and bicycles, compaction after planting, and elevated pH from building materials. Even the potential for automobile accidents can influence the location of trees. Changes in the design can reduce the impact of human influences. Tree planting areas must protect the tree, and the tree should be placed to respect other needs in the urban environment.

Figure 2.7.55. Not all overhead wires are the same. Lines lower on the pole generally have less pruning standoff requirements. Select trees that can fit into this mix.

Overhead Utility Lines

Local power companies have recommendations that define the spatial relationship between trees and power lines. Consult the project's local power company for its standards. Refinements to these recommendations can be made by working with the variables of power distribution. Pole heights vary and can affect the type of tree and location that are permissible.

Not all lines on the pole are the same. Lines vary by voltage and use. Limb standoff distances should increase as the voltage goes up. Lines at the top of the pole are often higher-voltage. Lower lines are either lower-voltage or communication lines such as telephone and cable TV and can often be closer to limbs. Often trees that grow between 30 and 40 feet can fit well under tall poles with little pruning needs.

Figure 2.7.56. Super-insulated wires can allow wider tree selection and location options without putting the wires underground.

Figure 2.7.57. Plane trees pruned around utility wires. If upper lines had higher voltage, the outcome would be less pleasing. Stricter utility pruning standards may make this vision impossible to achieve on new trees; however, plane remains one of the best trees to "absorb" wires.

Super-insulated power lines are available from some power companies that can further reduce the standoff distance. They are expensive and not generally in use in the United States. Canadian and English power companies are beginning to use this innovation to save on pruning and power outages, while allowing trees to be closer to lines.

Communities should not give up on large trees under power lines. When the line voltage is low enough, retain as many large trees as possible. Trees that have open branching habits with wide branch angles make the best trees to put under power lines. Species such as *Platanus*, *Sophora*, or *Prunus* are good examples. Even very large trees such as the plane tree and many oaks are fairly easy to train around lines, and many successful examples of lines running through canopies are observed. Trees with strong central leaders such as pin oak and willow oak and columnar trees are more difficult to train. Soft-wooded trees that do not compartmentalize (or wall off injury sites) well, such as silver maple, birch, poplar, and cherry, are not good candidates to place near lines where constant pruning may be required. See the list in the *Illustrated Guide to Pruning*, by Ed Gilman, for trees that are good and bad compartmentalizers.

Enlightened pruning can create peaceful coexistence between branches and wires. Some power companies are quite responsible and hire good arborists to manage line clearing. Local governments can successfully require higher pruning standards by power companies. Large trees can be placed on the side of the street opposite the lines or placed in a front yard in residential areas behind the wires. Building connection wires can get quite close to tree limbs, as they are lower voltage.

Cherry—Good and Bad

Note that cherry is recommended as a good tree to put under power lines and a bad tree for the same application. This is an example of the classic tree selection problem where subtle differences in situations can make the difference. Cherry does not compartmentalize well, so it may not fare well if constant pruning is required. However, this tree also has wide branch angles and an open structure, so it is a good tree to train around and through power lines, and in the right situation less pruning may be required. Wide branch angles make cherry inappropriate along a road where truck conflicts will inflict damage. The right answer? Look at all the variables and make an intelligent decision.

Alternatives to undergrounding the entire system. Putting utility lines underground is often proposed as the solution to the problem. However, this approach carries its own set of issues. Undergrounding existing utilities is extremely expensive. Even in new construction, it is much more expensive than aboveground lines. There simply may not be the political will to fund undergrounding of utility lines.

In existing communities, the root damage to mature trees is considerable. Underground transformers and manholes take up a lot of space, thus reducing the potential rooting volume for the trees. Construction damages soil structure, reducing rooting opportunities; however, lines can be installed using directional boring machines to reduce damage to existing trees and soil. Repairs of underground utility lines are also more expensive and can be damaging to the roots of mature trees.

Not all wires are the same in terms of the degree of difficulty to put them underground. Communities should examine all aspects of the problem before jumping to the conclusion that undergrounding all lines is the best option. A multi-option approach must be considered to find the compromise among the needs of trees, utilities, and budgets. Figure 2.7.58 illustrates approaches that can reduce cost, while making space for trees both above and below ground.

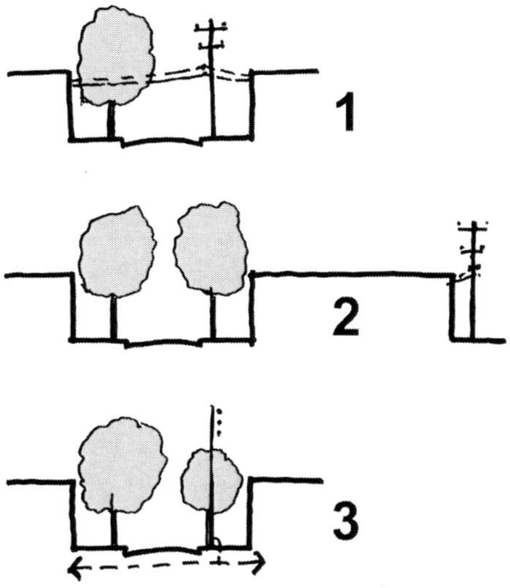

Figure 2.7.58. Alternatives to undergrounding utility wires.

1. Consolidate all wires to one side of the street.
2. Use alleys or rear feeds to remove poles from street.
3. Consolidate high-voltage wires to tall poles and underground local feeds and communication wires. Plant small trees under high wires.

Underground utilities. Underground utilities compete for soil volume. Installation can increase the compaction rate in the soil or, ironically, may leave large areas of lower compaction that are favorable for root growth, drawing the roots closer to pipes, which can be good for the tree but unacceptable to the engineer. It is important to find solutions to these conflicts that respect the needs of the tree and the utility.

Roots do not cause utility conflicts, but they do exploit existing cracks due to poor workmanship. Research indicates that a defect in the utility line often preceded the problem with a root. Roots are able to deform and even crush pipes. Sanitary and combined sanitary/storm sewer lines are at the greatest risk. Pressurized utility pipes and water, irrigation, and gas pipes are more at risk than underground wires. Tree roots have broken small gas and water lines and clogged sewer lines.

Older utility lines are much more vulnerable to problems than newer lines. Schedule 40 or heavier plastic utilities have glued joints that are impenetrable by roots, and the flexibility of plastic allows for minor line deformation without interrupting service. Concrete and cast-iron pipes with gasket joints also have fewer problems due to pipe strength and joint systems. Deeper pipes, with greater than 4 feet of cover, are less vulnerable than shallow pipes. In new construction, it is relatively easy to isolate lines by installing sheets of 4- to 6-mil plastic sheeting to the sides and top of the utility trenches.

In newly constructed urban environments, placing the utilities in a utility zone within the driving surface is the best way to avoid tree-root conflicts. Unfortunately, engineers would like to avoid this location, as traffic must be stopped during repairs. An argument could be made that pedestrian pavers, lights, and other urban features are expensive to repair and putting the utilities in the roadbed is actually cost-effective. It is a complex set of relationships, and there is no set answer. Designers are often the only tree advocates on the project when these infrastructure decisions are being made.

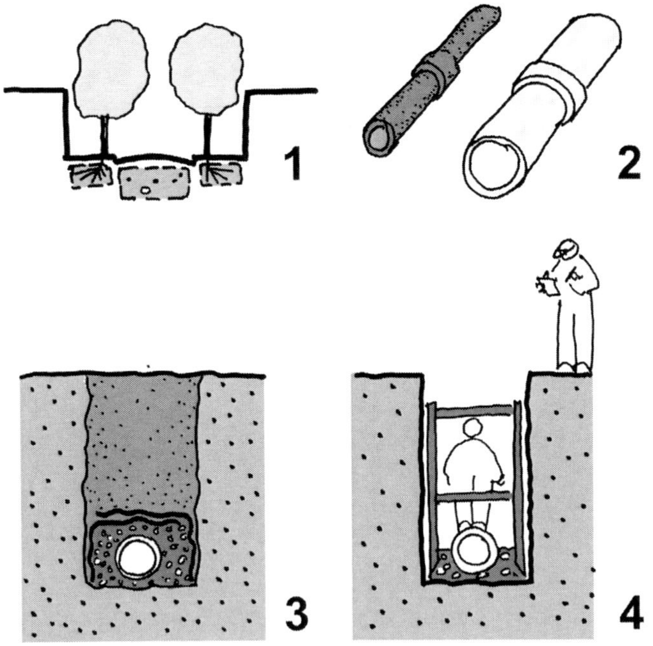

Figure 2.7.59. Methods to reduce root and underground utility conflicts.

1. Create separate zones for tree roots and utilities.
2. Use stronger pipes and joint systems.
3. Wrap pipe bedding material in heavy plastic with full trench-width overlaps.
4. Improve installation workmanship and inspections to produce a tighter system.

Figure 2.7.60. Thinning canopy in tree near gas line break.

Trees that are adaptable to wet soils are more likely to grow into sewer pipes than dry-site species. Smaller, slow-growing trees will cause fewer problems than more rapidly growing trees. Many cities have prohibitions against planting trees within certain distances of utility lines. Most of the time these distances are between 5 and 10 feet, which is actually too small a distance to be effective at stopping long-term problems. If cities really want to stop root-utility conflicts, trees would have to be kept 20 feet or more from lines—so far that no large trees could be planted. A better set of requirements would be to make incremental changes to the entire tree-utility system to obtain the most meaningful conflict reductions at the lowest cost (see Figure 2.7.59).

Root intrusion and pipe maintenance. When roots do enter the line, they can be removed. This is expensive maintenance, and the roots will return and fill the line again. A new technology can line the pipe after the roots are removed so that the roots will no longer grow there (see www.easy-liner.com).

Steam and gas lines. When steam or gas lines leak, they can kill trees. In many cities and universities, steam distribution lines from central heating plants cause considerable damage to trees by heating the soil. Soil temperatures greater than 95°F limit root growth and over 120°F will kill roots. These lines occasionally rupture, killing all roots in the area near the break. Heat recovery barriers have been shown to reduce this problem.

Gas lines occasionally leak. The gas displaces the oxygen in the soil and kills the trees. The symptoms are very small, curled leaves. When the eastern part of Berlin, Germany, changed gas type after reunification, the foresters found that the different gas formulation caused leaks in the pipe joints and many large trees in the city were killed.

A successful heat and gas line barrier for use over utility lines is discussed in Part 2, Chapter Four.

Urban Abuse

Car Accidents

Car accidents kill trees as well as people. Aggressive highway regulation often restricts the proximity of trees to the edge of the pavement. The interstate highway standard is approximately 30 feet from the lane edge stripe, although wider standoff distances are often observed. Standoff distances on state and local roads vary, and there is an increasing movement to force trees back from the road edge for safety reasons.

Ironically, studies indicate that adding trees near a road actually reduces the number of accidents and in particular the number of car-to-car head-on collisions due to the traffic calming effect of the tree. Communities that value trees must fight for laws that allow closer proximity of trees to roads.

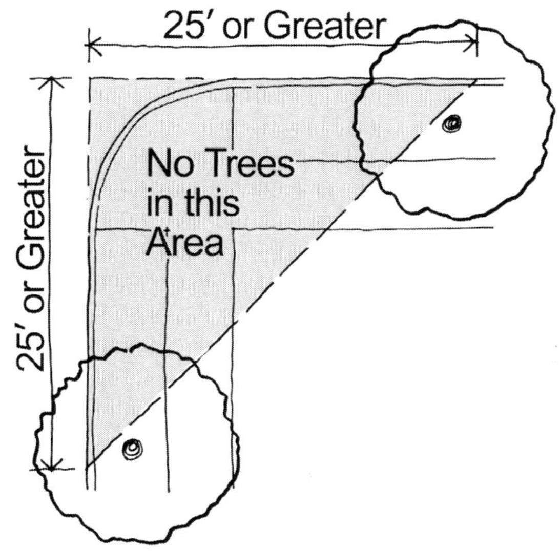

Figure 2.7.61. Sight distance triangle. Most jurisdictions have minimum sight distance triangles, which restrict trees and other obstructions from being placed near intersections. Check local regulations.

Vehicle Sight distances

Sight distance requirements reduce the number of trees along roads. At street intersections, most jurisdictions have a 25-foot or wider triangle where trees may not be planted. This triangle normally also applies to driveways; however, in some jurisdictions a smaller triangle may be permitted. Check local regulations. Use trees with ascending branches, and specify clear trunks taller than 8 feet to improve sight distances.

Tree–Vehicle Conflicts

In parking lots, bumpers and car doors can damage trees. Avoid placing trees in locations where they are vulnerable, and remember to calculate the growth of the tree, including the trunk flare. Install barriers, curbs, and guardrails where appropriate.

Trees near roads lose lower branches to trucks. It is advisable to prune lower branches from the street side of the tree as high as reasonable immediately after planting. Ultimately, street trees should develop clear trunks at least 14 feet high on the street side. This requires that the designer select trees in the nursery that have clear trunks to the top of the tree. Most of the lateral branches of a tree at planting are not permanent and will be removed over time to create long, clear trunks. In Europe, trees are often installed with tall, clear trunks to accelerate this form. American nurseries must begin to produce trees with similar proportions.

Figure 2.7.62. Purchase trees that can be limbed up to a minimum of 8 feet of clear trunk for adequate clearances near vehicle areas. Ultimately this tree will need to be pruned to a 14-foot branch height over the road. Be sure that there is a clear trunk to at least that height.

Figure 2.7.63. Damage from cars if tree is located too close to the parking space.

a. Tree damage after encouraging car parking in proximity of tree trunk.
b. Constant bumping of cars has caused significant rot within the trunk of this tree.
c. Maintain a minimum of 3 feet from the tree to the curb in head-on parking.

Trees along the edges of parking lots should be set back a minimum of 3 feet from the back of the curb. Where planting strips are restrictive, adding a bumper set inside the overhang of the car can protect the tree. Aligning the parking stripe and the trunk reduces the conflict.

Structural cell technology to permit large soil volumes under parking lots allows trees to be placed directly in the pavement. When this detail is used, be sure to provide a large curb space around the trunk.

Overflow Parking

Overflow parking on lawns compacts the soil, and people love to park under trees. If a lawn is to be used only a few times a year for parking, the tree will likely not be damaged. If lawn parking is frequent enough to damage the lawn, it is likely to be damaging the tree roots. Sandy soil and soils with strong structure can withstand more parking events than silty soil and soil with poor structure. Events during dry weather do less damage than when soil is wet.

The various systems of plastic rings, soil stabilizing grids, or concrete grids are all effective at protecting lower soil structure if the subgrade is not compacted during their installation. Unfortunately, most of the suppliers of these systems require 95 percent compaction of the subgrade, which ensures that the subgrade will not support tree roots. Do not require full compaction of subgrades unless the surface is to be used frequently. When the soil is required to be compacted, use an alternative soil system such as structural cells to support the tree roots.

Figure 2.7.64. Grass geobloc driving space will support the lawn, but 95 percent compaction requirement under the grass paving system is no better for tree roots than other paving types. *(Photo courtesy Presto-Geosystems, Inc.)*

Attacks on Trees

Abrasions, lawn mowers, dog urine, bike chains, and temporary signs tied to trunks all take their toll on a tree. Pit bull dog bites and even deer antler rub damage have been observed in urban situations. The trees near the entrance to a park or at a street corner often get the most abuse. Study the dynamics of how people use a space, and apply special protection to the more vulnerable trees. In intense areas, low fences at the perimeter of the tree opening will be necessary.

To protect the tree from attacks, the tree type, tree location within the plan and the need to include protection must be considered in making decisions related to putting the right tree in the right place.

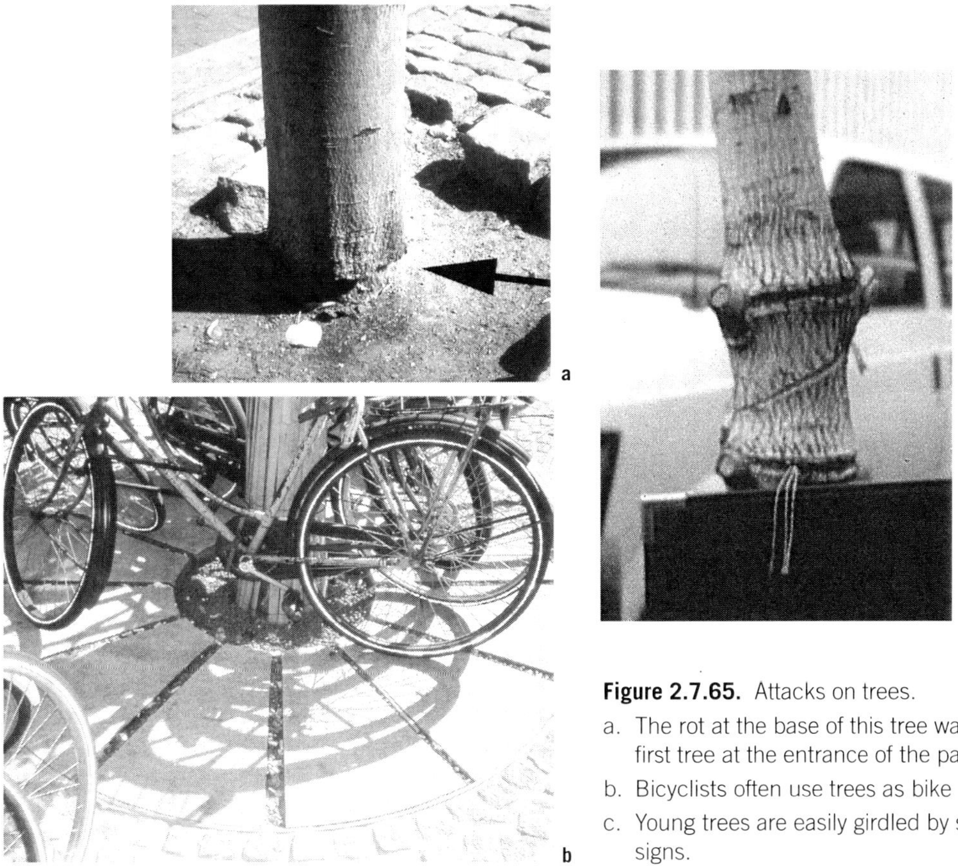

a b c

Figure 2.7.65. Attacks on trees.

a. The rot at the base of this tree was caused by dog urine. This is the first tree at the entrance of the park—a prime target for dog walkers.
b. Bicyclists often use trees as bike racks, damaging the bark.
c. Young trees are easily girdled by strings used to attach temporary signs.

Tree guards, if used, must be very large to accommodate growth and be easily removable. A tree guard should be no smaller than the size of the root ball if not easily removable.

Annual flowers or groundcover planting within the tree opening may serve to protect the base of the tree and signal a special place that commands greater respect. Remember never to plant within the root ball of the tree.

Elevated pH

pH is a constant issue for all urban trees and must be considered in tree selection and location. Lime in building materials migrates into the soil and raises the pH. Avoid selecting pH-sensitive trees in urban areas, particularly near large concrete, masonry, or limestone buildings, or protect the soil from leaching by controlling runoff into the tree opening.

Change in pH is proportional to the amount of soil being impacted by the runoff. The larger the soil volume provided, the lower the incidence of elevated pH. Consider the use of pH-tolerant trees near large concrete or masonry buildings or mound soil to reduce water flow from lime sources into the planting soil.

Figure 2.7.66. Tree guards should be as large as possible to avoid damaging the tree.

a. This tree guard is about as small a diameter as should be recommended.
b. Low tree guard to protect from car bumpers. Higher wooden staking system is temporary for only one growing season.
c. and d. Simple and effective tree guards.

a

b

c

d

SUMMARY

- Begin the tree selection process only after the site conditions and possible soil improvement options are understood. Make the place right for the tree and then select the right tree.
- Use a wide range of resources to gather information on the requirements of trees. Personal experience and local knowledge are the best resources.
- There are subtle regional differences in soil, climate, and adaptable cultivars that need to be understood when making tree selections.
- Taxonomic features and nomenclature are not always consistent within the industry. Use quality growers. Know the taxonomic features of the tree being specified.
- The size, shape, habit, color, and growth rates of all plants are controlled by the site's growing conditions as well as genetics.
- Know the nuances of each plant's limitations, including temperature hardiness, heat tolerance, photoperiod adaptability, cultural requirements, disease and insect susceptibility, shade tolerance, wind resistance, drainage limitations, air pollution tolerance, and salt tolerance.
- Trees that produce pollen and volatile organic carbons (VOCs) fill other important roles in environments of cities that offset these negative aspects. Continue to use trees that produce pollen and VOCs.
- Neither designs with a monoculture nor a wildly diverse number of tree species are necessarily correct or incorrect. Find a balance between extremes of design.
- Neither all-native nor all-exotic-species designs are necessarily correct or incorrect. Use the best tree for the situation.
- Wider spacing generally produces a longer-lived and easier-to-maintain landscape. There are conditions where closely spaced trees may be appropriate.
- Spacing must anticipate impact of future canopy competition and the ability to manage this competition.
- Landscapes, particularly trees, change over long periods of time. A designer should not live long enough to see the full cycle of a landscape's maturation process.
- Planting trees at smaller caliper is generally better for long-term tree health than planting larger-caliper trees.
- It is critical that designers expand the number of trees used in the urban landscape to build resistance to future disease and insect infestation.
- Design spaces and select trees that accommodate and protect the tree from human influences, including such diverse issues as utilities, car accidents, rising soil pH, and dog walkers.

REFERENCES

Key References

Arnold, Henry F. 1993. *Trees in Urban Design.* 2nd ed. Van Nostrand Reinhold, New York, NY. 197 pp.

Burns, Russell M., and Barbara H. Honkala, tech coords. 1990. *Silvics of North America: Volume 2. Hardwoods.* Agricultural Handbook 654. U.S. Department of Agriculture, Forest Service, Washington, DC. 877 pp.

Costello, Laurence R., et al. 2003. *Abiotic Disorders of Landscape Plants.* University of California, Division of Agriculture and Natural Resources, Oakland, CA. 242 pp.

Dirr, Michael A. 1998. *Manual of Woody Landscape Plants.* Stipes Publishing, Champaign, IL. 1,187 pp.

Gilman, Edward F. 1997. *Trees for Urban and Suburban Landscapes.* Delmar Publishers, Albany, NY. 662 pp.

Hightshoe, Gary L. 1988. *Native Trees, Shrubs, and Vines for Urban and Rural America.* Van Nostrand Reinhold, New York, NY. 819 pp.

Other Resources

Cathey, H. Marc. *American Horticultural Society Heat Zone Map.* American Horticultural Society, Alexandria, VA.

Costello, Laurence R. and Katherine S. Jones. 2003. *Reducing Infrastructure Damage by Tree Roots: A Compendium of Strategies.* Western Chapter of the International Society of Arboriculture, Cohasset, CA. 119 pp.

Dirr, M.A. 1976. Salt injury to landscape plants. *Journal of Arboriculture* 2:209–215.

Dirr, Michael A. 1997. *Dirr's Hardy Tree and Shrubs: An Illustrated Encyclopedia.* Timber Press, Inc., Portland, OR. 493 pp.

Flint, Harrison L. 1983. *Landscape Plants for Eastern North America.* John Wiley & Sons, New York, NY. 677 pp.

Gerhold, Henry D., Norman L. Lacasse, and Willet N. Wandell, eds. 1993. *Street Tree Factsheets.* Penn State, College of Agricultural Sciences. University Park, PA.

Gilman, Edward F. 2002. *An Illustrated Guide to Pruning.* 2nd ed. Delmar Publishers, Albany, NY. 330 pp.

Gilman, Edward F., and Sharon J. Lilly. 2002. *Best Management Practices—Tree Pruning.* International Society of Arboriculture, Champaign, IL. 35 pp.

Harlow, William M., and Ellwood S. Harrar. 1968. *Textbook of Dendrology.* 5th ed. McGraw-Hill, New York, NY. 512 pp.

Harris, Richard W., James R. Clark, and Nelda P. Matheny. 2004. *Arboriculture: Integrated Management of Landscape Trees, Shrubs, and Vines.* 4th ed. Pearson Education, Inc., Upper Saddle River, NJ. 578 pp.

Horticopia. 2007. www.horticopia.com.

International Society of Arboriculture. 2003. *Introduction to Arboriculture: Tree Biology.* DVD-ROM. International Society of Arboriculture, Champaign, IL.

International Society of Arboriculture. 2005. *Introduction to Arboriculture: Tree Identification and Selection.* DVD-ROM. International Society of Arboriculture, Champaign, IL.

Johnson, Warren T. and Howard H. Lyon. 1991. *Insects That Feed on Trees and Shrubs.* 2nd ed. Cornell University Press, Ithaca, NY. 560 pp.

Lilly, Sharon J. 2001. *Arborists' Certification Study Guide.* International Society of Arboriculture, Champaign, IL. 222 pp.

Lloyd, John, ed. *Plant Health Care for Woody Ornamentals.* 1997. International Society of Arboriculture, Champaign, IL. 223 pp.

Ogren, Thomas L. 2000. *Allergy-Free Gardening: The Revolutionary Guide to Healthy Landscaping.* Ten Speed Press, Berkeley, CA. 267 pp.

Sinclair, Wayne A., Howard H. Lyon, and Warren T. Johnson. 1989. *Diseases of Trees and Shrubs.* Cornell University Press, Ithaca, NY. 575 pp.

Sternberg, Guy, and Jim Wilson. 1995. *Landscaping with Native Plants: Northwest, Midwest, Midsouth and Southeast Edition.* Firefly Books Ltd., Willowdale, ON. 287 pp.

Steuteville, Robert, ed. 2006. Research: Trees make streets safer, not deadlier. *New Urban News* 11(6):1-6.

Trowbridge, Peter J., and Nina L. Bassuk. 2004. *Trees in the Urban Landscape: Site Assessment Design and Installation.* John Wiley & Sons, Inc., Hoboken, NJ. 205 pp.

Whitcomb, Carl E. 1985. *Know It and Grow It, 'II': A Guide to the Identification and Use of Landscape Plants.* 2nd ed. Lacebark Publications, Stillwater, OK. 740 pp.

Whitcomb, Carl E. 1987. *Establishment and Maintenance of Landscape Plants.* Lacebark Publications, Stillwater, OK. 618 pp.

INTRODUCTION

Management-Based Strategies

Knowledge of science and appropriate designs can help designers plan successful tree plantings, but seeing those plans through to completion requires skills in budgeting, documentation, and people management. The project must be managed from beginning to end in a manner that reinforces the soil- and tree-based strategies.

Over the next three chapters, we'll look at the management principles required to guide the process of incorporating the first seven principles into the built landscape.

Principle 8: Establish Reasonable Tree and Soil Budgets

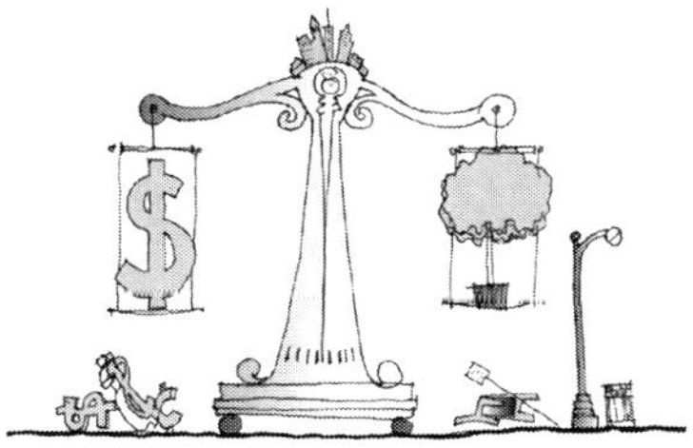

This principle directs designers to ensure adequate funding for the previous principles. Soil- and tree-based strategies often increase the cost of tree planting, but may also reduce long term maintenance cost and increase the benefits of the tree. Knowledge of these costs and benefits is critical to supporting the budgets needed to improve trees.

Principle 9: Create Detailed Tree and Soil Construction Documents

This principle helps the designer develop accurate, science-based construction documents to build landscapes that support functional trees.

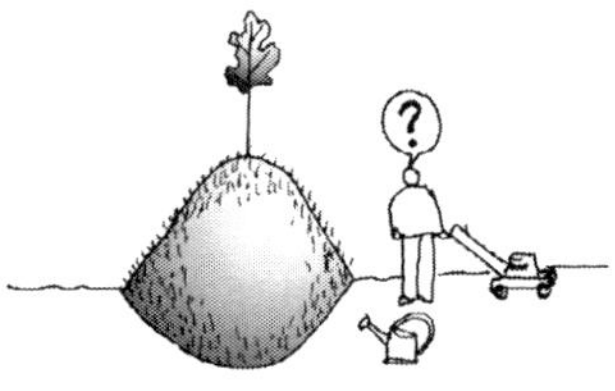

Principle 10: Design for Maintenance

This principle reminds the designer to conceive maintainable landscapes. This returns to the beginning of the design principles for its success. If the first nine principles are understood and implemented, projects should already be maintainable and sustainable.

PART TWO

8

Principle 8: Establish Reasonable Tree and Soil Budgets

Solving soil and tree problems can be surprisingly straightforward if you follow basic soil- and tree-based strategies. Obtaining the funds to pay for these ideas, however, can be more of a challenge. Start early to establish a soil budget. This will involve educating the client as to the biological requirements of trees and why "standard" practices may not be adequate to support long-term growth. Designers must be able to cite why improvements to soil are needed and the cost and benefits of functional trees to the project and the community. They must promote and defend soil costs compared to other project components competing for the same dollars.

It may be necessary to alter other design elements to establish a balanced budget, perhaps choosing a less expensive paving type or light fixture. Designers must make these choices early. Do not sell a particular design image where there is not enough soil to support long-term growth.

Begin the client's education about trees and soils at the master planning phase. Add drawings to master plan reports to indicate improved soil conditions. A schematic section of tree rooting provisions under proposed paving will become a placeholder in the budget outline.

Figure 2.8.1. Establish reasonable tree and soil budgets.

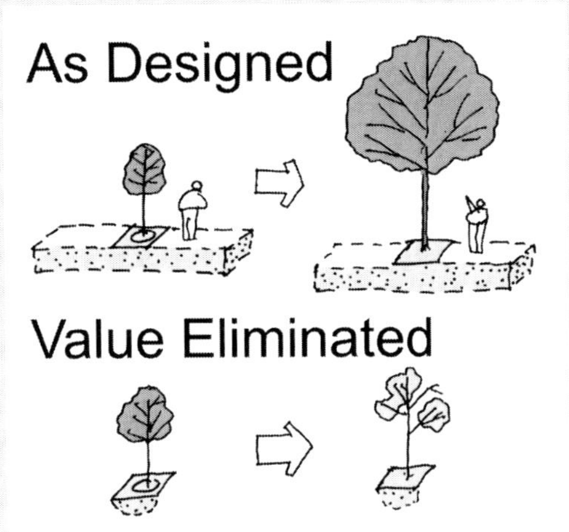

Figure 2.8.2. Value engineering: Slashing soil budget to reduce cost.

Value Engineering or Value Elimination?

The term "value engineering" is often shortened to simply VE. There is a joke in the design field that VE actually stands for "value elimination." At the end of the project, after the client and design team have worked out a careful balance of design, quality, and budget; a contractor (or, more often, a construction manager) is engaged with a mission of figuring out how to reduce costs. In theory, this person is supposed to show the client how to get the same project for less money. In a best-case situation, the construction manager brings ideas that reduce costs with minimum loss in value. However, most of the time, it is the project's quality, and thus its value to the client, that is lost. Too often, cost-cutting in one place undermines the rationale for other decisions, changing the fundamental success of the project.

Design sketches often depict trees as mature specimens, and clients expect that they are purchasing this view at some point in the future. However, this image may never appear if the soil to support that growth is not included in the budget. Client education and defense of the soils budget must continue all the way through construction. Value engineering (aka cost-cutting) continues right up to the time the soil is to be installed.To survive this process, the value of soil must be deeply imbedded in the project manager's mind.

ESTABLISH THE PLANTING BUDGET

Planting budgets based on a count of trees and other plants are easy to prepare, but most plant cost estimates assume only the minimum soil modifications needed to get the plant into the ground and survive the warranty period. Preparing a reasonable soil budget requires greater knowledge of conditions and should be its own budget category.

Tree sizes at planting, the spacing, and even the type of plants selected can have significant impacts on the budget. All too often, funds are expended on large-caliper trees to give an instant effect, without providing the resources to support the same tree over the long term. Be aware of budget relationships during preliminary design sketches and presentations. Present soil concepts during the first design meetings.

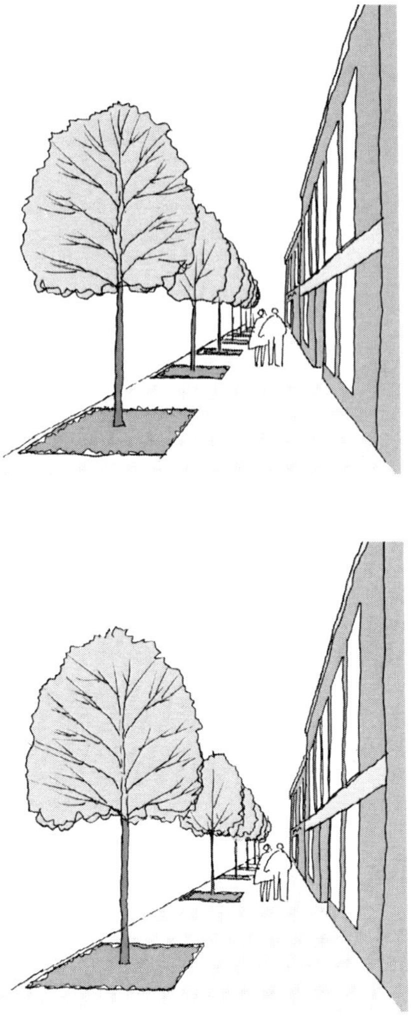

Figure 2.8.3. Use wider tree spacing to reduce cost without significantly reducing value. Wider spacing improves visibility and produces better sun/shade relationships.

a. Trees at 25-foot spacing.

b. Trees at 35-foot spacing.

Specify smaller-caliper trees to conserve cost. It may come as a surprise to some designers, but trees and shrubs actually grow. Smaller-caliper trees recover faster from transplant shock and require less maintenance in the early stages of the project life cycle. Increase the tree and shrub planting size only after the soil budget has been established. For most projects a 3- to 3-1/2-inch caliper tree is a good balance, large enough to make an impression and not so large to be difficult and expensive to install and maintain.

Smaller-caliper trees also require less energy to dig, move, and plant. Their smaller root packages contain less soil, reducing the impact on valuable resources. The cumulative effect of smaller trees is to reduce the project's environmental cost and carbon footprint.

While the recommendation is for smaller size trees to save money, this should not be interpreted as condoning the use of cheaper or inferior plants. Always specify trees from the best nurseries and require the highest quality. There are many "cheap" trees to be found in the market. Avoid them! See the in depth discussion on nursery practices as they impact tree quality in Part 2, Chapter Nine.

Space trees and shrubs at distances that anticipate long-term growth. Small changes in plant spacing make large differences in cost.

The cost per plant can vary significantly, depending on species and cultivar. Check established nursery catalog price lists when developing budgets.

Ensure that it is clear how larger plants are to be moved into position and handled in tight sites. Tree spades and other equipment need large amounts of room, both horizontally and vertically, to maneuver. Tree spades usually cannot operate on steep slopes. Consult contractors if you have questions about installation that may affect cost and bidding. If an installation technique is not obvious, add notes on the drawings to be clear about the intended methods.

Be aware of market forces, including supply and demand, seasonal fluctuations, weather, and disease outbreaks, which can alter the cost estimate. Specifying a plant that is not easily available in the size, type, or quantity required can make a big difference in contractor pricing. Maintain collections of nursery catalogs, attend nursery trade shows, and talk with local contractors to ensure that estimates reflect the reality of the market.

Cost estimating consultants are often not well versed in the nuances of estimating plants, planting soils, or special plant mixes. Work with the cost estimating consultant to ensure accurate estimates to avoid unpleasant surprises when bids are opened. Supply the cost estimator with plant and soil costs as needed to get an adequate budget picture. Do research with contractors to obtain pricing.

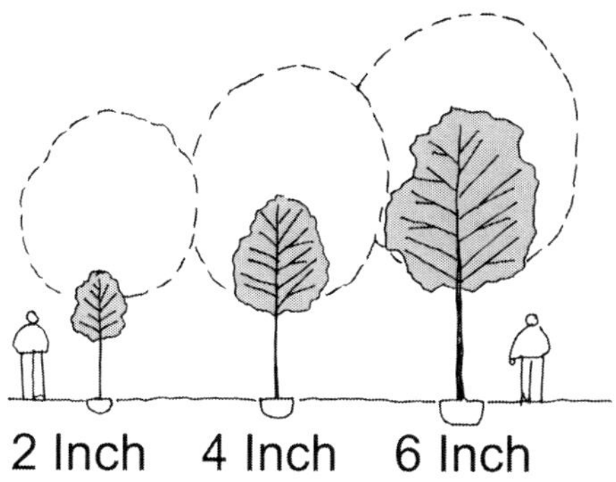

a

b

Figure 2.8.4. Different tree sizes at planting will produce roughly similar-sized trees after 10 years of growth if planted in good soil conditions.

a. Different size trees.

b. A 3- to 3-1/2-inch-caliper tree is the most economical size to specify in an urban landscape.

ESTABLISH THE SOIL AND DRAINAGE BUDGET

Soil and drainage features should be estimated separately from planting budgets. This allows the budgets and their value to be discussed independently from other landscape elements. Respond to proposed cuts in soils and drainage budgets with recommendations that the planting scheme and the quality of other site elements also be cut. Clients must be continually educated that the planting design is dependent on the soil and drainage for success. A cut in one must require a change in the other.

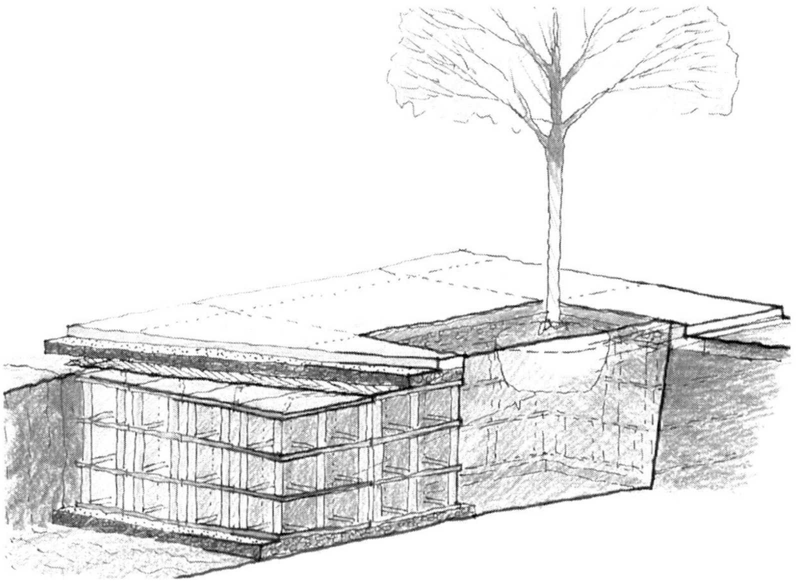

Figure 2.8.5. Building significant soil volumes into urban projects requires early development of budget line items for their construction.

Remove plants from the design when they are no longer provided with adequate soil. Until designers are willing to stand up for this principle, improvement to tree planting will remain an academic discussion. Designers will be surprised how easy it is to convince reasonable people that the money spent on soil is needed once the designer begins to speak with the authority gained from this book.

While soil improvement is vital to the success of trees, designers can reduce soil improvement costs during the design period by following the principles outlined in this book. Notice how the first four principles work with the existing resources and suggest inexpensive ways to provide for better planting conditions through a thorough understanding of site resources and creating designs that work with those resources. Planting the easy places first saves significant money.

Awareness of budget limitations during the design phase will lead to lower-cost alternatives being developed without sacrificing tree health. For planning purposes in urban sites, soil improvement cost should be, at a minimum, equal to the planting budget. For street tree plantings in dense urban areas, soil cost under pavement may be 10 times the cost of the tree! Street tree cost in a dense urban commercial district will be greater than $10,000 per tree (2006 evaluation) to include modification of soil conditions for long-term growth. However, these same trees will gradually increase in value to several times their installation cost. (See the valuation calculation later in this chapter.)

Understanding the existing soil is the first and most important step in reducing soil improvement cost. It is usually cheaper to work with existing soil. Follow the guidance in Part 1, Chapters Six and Seven to determine the usability of this soil. Recognize that preserving existing soil can add hidden costs to other parts of the project by restricting the area of the site usable by the contractor. Given how difficult it is to control contractor activity, assumptions that existing soil quality will remain at the end of construction may not be valid.

Soil improvements not covered by pavement are less costly and more effective than rooting zones created under pavement. Use Principles 1 and 2 if budgets are tight.

Soil improvement options vary dramatically in cost. Regional variations in the cost and sources of soil, sand, aggregate, and organic matter require that designers working outside their local area research material options and costs before preparing estimates and specifications. Some materials may not be available in all areas, or their trucking cost may be prohibitive.

$5 Tree in a $50 Hole

There is an old saying in the arborist profession: "Plant a $5 tree in a $50 hole." This may seem like an exaggeration, but it is surprisingly accurate in urban areas. The "hole" preparation needs to account for the long-term growth of the tree, while the tree should be as inexpensive as possible without sacrificing quality. Where budgets are tight, cut back on tree size, expand the spacing, and eliminate items such as tree grates that harm trees. But do not cut the soil work. A $1,000 tree in a $10,000 soil improvement zone under the pavement is about the right amount to budget for an urban streetscape.

Figure 2.8.6. An example where tree costs were out of balance with other site costs.

Figure 2.8.7. Trees and street lights have equal cost and equal value.

Trees and Street Lights Are Equal

It is illuminating to compare the cost and value of trees and street lights. The cost to correctly install and maintain one tree in an urban commercial district, including its soil, over a 30-year period is roughly equal to the cost to install and maintain one street light over that same period. Do they have equal value? Both are vital to the success of a vibrant retail space. This is not a comparison of the value of a street light to a newly planted tree but to a large, mature specimen. Consider the response by a community when a single mature tree is cut down, as opposed to when a street light is taken away. There is no comparison to the public outcry at the removal of a mature tree. When was the last time citizens chained themselves to a lamp post to save it from the bulldozer?

BALANCE TREE AND SOIL COST AND VALUE WITH OTHER SITE ELEMENTS

Each part of the designed landscape contributes to the whole image. Paving, streetlights, benches, trash receptacles, signs, fountains, planters, and trees each play their role in the image and usability of the site. The cost and value of each element must be evaluated relative to the overall budget. The value of each element is a combination of factors, from economic to environmental.

Designers must be honest about the value of more expensive finishes to the success of the project. Expensive paving around dead or declining trees is an inappropriate allocation of resources. One does not have to use expensive paving to ensure a respected landscape.

There are many examples of successful landscapes with less expensive paving types but great trees. Savannah, Ga., is a delightful example of a town built with concrete walks. Harvard

Figure 2.8.8. Great paving is not needed to assure a great public landscape.

a. Harvard University: Top-rated, historic campus with asphalt walks.

b. Savannah: A great city with concrete walks.

c. Brick pavers with custom precast steps and wall caps, but a dead tree.

d. Brick pavers and a slick invisible tree grate results in a 50 percent replacement rate and stunted, unstable trees due to poor distribution of budget funding.

University uses asphalt paving throughout its prestigious, historic campus. In both cases, great trees are what make these landscapes great. There is good science on the value of a large tree, but no scientific study has demonstrated that more-expensive paving will make a project more successful.

Of the many choices made during the design of a project, the decision to use tree grates and tree guards is perhaps most counterproductive to the success of the landscape and to the tree. The folly of the tree grate is thoroughly described in Principle 5. A tree grate contributes nothing positive to the health of the tree, but its high cost competes for budget resources with the soil systems needed to support the tree to maturity. The use of the tree grate is often justified as an important urban design element, but what is important about a handsome grate around a dead or declining tree? Find lower-cost solutions to fill the transition from the edge of the paving to the trunk of the tree. See Part 2, Chapter Five for alternative recommendations.

Figure 2.8.9. Tree grates are expensive and are not justified by any benefits to the tree.

ROLE OF GOVERNMENT REVIEW AGENCIES IN SUPPORTING ADEQUATE SOIL BUDGETS

It is not likely that developers will voluntarily approve larger budgets for planting soil. The altruism implied by this book is not going to rise up from an industry that competes for the bottom line. Most of the ideas in *Up By Roots* do not begin to have lasting impact until long after most projects are sold. Designers cannot force clients to think long-term. In larger development companies, the part of the company that makes decisions as to how much money is spent on the capital cost is a different group and, critically, has a different balance sheet than the part responsible for operations. The project team will likely be working for different companies and on different projects when the trees in a poor design begin to decline.

Government reviewers can raise the bar on development standards. For example, sediment control and rainwater management standards and requirements have improved over the past 20 years. These changes in regulations have added significant cost to projects, but the increase is considered as a part of the cost of business. Since everyone must comply, the added costs are passed on to buyers or renters. This approach must be applied to improving planting conditions.

Almost every jurisdiction in the United States has some form of planting requirement. These regulations are often erroneously called "landscape requirements," even though they only regulate plants. Almost none of these regulations require that the plants be accompanied with any soil other than a standard planting detail. Some regulations actually require that the plan provide designated amounts of canopy to shade parking surfaces, but fail to require the soil to produce that canopy. Soil volumes based on canopy requirements must become a standard. See Part 2, Chapter Four for further discussion on soil volumes.

A change in the prevailing attitude toward soil must emerge from regulation. Existing planting ordinances need to be amended to require soil improvements so that each plant has the required soil volume and soil quality to grow trees over the life of the project and to the sizes required by the ordinance. This will take political will, and that will may exist in environmentally focused voters and planners if only they can be educated to the problem. The introduction to this book was written as the beginning of that education.

Figure 2.8.10. Local ordinances for soil improvement can lead the way to tree-friendly cities changing logos into reality.

USE THE BENEFITS OF LARGE, HEALTHY TREES TO SUPPORT COST

Plant and cultivate client understanding of the importance of large, mature trees to the project. Many volumes have been written on the cultural and environmental benefits of large trees to urban areas. It has always been assumed that trees were good for us, and like chicken soup or an apple a day, scientific evidence supports these old assumptions. It is now clear that trees offer benefits that far outweigh their costs. There is substantial evidence that humans truly need to live among trees.

Early humans are thought to have evolved along the forested edges of the savannas of Africa and in other places where they could use the resources of trees and at the same time use the more open plain for hunting and gathering. This mixture afforded a competitive advantage for a two-legged creature who walked erect in a four-legged world. Modern humans may still carry this inner need to live among trees and not just any collection of trees, but groups of large trees at spacing similar to the savanna. Humans are most comfortable in open, park-like settings where there are long vistas through tall tree trunks, where there is a mix of sunny, grassy

Figure 2.8.11. Large trees help create healthy cities.

What Is a Fish Worth?

The shade of a tree cools the pavement, which then cools the water from a summer rain. That cooler water increases fish reproduction. But what are these fish worth, except to the fisherman? Would it not be cheaper to stock the stream from a fish hatchery than plant the number of trees needed to cool the water enough to increase fish reproduction? Or is more going on here? How long will it be before it is understood that the whole machine working together is worth more than the sum of its parts?

patches and clumps of shade, much like English or Olmstedian parks or the great estate landscapes of the 19th and early 20th centuries. Healthy large trees spaced at 50 feet or greater replicate this image.

Large vs. Small, Street vs. Park

Not all trees are equal in the cost/benefit discussion. Almost all of the benefits of living among trees come from the canopy. The larger the canopy, the greater the benefit. Climax forest species of trees generally live longer, further extending the benefits.

As large trees reach maturity, they tend to become more open in habit, casting a dappled shade rather than the denser shade of smaller trees. This allows a greater variety of plants to grow under their canopies. Larger trees develop tall, clear trunks so that the vista lines are open at human eye level, while smaller trees remain thickly branched at lower levels, obscuring sight lines. Smaller trees need to be planted closer together to create a continuous canopy, creating more trunk obstructions and taking up valuable ground space. Wherever possible, trees that mature to large sizes should be planted at wide spacing rather than smaller varieties at closer spacing. Larger trees, not smaller ones, have an urban scale.

A review of the environmental and cultural benefits of trees reveals that a tree located closer to human activity provides more benefits than the same tree located in a more remote location. The canopy provides much of that benefit by cooling the urban heat island, reducing energy use, absorbing dust, reducing rainwater flows, and transpiring groundwater. A tree shading a building, plaza, or parking lot does a lot more to mitigate human impact than a tree of the same type and size shading only soil in a park. Treed streets and spaces bind communities together and have been credited with measurable reductions in stress and crime while increasing the value of property. The problem is that it is much more difficult, and expensive, to grow trees in close proximity to zones of human use.

Environmental Benefits

Many people intuitively know trees help restore the balance between human communities and the other parts of the earth's environment. The International Society of Arboriculture uses the slogan "Trees Are Good," in part to summarize these benefits. But what are these environmental benefits, and do the benefits outweigh the cost to plant and maintain trees in close proximity to human habitat? Some of the benefits are easy to measure and value. Others may be difficult to quantify.

a b c d

Figure 2.8.12. Large and small trees, park and street trees have vastly different benefits.

a. Large trees like this oak block rainwater, cool the air, and change the city in significant ways.
b. Small trees such as these hollies have lesser benefits due to their smaller canopy volume.
c. Trees that overhang paving and shade buildings offer greater environmental benefits than trees in parks.
d. Trees in parks, while important, have fewer environmental benefits than the same size trees planted closer to human activity.

Tree size and location in the landscape can greatly increase or reduce a particular benefit. Larger-canopy trees such as oak are much more valuable than smaller trees such as dogwood. The closer a canopy is to activity, the greater the mitigation of our impact on the land through greater cooling and absorption or cleaning of rainwater.

Except for reductions in energy use, most of the environmental benefits from a single tree are small. It is the aggregate impacts of many trees in a city that become large enough to make a significant reduction in the impact cities have on the land. The knowledge base has not advanced sufficiently to place a dollar value on many of the benefits. Do not overstate the importance of the benefits of a single tree, but also do not underestimate the importance of the urban forest.

The following are the most important benefits that urban trees provide to the natural environment.

Heat Island Reduction

Shade and evaporative cooling provided by trees have a significant cooling effect. The air under a tree can be 5 to 10 degrees F cooler than in the direct sun. This cooling impact is greater when groups of trees provide canopy closure and in areas where large areas of canopy cover paving, particularly darker-paved surfaces like asphalt. Heat island reduction starts a chain of other environmental benefits as described below.

Figure 2.8.13. Canopy is responsible for most of trees' environmental benefits.

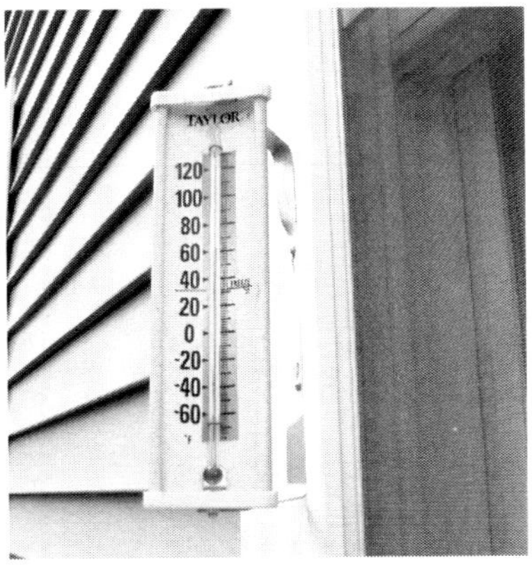

Energy Use and Conservation

Trees lower air temperatures, reduce solar loading by shading a building in summer, and still permit solar access in winter. Locating trees on the southeast and southwest sides of buildings offers the greatest compromise between winter and summer conditions. Large trees close to buildings lower wind speeds, reducing heat loss in winter. Trees shading parked cars reduce the amount of fuel that evaporates from cars and reduce the number of days the air conditioner in cars needs to be operated. Reduction in energy use by living among trees is significant.

Urban trees also require the use of energy during the planting, maintenance, and removal process, which reduces the net savings. The larger the size of the tree at planting or the shorter the tree's life span, the greater will be its energy consumption. In difficult soil situations, the tree's energy consumption will be greater than the savings it can provide—yet another reason to plant the easy places first.

Air Quality

Trees lower energy use with the resulting decrease in emissions. Trees emit volatile organic compounds (VOCs) but are also responsible for a net reduction in VOCs by reducing energy use. VOCs are responsible for smog and reductions in air quality. They can form ozone and contribute to global warming. The trees' improvement to air quality is offset by emissions of equipment during planting, maintenance, and removal. Even the design process results in emissions that reduce the net benefit of the tree, as designers fly around the country attending design meetings or go to nurseries to inspect trees. It is interesting to note that human activities also emit VOCs, but have no offsetting environmental benefit to justify their space in the landscape. Why is it that we do not have to justify our existence by a positive environmental balance sheet when the same is often asked of urban trees?

Table 2.8.1. Temperature inside cars parked in shaded vs. unshaded parking lot. The shaded car will evaporate less fuel while parked and use less air conditioning when driven. ***(Source: USDA Western Center for Urban Forest Research and Education)***

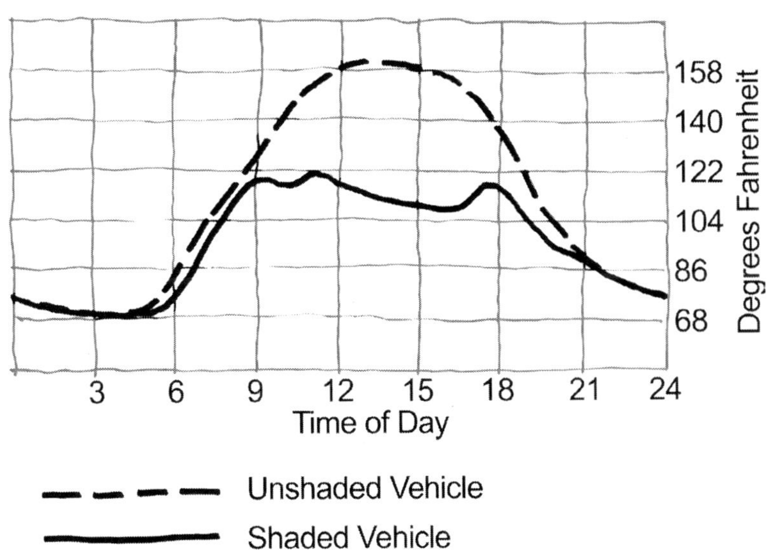

Figure 2.8.14. Trees planted to shade buildings and air-conditioning units reduce energy consumption.

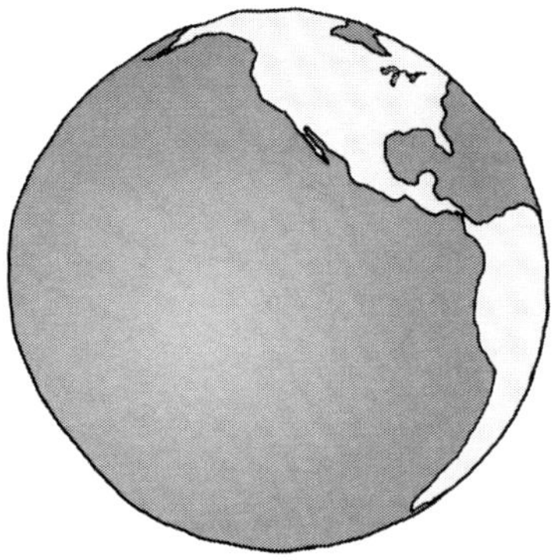

Breathe the Ocean Air

It is often stated that trees produce the oxygen needed to breathe. While it is true that trees produce a net flow of oxygen into the atmosphere, the amount of oxygen produced by all the trees in a city is quite small compared to the amount of oxygen required. In the 1991 Arizona Biosphere experiment, where 16 scientists tried to live in a sealed, self-sustaining environment, CO_2 buildup in the biosphere building required that oxygen be added. Most of the oxygen in the atmosphere actually comes from the oceans. Unfortunately, the biosphere designers forgot to make seventy percent of the space in the building an ocean.

Trees absorb dust and particulate matter, cleaning the air. On the other hand, trees create dust in the fall and contribute pollen into the air in the spring. But overall, a large tree has a net positive reduction of particulate matter.

Trees in urban areas provide a little bit of oxygen and reduce carbon dioxide buildup, but not in sufficient quantities to make a difference in the needs of humans.

Rainwater Runoff Quality

Trees slow down water velocity, filtering and cleaning runoff that flows through the soil and organic layers under the tree. The filtering function is reduced in areas where leaves are removed. Combining trees with other layers of plantings significantly boosts the rainwater quality benefits. Nitrogen and organic matter from decomposing leaves are deposited into the water, canceling some of the positive benefits. Runoff from tree-shaded paving is cooler when it reaches streams, an important factor in fish survival.

Rainwater Runoff Quantity

A tree in leaf can absorb about the first tenth of an inch of rain as leaves, twigs, and bark are coated with water. This water is held during the rain event, and much of it evaporates back into the air. However, the real rainwater benefit of trees is within the root system. Soil with bulk density low enough to support roots absorbs and filters more water than compacted soil.

Soil Erosion

The tree canopy absorbs the impact of rainfall. Roots and organisms in the root zone hold together soil particles. Soil erosion is lower in forested areas than in other types of planted environments due to the canopy, forest duff, soil biology, and roots.

Figure 2.8.15. Trees as a part of a rainwater management basin. Tree roots will serve as a pump to transpire water back into the atmosphere.

Soil Quality

Trees improve soil quality by adding to the organic content of the soil. Even if all the leaves are removed, decaying roots and root secretions, called exudates, add carbon to the soil immediately around the root, which feeds important parts of the soil food web. Decaying roots form channels and open the soil for better drainage.

Carbon Sequestration

Trees remove carbon from the air and store it in their cells. This carbon remains sequestered until the wood rots or is burned, whereupon it is released back into the atmosphere. A healthy, mature forest is a huge carbon sink. As the forest matures further, existing wood is rotting and releasing carbon almost as fast as new wood is added. Large open-grown trees in low-maintenance environments will add carbon each year until they reach maturity or crown closure with the adjacent trees. Large, long-lived trees sequester more carbon than small and short-lived trees.

A significant amount of carbon is added to the soil by the tree. This is in the form of decaying roots and exudates added to the area around the root as it grows. Healthy soil biology plays a major role in this process. The amount of carbon sequestered in the soil as the tree grows is larger and more permanent than the carbon sequestered in the woody parts of the tree.

Urban trees are not good examples of carbon sequestration. The use of gasoline-powered equipment to improve soil and plant and maintain urban trees releases as much or more carbon into the air as the tree is sequestering. Preserving large existing trees is important in the carbon cycle by maintaining existing carbon in the tree.

Animal Habitat

Large, mature trees provide significant habitat for animals, birds, and insects. Urban trees can support diverse populations. This habitat diversity is improved as understory plantings are increased and diversify, and is reduced as paving increases.

Figure 2.8.16. The carbon cycle of urban trees is not what we might want to believe.

a. The energy to dig, move, plant, fix the soil, prune, maintain, and remove an urban tree introduces as much carbon into the atmosphere as is later sequestered by the tree as it grows.
b. Specifying large-caliper trees further reduces the environmental value of planting the tree due to the huge energy expenditure to move the tree from the nursery to the landscape.

a

b

Summary of Environmental Benefits

What are all these environmental benefits worth? Actual amounts will vary from tree to tree, depending on tree type, size, and location. Each year additional research improves our awareness of the value of trees.

The measurable dollar value of most environmental benefits when applied to a single tree is small and barely justifiable in strict economic terms. When multiplied by all the trees in the urban forest, they represent a significant benefit to the community.

Speak the truth and cite facts, not generalities, relative to the environmental importance of trees. Many environmental benefits are not sufficiently understood to reasonably apply a dollar cost per tree, but may still have significant value to the interconnections of the environment. Use the references cited at the end of this chapter to find the most current values of urban trees.

Cultural Benefits

Cultural benefits of trees improve the quality of life, reduce the cost of living, and increase the value of a piece of land or its commercial activity. It is not surprising that more is known about cultural tree benefits and that cultural benefits are considered to have greater value than environmental benefits. Most cultural benefits of trees are directly tied to financial conditions of property.

Increasing our knowledge of the benefits of trees will help justify spending additional funds to create conditions that ensure the long-term growth of large trees.

Rich People Know About Trees

It is no coincidence that in most cities, the best and most expensive neighborhoods often have the best urban forests. This may be partially due to having more funds to plant and care for trees, but these neighborhoods are also often located in the portion of the city with the best soil conditions for large trees, in areas where large trees are already growing, implying that people instinctively value larger trees and the soil conditions they need.

Figure 2.8.17. The Georgetown neighborhood in the District of Columbia has great soil to grow trees. It is not surprising that wealthier people tend to live there.

Land Value

Trees add legally definable value to a property. This value reflects the sum of all the cultural benefits and is the best cost basis to justify the expense of large, urban trees. There is an easy and defendable way to determine the value that any tree contributes to overall land value. Assume that your neighbor comes over one night and cuts your tree down to improve their view or just because they don't like trees. You take your neighbor to court to regain the value of the lost tree. There is significant case law that can be used to support the notion that this tree has value. You—and particularly your neighbor—may be surprised at how high this value can be.

The primary reference to determine tree value is the *Guide for Plant Appraisal*, prepared by the Council of Tree and Landscape Appraisers and published by the International Society of Arboriculture. Table 2.8.2 is a comparison of the values of several different trees to indicate the importance that courts place on the value of trees in the landscape. Several types of growing conditions are used in the calculations to indicate how fixing soil problems can add value to trees as they mature.

The value of a large tree planted in good growing conditions easily recoups the cost of substantial investment to improve the soil over time, while the small tree makes only small gains in value. Trees at sites with poor soil resources do not gain in value due to their smaller size and poor condition, and the value can be less than the initial planting cost.

Figure 2.8.18. Trees add considerable value to the purchase price of a house.

Table 2.8.2. Appraised value of various trees as affected by soil conditions. (Appraisals prepared by Keith Pitchford using the *Guide for Plant Appraisal* 2005 values.)

Description	Appraised value
Newly planted tree	
• Willow oak, 3.5-inch dbh, in good condition in a residential front yard	$840
• Single-stemmed crabapple, 3.5-inch dbh, in good condition in a residential front yard	$720
• Willow oak, 3.5-inch dbh, in good condition; street tree in a commercial district	$720
• Single-stemmed crabapple, 3.5-inch dbh, in good condition; street tree in a commercial district	$660
Mature tree at site with good soil conditions	
• Willow oak, 30-inch dbh, in good condition in a residential front yard	$24,300
• Single-stemmed crabapple, 15-inch dbh in good condition in a residential front yard	$5,000
• Willow oak, 30-inch dbh, in good condition; street tree in a commercial district	$19,700
• Single-stemmed crabapple, 15-inch dbh, in good condition; street tree in a commercial district	$4,950
Mature tree at sites with poor soil conditions	
These trees were assumed to grow at a much slower rate and to be in a stressed condition.	
• Willow oak, 10-inch dbh, in poor condition in a residential front yard	$1,170
• Single-stemmed crabapple, 8-inch dbh, in poor condition in a residential front yard	$700
• Willow oak, 10-inch dbh, in poor condition; street tree in a commercial district	$1,100
• Single-stemmed crabapple, 8-inch dbh, in poor condition; street tree in a commercial district	$700

Lower Energy Bills

Less energy use has obvious environmental benefits, but it also lowers consumer energy bills. Large trees near a building save the decision-maker money. Of course, other factors weigh in the equation, including regional location; building type and construction; and tree type, size, and proximity to the building. Yet in many cases, energy savings of trees near buildings for heating and cooling can range from 25 percent to 50 percent. That savings alone can justify careful tree planting decisions, improvement in soil, and tree maintenance costs.

Retail Sales

Consumers have indicated that they will pay up to 10 percent more for items purchased at stores on streets lined with mature trees.

Commercial Rents

Developers report that they can charge up to 8 percent more rent for retail and office space in commercial environments with mature tree canopies.

Reduction in Air Temperatures

Cooler, tree-covered neighborhoods are more pleasant places in which to live and work because the urban heat island effect is reduced.

Improved Health

Living, working, and driving in areas covered with large trees can make a difference to physical and mental health. People are calmer around trees, and their blood pressure is lower. Patients whose hospital beds have a tree view spend one less day in the hospital on average than patients who cannot see trees. Placing patients in green garden spaces has been demonstrated to offer significant, measurable improvements to their physical and mental outlook.

Figure 2.8.19. Tree-shaded neighborhoods of Georgetown in the District of Columbia are cooler than adjacent parts of the city. *(Photo courtesy National Park Service)*

Community Cohesion

Time after time, communities that have good urban forests are also the same communities with strong support networks. This was found in studies of public housing in Chicago and is also observed in established, exclusive neighborhoods on the north side of that same city.

Crime Reduction

Neighborhoods with successful trees have lower crime rates. Adding trees to tough neighborhoods lowers the crime rate. This effect was first noticed in New York in the 1980s and is more accurately measured in a large Chicago study. See "The role of arboriculture in a healthy social ecology" by Frances Kuo in the May 2003 issue of the *Journal of Arboriculture*.

Improved Test Scores

Frances Kuo and her team, again in Chicago, found that students in public housing who could see trees from their home study areas had higher test scores in school than students from similar homes who could not see trees. See www.lhhl.uiuc.edu for more on this research and findings that support the social importance of trees in cities.

Summary of Cultural Benefits

All of the above benefits have clear value, and they may be summarized in the appraisal value of a tree, which represents an averaging of many factors. This list also suggests that the size, location, tree type, and condition of the tree play a role in the value of any individual tree. It should be no surprise that size, location, tree type, and condition are the most significant factors in the *Guide for Plant Appraisal* used to determine tree value. Large, healthy canopy trees in locations that are important to humans provide the most benefits and repay the communities that support funding for improved growing conditions.

Designers should use this information to support increased soil improvements for trees in difficult sites.

a b

Figure 2.8.20. Public housing with identical architecture but successful and unsuccessful tree plantings had significantly different outcomes in community cohesion, crime, and school test scores.

a. Successful trees.

b. Unsuccessful trees.

LIFE CYCLE COST

Forest trees are able to plant and manage themselves, as long as humans do not intervene and accept the results, which can be chaotic and unpredictable. Natural and random tree failure, disease, and regrowth often conflict with human management goals.

Humans are unwilling to let nature plant or maintain trees. They desire to control the trees' precise location and species, remove and replace lost trees, and control the size and shape of the crown. They plant trees in places where the trees struggle to survive, and avoid planting in places where trees might thrive. Find a tree near people, and you will soon find someone cleaning up leaves, removing untidy or hazardous parts, and generally making the landscape safe for humanity. Much of this control is needed to make orderly places to live and to meet perceived standards for the "proper" relationships of trees and humans. This all costs money, thus making it necessary to quantify the life cycle cost.

Quantifying a tree's life cycle cost requires knowledge of the existing and proposed site conditions, soil, and the decision-maker's preferences for quality and risk. Generally, the better the growing conditions, the less disease and maintenance may be experienced. In most areas of the United States, adequate soil provisions can eliminate the need for automatic watering systems. The larger the soil volume, the greater the period between removal and replacement; however, pruning costs will incrementally increase with tree size, as will removal cost.

a

b

c

d

Figure 2.8.21. Trees at various life stages. Maintenance tasks and costs change with time.

a. Newly installed tree.
b. Maturing, functional tree.
c. Mature tree.
d. Declining tree.

Large trees have a dark side if planted too close to buildings and pavement. U.S. cities spend more on sidewalk damage from tree roots each year than national annual lost value from forest fires. Follow Principle 5 to avoid conflicts between trees and pavement that can cause costly repairs that must be factored into the life cycle cost. If trees are placed in small openings, the cost of pavement repair can easily erase accrued economic benefits of the tree.

SUMMARY

- Establish a reasonable tree-planting budget.
- Establish a separate soil and drainage budget.
- Work with local planning agencies to add requirements for soil improvement to planting ordinances.
- Balance the costs of tree planting, soil, and drainage with the costs of other elements in the landscape. Avoid expensive materials if there are inadequate funds to support soil and drainage requirements.
- Use the benefits of trees to support the cost of soil and drainage improvements.
- Learn the environmental and cultural benefits of trees. Be realistic and do not overstate their value.
- Become familiar with the life cycle cost of planting, soil improvement, maintenance, and removal of trees.

REFERENCES

The science of determining the environmental and cultural value of trees is rapidly emerging. The following references and institution Web sites are the best resources for current information.

General Information

Marcus, Clare Cooper, and Marni Barnes, 1999. *Healing Gardens: Therapeutic Benefits and Design Recommendations*. John Wiley & Sons, New York, NY. 610 pp.

Tree Link. www.treelink.org.

United States Department of Agriculture Forest Service. Pacific Southwest Region. www.fs.fed.us/psw

Environmental Benefits

Center for Urban Forest Research
USDA Forest Service
University of California
One Shields Avenue
Davis, CA 95616-8780
wcufre.ucdavis.edu

Cultural Benefits
Center for Urban Horticulture
Human Dimensions of Urban Forestry
University of Washington
College of Forest Resources
Box 352100
Seattle, WA 98195-2100
www.cfr.washington.edu/research.envmind

University of Illinois at Champaign-Urbana
Human-Environment Research Laboratory
1103 South Dorner Drive
Urbana, IL 61801-4778
www.lhhl.uiuc.edu/crime.htm

Urban Forestry South
Southern Center for Urban Forestry Research and Information
320 Green Street
Athens, GA 30602-2044
www.urbanforestrysouth.org

PART TWO

9

Principle 9—Create Detailed Tree and Soil Construction Documents

Construction documents must be sufficiently detailed to correctly implement tree and soil concepts. The designer must then enforce these documents with diligent field review. The installation of trees and soils in urban landscapes is not well understood, and the industry is not yet committed to the science that creates the environment for large, healthy trees. Roadblocks and detours on the road to successful urban trees are numerous and difficult to overcome. Other project interests and goals compete for space above and below ground and in budget allocations. A well-detailed set of construction documents must be prepared to meet the challenge.

To enforce the documents, vigilance must be maintained during construction. Soil and plant quality are difficult to determine and control. Subtle changes to soil composition can make the difference between too much and too little drainage. Subgrade conditions and soil depths, volumes, and compaction levels

Figure 2.9.1. Create detailed tree and soil construction documents.

Figure 2.9.2. Construction is a complex undertaking requiring coordination among trades at every step.

are almost impossible to check or to change once the work is completed. Some nursery practices produce poor-quality trees with insufficient or girdling roots, roots too deep in the root package (root ball), co-dominant leaders, and weak branching junctions. It is difficult to obtain quality nursery stock, even from reliable nurseries.

Installing trees and soils is one of the last parts of the project. There is pressure from the decision-maker, the general contractor, and the installing contractor to cut corners, speed up the process, and save money. Nursery inspections may be suspended or substandard. Previously rejected materials may be accepted, and poor workmanship overlooked. The team is fatigued from the long construction process. The designer may be out of fee, forcing hard business decisions of quality over profit.

Success requires that the entire team, from the decision-maker to the last contractor, understand the importance of the process and be committed to its outcome. One person or contractor on the team can change the outcome for the better—or the worse.

CONTROL THE CONSTRUCTION DOCUMENTS

The designer who is preparing the planting plan must negotiate fees to prepare the construction documentation for all planting soils, including grading, installation, interface with adjacent materials, and drainage requirements. For various reasons, the plant designer often controls only the planting plan, while architectural or engineering disciplines control the grading, soil, and drainage design. Without single consultant control of all parts of the planting/grading/soil/drainage equation, or a collaborative culture among the design team, omissions or different priorities may create conditions that can lead trees to fail. It is amazing how often this first step is missed. The professions that claim to design trees must claim authorship of all the parts of the design that allow the tree to be successful.

Who Is the Lorax on Your Project?

Construction is a complex endeavor, with hundreds of people affecting the outcome. Team members, even if they understand the importance of trees, may need to be educated as to their requirements. It is easy for decision-makers to support trees during the design phase, and also easy for them to cut soil budgets in the value engineering and contract document phase. If you have read this far, you are the project Lorax, the mythical character given to us by Dr. Seuss. Now is the time to "speak for the trees."

Photo courtesy office of Michael Vergason.

Start the education process about the importance of trees and soils during the initial interviews and consultant selection process. Firms can make community advocacy work related to trees part of their marketing program to set themselves apart from the competition by demonstrating expert knowledge in this field. Educate clients about the need to have landscape design contracts include the designs for grading, planting, soil, and drainage.

Challenging areas of the practice controlled by other design disciplines can have negative effects. Cross these professional turf barriers slowly and with care. Build firm expertise first, and let knowledge lead the way to broader participation.

Figure 2.9.3. The designer of the trees must also control the design and documentation of planting soil, drainage, and grading. *(Photo courtesy office of Michael Vergason.)*

PREPARE DETAILED, ACCURATE PLANS AND SPECIFICATIONS

Landscape design firms typically prepare planting plans and include any reference to soil modifications within those plan documents. Soil and drainage, even on simple projects, deserve their own set of drawings and specification sections. Think of soil and drainage as another system in the construction sequence. Draw these plans and details to scale to show the contractor exactly what is supposed to be built. Details need to be clearly referenced from the plan. Draw many sections. Write clear and scientifically accurate specifications to support the drawings. Do not rely on typical details or a few lines in the planting specifications to instruct the contractor on what should be complex soil and drainage requirements.

The types of plans and level of detail needed are depicted on the typical plans that follow. Detailed sections have been shown throughout the book related to each of the principles discussed. *None of these details should be used verbatim, and they need to be adapted to the specific requirements of the project.* There is no such thing as a typical detail, and each set of drawings should develop a unique approach based on the design, site conditions, project goals, and budget. Designers must think outside the confines of current practice to improve the construction of spaces for trees.

Figure 2.9.4. Planting plan should reference only plants. Soil and other considerations should be depicted on separate plan views.

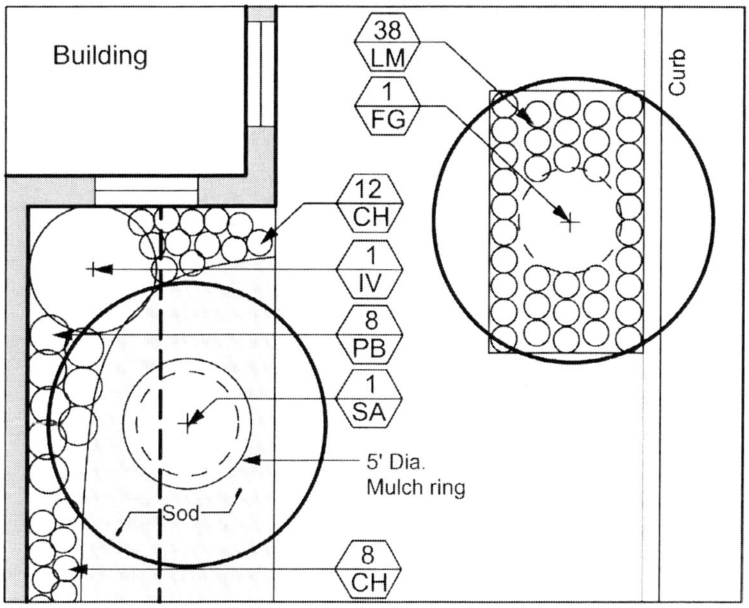

PLANTING PLAN

The planting plan defines the number, location, and type of plants to be installed. It should not include information on soils and drainage. Drawings that combine too many layers are difficult to read, and the soil and drainage may be installed by two different contractors.

Landscape architects currently do a good job in documenting plant requirements. The following are a few changes to the planting plan that can improve the communication of the work to the contractor and avoid conflicts.

Drawing Crown Dimensions

There is a difference of opinion within the profession as to how large to draw the crown of a tree on the plan. Most often, the crown is drawn at a size that looks good on the illustrative design plan but bears no relationship to the size that the tree might actually grow. Rarely is the tree drawn to the size it will be at planting. Drawing the tree size at planting may be the most reasonable approach, showing an honest representation of what the client is buying. Unfortunately, this approach does not reveal long-term spacing conflicts. It may also lure the designer into adding more trees to make the initial plan look better, a common error in the profession.

Showing the crown area at its maximum size given the soil conditions is a good alternative. The designer will need to calculate the soil resources and make canopies different for each tree based on soil provided and species. While this requires more work, it allows the designer to accurately depict the expectation of the plan and may help to obtain approval for the required soil improvements. It may be best to show both the size of the tree canopy at planting and a dashed line of the canopy at expected maturity.

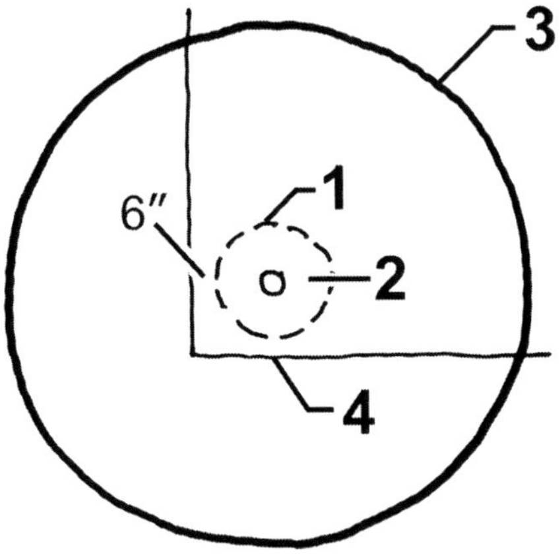

Figure 2.9.5. The root package should be a part of every tree plan symbol and its size calculated for the size tree specified.

1. Limit of root package per ANLA standards.
2. Never indicate ground cover planting within the area of the root package.
3. Draw limit of the canopy at the mature size expected based on the soil volume provided.
4. Edge of paving or other obstruction.

Plan Views of Root Packages (aka the Root Ball)

Trees are planted with roots. It may seem obvious, but it is incredible how often planting plans and details show trees to be planted into spaces where there is not enough room for the root package. Draw the root package at its correct size to the American Nursery & Landscape Association (ANLA) standards for the type and size of tree to be planted. Include the root package as a dashed line as part of the tree symbol. This circle must fit easily into the space required.

A minimum of 6 inches of tolerance between the side of the root package and the edge of any paving or obstruction is needed to ensure that soil can be placed around the tree. Never develop a detail that relies on shaving a root package to fit the planting location. While this 6-inch tolerance is a reasonable dimension for a partial obstruction, this does not mean that the tree can be fit into a confined space just 6 inches bigger in all directions than the root package. When the tree is confined on all sides by paving, a minimum of 8 to 12 inches is a better space between the edge of the root package and the paving.

Planting Within the Root Package

Never indicate shrub or ground cover plants to be planted within the root package of the tree! Be clear in the planting plans and details that the root package area is dedicated to mulch covering only.

Tree Location

Most planting plans do not show dimensions for the locations of plants. It is assumed that the contractor will scale the drawing. On one hand, this allows a bit of adjustment to plant locations, as the landscape is never built as precisely as plans suggest. On the other hand, if the location of a tree is critical, it must be dimensioned. A tree is not a very precise object, and finding its assumed center point is difficult. Build in tolerance into the dimensioning requirements and be prepared to make field adjustments.

Conflicts with Other Objects

Planting plans must resolve conflicts with other objects that compete for space in the landscape. The same plan that includes the root package sizes must indicate utilities, foundations, vaults, and other objects near the trees. Unfortunately, other design team members are not drawing all their requirements to scale, and utility plans are often strictly diagrammatic. Electric lines, wire splice boxes, irrigation lines, and valve boxes are not likely to show on the drawings in the correct locations or even at the correct sizes. Constant vigilance and field adjustment are requirements for success. Plans and specifications must repeatedly require coordination with other trades working on the site. The tree opening is for trees!

Figure 2.9.6. Coordinate tree and conduit locations to avoid conflicts with the root package.

Plant Spacing and Canopy Competition

Designers often plant trees too close and plant too many trees for the size of the space. Ensure that the design meets the spacing requirements discussed in Part 2, Chapter Seven.

PLANTING DETAILS

Tree planting details reflect conditions that change from tree to tree and project to project. There should not be an "office standard" or "industry standard." Details must vary by region, project requirements, the nursery practices that produce the tree, and the size of the tree as purchased. The planting detail should not be the place to discuss soil improvements, except to refer to the soil plan. Trees planted in good soil may be the one exception to this recommendation, where the amount of cultivation of soil within the hole may be shown.

The following section discusses all the elements that go into the development of a good planting detail. The detail process must be changed from a single detail to multiple details that reflect different conditions and requirements. The information in this section is not intended to be copied directly into the drawings, but should guide the design of details.

Root Package Options and Planting Details

The type of root package (root ball) specified must be shown on the details to show the contractor how to treat each package. This means a different detail for each package type.

Nurseries use different techniques to grow and package tree roots for shipping. The term "package" is being suggested as the preferred term in some areas of the industry to describe all the various systems used to grow and protect the roots of the

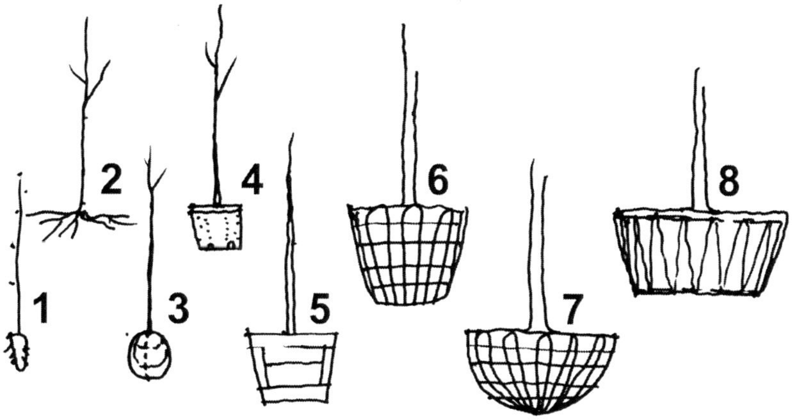

Figure 2.9.7. Typical root packages.

1. Reforestation liner.
2. Bare root.
3. Grow bag.
4. Container.
5. Boxed.
6. Tapered spade-dug with burlapped wire basket.
7. Concave spade-dug with burlapped wire basket.
8. Hand-dug, drum-laced, balled, and burlapped.

tree during shipping. While "package" may sound too industrial for an agricultural business, it reflects the transition of nurseries from a family farming activity to a commercial, industrial operation. Root packaging varies regionally, although with national distribution of nursery material, almost all types of root packages are likely to show up in any section of the country.

Nursery production methods change the root system of the tree in dramatic ways. Assumptions about roots based on trees grown from seed and in nature are not good starting points when discussing roots of nursery-produced trees. Nursery-grown tree roots are likely to be deeper in the package, may not have a definable trunk flare, may be more fibrous, and have more circling and girdling roots. Often the plant top is grafted or budded onto the roots. The roots and top may even be a different species.

Root package sizes are supposed to be proportional to the tree size and type. Use the American Standard for Nursery Stock ANSI Z60.1, published by the American Nursery & Landscape Association, for standards. Note that these standards only discuss ball size, grading, and measuring systems. Plant and root quality are not generally discussed. The designer must specify plant quality for each project.

a

b

Figure 2.9.8. Remove all constricting elements from the trunk.

a. Burlap wrapped around the trunk should be removed.

b. This synthetic twine, left on the root package, will kill the tree just about the time it is beginning to mature.

Balled and Burlapped

Balled and burlapped (B&B) trees remain the most common root package. This is one of the better ways to harvest and ship trees. B&B trees recover quickly from transplant, with minimum root problems, if propagated and dug correctly. The burlap does slightly delay the movement of roots into the soil. B&B trees may be either hand- or mechanically dug. They may be in a wire basket or the burlap secured around the earth ball with jute twine called drum lacing.

Digging and moving large balls of earth has obvious environmental costs. A large amount of energy is used to dig, lift, ship, and install. Soil is moved from farm sites and field soil becomes exhausted.

Burlap must be biodegradable. Synthetic burlap or natural burlap that has been treated to resist rot is used on trees with great regularity. Reject trees with these materials, or remove all non-biodegradable material from the ball. Removing the burlap will weaken the ball, and staking may then be required. Twine or string holding the ball together should also be a natural and biodegradable material. It is more common for this to be synthetic twine. It is critical to remove the twine from around the trunk and to cut any synthetic twine that crosses over the top of the root package. Synthetic and non-biodegradable burlap materials must be removed because they will girdle the trunk and roots as the tree grows.

Synthetic material melts rather than burns. Individual fibers have a high luster and reflect more light than natural fibers. These are good field tests to determine which type of material has been use. Treated natural burlap is sometimes green in color, but this must not be confused with algae growth on the burlap.

Even if the burlap and twine are biodegradable, it is still important to remove the material wrapped around the trunk. Thick layers of burlap and twine can damage the trunk base by holding water against the bark. In dryer climates, the twine may not rot fast enough to avoid

Figure 2.9.9. Concave spade-dug trees in wire baskets.

Figure 2.9.10. Large, hand-dug, drum-laced root package with flat side for shipping.

trunk girdling. This may be done at planting or after the first growing season as part of the final inspection. Trees where twine has been cut at planting may require staking if there is concern about the structural integrity of the root package.

Most B&B trees are machine-dug. When a tree is dug with a tree spade at the nursery, it will have a deeper root package than a hand-dug ball. The American Standard for Nursery Stock ball depth standards are for hand-dug balls, but few trees are actually hand-dug due to labor costs. Newer concave tree spades dig a shallower ball. If there is a shallow building foundation or other structure under the tree, specifying the root package depth may be important.

Large, hand-dug B&B trees are often dug with one side flat so the ball is stable on the shipping trailer. The flat side can be specified on a particular side of the tree to allow a large tree to be placed closer to an obstruction.

Most B&B trees are placed inside a wire basket. The wires can harm the roots and trunk flare of the tree where the top wires protrude above or near the top of the root packages.

The planting detail should indicate that the top 12 inches of the wire basket must be cut vertically and folded down into the soil. Complete removal of the basket is not needed. Show the wire basket on the tree planting detail and how it is to be cut away. A new type of basket that stops short of the top of the root package, called a low-rise basket, can be installed without

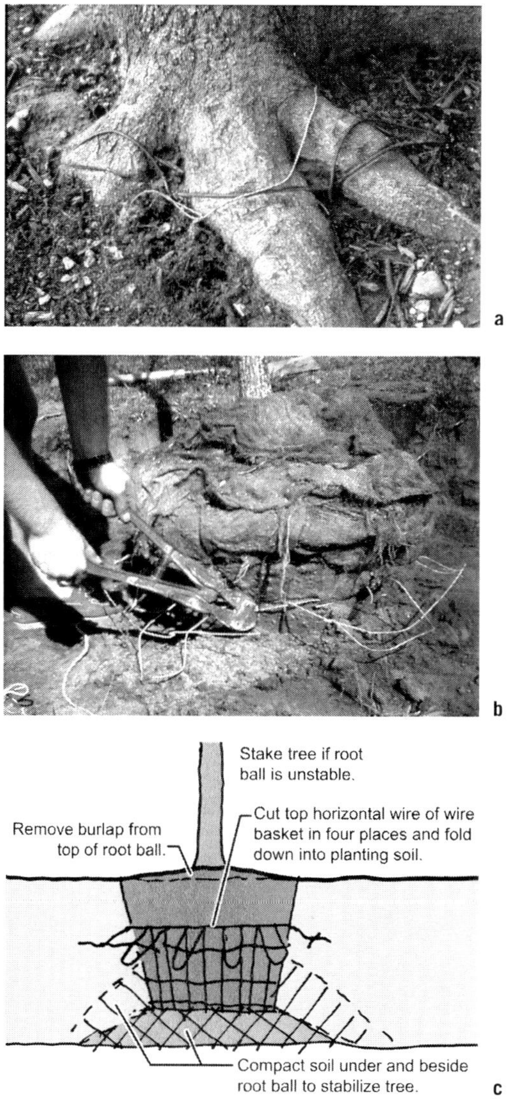

Figure 2.9.11. Wire basket damage.
a. Wire baskets left on the surface can damage future buttress roots.
b. Cut and fold down the top ring of the basket at time of planting.
c. Planting detail for B&B tree with a wire basket.

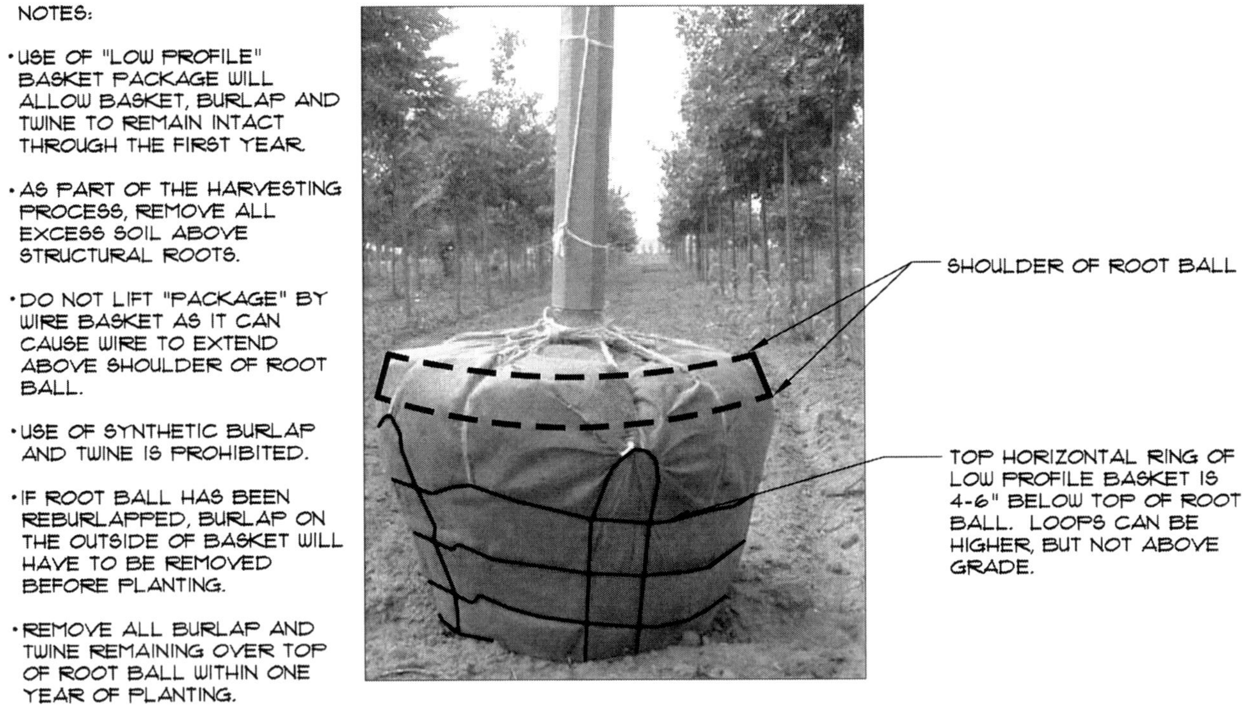
NOTES:
•USE OF "LOW PROFILE" BASKET PACKAGE WILL ALLOW BASKET, BURLAP AND TWINE TO REMAIN INTACT THROUGH THE FIRST YEAR.
•AS PART OF THE HARVESTING PROCESS, REMOVE ALL EXCESS SOIL ABOVE STRUCTURAL ROOTS.
•DO NOT LIFT "PACKAGE" BY WIRE BASKET AS IT CAN CAUSE WIRE TO EXTEND ABOVE SHOULDER OF ROOT BALL.
•USE OF SYNTHETIC BURLAP AND TWINE IS PROHIBITED.
•IF ROOT BALL HAS BEEN REBURLAPPED, BURLAP ON THE OUTSIDE OF BASKET WILL HAVE TO BE REMOVED BEFORE PLANTING.
•REMOVE ALL BURLAP AND TWINE REMAINING OVER TOP OF ROOT BALL WITHIN ONE YEAR OF PLANTING.
SHOULDER OF ROOT BALL
TOP HORIZONTAL RING OF LOW PROFILE BASKET IS 4-6" BELOW TOP OF ROOT BALL. LOOPS CAN BE HIGHER, BUT NOT ABOVE GRADE.

Figure 2.9.12. Tapered spade-dug root package in low-rise basket to reduce damage to buttress roots. Low-rise basket does not need to be cut down. *(Source: Illinois Tree Specification Review Committee)*

removing the top wires. Additional information on root package and tree planting details may be found at the Illinois Nurserymen's Association Web site, www.ina-online.org.

B&B trees are subject to many of the root and canopy problems found in other types of root packages. They are often harvested too deeply and have poorly pruned canopy structure. B&B trees may also have been grown in a container and have the same girdling root discussed in container plants. Read further in this chapter to understand these problems and solutions.

Pre-Dug Balled-and-Burlapped Trees

Trees are best dug when dormant. To plant out of the normal digging season for B&B trees, nurseries will often dig hard-to-transplant trees during the spring, before bud break, and hold them until later in the summer. Consult with local nurseries for lists of hard-to-transplant species.

If the trees are well watered and cared for, pre-digging is an acceptable practice and is preferable to digging in full leaf. Often, the burlap may start to rot if the tree is held too long, or these trees may have been wrapped in synthetic burlap. In the case of the rotting burlap, the tree is often rewrapped for shipping over the wire basket. In this case, the outer burlap, whether natural or synthetic, should be removed. The wire basket, if covering the top portion of the root package, must also be removed to a depth of 12 inches.

Some growers are shrink-wrapping balls of trees that must be held. This is a good system, but the plastic sheeting must be removed prior to planting. (Green side up? Duh? Yes, trees have been planted with the plastic covering intact!)

For very large, long lead time projects and where budget allows special handling, large trees can be prepurchased and boxed. This practice reduces the transplant shock, permits the trees to be held for extended periods, and allows the trees to be planted at almost any time during the year. Trees boxed in this manner need a minimum of two growing seasons to fully recover from the initial boxing.

a b

Figure 2.9.13. Trees to be planted out of season.

a. Trees dug before budbreak the previous spring and held in the nursery. Shrink-wrapping the root balls allows extended storage time.
b. Boxed trees being held for several years to increase planting season and extend holding time.

Processed and Containerized Root Packages

Trees may be field-grown and dug bare-root. The grower then packages the tree with soil formed around the roots to make the tree look like a B&B or container tree. B&B trees are called "processed root balls." Trees placed in containers are called "containerized" trees. Be cautious when purchasing this type of root package. Trees loosen in their balls, and some trees may have poorly developed root systems. It is best to simply prohibit processed or containerized root packages in the specifications.

Container Trees

Trees grown in containers are rapidly becoming the primary root package offered by growers, especially for small-caliper trees. This practice is particularly dominant in the southern and western parts of the United States. Typically, the tree is grown in a bark potting medium. Circling roots, kinked roots, and roots too deep in the container are common problems with container plants. Circling roots are the result of leaving the trees in the container too long. Deep roots are the result of production processes.

Figure 2.9.14. Container trees are becoming the dominant root package for smaller trees.

Technical problems with container plants often do not manifest themselves during the guarantee period. Girdling roots and roots too deep in soil start a process that may take 10 or more years to kill the tree. This leaves the tree owner with an expensive problem to solve and time lost to grow a large tree.

Container sizes and nomenclature are not standardized. The American Standard for Nursery Stock ANSI Z60.1 has a table that establishes standard sizes. These standards permit very large ranges of volume within each class size. Note that container class sizes are named by number, not volume size. For example, a number 5 container may range from 3.4 to 5.4 gallons. Specifying a 5-gallon container has no standard meaning in the industry. Check the most current version of ANSI Z60 as the organization is working to further standardize container sizes.

There are many different container types and sizes. The traditional container is plastic, with drain holes in the bottom, or a wood box. There may be vertical ribs to try to reduce circling roots. To reduce root problems, containers may have various holes, slits, and/or angles, be made from wire frame/filter cloth, or be coated in copper paint. Containers can also air-prune some of the roots. The containers that use air pruning by exposing the edge of the container to an airflow appear best at reducing the incidence of circling roots; however, any tree left in any container long enough will have circling roots. Even in an air-pruning container, circling roots may appear in a single year.

A more sinister problem with containers is that trees are normally repotted into ever-larger planters as they grow. With each transplant, a new set of girdling roots is likely to be created. The circling roots on the last pot can be cut away, but the interior set of roots cannot easily be removed without causing severe damage to the tree.

The constant repotting also may produce vertically layered rooting systems. The root system from the smaller container is placed in the larger container on top of a base of potting mix and additional potting mix is added over the top of the original root system to fill the container. Depending on the watering system, few roots grow into the lower level, while dense roots grow around the trunk in the upper zone. Both the loose potting mix at the bottom and the new roots on top of the original rooting system must be removed before planting to reduce settling and the tree being planted too deeply. This aggressive action may kill the tree, but better to die during the guarantee period than after the tree struggles for ten years.

The soilless growing medium or substrate used in the containers becomes a problem when planted. The low water-holding qualities of the bark mix tend to form an interface against the adjacent soil. Water and roots do not move across the interface easily, and roots often stay within the container root package. The root package may dry out or become waterlogged, depending on adjacent soil conditions. Dead plants are often removed with no roots that emerged from the root package.

Solving each of the these problems adds to the difficulty and cost of using container trees. It is currently impractical to think that any but the best contractors will take time to perform the labor-intensive process described in Figure 2.9.17 to fix the container tree. The interior circling roots may not be a condition that can be fixed, and girdling roots will eventually kill the tree.

These problems are so threatening to the future of the tree that I have stopped using container trees until the nursery industry can implement solutions. Other designers and tree specifiers should consider the same position. The solution

must be industry-wide. Propagators, growers, contractors, designers, and arborists are currently working together to find useful solutions. It may be too late for the millions of trees already in the production line.

Shrubs are less bothered by girdling roots but the problem with roots too deep and the soil-to-root-package interface persists. Container shrub use may be acceptable provided the potting medium is removed and the roots pulled out into the soil.

Florida Has It Right

Florida has statewide tree grading requirements. This system states that a "Tree is a cull if it has a root greater than 1/10 the diameter of the trunk circling around more than 1/3 of the trunk in the top half of the root ball." By this standard, which unfortunately is rarely enforced, most container trees are culls, particularly when the interior girdling roots are examined. Never look at just the roots on outside of the container, inspect the interior parts of the container.

Figure 2.9.15. Circling roots in container tree root packages.

a. Typical circling roots. These roots should be pulled out of the root package.
b. Air pruning style containers produce circling roots in less than one growing season.
c. Typical three-layered root system.
   1. Upper rooting to be removed to eliminate circling roots and obtain proper planting depth.
   2. Middle original rooting system, to be retained.
   3. Lower potting mix with few roots. Remove this soil before planting.
d. Telltale roots stopping at the limit of an old container diameter. A surveyor's pin is used to detect root locations (dashed line).
e. Container root package cut in half to reveal many circling roots at the position of a previous container (dashed line).
f. Container-grown tree with large circling roots at the edge of the container. These roots will kill this tree.

Figure 2.9.16. Traditional preparation of a container plant (left) by butterflying the root package with deep cuts in two directions. This technique does not address interior circling roots in the upper part of the root package.

Preparing Container Trees for Planting

An outright prohibition on the use of container trees is impractical for many projects, so designers must implement methods to use existing container trees. Traditional planting details for container plants indicate cutting circling roots on the outside of the root package and, in some specifications, slicing the root package deeply into the bottom of the root mass (called "butterflying the ball"). Neither of these techniques solves the interior circling root and interface problems outlined above.

To remediate the interior circling roots, potting medium interface, and too-deep roots, it may be advisable to remove as much potting medium as possible and pull the roots out into the new soil. This process, known as "bare rooting," is an aggressive approach, which may appear to endanger the tree. Practitioners who use this technique report no increase in loss over conventional methods.

Dipping the exposed root system in a hydrogel polymer may improve transplant success. Hydrogel is a potassium-based polyacrylamide substance that absorbs and holds water. It is available from many suppliers. Research into this technique is progressing.

If the tree dies normally, it will do so within the warranty period. Since plants with interior circling roots should be considered as stock to be rejected, the plant warranty should be enforceable. Note that almost all container trees have these problems. Work out this issue in advance with the contractor. If the contractor refuses to honor the warranty because of techniques to eliminate circling roots, plant rejection is the only alternative. Get agreements in writing.

Once the roots have been severely cut to reduce circling roots, trees will initially fade from lack of water uptake, but then recover as roots break out into the soil. Spot-watering the root package area is vital during the transplant recovery period. Use of watering bags is recommended, but do not leave them on the tree when not in use. Watering bag systems can become a perfect insect habitat. See further discussions on watering bags later in this chapter.

Spray irrigation may not provide enough water at the root package without over watering the adjacent soil. Do not depend on spray irrigation as the primary watering method.

Figure 2.9.17. Aggressive removal of soil with pulling and cutting of circling roots. Roots will be pulled out into the soil during planting.

a. Aggressive bare-root technique (left) compared to a butterflied root package (right).

b. Tree with all potting soil removed. The large root on the left side of the tree that is a remnant circling root must be either removed or directed into the soil away from the tree.

c. Small fork used to remove potting mix from the root-bound plant. Air knife or water can also be used to remove the soil.

d. Polymer gel to be applied to the wet root system.

e. Washing soil from roots to inspect root system and plant bare-root. *(Photo: Bonnie Appleton)*

f. Soak container trees in water to make washing the roots easier *(Photo: Bonnie Appleton)*

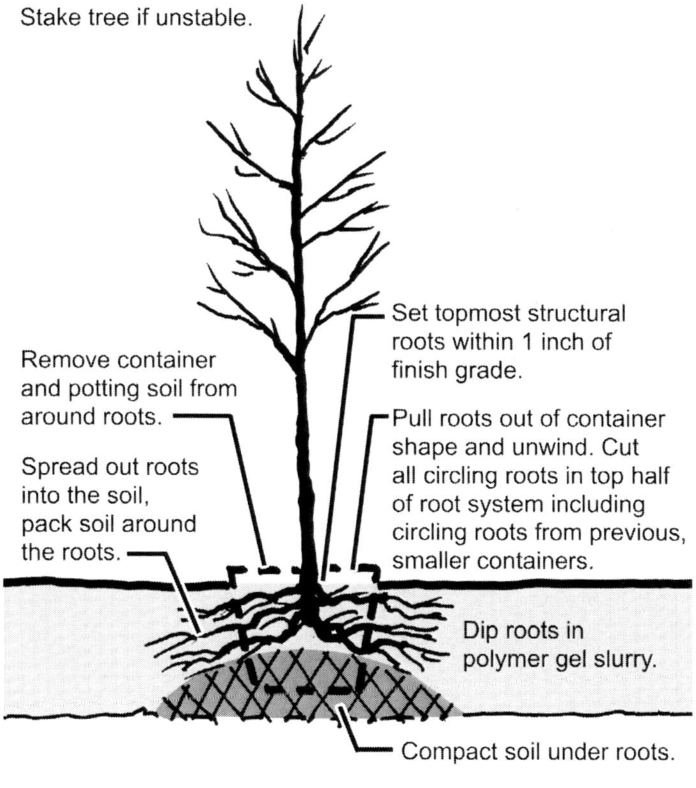
Stake tree if unstable.
Remove container and potting soil from around roots.
Spread out roots into the soil, pack soil around the roots.
Set topmost structural roots within 1 inch of finish grade.
Pull roots out of container shape and unwind. Cut all circling roots in top half of root system including circling roots from previous, smaller containers.
Dip roots in polymer gel slurry.
Compact soil under roots.

Figure 2.9.18. Planting detail for container tree.

Figure 2.9.19. Trees blown over with grow bags still intact. Always remove the grow bag before planting.

Figure 2.9.20. Boxed trees. Plant the same as any container tree.

Grow Bags

Grow bags are a type of in-ground container. Small roots grow through the bag, made of filter cloth, into the soil. Roots growing through the cloth are girdled, forcing more root development inside the bag.

The bag must be removed before planting. Figure 2.9.19 shows trees in Florida planted with the grow bags intact.

There is a limit to how long the plant can remain in the bag without harvesting or replanting into a larger bag. Circling roots will develop if the tree is kept in the bag too long. Trees in grow bags may have been started in a smaller container and likely share the internal girdling root problem mentioned in the discussion of container trees. For some hard-to-transplant species, grow bags may be a good way to improve transplant success. The planting detail for trees shipped with grow bags should be similar to that for a container tree.

Boxed Trees

Boxed trees are grown in square containers made of wood or plastic. They are primarily found in western nurseries and are specified by box size. The box is removed after the tree is in its proper position. The bottom of the box may be left in place for larger trees. As with any container, once the box is removed, the root package needs to be checked for circling roots and main roots too deep or circling in the interior of the container. The planting detail for boxed trees should be similar to that for a container tree including removing the box, pulling the roots out of the container, and cutting interior circling roots.

Bare-Root Trees

Bare-root trees can be transplanted quite successfully. They are ecologically preferable to all other forms of root packages, since no soil is removed from the nursery and energy consumption to dig, transport, and plant the tree is reduced. Bare-root trees are less expensive and have more roots intact. The roots can be inspected for quality and planted at the correct depth, and girdling roots can be removed. Bare-root trees may need to be staked, although small trees have been planted without staking.

Recent improvements in bare-root planting techniques, developed at Cornell University, increase the success rate of bare-root plantings, broaden the number of species that can be transplanted, and increase the size of tree that can be moved. Dipping the roots into a slurry of water and hydrogel holds moisture in the roots. Storing the roots in individual plastic bags after dipping in the hydrogel slurry helps reduce loss, as does storing and shipping in enclosed containers. Refrigerated shipping and storage facilities are needed.

A good description of bare-root transplanting is found in *Trees in the Urban Landscape*, which should be consulted when specifying bare-root planting.

Bare-root transplants deserve wider adoption in the industry. Historically, this was the preferred method of moving trees. Air knives and hydrogels have allowed large trees over 15 inches dbh to be moved bare-root.

It is generally thought that bare-root plants must be moved only when dormant, but research is demonstrating ways to extend the size and type of tree suitable and expand the planting season to allow planting while the trees are in full leaf.

If bare-root plantings are specified, discuss the project with potential nurseries. Not all nurseries will dig bare-root. Nurseries with heavier soils may experience difficulty digging. The different system disrupts their production, and they may not feel there is sufficient profit to make the trees available. Proper cool storage must be available. Each of these complications reduces the number of nurseries willing to supply bare-root trees. There may not be substantial cost savings until the industry adapts to wider use of bare-root techniques. For the near term,

a

b

Figure 2.9.21. Bare-root trees were historically the preferred method to transplant.

a. The Minneapolis Parks Board planting trees 100 years ago. *(Photo courtesy Minneapolis Park and Recreation archives)*

b. Bare-root liners in cold storage. *(Photo: Bernie Jacobs)*

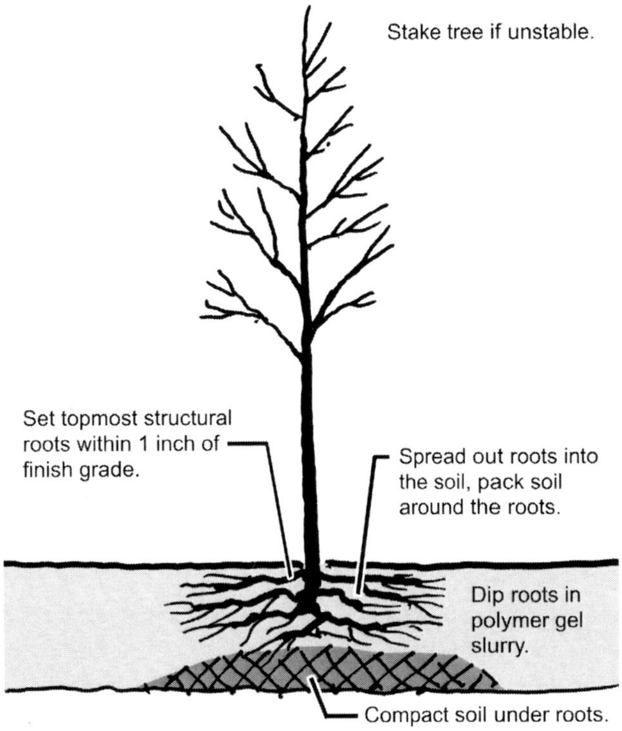
Stake tree if unstable.
Set topmost structural roots within 1 inch of finish grade.
Spread out roots into the soil, pack soil around the roots.
Dip roots in polymer gel slurry.
Compact soil under roots.

Figure 2.9.22. Planting detail, bare-root trees.

each project must identify the supplying nursery in advance. In many markets, this restriction may make it more difficult to conduct competitive bidding on plant sources due to the limited number of nurseries willing to participate.

Reforestation Liners

Liners are a specialized type of bare-root planting used to plant large areas of land. These trees often receive limited or no supplemental water, although spot watering even a few times during the first summer significantly improves survival. Survival is dependent on soil conditions and weather. First-year loss rates of 25 percent or greater are common, and sites are generally over planted to compensate for the loss.

Small 12- to 24-inch high trees are planted. Trees are specified as first-year or second-year plants, referring to the time since the tree was propagated. Hydrogel dips and storing the trees in cool, moist locations before planting are important. Reforestation plants are often moved when dormant. The roots must be placed in the ground such that they extend out from the plant and do not get kinked or turned into a "J" as they are placed into the hole. Liners will need protection from weed competition and animal damage.

Tree shelters are effective to reduce deer and rodent loss and improve initial growth rates. Chemical weed control or mulch around each tree will reduce competition and improve survival. When preparing a specification for reforestation, consult a firm that specializes in reforestation planting.

a b

Figure 2.9.23. Reforestation liners.
a. Reforestation liners in tree shelters to protect the young tree. *(Photo: Jeremy Barrell)*
b. Liners used at a school planting project, five years after planting.

Tree-Spade-Dug and Planted Trees

Trees are transplanted directly from their growing location to the final planting site by the tree spade. This is most often used for transplanting large existing trees, but transplanting from the nursery directly to the final planting site also is a practical application. The spade first goes to the planting site and digs the hole. Then the tree is dug, and the truck returns to the planting site with the tree. If the tree spade is properly sized for the tree, the tree is moved with the least harm to the roots and normally with a very large root mass. Trees of many species can often be moved in full leaf.

The tree spade must be sized to the tree size and species. Location and season of planting are factors in determining the size spade to be used. A tree spade can be quite large. Truck weight and turning requirements, slope, soil conditions, and underground or above-ground utility lines will limit the trees that can be moved with this equipment. Tree spades often create significant damage to soil and paving while moving in and out of the site. Underground utilities must be located at both ends of the operation, as the spade cuts through anything in its path. The longer the distance from the tree's initial location to its final destination, the greater the cost. Always consult with a firm with experience in moving large trees to understand the requirements and limitations.

The spade may leave large air pockets between the soil and the root package particularly near the ground line. These voids must be filled with loose soil or a soil slurry. In fine-grained soil, the spade makes a glazed soil interface between the root package and the soil. Loosening the soil at the top foot of depth around the joint between the ball and the soil will help water and roots to move across this interface. Spot watering the root package for several seasons is critical to success.

Like other methods that move trees with the earth intact, use of tree spades is not environmentally friendly. The equipment consumes large amounts of energy and damages farm soil. Sustainable designers are better off to plant smaller-caliper trees, bare-root if possible.

a

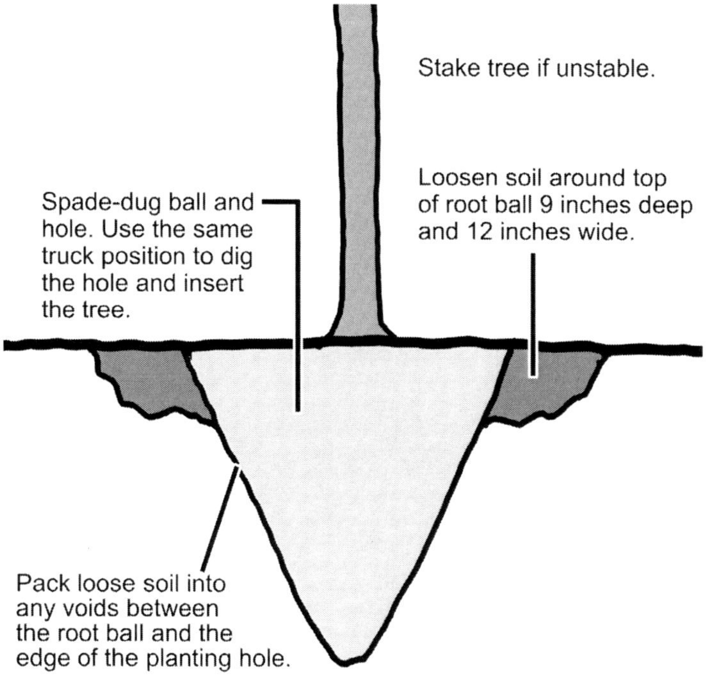
Stake tree if unstable.
Loosen soil around top of root ball 9 inches deep and 12 inches wide.
Spade-dug ball and hole. Use the same truck position to dig the hole and insert the tree.
Pack loose soil into any voids between the root ball and the edge of the planting hole.

b

Figure 2.9.24. Trees transported by tree spades.

a. 90-inch tree spade requires significant space to maneuver. *(Photo courtesy Ace Tree Movers Inc.)*

b. Planting detail: Spade-moved trees.

a

b

Figure 2.9.25. Exceptionally large trees.

a. Pipe system under root package to lift the tree. Note the large amount of space required around the tree for operation. *(Photo courtesy Ace Tree Movers Inc.)*

b. Exceptionally large trees can be successfully moved, at great expense, such as this tree in Holland.

Moving Exceptionally Large Trees

It is possible to move exceptionally large trees with reasonable success. Trees up to 30 inches in trunk diameter or larger are regularly transplanted. Five factors appear to limit success:

- Moving large trees is expensive, and adequate budgets and maintenance budgets must be provided.
- There needs to be sufficient area to maneuver large equipment and excavate large volumes of soil.
- There must be adequate time, more than a year, to prep the tree, and it must be moved in the most advantageous season of the year.
- The tree species and soil type must be appropriate for the operation.
- Follow-up care will be necessary for many years after transplanting, including water monitoring in the soil, canopy misting, and other mitigation techniques.

Most trees are moved with large sections of earth supported on pipe beds driven under the soil. Large trees have been moved bare-root after being dug by an air knife, a tool that blows the soil away from the roots with little damage to the root structure. These trees are easier to handle with smaller equipment, and trees in close proximity to buildings or other tight spaces can still be moved.

Moving exceptionally large trees is a specialized operation, and explaining the details to move them is beyond the scope of this book. Each tree situation is unique. Consult a firm specializing in this work.

TREES HARVESTED TOO DEEP

Many trees are harvested with roots too deep below the top of the root package. This condition is the result of nursery practices that may start during propagation and continuing to harvest. Roots too deep can be found in all types of root packages including field grown trees.

The grower may plant the tree deeply to ensure that it remains upright in the row. Some trees are planted too deeply to conceal irregularities at the base of the trunk.

If the tree was grafted or budded, a crook in the trunk will often develop just below the graft or bud point. Trees on their own roots are often allowed to grow for a season to establish roots and then cut off at ground level. The resulting sprout grows faster and is easier to train as a straight trunk. This technique also produces a crook at the base of the tree. Though these kinks will disappear as the tree grows, the grower may think that the tree will be more salable if the crook is below the soil line, causing the main roots to be too deep.

a

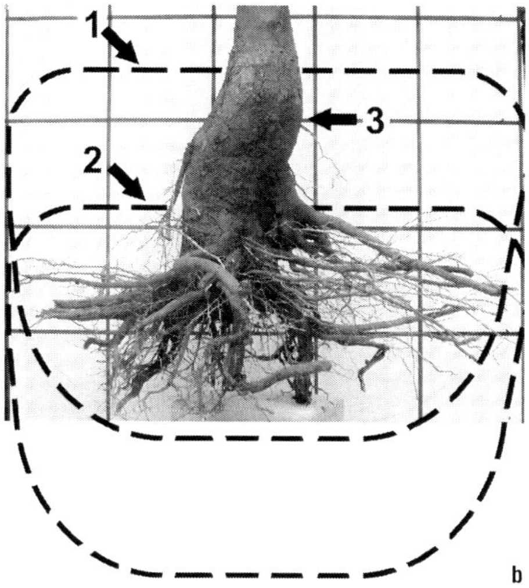

b

c

d

Figure 2.9.26 Trees harvested with roots too deep.

a. Too much soil over the roots.
   1. 6 inches of soil.
   2. Main roots.
   3. Adventitious root growing in soft soil above the main roots. This root may become a girdling root.
b. Roots too deep to conceal graft crook in trunk.
   1. Root package as harvested.
   2. Root package as it should have been harvested. Note large amounts of roots lost at the bottom.
   3. Graft. Designers must look for the graft and be willing to purchase trees with this slight bend.
c. Extreme example of roots harvested too deep. This tree survived after removal of more than a foot of soil from the root package.
   1. Level of soil in root package when delivered.
   2. First main root emerging from the trunk.
d. Tree with roots harvested too deep. Trunk growth limited by girdling roots. This tree simply fell over.

As the trees are maintained in the nursery, cultivation machines may pile soil on top of the roots, burying them deeper in the soil. Trees that are machine-dug may have extra soil pushed up on top of the root package from the pressure of the cutting blades.

Whatever the reason for soil accumulation over the main root system, it must be removed before the tree is harvested. When the main roots are found deep in the root package, significant lengths of trunk are buried in the soil. Harvesting a tree too deeply means that the purchaser is buying dirt without roots at the top of the ball and leaving roots in the nursery that were cut during harvest. These trees may be unstable and require staking, suffer from additional transplant shock, or develop bark rot. Girdling roots may develop in the soil above the main roots. Each of these conditions results in additional stress on the tree, contributing to poor establishment and long-term decline.

Too-deep harvesting and planting has been the direct cause of death in many trees. In other cases, the extra soil over the roots was the beginning of a process that resulted in the loss of the tree from secondary causes.

Removing the soil before the tree is harvested results in a root package where the maximum roots are shipped in the root package. These trees will recover faster from the transplant.

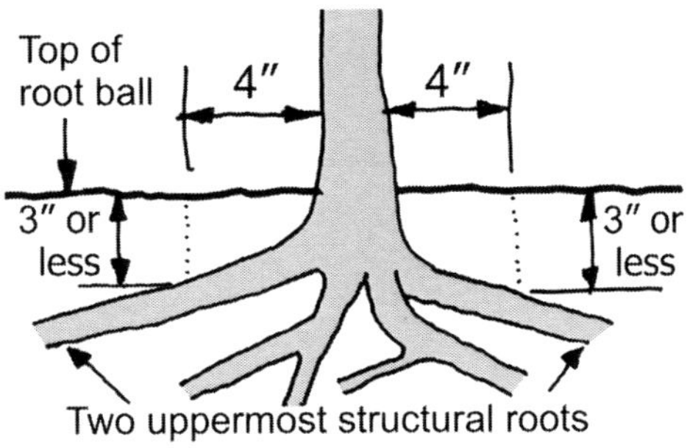

Figure 2.9.27. ANLA standard for root depth in the root package.

A Standard for Depth of Roots

A joint committee of the American Nursery and Landscape Association (ANLA), International Society of Arboriculture (ISA) and the American Society of Landscape Architects (ASLA), have developed a new standard for harvesting trees. This standard, adopted in 2005, states that a minimum of two main roots must be within three inches of the root package soil line as measured four inches from the trunk. This standard has been published by ANLA as a Best Management Practice bulletin titled "Avoiding Excessive Soil Over the Root System of Trees" and is available from ANLA.

PROPAGATION, LINERS, AND OTHER NURSERY PRACTICES

While a limited number of trees are produced from seed, all named cultivars are produced by various asexual reproduction techniques. These include:

- **Budding:** a bud from the tree to be cloned is inserted under the bark of the tree that is to be the root stock. Once the bud begins to grow, the top of the root-stock tree above the bud is cut off. A crook in the trunk should be visible just above the soil line.
- **Grafting:** a stem of the tree to be cloned is inserted into the top of the stem of the root stock. Graft line should be visible just above the soil line
- **Rooted cuttings:** stems of the tree to be cloned are treated with root hormones and inserted in rooting beds where roots begin to form directly from the stem.
- **Tissue culture:** tiny bits of tissue from the tree to be cloned are grown under controlled conditions to form a new tree.

Trees grown from seed, rooted cuttings, or tissue culture are often referred to as being "on their own roots," while grafted or budded trees have a totally different tree, even a different species, for the roots. Grafted trees sometimes reject the graft if the wrong root stock is used. This can happen many years after transplanting.

Liner Production

Most trees are propagated in large specialty nurseries and sold to wholesale growing nurseries as a liner. Some liners are produced in containers, while others are produced in field soil and harvested bare-root. Young trees are transplanted many times as they move through the propagation process. Each time the tree is transplanted, it should be root pruned.

J-Rooting

If the tree is machine-planted, the liner roots will often be swept back along the furrow as the machine moves through the field, causing the roots to grow only in one direction. The softer soil within the furrow will tend to cause the initial set of roots to stay within the furrow. This will result in a root package with the roots unevenly distributed. Some portions of the root package will not have roots.

Figure 2.9.28. Propagation.

a. Budded tree after the stem of the root stock was cut away. This crook in the trunk will eventually straighten out. Designers should select grafted and budded trees with the union above the soil line.

b. Grafted tree. It is common for the root stock and first part of trunk to grow faster than the grafted portion above. The graft is normally lower on the stem.

c. Tree rejecting its graft. The top portion grows reaction wood over the root stock.

d. Oak trees propagated from seed. Seed-produced trees tend to have a well-developed trunk flare.

e. Tree that snapped at the rejected graft site.

Figure 2.9.29. J-rooted trees have one-sided root systems.

a. J-rooting can be detected with a metal pin.

b. Roots swept back in the furrow.

Wholesale Nursery Production

From the liner stage, the tree is moved into a production field where it is planted on wider spacing. Planting may be by hand or by a mechanical tree planter. Small trees, 2 to 3 inches in diameter, may go directly from this field to the point of sale, while larger trees may be transplanted at least one more time. Nurseries may grow the trees in field soil or in plastic, wood, or other types of containers.

INSPECTING TREES IN THE NURSERY FOR ROOT PROBLEMS

Identify root problems in the nursery before any digging takes place. Each tree should be inspected. A technique developed by Gary Johnson of the University of Minnesota uses a short pin to probe for the roots in the nursery or at the time of planting. A surveyor's chaining pin, which is about 12 inches long and 3/16 inch in diameter, is an ideal size probe. The pin has a small circular handle, is marked in 1-inch increments, and is available from forestry or surveying supply companies. Push the pin repeatedly into the ground starting next to the trunk and moving out as roots are found. Roots can be felt and differentiated from rocks. With a little practice, the main root depth and the presence of interior circling roots can be determined in about 60 seconds per tree. This technique can also be used for container trees.

Nursery production is reasonably consistent. In a large block of trees, it may only be required to randomly inspect the roots of a few trees. If consistent rooting is found in a small sampling of the trees, it is reasonable to assume that all the trees in that block are similar. However, note that the same species of tree in two different field locations may be different.

Figure 2.9.30. Nursery inspections for root problems.

a. A surveyor's chain pin is a perfect tool to probe for roots in a nursery. Note adventitious roots emerging above the tree's trunk flare. The black mark on the tree was the level of the soil before digging.
b. The pin is useful to inspect trees at all points in the purchase and planting process.
c. Marking a point on the trunk 12 inches above the trunk flare to aid in field inspection once trees are delivered.
d. Trees with roots too deep will open a slight crack at the soil line when the trunk is pushed sideways.

Other indicators of a tree being too deep in the root package are trees with no trunk flare and trees with no visible graft union. Do not be fooled into thinking that the normal swelling at the graft union is the trunk flare. Push on the trunk; if a crack appears between the bark and the soil, there is a good chance that there is soil piled on top of the main roots. Depending on how long the tree was in the nursery, small adventitious roots may be in the soil above the main roots. These should be removed.

J-rooting can be discovered with a pin to locate the upper root system. Look for most of the roots on one side in the direction of the tree rows. Often the pin can be pushed under the bottom of the trunk.

Each tree should be sealed with a numbered tag. This practice is already common in most landscape architects' offices. Root depth should be recorded on a log by tree number and given to the nursery to indicate how much soil must be removed prior to digging. Apply a small dot of white paint on the trunk 12 inches above the highest root found to aid in determining that the nursery removed the soil before digging. This dot should be put on the north side of the tree to assist in proper orientation at planting. Alternatively, for smooth-bark trees, a black Sharpie pen is suitable to mark the bark.

Visible Grafts Are Good

Removing the soil means that designers must be willing to accept a slight crook in the trunk the time of planting. This will disappear as the tree matures, leaving a straight trunk. If the crook is not visible, assume the soil over the roots is too deep. Note that trees grown from seed may have straight trunks.

Many nurseries report that designers insist on not seeing the graft and that is why they bury it. The design profession must change this paradigm and insist on seeing the graft union and surface roots at the base of the tree. This crooked base will grow to become straight as the tree grows.

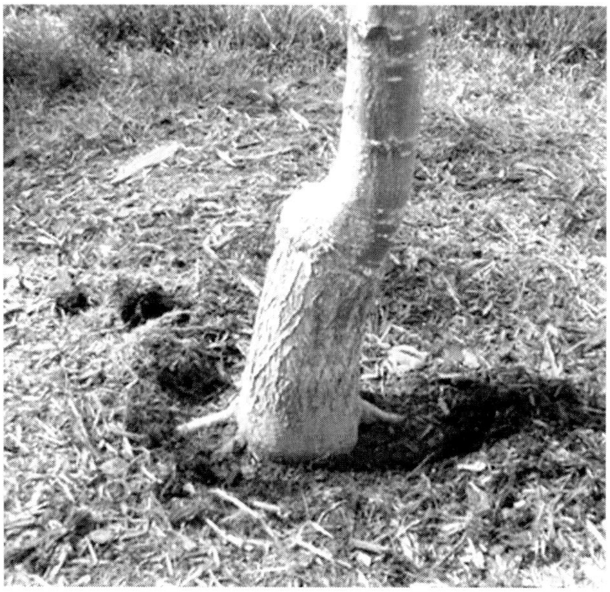

Figure 2.9.31. The graft and top set of roots should be visible in a well-grown and -dug tree.

Nursery Inspections

Root inspection increases the amount of time needed to inspect and tag an individual tree. Roots cannot be probed when the ground is frozen or very dry, reducing the time period when trees can be tagged. Root inspections require that the inspector go to the nursery, even as nursery inspections are being cut from construction administration fees.

Some nurseries will agree to remove the soil, but the trees show up on the site with the soil still on top of the root package. The quality control procedures in the nursery and landscape industry are not sufficient to control this problem and it remains the designer's responsibility to field-check all aspects of the work.

The number of available trees that do not have too-deep roots is depressingly small. Even the best nurseries have some percentage of stock too deep. It is not practical to simply specify that tress will be properly grown and harvested or to rely on quality nurseries. Modification at harvest is the only solution and achieving this will take diligence on the part of the designer and contractors. Since these problems do not manifest themselves until long after the warranty period has expired, it is not sufficient to rely on warranties to protect the property owner.

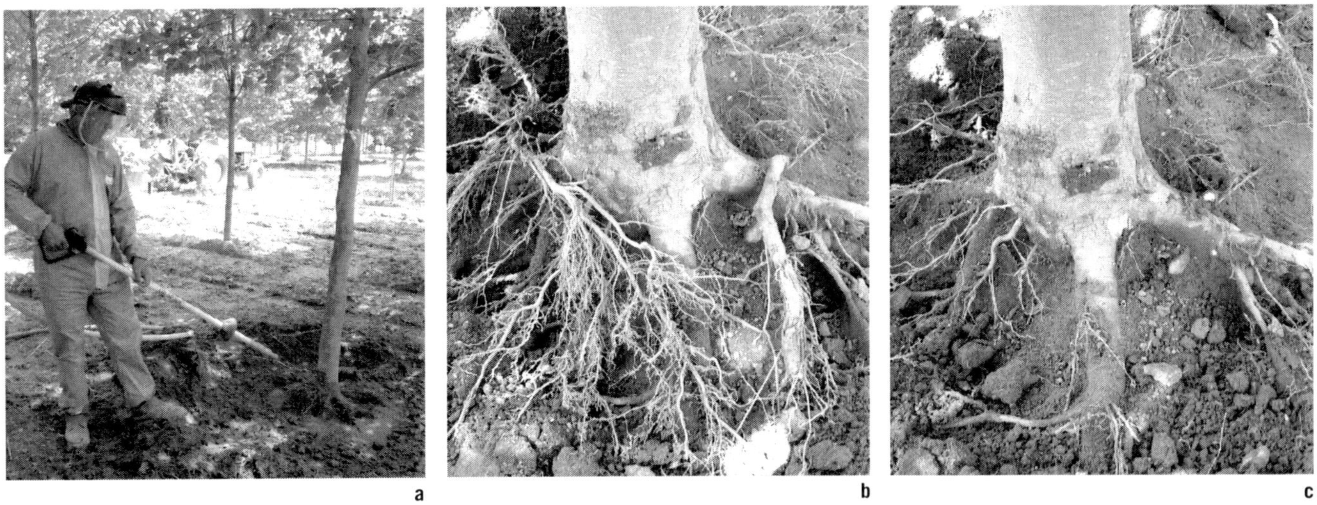
a
b
c

Figure 2.9.32. Air knife root collar inspection in the nursery.

a. Air knife removal of soil approximately 3 feet in diameter to expose the trunk flare.
b. Trunk flare and girdling roots exposed.
c. Girdling roots removed.

Air Knife Root Collar Inspection

For important trees where elimination of girdling roots is critical, the only way to ensure that the tree is harvested and planted correctly is to perform a root collar inspection in the nursery using an air knife. The root collar of each tree is exposed at the time of tagging. All adventitious and girdling roots are cut and the proper elevation of the trunk flare or main roots marked and recorded. This is a labor-intensive process but necessary if the designer wants to do proper diligence to purchase quality trees.

Correcting Root Depth Problems at Installation

If the tree is shipped with roots too deep, the designer should reject it and obtain a substitute. Often, however, there is not time to reject the tree. The following options are last resorts if you must utilize the tree. Up to 4 inches of soil may be removed from the top of the root package at the time of planting. An inch or so of soil should be left over the roots to avoid damaging the root surface. Always cut away any girdling and adventitious roots encountered.

If more than 4 inches of soil has to be removed, and the tree cannot be rejected, plant the tree with the main roots one inch below the correct planting grade. Remove the first 4 inches of soil at the time of planting, leaving the tree on a slight mound. After the first growing season, return and remove the additional soil.

The greater the amount of soil to be removed, the greater the stress on the plant. There is no agreement as to a specific soil depth after which the plant should be thrown away. It depends on the type of plant, size, and other factors. It is reasonable that trees delivered with greater than 6 inches of soil over the main roots should be rejected.

Trees where soil has been removed at planting are likely to need staking for support, along with more water to compensate for what amounts to an undersized root package. Higher loss rates should be expected. It is always simply better, but often impractical, to reject trees.

Figure 2.9.33. Planting detail for trees harvested with roots too deep.

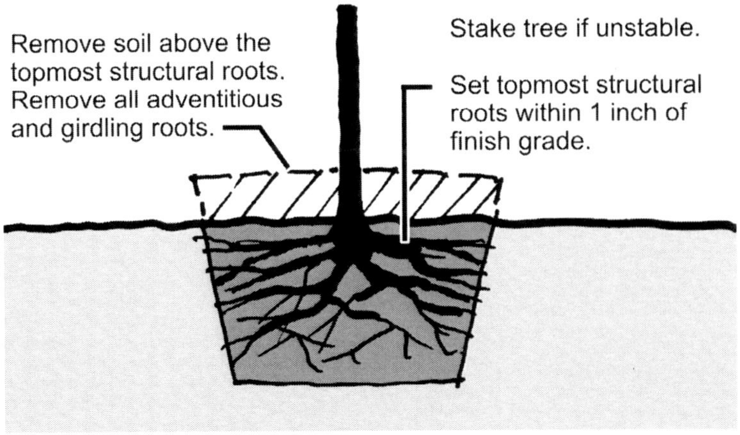
Remove soil above the topmost structural roots. Remove all adventitious and girdling roots.
Stake tree if unstable.
Set topmost structural roots within 1 inch of finish grade.

OTHER PLANTING DETAIL CONSIDERATIONS

Top of Root Package Elevation Relative to Grade

There is no standard relationship between the root package and the adjacent finished grade. Many factors including soil, type and size of trees, root package condition, climate, and adjacent grades will dictate the root-package-to-grade relationship. In well-drained loam soils, in a temperate climate and on slopes less than 10 percent, a quality root package with the roots at the surface should be set even to the adjacent grade. When this ideal set of conditions changes, the root package may need to be set a bit higher or lower.

As soil becomes less well-drained, set the root package higher, and mound the soil up around the raised ball. In heavy soil, an eighth of the ball depth out of the soil is a good standard. In extremely poor drainage conditions, rising up to half of the root package out of the ground might be appropriate, in addition to specifying a tree that will adapt to mesic (moist) conditions. The more of the root package that is out of the ground, the wider the mound of soil around the tree should be. Avoid slopes greater than 3:1 away from the tree to avoid having the root package dry out.

Trees that may be adaptable to wet locations are often grown in well-drained nursery soil and will need time to adapt to wetter conditions. Placing a nursery-grown red maple flush to grade in wet soil is likely to kill the tree, even though the species can tolerate wet sites. Seasonally wet sites are different from sites where soil water is trapped to the point where the soil becomes anaerobic. Few trees can survive in anaerobic conditions.

In extremely well-drained soil or dry climates, lowering the root package a couple of inches below the adjacent grade will help conserve water. This does not mean placing soil over the root package, but just creating a slight depression.

Drought-intolerant trees can be planted lower, while trees intolerant of wet conditions can be planted higher.

Trees planted on steeper slopes should be planted lower as the slope increases to avoid the root package sticking out of the soil on the downhill side. Making a slight depression on a slope will increase its ability to hold water near the root package.

Each variable creates a different situation, and several drawings may be needed in the planting details to cover multiple conditions. Large root packages or mounded planting sites may need to be reflected in the grading plan contour configuration. It is a lot of extra work to draw these subtle changes, but they will reveal any conflicts with grading and show the contractor exactly what to build.

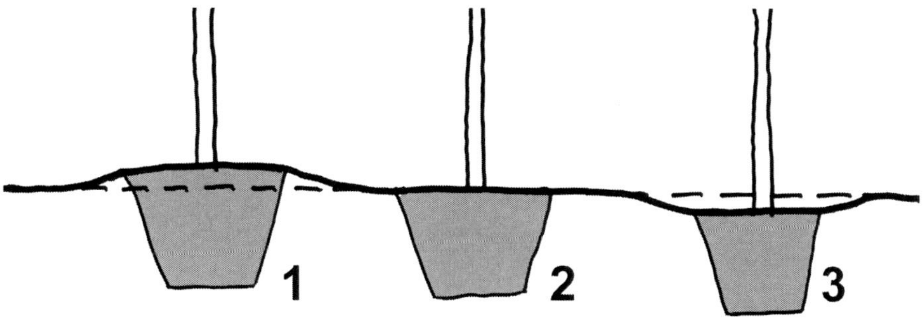

Figure 2.9.34. Top of root package relative to finished grade.

1. In slowly draining soil, plant package higher than grade 1/8 to 1/4 of the package depth.
2. In well-drained soil, plant package flush to grade.
3. In dry regions and minimum irrigation, plant package a few inches below finish grade in a slight depression.

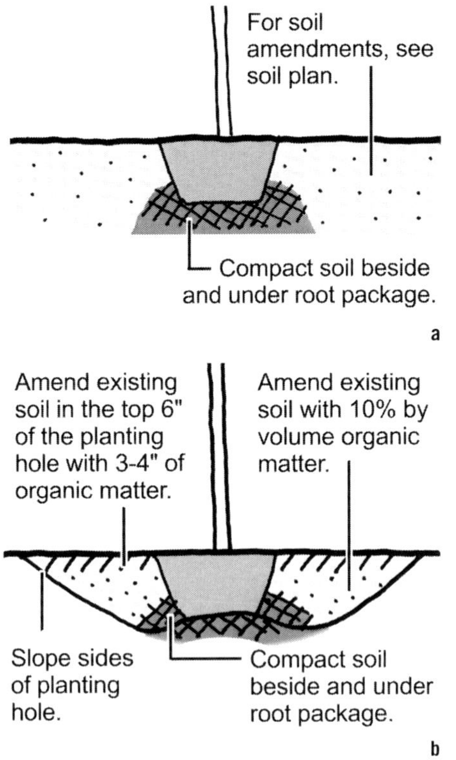

Figure 2.9.35. Soil amendments around planting hole.

a. Soil amendment notes for typical planting detail.
b. Soil amendment notes for planting detail where soil beyond the planting hole is not amended. The hole diameter is dependent on the quality of the existing soil.

Soil Compaction Around the Root Package

Soil under and around the lower portion of the root package must be compacted sufficiently to support the tree in place and keep it from settling. The soil under the root package must either not be excavated or be compacted to about 90 percent of dry density to support the ball. Around the lower half of the root package, compact the soil firmly to keep the ball from rotating or pivoting in the planting hole. The soil around the upper half of the root package should be only lightly compacted.

Soil Amendment Around the Root Package

Soil amendment should generally not be shown on the planting detail. In situations where there is to be bed wide soil improvement, the planting detail should simply refer to the soil and drainage plan for modifications to soil around the tree. The one exception to this suggestion is where the tree is to be planted in reasonably good-quality existing soil. In this case, it may be appropriate to draw the proposed soil conditions on the planting detail. A small amount of organic matter, no more than 10 percent by volume, can be added to the backfill. Three or four inches of organic matter can be tilled into the top layer of the soil. The sides of the hole should be dug with sloped sides, and the top of the hole should be a minimum of three times the ball diameter. In excellent soil, the hole diameter can be much smaller. In marginal soil conditions, the hole may need to be much larger. Please note that this detail should be used only when the soil beyond the planting hole is not being changed and is of sufficient quality to support tree rooting. The soil condition within the planting hole and beyond should both be designed to support tree rooting.

Auger Planting Holes

Planting holes dug with augers have smooth, vertical sides, and in fine-grained soils, the auger may glaze the face of the hole. As the au-

Figure 2.9.36. Auger planting holes.

a. Prohibit auger-dug planting holes.
b. Roots growing in an auger-dug hole circled around the soil cylinder.
c. Handwork required to disturb the glazing of an auger-dug hole.

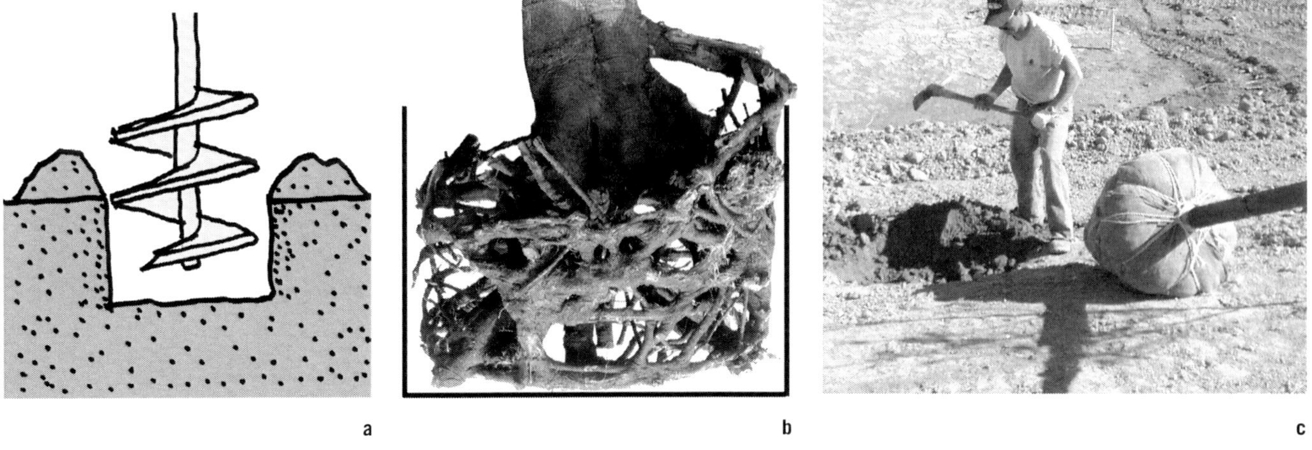

ger rotates, fine soil particles are compressed together, making an impenetrable layer completely around the edge. The smooth walls and particularly the glazed soil are quite restrictive to root penetration. Planting specifications must specifically prohibit the use of soil augers to dig planting holes unless the hole edges are disturbed using hand tools prior to planting. If a machine is required to dig the planting hole use a back hoe to dig an irregularly shaped hole.

Watering Saucers and Watering Bags

Build water retention saucers around the outside edge of the root package. The saucer should be formed from packed soil, not mulch, and be large enough to hold a minimum of 3 inches of water. On sloped ground, make the downhill side height enough to retain the required water depth and to harvest water running down the slope. The saucer is primarily needed for the first year of watering, when saturation of the root package is critical.

Tree watering bags are available to improve the effectiveness of spot watering during the first year after planting. They allow a rapid filling of the bag and slow drip into the root package. Be sure that the watering bag is removed at the end of the first growing season. The space between the bag and the tree will remain moist and become an ideal insect habitat. If the bags are needed for a second season, reinstall them once the second watering season begins.

On steep slopes, a wider dam feature built in the downhill side can harvest larger amounts of runoff and funnel them into the tree. These dams are particularly useful at sites where little watering is expected.

In poorly drained soil, where the tree is to be planted high, a saucer and/or watering bag may still be required to assist in spot watering.

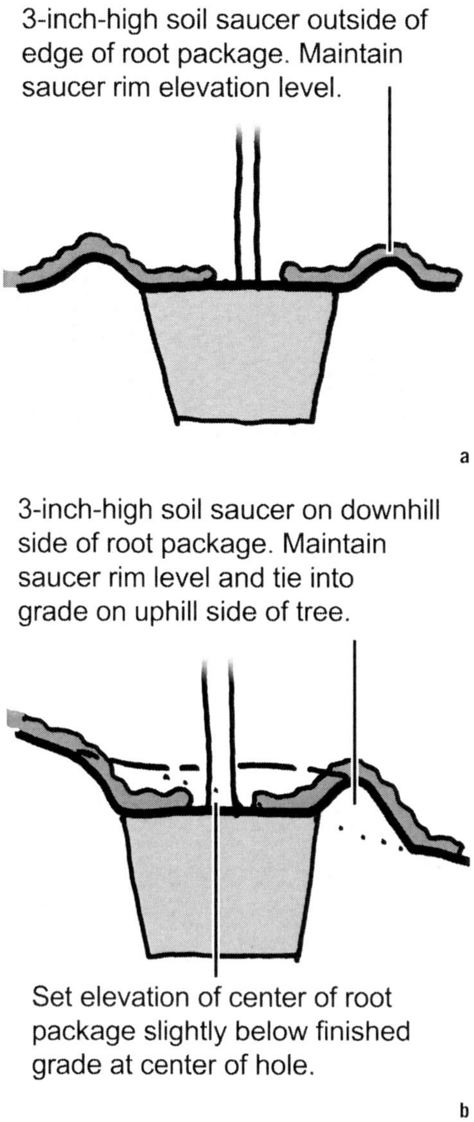
3-inch-high soil saucer outside of edge of root package. Maintain saucer rim elevation level.
a
3-inch-high soil saucer on downhill side of root package. Maintain saucer rim level and tie into grade on uphill side of tree.
Set elevation of center of root package slightly below finished grade at center of hole.
b

Figure 2.9.37. Watering saucer detail.

a. Saucer on flat areas.

b. Saucer on slopes.

Figure 2.9.38. Tree watering bags are effective ways to maintain water in the root package. *(Photo: OozeTube by Engineering Water Solutions Inc.)*

Mulch

Mulch reduces evaporation of water from the soil and provides carbon to the soil food web. During a light rain or misting irrigation cycle, mulch can actually keep water from penetrating to the root zone. Apply mulch 1 to 2 inches thick over all areas of soil, except on lawns. In lawn areas, make 6- to 8-foot-diameter circles of mulch around the tree, and keep the mulch free of plants (including ground cover) during the first two to five years. This plant-free area will significantly boost the tree's ability to recover from transplant shock. Never allow lawn within 24 inches of the trunk until the tree has matured. Lawn mowers and trimmers do significant damage to the trunk flare and surface roots.

A little mulch is great, but too much of anything will become a problem. Do not place mulch against the trunk. Educate the decision-maker that he or she should not permit the maintenance company to mound mulch against the trunk, creating the dreaded mulch "volcano." Mulch against the trunk can cause bark rot and contribute to girdling roots. Overly thick mulch can keep water from getting to the root package, particularly if spray irrigation is used to water the tree. The mulch absorbs significant amounts of water and holds it above the soil.

Almost any organic mulch or compost material will work. Composts with lower C/N ratios, such as bark mulches, are better, as they decompose more slowly. Pine bark mulches are better than hardwood mulches. In the mid-Atlantic area, hardwood mulch appears to be contributing to an elevation of manganese in the soil. Mulch that is not aged will cause a slight nitrogen drop in the upper soil level as soil biology concentrates on breaking down the material, a process that uses soil nitrogen.

Use of cypress mulch has been noted as having a significant negative impact on natural cypress forests, which are difficult to re-establish. Environmental advocates in the South are requesting that the use of cypress mulch be eliminated.

Figure 2.9.39. Mulch.

a. Properly mulched trees keep the lawn from conflicting with early root development and keep the lawnmower away from the trunk of the tree.

b. Mulch volcano. Too much mulch piled against the trunk.

a

b

Fertilizer

It is not critical to fertilize a newly planted tree, and fertilizers should only be added if the soil test shows significant deficiencies. Newly planted trees need water and loose soil free of competitive plants. If the soil carbon cycle is functional, the soil food web can provide the tree with most of the chemicals it needs. Never add chemicals to the soil without first conducting a soil test. The soil test should include a bioassay of the soil food web to determine the health of the soil biology. The lab undertaking the bioassay will supply the interpretation of the information and recommend remedial action to bring the soil biology in balance. Making slight changes to the soil's organic composition combined with using compost tea may eliminate the need for fertilizer.

Trunk Wrapping

Trunk wrapping is supposed to prevent bark frost cracks, but is not needed if the tree is properly planted and maintained. Trees with adequate water during the establishment period and that are oriented in the same solar direction as they were in the nursery rarely have frost cracks. Leaving lower branches on the trunk will also reduce trunk cracks. Note that container-grown trees do not have a defined solar orientation due to frequent movement of the plants in the production and shipping process. If the solar orientation has been lost or the trees poorly watered, wrapping may be advisable for thinner-barked trees in northern climates. A white, thin filter cloth wrap offers the best protection when wrapping is needed.

Corrugated plastic tubes or grids of plastic mesh, sold as tree shelters and designed to protect reforestation saplings, are also effective devices to protect the lower trunk from winter sun damage, small animal damage, or deer antler rubs.

Wrapping can be excellent insect habitat. Attachment straps and strings can girdle the trunk. In general, most trees are no longer wrapped and wrapping should only be allowed when special circumstances suggest that it will do more good than harm. Wrapping should only be applied for the winter and removed in the spring. Be sure to remove all tape or anything used to secure the wrapping material to the tree. Young trees can be killed by a single piece of cotton twine, electric wire or plastic tape.

a

b

Figure 2.9.40. Trunk wrapping.

a. Plastic tubes or white filter fabric wrapping are suitable trunk wraps if needed.
b. Trunk wrap does not necessarily prevent bark cracks and so-called sun scald. Too-deep planting caused this trunk crack and rot. Correct planting depth, keeping the north side of the tree in the nursery in the same direction at planting, and proper watering prevent many trunk problems.

Loose or Damaged Root Packages

These are the result of harvesting the tree with too much soil on top of the roots and/or improper handling during digging, shipping, and storage. The roots of trees in sandy soils will often be loose. Handling or shipping when the soil is saturated may contribute to slumped and distorted root packages, resulting in roots being displaced within the ball. Balls that are cracked or broken may also be loose. Compensatory provisions such as staking or additional watering may be specified for these trees.

Whether or not the tree is rejected based on these conditions needs to be a field decision; however, rejecting the tree is normally the best option. These are simply bad trees. Staking just masks issues that should not be passed on to the owner.

Staking and Bracing

Staking is usually not needed if the tree's crown and trunk are in proportion; it has a quality root package and is properly planted. The most common cause of trees not remaining plumb is poor soil compaction within, under, or around the root package. Trees out of plumb may not be "blowing over," but may actually be settling in the soil. There are some valid reasons to stake or brace trees, including:

- Trees loose in their root packages, where the ball package has been disturbed.
- Trees that need to have soil removed from the top of the ball due to being harvested with roots too deep.
- Undersized balls relative to their canopy size.
- Unusually dense or high crowns on thin, weak trunks due to being grown too closely in the nursery.
- Sandy soil or bark potting medium root packages.
- Bare-root trees.
- Trees in extremely windy or wet locations.

Specifications should call for no staking unless there is a specific reason to require additional stabilization. Details for stabilization are specific to the project location and the

a b

Figure 2.9.41. Most staking is not needed and not effective.

a. This tree is falling over due to unstable soil conditions in the tree opening. Staking would not have helped much.

b. Stake and tree failing together. Never locate the stake within the root package. The upper portion of the stake will damage the tree.

Another California Fad Moves East?

On the western edge of the United States, nursery practices are creating rather tall trees with very small trunk diameters and small root packages, the result of close spacing in the nursery and the use of container material. These trees are not able to stand straight by themselves because of their weak trunks and undersized root packages. Designers and arborists must work with growers to improve tree quality. Until then, continued staking may be the only answer. The trend toward container trees in southeastern nurseries is spreading this problem beyond California.

response should be based on the many reasons for staking. Details should be developed at the time with the contractor.

When staking or bracing, use the simplest, least restrictive method to solve the problem. Stake or brace the tree at the lowest possible position so the top of the tree can move. Movement in the tree trunk increases root growth and lower-trunk caliper growth. Trees that are rigidly braced tend to grow fewer roots, add less trunk diameter, and more top growth.

Most trees should have sufficient roots after one growing season to remove the stakes. If not, consider replacing the tree or determine why the tree has not become stable. This may be due to the tree having been harvested or planted too deep, overly wet or dry soil, use of synthetic burlap, or poor soil conditions around the planting site.

Always place the stakes outside the root package. There is a tendency in the western United States, in response to weak trunks, to drive a single stake close to the tree. These stakes often damage the trunk.

While staking can be done in non-damaging ways, the best solution is not to do it at all. Designers should work for improved nursery stock quality in order to eliminate the need for staking and bracing.

Figure 2.9.42. Damage from leaving guy attachments on too long.

a b

Figure 2.9.43. Staking.

a. Stakes rubbing on trunk. Note co-dominant leader, which is contributing to an overly dense head, which increases the tendency of the tree to fall over.
b. Set stakes outside root package limit and use webbed strapping to attach. Note loop attachment rather than a knot at the trunk. This approach allows more time before the attachment girdles the tree.

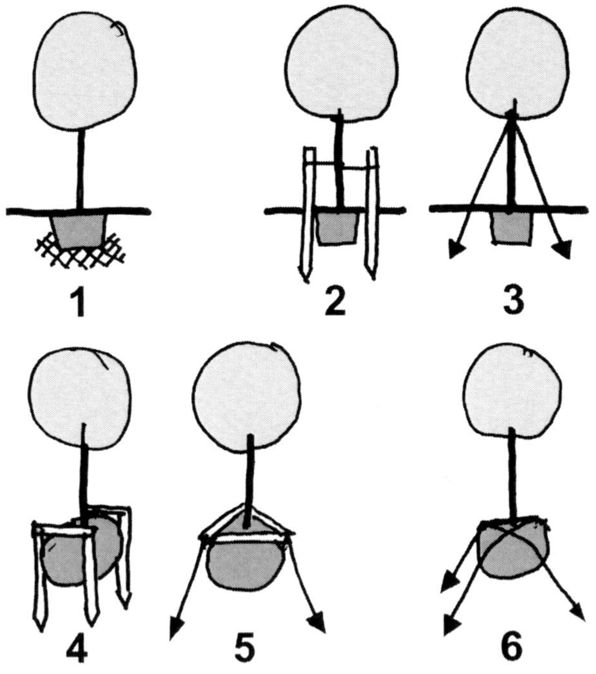

Figure 2.9.44. Tree staking options.

1. The best option is no staking. Use proper nursery and planting practices.
2. Side stakes: Stakes outside the root package, attachments as low on the trunk as possible. Use webbing tie material, not wire and hose.
3. Ground anchors generally stake the tree too high.
4. Simple wood bracket over the top of the root package. Use non-treated wood.
5. Non-treated wood frame with ground anchors. Do not connect attachment wires across the top of the root package.
6. Ground anchors with straps over the top of the root package close to the trunk. Do not use this system.

(Note that options 4 and 5 work only where the root ball is solid.)

Use of webbed straps such as Arbor Tie for guying trunks to stakes avoids the problems of wire/hose systems, which can cut the tree if the hose slips. The strapping should not be tied to the trunk, but rather attached to the stake with a figure-eight loop around the trunk.

Be sure to require the removal of all staking material before the beginning of the second growing season. Leaving stakes attached, which will girdle the tree if not removed, has damaged or killed many trees.

There are many manufactured systems for staking trees. Different systems may not eliminate all the problems that led to the need to stake. If trees are being staked or braced because of a loose root package or root packages that have had significant soil removed after harvest, staking systems that stabilize just the ball will not be effective. Tree anchors may not be effective in unconsolidated sandy loam soils such as are used on roof gardens and in large-scale installed soil planters.

Below-Grade Root Ball Stabilization

Designers in urban areas often use straps over the top of the ball in tree openings where they do not want to use aboveground guys. This is a practice that needs to change. If left in place, the straps will girdle the trunk or the zone-of-rapid-taper roots as the trunk diameter becomes larger. If a belowground guying system is required, use a simple untreated wood frame spanning over the root package, connected to the anchoring system at the three corners. The wood will rot away after the anchor is no longer needed.

Below-grade ball stabilization systems will stabilize only a well-planted tree, with a firm, correctly sized ball, proper trunk proportion, and roots at the top of the root package. Eliminating the need for belowground stabilization supports the basic thesis of this book—make larger planting spaces. If the planting space is so small that aboveground staking may be hazardous to pedestrians, the planting space is just too small.

Most trees do not need to be staked or guyed. When they do, make it simple and remove the system as soon as possible.

Trunk Protectors

Newly planted trees may benefit from tall trunk protectors depending on their location and type. Deer damage occurs in surprisingly densely developed areas and bicycle damage is common in commercial areas. Plastic grid tree bark protectors, such as manufactured by NSW (www.nswplastics.com), are an excellent protection system that is open enough to allow light and air around the trunk and stiff enough to provide good protection. This protector also provides limited trunk sunscald protection.

Trunk protection in close proximity to the tree must consider the conflict between the protection device and the growing trunk. The attachment system, if required, must be strong enough to hold the material around the trunk when bumped by deer, pedestrians, or inadvertent removal but not so strong that it will girdle the tree if no one removes it as the tree grows. This is a narrow range

a b c

Figure 2.9.45. Tree trunk protectors.

a. Tall mesh protector by NSW, useful for protection from sunscald, deer rub, and other mechanical damage. Requires taped connection fastener.
b. Short plastic guard is useful to defend against rodent and lawnmower damage. This design requires no connection device.
c. Tree with lawnmower damage. This tree should be removed.

between too strong and too weak. Plastic tapes that are biodegradable in sunlight must be used.

Shorter bumper systems are useful in protecting bark from rodents, lawnmowers and string trimmers. These smaller devices generally snap onto the tree trunk and expand as the tree grows.

Keeping a large area of weed-free mulch around the base of the newly planted tree for five or more years is the most effective method to protect the trunk from lawn mowers. As the tree matures, the developing trunk flare and thickening bark are sufficient to protect the tree.

Pruning

Normally only minimal pruning should be performed at planting. Pruning instructions should be included on the planting details, but the less pruning at the time of planting is best. The more buds and leaves left on the tree during the initial transplant period, the faster the tree will recover. The carbohydrates produced by these leaves are used to grow replacement roots, and the tree must use resources to heal over each pruning cut. Pruning to reduce the crown area, as often shown in typical planting details, is not recommended. The terminal leader should never be pruned.

The goal of any pruning should be to create sound, long-term structure. On canopy trees, most of the canopy branches that arrive with the tree at the time of planting are only temporary branches. The permanent branches will develop as the tree grows. If no central leader exists, prune to create a dominant side branch that will develop into one. Remove closely spaced branches and co-dominant leaders. Remove crossover branches and branches that are in conflict with adjacent structures. Minor crown shaping can also be performed at the time of planting. Reference the specifications in An *Illustrated Guide to Pruning* for techniques and standards. If a tree requires significant pruning at planting, it is not a quality tree.

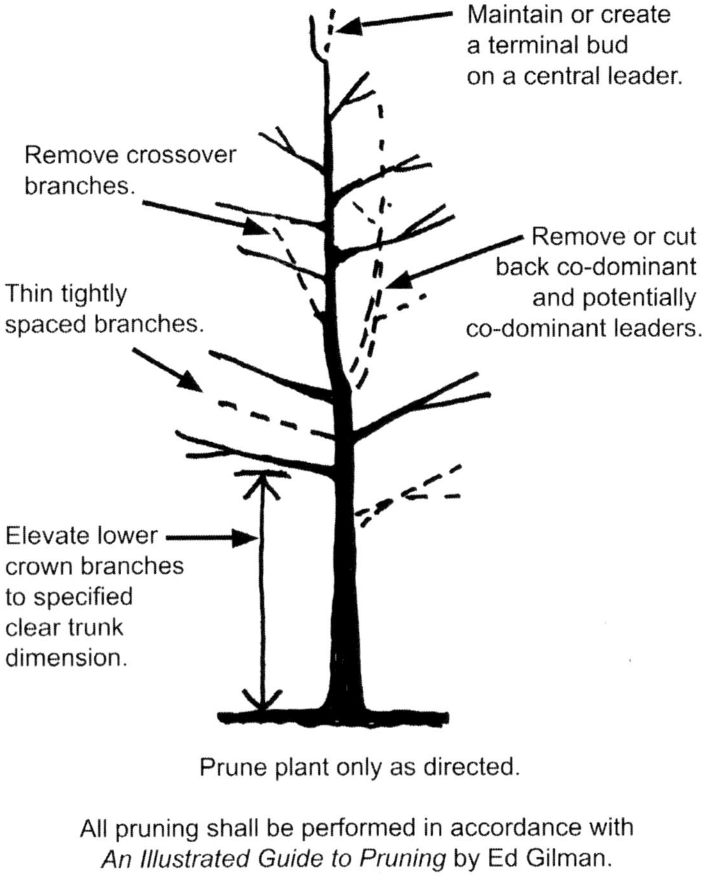
Maintain or create
a terminal bud
on a central leader.
Remove crossover
branches.
Remove or cut
back co-dominant
and potentially
co-dominant leaders.
Thin tightly
spaced branches.
Elevate lower
crown branches
to specified
clear trunk
dimension.
Prune plant only as directed.
All pruning shall be performed in accordance with
An Illustrated Guide to Pruning by Ed Gilman.

Figure 2.9.46. Standard pruning notes.

Occasionally, special notes may be required if pollarding, shearing, or other specialized effects such as topiary are desired. These should be on a separate tree planting detail for those trees, to limit any confusion. If a tree is to be sheared or pollarded, it may not be big enough to start this process for several years after planting.

Composite Planting Detail

The previous sections have discussed many elements that go into a planting detail. It is up to the designer to incorporate the relevant parts into a compost detail or details that go on the project planting plan. Most projects will have several details that reflect different conditions. There is no standard detail, and designers must resist the temptation to develop one.

SOIL, GRADING, AND DRAINAGE PLANS

Up By Roots encourages designers to look at planting soil and drainage from an entirely new perspective. As they do, design and construction will increase in complexity, and it will no longer be sufficient to put a few lines in the planting specifications instructing the contractor about minimum soil amendment. A separate set of soil, grading, and drainage plans, details, and specifications are required to communicate this information clearly. Planting, soil, and drainage specifications will each need their own CSI format section number. Separate contractors may install plants, soil, and drainage.

The planting plan controls the installation of plants. A grading plan, with contours, controls the sculpting of soils as well as the grades of all structural site elements. The soil and drainage plan controls the types, limits, transitions, and depths of soil and how excess water is to be removed from the soil. The requirements of preserving soil and root zones under existing trees are better left to a separate tree preservation plan.

Grading Plan

A grading plan should be part of the soil drawings. Grading determines where water will flow and how much will be absorbed into the soil versus put into pipes. The grading of a site is an interrelated set of design decisions affecting all the elements of the site design. The designer who controls the soil design should also have authority over the surface of the soil and the paved areas around it.

Many designers, particularly civil engineers, have shifted away from using contours to show grades, instead depicting the design of the grades by numerous spot elevations. While spot elevations may better depict points, they are very cumbersome at showing fluid surfaces like soil. Contours reveal the way a design actually will look, even to a person with little experience in reading plans. Contours can be drawn at one-foot or half-foot intervals, or even closer intervals, up to one-tenth foot, in areas of the site where the surface is flat or has a high level of fluidity. Contours best show the shapes of swales and mounds. They better reveal mistakes in design drawings. Finding a dropped contour is far easier than locating a spot elevation with the wrong number.

Unfortunately, site designers do not often control the grading process. Civil engineers have increasingly included this part of project documentation in their contracts. This blocks the site designer from influencing a critical aspect of landscape design—soil and drainage—during the project documentation phase. Site designers need to become proficient at drawing contours, a task made much easier by computers. Site designers can better negotiate the grading plan into their design contracts by demonstrating mastery of this skill and the importance of having all aspects of soil and drainage under one discipline. Consumers of site design services should award contracts to firms or teams where the landscape architect prepares the grading plan.

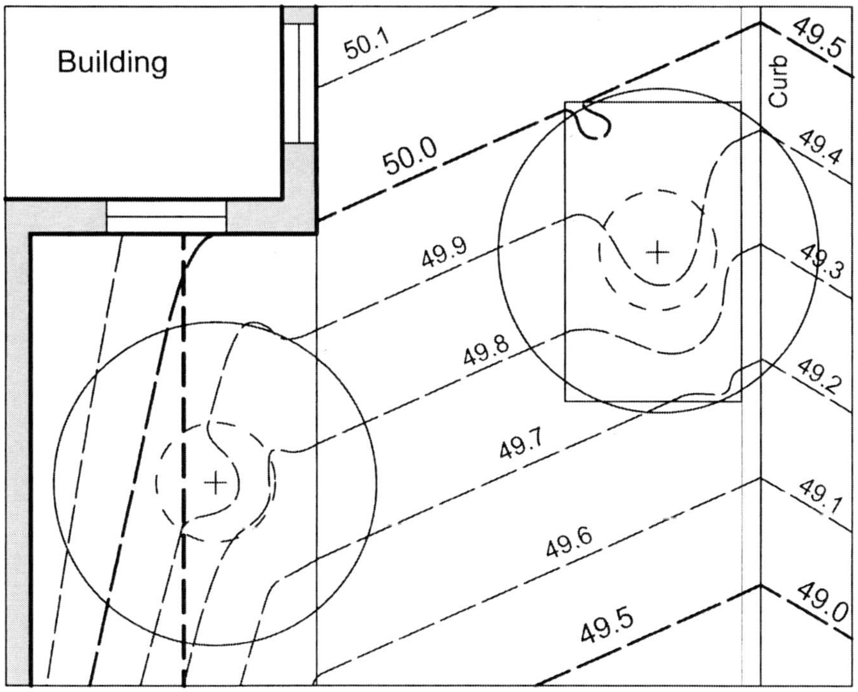

Figure 2.9.47. Grading plan.

Areas of planting soil function better for the plants if they have sufficient slopes to drain away excess water. Slight mounding above the elevation of adjacent paved surfaces will improve tree and plant health. Slope lawn areas at 2 percent or greater, planting beds at 5 to 10 percent. On overly steep slopes (greater than 3:1), soil may be too dry and newly placed soil easily eroded. Planting soil beds should be illustrated as being slightly mounded in anticipation of soil settlement. Even well-placed planting soil will settle to some degree. See the discussion on soil settlement in Part 2, Chapter Four.

The above comment on mounding planting areas is counter to new theories on urban rain water management. When rain water harvesting is added to the design goals, planting areas tend to become depressed to gather and hold water. This puts a greater demand on the soil and subsurface drainage design to create conditions that work both for rain water and trees. Soil type, relationship of the drainage area size to the absorbing soil volume, plant choices, subtle variation in grading to mound the tree root package while still creating the water harvesting depression requires great grading dexterity and understanding of materials/water relationships.

Soil Plan

A soil plan is a diagram of zones of different soil treatments drawn over a site plan, with the grading and planting layer turned off. Different soil types, areas where the subsoil needs to be loosened, root paths, and the limits and types of tree soil under paving should be included and dimensioned where needed for clarity. Each soil treatment type references a detail section. The transitions between different soil treatments will be detailed and referenced on the diagram using typical detail targets.

Calculate soil volumes relative to tree size and tree life expectancy desired as described in Part 2, Chapter Four. Understand how much of the existing soil may be usable. Establish connectivity across the plan of different types of root zones by using the principles in Part 2, Chapter Six.

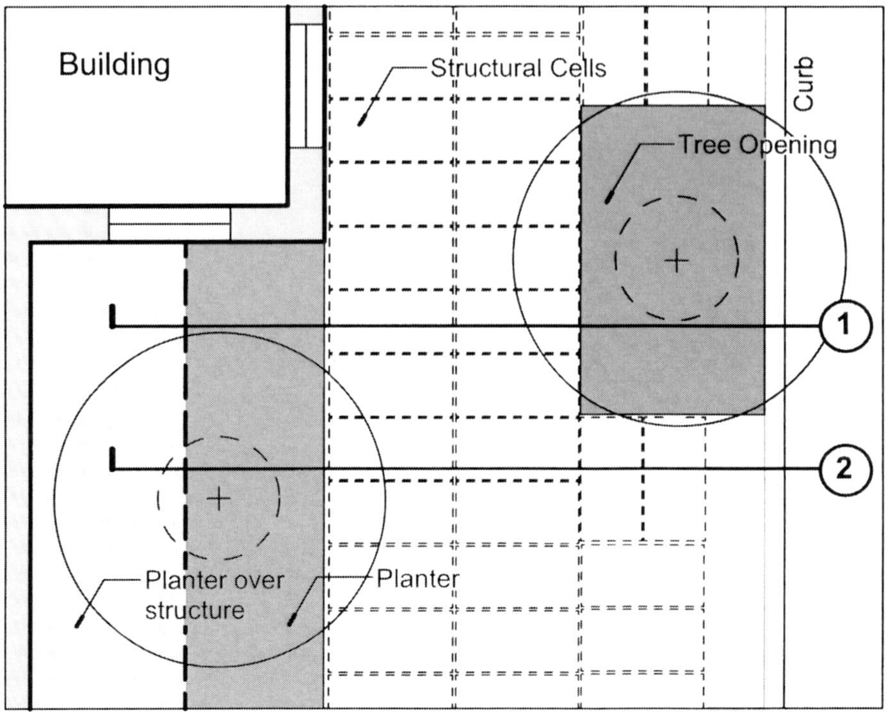

Figure 2.9.48. Soil plan.

Include fencing and other protective devices on the soil plan to protect existing soil resources from compaction and contamination during construction. Think of soil preservation in the same way as tree preservation. The only real difference is that soil preservation is about future tree establishment and growth.

It is useful to have a clear legend on the soil plan that references the details and gives a summary description of each planting soil type. The summary should include the type of soil and the minimum depth of installation. Do not overly describe the soil type, as this is better left to the details. The plans will often be reduced to an 11-by-17-inch sheet and rattle around in the contractor's truck, covered in dust, and folded into the foreman's pocket. Be sure the graphics are readable at a greatly reduced scale.

Drainage Plan

Drainage lines, inspection risers, dry wells, wall sleeves, and connection points to storm lines should be added to this diagram. Show drainage plans to include inverts and other line elevation information at cleanout risers, outfalls, and storm sewer connections. For complex projects, the drainage plan may need to be a separate drawing.

Also show site utilities, footings, underground structures, and access limitations where they directly impact the soil work. Site utilities including water, electric, irrigation, and communication distribution tend to be drawn diagrammatically on the engineering plans. The final location of lines is often left to the contractor. Where it is critical, coordinate exact locations of lines with the engineer to reduce conflicts with soil areas. This may require notes on the engineer's plans as well as on the soil plans. A note on a soil plan that the other contractors are not to locate lines in the areas of planting soil will be ignored once construction starts. Utility contractors are on the site before the landscape contractor, and "Possession is nine-tenths of the law" prevails.

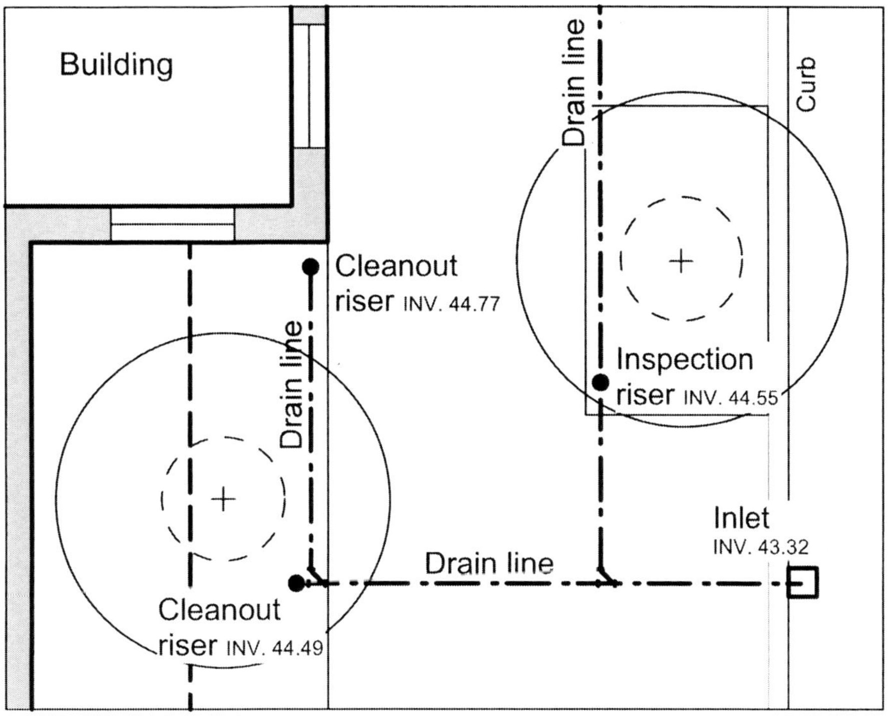

Figure 2.9.49. Drainage plan.

SOIL AND DRAINAGE DETAILS

The soil plan should reference sections through each soil treatment, the transitions between treatments, and drainage provisions. These sections explain the plan and reinforce the specifications. Soil sections give a visual reality of the requirements to the contractor. Drawing these sections will show transitions to adjacent materials and reveal conflicts with other site conditions and between different soil treatments. It is critical not to rely only on specifications or written text to describe the installation of soil.

There should be no standard details. Relying on standard details increases the chance for errors and omissions! Details are always project-specific. Parts of details can be used from project to project, but the designer must always revise nearly every detail from project to project. The computer should make this easier; however, this labor-saving device also makes it easier to repeatedly copy the same detail even when it is inappropriate.

Soil treatments range from strict soil protection, preservation, and minor interventions to complete removal and replacement of soil. The strategies and detailed sections for different types of soil and drainage treatments are described in Principle 3 ("Preserve and reuse soil"), Principle 4 ("Improve soil and drainage"), and Principle 6 ("Make space for roots"). Use this previous information as the basis for preparing project-specific details.

Each detail must address the "Key Factors of Soil and Drainage Improvement" described at the beginning of Part 2, Chapter Four. These factors control the success of the soil and drainage design.

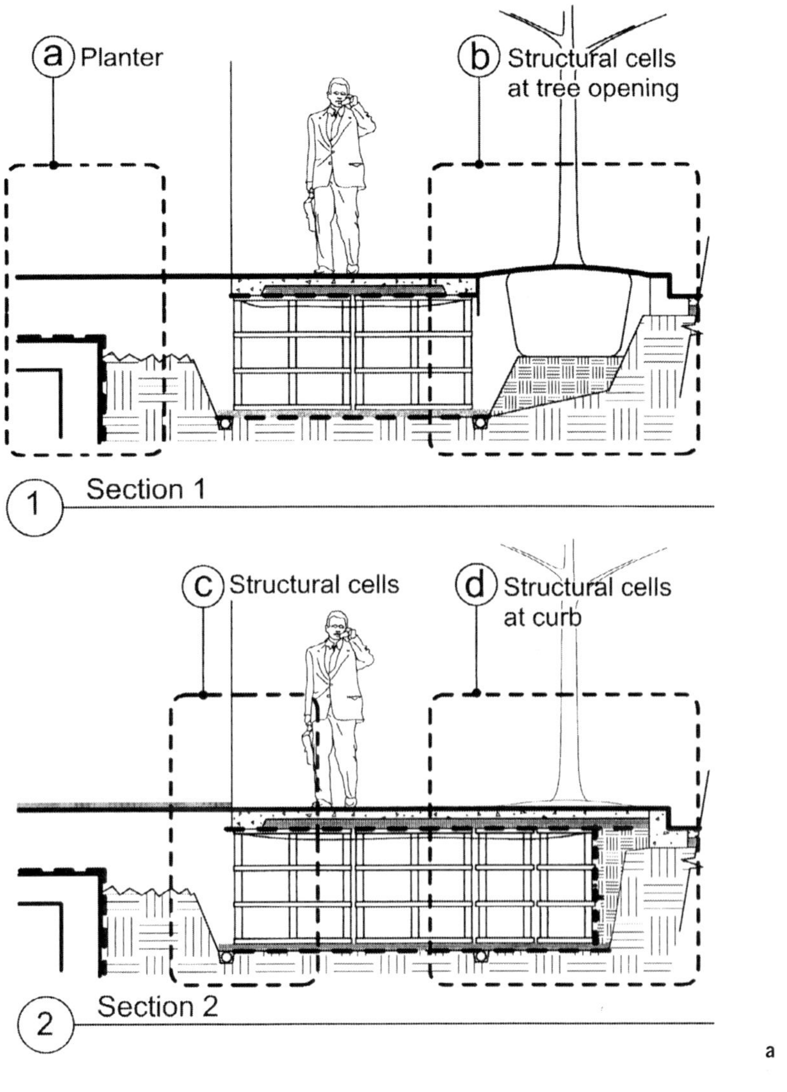

Figure 2.9.50. Examples of soil details referenced in the soil plan in Figure 2.9.47.

a. Section through the site shows the interrelationships of different soil systems.
b. Detailed sections show the precise relationships of the various components of individual soil systems. These details are representative of typical details. Additional details would be required to depict drainage and paving interfaces.

Use consistent terminology and definitions in describing materials. This is particularly important with soil amendments. Use the terms suggested in Part 2, Chapter Four. Understand that material types, cost, and terminology vary from location to location. Do not assume that the same details and products on a project in Chicago will work well or be available in New York.

Reduce and control compaction in the subgrade and installed soil. Lack of attention to compaction is a major cause of soil failure. Compaction levels at the site during the design phase are likely to increase during construction. Specify compaction ranges on the details in percent of dry density as determined by Proctor or as bulk density values. Be sure that the required values are appropriate for the soil type and application as determined by soil testing.

Draw sets of details for soil improvement within the root zones of existing trees that are to remain. Draw different details for modifying existing surface soils as opposed to new soil installations. Details should reflect the preservation or development of soil profiles. Sections should detail the transitions between different materials, both horizontally and vertically.

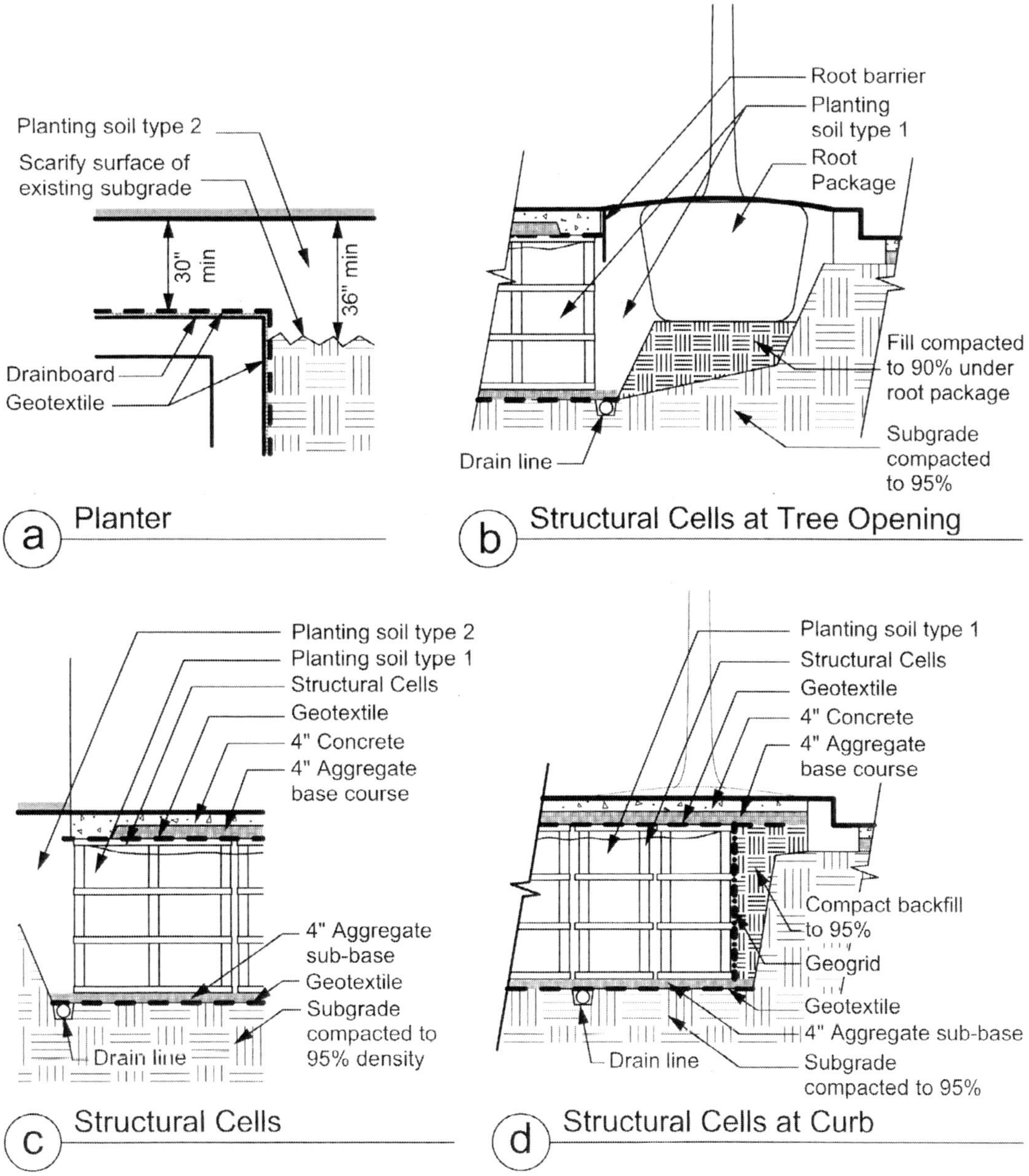

b

Prepare different sections that reflect changes to plant types and surface materials. Mulched beds, lawns, flexible paving, and rigid paving each have different subgrade requirements relative to the installation of planting soil.

Soils to support rooting under pavement are described and detailed in Principle 6 ("Make space for roots"). The details of each system need to be drawn at each change in conditions. At a minimum, two details should be drawn—one at the point where the soil transitions from the tree opening to the soil under the pavement and the second showing the transitions under the pavement from the planting soil to the various other soils that are adjacent to the planting soil. Drawing sufficient details of these critical soil types will anticipate conflicts and make acceptance by permit reviewers easier.

Draw separate sets of details for soil improvements on steeply sloped areas and flat areas. Draw the sloped details, accurately depicting the maximum slope. There is a tendency to draw all soil sections as flat, which can lead to details that do not work.

Utilities need to be shown on the soil sections if they are a significant factor in soil installation. Locate existing utilities. Coordinate proposed utility line locations with other consultants. Where possible, utility lines should be located below or beside the planting soil. Any lines that are near or within soil installation areas should be reflected in the section. Draw the conflict points and any special modifications needed to solve conflicts. Use steam heat intercepts and root barriers over the top of utility lines to reduce conflicts.

Tree preservation requirements are often at odds with soil improvement goals. Mechanical disturbance of the soil to improve compaction or incorporate amendments within the root zone will damage tree roots. The use of an air knife to break compaction and remove soil allows significant soil modification around existing tree roots. Draw sections through the tree preservation soils indicating roots, vertical mulching, root pruning requirements, fencing details, and sediment control devices. Resolve conflicts indicated by those sections.

Whenever any detail is drawn, imagine the work being performed. Is it possible to build? What kinds of equipment are needed? Is it possible to actually get the equipment to that point in the site? It is amazing how many details are drawn that are physically impossible to execute much less actually solve the problem being studied. Often it is the contractor who saves the designer by simply building something logical that is in the end successful.

SPECIFICATIONS

Specifications are the support document of the plans and details. They do not replace the plans and details. Prepare separate specification sections for planting, soil preparation, and drainage installation. It is critical to separate work into different specification sections, which is of substantially different natures and requires different skill sets or contractors to perform.

Specifications must be based on the research available at the time. However, remember that the scientific method is one of testing ideas against a controlled set of conditions. Rarely does scientific study prove a principle over a wide range of situations. The science of trees and soils is fluid and changing. The specification writer must make assessments as to which science to accept and which findings to balance with experience and industry practices.

Specifications are also based on local industry practices and product availability. Industry standards are often the blending of many people's experience as to what works most of the time. They may reflect a compromise between what may be known about a particular problem and what practices may be practical while still making a profit.

Figure 2.9.51. Installation of planting, soil, and drainage are different types of work and should be given separate specification sections.

Most soil products are natural materials, and transporting them over long distances is both expensive and environmentally bad practice. To use local materials requires knowledge of local sources and suppliers and the peculiarities of the product composition. The compost source specification for Baltimore is likely different from the specification for a similar type of compost in Chicago. Materials also respond in different ways based on climate, soil, plant type, and installation methods. Local practices develop in response to these changes. Soil amendment practices in Phoenix will be different from those in Boston.

Designers will often find a particular need to make a recommendation that fits neither the scientific information nor the industry standard. The scientific evidence may be limited, or studies of a particular topic may have only looked at a very limited number of variables and the problem at hand may fall outside of those variables. Designers must synthesize current research with their own experience and the standards of the industry.

When a new scientific study challenges conventional wisdom, designers must decide whether this new information is reliable enough to change the conventional specification. A good test is to imagine the failures or unintended consequences that might result from the change, and then imagine yourself in court testifying in the "errors and omissions" trial of your work. Can an adequate defense of the change be made. This is where professional societies like the International Society of Arboriculture or the American Society of Landscape Architects (ASLA) must get involved to endorse changes in the standards of practice that have the consensus of respected practitioners.

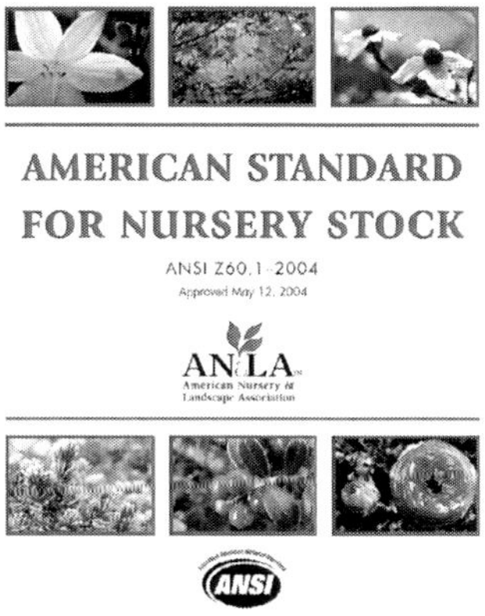

Plant Standards

Most specifications reference the *American Standard for Nursery Stock* (ANSI Z60.1), published by the American Nursery & Landscape Association. This standard was updated in 2004 and is available free from www.ANLA.org/publications. Designers must have the most current version in their office and be aware of its requirements. However, this document is only a standard for plant sizes and nomenclature descriptions of nursery stock. It does not set standards for quality of plants or roots. Designers must set their own standards for quality in their specifications and enforce those standards during the construction period. ANSI Z60.1 is also silent on all shipping, delivery, installation, warrantee and maintenance issues related to plants.

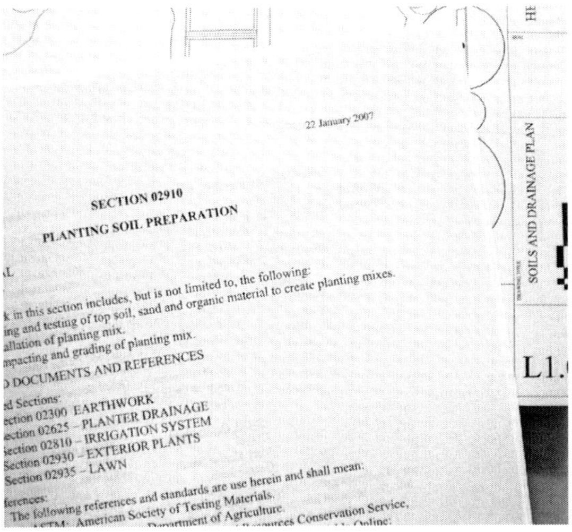

Figure 2.9.52. Specifications must be project-specific.

Figure 2.9.53. Discussing compaction tolerance and the use of penetrometers with the contractor to establish quality control. *(Photo courtesy office of Michael Vergason)*

Writing a Good Specification

Writing a good specification requires practice and study of other specifications. The specification format and numbering system should be based on the standards of the Construction Specification Institute, www.csinet.org. It is beyond the scope of this book to provide a specification example or to teach specification writing. Example language may tend to become the de facto standard, whereas a good designer should create specifications that reflect thorough understanding of each project.

Specifications, like details, have tended to become standardized within an office and are repeated project after project. This leads to bad specifications. Edit the master specification for every application. Remove parts that do not apply, and modify or create new text for unique situations.

The field foreman is rarely reading the specifications. If information is critical to the person doing the installation, it needs to be on the drawings. On the other hand, field personnel do not need to know much about the particulars of product specifications, warranties, and other contractual issues. Cluttering up the drawings with information that should be in the specifications deflects the attention of the people in the field from the issues they need to know.

Some installation process issues may need to be in the specifications because of their complexity, but may also need to be included on the drawings in a simplified version to instruct the contractor in the field. For example, the drawings may note that a particular section of soil be "compacted," or "compacted to between 80 and 85 percent," or "compacted to between 80 and 85 percent of maximum dry density." Each of these notes guides the contractor to a different level of specificity, but none of them is adequate to describe to what level a soil is compacted.

To accurately describe the required compaction level, the note would have to read "compacted to between 80 and 85 percent of maximum dry density as determined by the Proctor test, ASTM D 698-91." This longer version belongs in the specifications. This level of detail will clutter the drawing to the point where the field installer may push the drawings aside, with the often-heard comment, "We know how to do this." Moreover, putting information in both places raises the dangerous possibility of giving conflicting instructions. Be careful to confirm that the instructions on the drawings are the same as the instructions in the specifications. A good compromise is a set of more detailed notes on the drawing sheet that define important but complex terms needed by the installer, so that the details can use simpler terms.

Dimensional Tolerance

All dimensional and measuring standards must have a range of values. It is impossible for the contractor to compact all the soil to exactly 85 percent. The upper and lower limits tell the contractor to stay between the two values. Some specifications may set only an upper or lower limit—"compacted to 95 percent or greater," for example. Be sure you understand the ramifications of getting too high or too low. Do not set the window too narrow or too wide. Most contractors are used to compaction values being a lowest allowable number. Too much compaction is not a problem for engineering soils. Dealing with upper and lower compaction limits is going to be a new concept. This concept of tolerance must apply to all items of measurement in the specifications.

Consistent Terminology

Maintaining consistent terminology among the plans, details, and specifications is critical. "Top soil" and "topsoil" are often used interchangeably—pick one and stick with it. Are "plant mix," "planting mix," and "soil mix" the same material? Is it "lawn" or "sod"? Is some of the lawn "sod" and some "seeded" lawn? Are "compost," "organic matter," and "mulch" different materials? Are there different types of "mulch" and "organic matter" on the job? Keeping these terms consistent is difficult. Make one person on the project responsible for setting the standard and coordinating specifications with drawings.

Designers must have a firsthand understanding of the specifications they are writing. They must experience the processes in the field and be competent to observe if the contractor is following the instructions. If a sandy loam soil is specified, can the designer pick up some of the soil at the site and tell its approximate texture? Can the designer tell if the soil is under or over the specified compaction rate? Can the designer tell if the tree was harvested too deeply? Only continuous field experience builds this knowledge. The owners of design firms must fight for the required fees to get their design team out into the field during the installation process so that they can build this level of experience. Periodic field trips to construction sites as continuing education is a critical part of the apprenticeship process of growing the next generation of competent design professionals.

Submittals

In the first part of the specifications, include a submittal section that covers approval of plants, soil, and other products. The submittal process for plants is well understood, although greater attention to detail and nursery site visits are needed to ensure quality. *Each tree must be examined at the growing nursery to ensure quality control.*

Correct soil submittal processes are not well understood. Soil in particular is a very elusive material. Availability and quality in the marketplace fluctuate. The specification writer must be well-versed in the soil products that are regionally available and the critical issues that control quality. Information important to developing submittal requirements and reviewing soil materials is included in previous chapters.

Critical to the soil submittal process is providing enough time to complete this process before the material is needed at the construction site. Submitting different products for testing and then further testing the mixture of the different products takes many weeks. Add to that the time for review, rejection and re-submittal, and up to four months is not an unreasonable amount of time to secure approval for the products to be used on a large project. Be sure that all members of the construction team are aware of the need for this much time. If the project schedule becomes an issue in the process, more often than not the client will suspend the submittal process, accept the best information available, and proceed. This situation will cause problems on the project.

The submittal process can sometimes extend to the point where soil supplies previously agreed upon have been sold out and no longer available. Require the contractor to secure any source submitted.

A Standard Specification

This book will not attempt to provide a sample or standard specification. A standard specification should be the work of an industry working group so that consensus is reached and the wording is well developed. Several regional attempts have been made at standard specifications and the ASLA, in conjunction with Master Spec, has developed a national template specification. At the time of the publication of this book, the Master Spec document is still a work in progress, and designers are advised to consider it as a beginning point. Many of the recommendations of this book remain to be woven into the Master Spec document.

CONSTRUCTION ADMINISTRATION

Without diligent construction administration, all the planning and details can evaporate. This phase can be the most frustrating part of a project for the designer.

Adequate Construction Administration Fees

Designers must negotiate sufficient construction oversight fees to ensure their design work is followed. This must include soil inspections, nursery review visits, and sufficient time at the job site during construction.

Design elements that are covered with soil or pavement cannot be inspected at the end of the project. The only way to know if things were incorrectly installed may be upon failure or underperformance of the resulting trees, and this may not be noticeable until long after the warranty has expired. A knowledgeable designer who is representing the interests of the trees as well as the owner must be at the site to ensure the plans are followed.

Establish early in the process that site visits will be regular and may be unannounced. Get to know the general contractor's personnel assigned to the job. Compliment and thank them for jobs well done. Compromise when a field adjustment will not make a significant difference to the project outcome. Work with the contractors to modify requirements that may make things easier for the contractor and still achieve the same goals.

Figure 2.9.54. Field-checking delivered soil quality against the approved sample. Water is added to both soils and a texture by feel test undertaken. Sample color is also examined. *(Photo courtesy office of Michael Vergason)*

Listen to contractors when they notice something that may not be correct on the plans and specifications. Designers must recognize that the contractor's ideas have validity and may be a better solution. Stand firm when you are sure you are correct and it is important to the outcome.

Designers overseeing construction must understand the plans, specifications, and what is expected from the contractor. They must be skilled in observing planting, soils, and drainage installation, as well as be able to make judgments of soil quality based on color, texture, feel, and smell. They need to carry and know how to use a soil probe, penetrometer, and other equipment to inspect various soil requirements including compaction. This is not the best task for a new employee or recent graduate. Training and mentoring in the art of construction oversight are critical.

Subcontractors not under contract to deal with soil and tree issues can have significant impact on the outcome of trees, such as washing out concrete trucks in an area excavated for subgrades or building foundations and pavements that are larger or in the wrong place. In one project, sheets of drywall buried in the backfill made a large area that did not drain and killed the plants above. If something can go wrong, it will. The only way to find mistakes is to visit the site regularly. Even if things are going well, often only a portion of a site is ready for subgrade review, requiring repeated visits as the contractor backs out of the site. This is the nature of construction work.

At the end of a long design and construction period, owner, designer, and contractor are usually suffering from fatigue. There have already been conflicts with quality, scheduling, and budgeting issues related to other parts of the project. The client may never have been vested in the importance of large, healthy trees. Ideas that garnered support during the project approval phase may no longer have the backing of the client. No one is in the mood to hear that the subgrade or installed soil quality has been rejected and there will be a week's delay to fix the problem. Maintaining the client's support is vital and often the deciding factor in the success or failure of the work.

The designer may also be suffering from fatigue. The office may have experienced cost overruns in the production of the construction documents. Key personnel may have left, or exciting new design projects may vie for principals' time and attention. Significant budget cuts may have eliminated important features of the designer's work, lowering this person's enthusiasm or sense that the project will be a good addition to the firm's body of work. The designer may not have the energy or financial resources to remain diligent. The contractor may be counting on the designer's and owner's fatigue to gain acceptance of substandard work.

The farther a designer's office is from the project site, the more difficult it is to perform adequate site visits. More than an hour of travel time from the office to the site becomes limiting to the process. Designers who work on projects in distant cities need to arrange with a local, trusted, and competent professional to perform oversight duties. Project managers would be well advised to hire local design firms to ensure adequate construction oversight.

Each of these obstacles has ripple effects on the success of the project. Advocates for trees must anticipate the problems at the end of the project and not assume that good things will happen just because the developer promised to do them at a public meeting three years earlier.

Actively Engage in Materials Approval

The specifications set the requirements and timing for the submission and approval of materials to be used in the work. Requirements include manufacturer information, samples, product testing, and visits to suppliers or growers discussed earlier in this chapter.

Figure 2.9.55. Somewhere in this image are locations where trees will be planted in just a few more months. Is the designer in a position to obtain the growing conditions for these trees discussed in the previous two years of preparation?

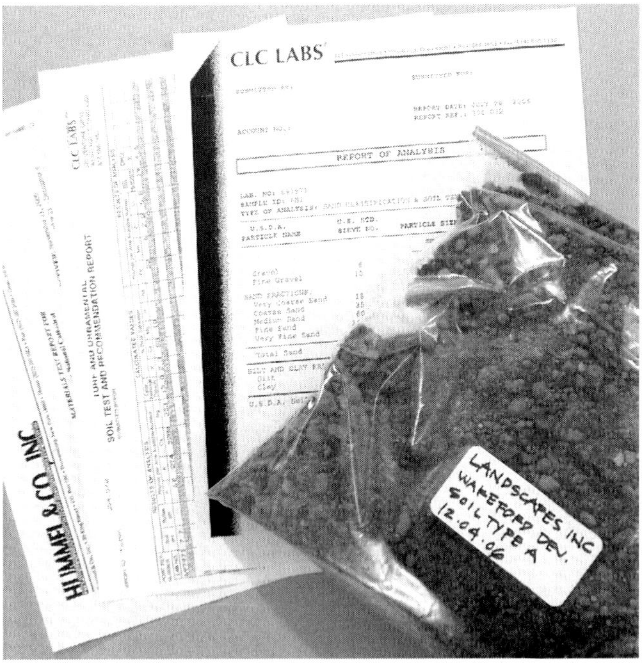

Figure 2.9.56. Soil submittal must include samples as well as testing data.

Soil Approvals

Soil, soil mixes, and other natural materials are hard to accurately define, and it is therefore difficult to set specific quality control requirements for them. Submittal samples become the basis for determining whether the contractor is delivering or installing the approved material to the site. Sample bags of approved sand, soil, and soil mixes will begin to pile up in the designer's storeroom and the vehicles used to make site visits. Managing these samples, which need to be kept until the end of the warranty period, requires a dedicated storage space and good record keeping.

Soil testing labs vary in capability and orientation. Agricultural soil labs may not be sufficiently well versed in sand-based soil mixes, while geotechnical labs may cover only textural and structural factors. Specify the soil testing lab to be used. These labs should have demonstrated expertise in testing and evaluating landscape soil mixes. Labs that specialize in golf course and athletic turf soil testing are often good choices; however, be sure that they are aware that the soil is for trees, not turf.

Soil and soil mix testing may take several submissions, with rejections and retesting to find the right combinations of materials. Designers must be proactive in getting contractors to begin the process in advance of the expected date of installation.

Construction Mockups

In addition to the material submissions, require full-scale mockups of construction assemblies particularly soil and drainage installations to demonstrate that means and methods selected by the contractor do achieve the desired results. Mockups are an important part of other areas of construction and should be used more in the construction of landscapes. This is the best method to determine if the contractor understands the specifications and also allows minor tweaking of the specifications to better fit the available materials, project conditions and the contractor's skills, equipment and experience. The mock up process should be a time when the entire construction team can discuss better ways to solve problems.

Plant Approvals and Nursery Inspections

Nursery practices create a wide range of plant quality, even within the same field of the same trees. Co-dominant leaders, weak branch attachments, too much soil over the roots, and circling roots must be observed firsthand. It is easy to reject plants at the nursery and much more difficult, if not impossible, at the job site.

Nursery inspections are a critical part of the designer's education. Designers committed to quality trees need to visit nurseries on a regular basis, for their own benefit as well as to benefit their projects. Growers, more than any other people in the industry, are in tune with the issues of moving a tree from propagation to maturity. The time spent in a pickup truck driving through fields of trees, discussing the nuances of soil, species, and the marketplace, is one of the most memorable and educational experiences a designer can ever have.

During the nursery inspection, the designer gets to eliminate many of the long-term problems with trees. The principal task is not to get great-looking trees at the time of installation; the real task is to get well-formed trees that have the structure and roots needed to become mature specimens. Often that may mean rejecting the tree with a perfectly symmetrical full head for a tree with a more open crown but properly spaced branches and a well-defined central leader. Many of the nursery pruning practices that create full, symmetrical heads also introduce branch habits with significant problems that may not be easy to correct in the future. It is easier to reject the tree at this point than to have to cut away co-dominant leaders later.

The best source for determining whether a tree has been well pruned is the State of Florida "Grades and Standards for Nursery Plants." This is available free on the Web at http://prohort.ifas.ufl.edu/grades_standards.htm. The ten-step grading process covers all the questions one needs to consider to select a well-grown and pruned tree. Despite its southern origins, the methodology is useful in all regions of the United States.

In addition to looking for branch structure, top inspection should include looking for borer holes, branch and trunk abrasions, and weak grafts. Large amounts of branch suckers emerging from the base of the tree may indicate a weak graft of bud, an aggressive rootstock or a girdling root. Each of these problems will haunt the tree far into its future, causing its premature decline.

Use the pin probing method or root collar inspections, described earlier in this chapter, to find root elevations, girdling roots, J-roots or roots that are not well distributed around the trunk. Require that excess soil be removed before harvesting. Reject trees with girdling roots, J-roots, or poorly distributed roots.

Mark the north side of trees so they may be oriented correctly at the time of planting. Tag each tree with a numbered tag that has a secure locking mechanism. Note each tree by number in the field report with any special requirements.

Many designers say they find it difficult to get clients to include nursery inspection services in their contracts. Designers must fight for this service. It is the best and easiest way to ensure quality control.

a

b

c d

Figure 2.9.57. Nursery inspections are critical.

a. The top standard inspection. Was the co-dominant leader in this tree marked for removal? Note the soil piled on top of the root ball.
b. Spot checking for soil over the main roots. It is reasonable to assume that all the trees in this row have the same condition. Require soil to be removed before harvesting.
c. Tree with perfect head but multiple developing co-dominant leaders.
d. The same tree pruned properly to eliminate co-dominant leaders. Its canopy is not as full, but a thoughtful designer will prefer it because of its capacity to develop into a superior mature tree.

Figure 2.9.58. Nursery inspections to approve both the top and roots of each tree are critical. Purchase trees from growers that are close enough to easily make nursery inspections.
(Photo: Bob Benjamin)

One reason designers may be having trouble getting nursery inspections included in their contract is the practice of buying trees from locations quite distant from the project site. Purchasing trees from distant nurseries has several negative side effects besides the costs to inspect them.

From a sustainability perspective, the farther the tree is transported, the greater the environmental cost, based on fuel consumption alone. This includes the fuel to transport the designer to inspect the tree. The designer's carbon footprint must be factored into the sustainability equation.

Trees may be coming from a latitude that is quite different from the project site, particularly if the site is greater than 200 miles north or south of the project. While the tree may be adaptable, many factors determine whether it will adapt. The years of growing the tree in the same latitude helps reduce these variables. The longer the trip, the greater the stress on the tree. It is difficult to know whether the tree was handled correctly during a long transport. Think globally, specify locally.

Re-Wholesale Nurseries

In most metropolitan areas, large re-wholesale plant sellers have become a common source for trees, particularly when only a few trees are needed or projects are on short schedules. For many reasons, this is not a preferred source for trees and should be avoided.

It is critical to inspect the tree before it is harvested. Once the tree has been dug and packaged, finding the main roots, grafts, and other root features becomes much more difficult. Excess soil over the roots must be removed before the tree is harvested so that a proper root package can be prepared. Once the tree is dug, the soil can be removed, however, roots have been cut and the root package will no longer meet ANLA standards. Once the tree is harvested, the trunk's north orientation is lost. Keeping north the same in the nursery and the final location is important to stress reduction.

Selecting the tree in the re-wholesale yard significantly reduces the number of trees available for inspection and therefore the possibility of getting the best tree. Seeing the grower's fields gives the designer valuable information about the soil, drainage conditions, and the grower's operation quality that may be critical to determining if that grower is the best choice for the project. In the case of a re-wholesale yard, the actual grower's location may not be known and issues of climate, photoperiod, and transportation stress cannot be discussed. Less is known about the tree and the chance of problems increases.

Insist on the landscape contractor purchasing trees from the nursery that grows the tree!

Figure 2.9.59. Re-wholesale plant yards should be the source of last resort to purchase trees.

SUMMARY

- Prepare detailed and accurate plans and specifications documents that are based on the current science of soil and trees.
- Draw planting plans that include properly sized tree crowns and root packages.
- Dimension tree locations and space plants to reflect long-term growth and plant competition dynamics.
- Include all conflicting objects, such as utilities, vaults, and footings on the planting plan.
- Draw planting details unique to each project. There are no standard details!
- Do not show soil information on the planting plan or planting details. Reference soil plans and details for this information.
- Draw different details for different types of root packages to clearly inform the contractor how to treat each root package.
- Understand and reflect the correct relationship of the top of the root package to finish grade. Draw different details for each condition.
- Require compaction of the planting soil under and around the base of the root package.
- Consider different details for when to mulch, build water saucers, wrap trunks, or stake the tree.
- Include pruning requirements on the details. Note that pruning at planting should be the least amount required.
- Prepare or control the grading plan for soil installation. Draw the plan using as fine a contour interval as possible.
- Prepare a separate soil plan to guide the preparation and installation of planting soil.
- On complex projects, prepare a separate drainage plan to control the installation of subsurface drain lines.
- Prepare soil and drainage details depicting sections through each soil condition and the transitions between different conditions and adjacent materials. Make the details clear, project-specific, and drawn to scale.
- Prepare soil and drainage specification sections that are separate from the planting specifications.
- Do not rely on standard specifications. They must be project-specific.
- Include adequate construction administration services in design contracts. Soil and drainage must be inspected while it is being installed.
- Nursery inspections and approving quality trees are critical to the long-term success of the tree.

REFERENCES

Key References

Craul, Phillip J. 1999. *Urban Soils: Applications and Practices.* John Wiley & Sons, New York, NY. 366 pp.

Craul, Timothy A., and Phillip J. Craul. 2006. *Soil Design Protocols: For Landscape Architects and Contractors.* John Wiley & Sons, New York, NY. 339 pp.

Ferguson, Bruce K. 2005. *Porous Pavements.* CRC Press, Boca Raton, FL. 577 pp.

Harris, Richard W., James R. Clark, and Nelda P. Matheny. 2004. *Arboriculture: Integrated Management of Landscape Trees, Shrubs, and Vines.* 4th ed. Pearson Education, Upper Saddle River, NJ. 578 pp.

Hoke, John, ed. 2000. *Ramsey Sleeper-Architectural Graphic Standards.* 10th ed. John Wiley & Sons, New York, NY.

Matheny, Nelda, and James R. Clark. 1998. *Trees and Development: A Technical Guide to Preservation of Trees During Land Development.* International Society of Arboriculture, Champaign, IL. 183 pp.

Trowbridge, Peter J., and Nina L. Bassuk. 2004. *Trees in the Urban Landscape: Site Assessment Design and Installation.* John Wiley & Sons, Hoboken, NJ. 205 pp.

Other Resources

American Nursery & Landscape Association. 2004. *American Standard for Nursery Stock.* American Nursery & Landscape Association, Washington, DC. 112 pp.

Appleton, B. 2003. Tree trunk protection: Are trees getting a bum wrap? pp. 51–54. In *Tree Selection and Planting* (CEU compendium). International Society of Arboriculture, Champaign, IL.

Appleton, B.L. 2004. To stake or not to stake? *Landscape Architecture* 94(4):44–50.

Appleton, B., and S.A. Floyd. 2004. Wire baskets—Current products and their handling at planting. *Journal of Arboriculture* 30(4):261–265.

Appleton, B., J. Koci, S. French, M. Lestyan, and R. Harris. 2003. Mycorrhizal fungal inoculation of established street trees. *Journal of Arboriculture* 29(2):107–110.

Arnold, Henry F. 1993. *Trees in Urban Design.* 2nd ed. Van Nostrand Reinhold, New York, NY. 197 pp.

Brinton, William F. 2002. *Earth Plant and Compost.* BIO-Dynamic Farming and Gardening Association, San Francisco, CA. 73 pp.

Costello, Laurence R., and Katherine S. Jones. 2003. *Reducing Infrastructure Damage by Tree Roots: A Compendium of Strategies.* Western Chapter of the International Society of Arboriculture, Cohasset, CA. 119 pp.

Craul, Phillip J. 1992. *Urban Soil in Landscape Design.* John Wiley & Sons, New York, NY. 396 pp.

Derr, Jeffery F., and Bonnie Lee Appleton. 1988. *Herbicide Injury to Trees and Shrubs: A Pictorial Guide to Symptom Diagnosis.* Blue Crab Press, Virginia Beach, VA. 72 pp.

Gilman, Edward F. 1997. *Trees for Urban and Suburban Landscapes.* Delmar, Albany, NY. 662 pp.

Gilman, Edward F. 2002. *An Illustrated Guide to Pruning.* 2nd ed. Delmar, Albany, NY. 330 pp.

Gilman, Edward F., and Sharon J. Lilly. 2002. *Best Management Practices—Tree Pruning.* International Society of Arboriculture, Champaign, IL. 35 pp.

Halfacre, R. Gordon, and Anne Rogers Shawcroft. 1999. *Landscape Plants of the Southeast.* 5th ed. Sparks Press, Raleigh, NC. 426 pp.

Hightshoe, Gary L. 1988. *Native Trees, Shrubs, and Vines for Urban and Rural America.* Van Nostrand Reinhold, New York, NY. 819 pp.

Hopper, Leonard J., ed. 2007. *Landscape Architectural Graphic Standards.* John Wiley & Sons, Hoboken, NJ. 1074 pp.

Ingham, Elaine R. 2003. *The Compost Tea Brewing Manual.* 4th ed. Soil Food Web Incorporated, Corvallis, OR. 88 pp.

International Society of Arboriculture. 2006. *American National Standard for Arboricultural Operations—Safety Requirements* (Z133.1). International Society of Arboriculture, Champaign, IL.

International Society of Arboriculture. 2005. *Introduction to Arboriculture: Pruning.* DVD-ROM. International Society of Arboriculture, Champaign, IL.

International Society of Arboriculture. 2003. *Introduction to Arboriculture: Tree Biology.* DVD-ROM. International Society of Arboriculture, Champaign, IL.

Lloyd, John, ed. 1997. *Plant Health Care for Woody Ornamentals.* International Society of Arboriculture, Champaign, IL. 223 pp.

Matheny, Nelda P., and James R. Clark. 1991. *A Photographic Guide to the Evaluation of Hazard Trees in Urban Areas.* International Society of Arboriculture, Champaign, IL. 72 pp.

Plaster, Edward J. 2003. *Soil Science & Management.* 4th ed. Delmar, Clifton Park, NY. 384 pp.

Puhalla, Jim, Jeff Krans, and Mike Goatley. 1999. *Sports Fields: A Manual for Design Construction and Maintenance.* John Wiley & Sons, Hoboken, NJ. 464 pp.

Shigo, Alex L. 1989. *Tree Pruning: A Worldwide Photo Guide.* Shigo and Trees, Associates, Durham, NH. 186 pp.

Shigo, Alex L. 1991. *Modern Arboriculture.* Shigo and Trees, Associates, Durham, NH. 424 pp.

Singer, Michael J., and Donald N. Munns. 2002. *Soils: An Introduction.* 5th ed. Pearson Education, Upper Saddle River, NJ. 429 pp.

Smiley, E. Thomas, and Sharon J. Lilly. 2001. *Best Management Practices—Tree Support Systems: Cabling, Bracing, and Guying.* International Society of Arboriculture, Champaign, IL. 30 pp.

Spencer, Eugene R., ed. 2003. *R S Means Site Work & Landscape Cost Data.* 23rd ed. Construction Publishers & Consultants, Kingston, MA. 630 pp.

Tree Care Industry Association. 1998. *American National Standard for Tree Care Operations—Tree, Shrub, and Other Woody Plant Maintenance—Standard Practices (Fertilization)* (A300, Part 2). Tree Care Industry Association, Manchester, NH. 9 pp.

Tree Care Industry Association. 2000. *American National Standard for Tree Care Operations—Tree, Shrub, and Other Woody Plant Maintenance—Standard Practices (Support Systems a. Cabling, Bracing, and Guying)* (A300, Part 3). Tree Care Industry Association, Manchester, NH. 29 pp.

Tree Care Industry Association. 2001. *American National Standard for Tree Care Operations—Tree, Shrub, and Other Woody Plant Maintenance—Standard Practices (Pruning)* (A300, Part 1). Tree Care Industry Association, Manchester, NH. 9 pp.

Watson, Gary W., and Dan Neely, eds. 1994. *The Landscape Below Ground.* International Society of Arboriculture, Champaign, IL. 222 pp.

Watson, Gary W., and Dan Neely, eds. 1998. *The Landscape Below Ground II.* International Society of Arboriculture, Champaign, IL. 265 pp.

Watson, Gary W., and E.B. Himelick. 1997. *Principles and Practice of Planting Trees and Shrubs.* International Society of Arboriculture, Champaign, IL. 199 pp.

Whitcomb, Carl E. 1987. *Establishment and Maintenance of Landscape Plants.* Lacebark Publications, Stillwater, OK. 618 pp.

Information Resources

U.S. Department of Agriculture, Natural Resources Conservation Service, 2002. *National Soil Survey Handbook,* title 430-VI. http://soils.gov/technical/handbook

Soil Foodweb, Inc. www.soilfoodweb.com

PART TWO

10

Principle 10: Design for Maintenance

Figure 2.10.1. How many times do we applaud great designs that simply cannot be maintained, then blame lack of maintenance for the project's failure?

If you have followed all the requirements of the first nine principles, or if you correct the few places where you strayed from the principles, the site will already be designed for easy maintenance. The more you deviates from these principles, the harder it will be to maintain the landscape. This chapter will not go into extensive maintenance requirements. Designing for these requirements has already been covered in previous chapters.

Figure 2.10.2. A lack of maintenance is not the reason these trees are in decline.

Designers often conclude that trees or other plants in the design failed because of lack of maintenance. Did they know and anticipate the owner's maintenance capabilities during the design phase? Were those assumptions based on client discussions or observation of past maintenance levels? Or did the designer simply assume a certain level of maintenance would be provided? Were the trees able to survive at any reasonable level of maintenance?

RESPECT THE EXPECTED MAINTENANCE

Designers must adjust their plans to fit the expected maintenance. For example, the usual maintenance for street trees is often installation and removal, with maybe one or two pruning cycles if the tree lives beyond its tenth year. While this maintenance level should not be acceptable, the design should not depend on anything more.

Large institutions do not change their maintenance practices easily. Do not expect to have new projects well maintained if the developer's other buildings or a city's other streets have trees in decline. A larger soil volume is the one way to overcome low maintenance. Trees growing in good soil resources can, to a great extent, maintain themselves after they become established.

Often designers will draw inspiration from a detail or design of another landscape, and try to re-create it in a new setting. When doing this, it's important to find out whether maintenance is a factor in the success. The

Figure 2.10.3. Bonsai tree visited several times a week to perform carefully regulated maintenance.

Bonsai

The art of tree bonsai, where trees are kept alive and at very small sizes for centuries in small dishes is the ultimate in high-level maintenance. The soil volume to canopy volume in the typical bonsai dish is only slightly lower than the proportions cited earlier in the soil volume/tree canopy table. Weekly or even daily maintenance is required. The beauty of the plant lies as much in the knowledge of continuously provided care over many generations as in the elegance of the result. If that level of care were provided to every urban tree, this book would not be needed. An extreme point, but it emphasizes that different maintenance levels create different results.

a b

original may be working well because maintenance is overcoming limitations. Limitations may include soil quality, small soil volumes, improper drainage, inappropriate plant choices, lack of water, improper pH, or a low ability of the soil to hold chemicals. The original may require extraordinary maintenance, or even frequent replacement with large-caliper trees to create the illusion that the trees are healthy.

Climate and location play big parts, so a tree growing in one location may not be maintainable in a different climate region, even if it receives the same maintenance and is growing in the same cultural conditions. Designers must know all the circumstances around a design that works and be sure the new design replicates or improves upon the elements responsible for the initial success.

On the other hand, even small maintenance changes can make a big difference. At a major resort, an extremely large tree was transplanted, and for years, a single individual was responsible for its maintenance. That person retired, but his replacement was not as well trained in the tree's special requirements. The tree went into decline within the year. Only by recalling the original caregiver to better train the new person was the situation reversed.

Figure 2.10.4. Similar trees in paving design, with similar maintenance but different results. It would be a mistake to make any assumptions about the correctness of the design without knowing all the differences in the growing conditions.

a. 20-year-old plane trees in granular, free-draining urban soil and a high water table, producing large, healthy trees.
b. 20-year-old plane trees in compacted clay soil struggle to grow.

MAINTENANCE CHECKLIST

The following is a list of questions the designer needs to ask during the design process.

- What is the client's commitment to maintenance? Will it be by the owner's staff, a contract maintenance service, or maintenance only when the building manager sees a problem? The commitment to maintenance starts at the top of the organization chart.
- What is the maintenance history of existing landscapes managed by the same person or department?
- Will the person on the client's team who is managing and approving the design be the same person who will manage and approve maintenance decisions? This shift in responsibility means that maintenance requirements discussed during design meetings may not be passed on to the maintenance team, or the maintenance team may not have the resources to complete the task.

a

b

Figure 2.10.5. Maintenance practices to balance tree growth with soil conditions. Providing adequate soil in the design would eliminate the need for both practices.

a. In London, large numbers of trees are cut back to reduce soil volume requirements.

b. In Germany, compacted, poor-quality soil is replaced around trees to enlarge root space.

- Will the current owner of the property be the same person who owns the property when the project is completed? If not, then there may be no way of knowing future maintenance capability or transferring knowledge.
- Does the designer believe he or she will continue to have a relationship with the project after completion, so that special maintenance requirements can be discussed? Landscape projects often are more successful if the designer stays involved, assuming this person is sufficiently knowledgeable about maintenance requirements.
- Are there budget commitments to buy soil, drainage, and irrigation improvements? If they are cut, will the design still work? The value elimination (VE) process is a big issue with any project. Designers must know when client VE cuts have crossed the line from success to failure, and be prepared to state in writing that the design no longer works.
- What are the maintenance provisions for rooting soil under the pavement? How will it be inspected, tested, and amended if there are problems? Seldom is anyone aware of the soil under the pavement.
- Is the owner prepared to replenish settled soil, replace plants, and remove plants when they become overcrowded or shaded? Owners may see landscapes as static, unchanging objects, but all landscapes must change over time as trees and plants grow, die.

In addition to understanding the end user's maintenance capability, the designer must make design decisions that allow a landscape to be maintained. Read and follow the requirements of Principles 1 through 9 in this book in order to achieve Principle 10. Ignoring a single step starts a spiral of maintenance problems that may be difficult to reverse. Inform the owner whenever a principle is not being followed. Explain how not following the requirement will increase maintenance costs of the trees.

Figure 2.10.6. Arborist inspecting a girdling root prior to removal. Arborists should be included in the development of management programs.

MAINTENANCE MANUALS

The designer may be asked to make maintenance recommendations to the owner or client, and even to prepare maintenance manuals or write maintenance contracts. These recommendations should be based on scientific findings and industry standards based on current research. The International Society of Arboriculture should be the first reference point for best practices of tree management.

Designers who encounter unfamiliar maintenance problems have an obligation to explain that the situation is not within their expertise. They also have an obligation to stay current on maintenance practices and to familiarize themselves with references. Answers to almost any question related to the maintenance of trees in the urban landscape can be found in resources listed at the end of this chapter. Research has challenged many landscape maintenance practices such as piling mulch up the trunks of trees and applying water, fertilizer, or other chemicals as the first response to any problem.

EXAMPLES OF THE RELATIONSHIP OF MAINTENANCE AND DESIGN

Sustainable maintenance practices are evolving along with sustainable design concepts. Large commercial landscapes such as Battery Park City are now maintained entirely with sustainable organic solutions.

Battery Park City's Organic Maintenance Program

Battery Park City, located in Manhattan, includes more than 30 acres of open space. A force of about 25 gardeners uses organic techniques whenever possible to maintain this landscape. With compost tea and compost top dressing as their primary tools, the quality of the plants is amazing, given the intensity of use that

Figure 2.10.7. Battery Park City, New York.

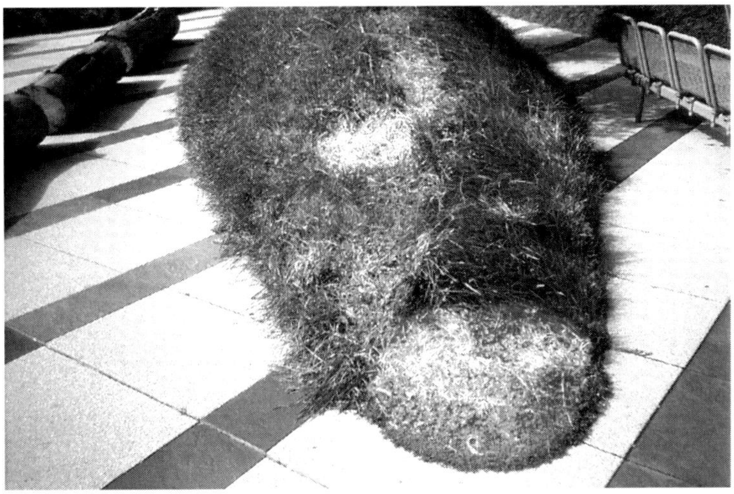

Figure 2.10.8. Minneapolis Federal Court House.

surrounds each bed. The maintenance staff has an intimate understanding of how a healthy soil food web can reduce water, fertilizer, disease, and insect problems.

Making sure the design of each landscape is sensitive to maintenance requirements is a critical element in its success. The maintenance staff regularly meets with design consultants and critiques designs. Battery Park City has won numerous design awards, a testimony to the fact that projects designed with input from maintenance staff and sustainable maintenance can be beautiful.

Halfway across the United States, the landscape of the Minneapolis Federal Court House has the opposite reputation from Battery Park City's. This landscape, with its signature steep-sided mounds, ignored maintenance requirements of trees and soil. Less than five years after it was built, the plantings required reconstruction. It has become a national symbol of what is wrong with the profession that would design such a landscape.

Few argue that the aesthetic design of the space is the problem. In concept, it is an interesting landscape. But the detailing of the soil and trees has created a landscape that is so unmaintainable as to have become a local joke. Had the principles of trees and soils been followed, the design may have been different, but probably not radically so. It should have been the designer's challenge to find a way to implement the basic concept in a maintainable way or modify the concept to the point that the landscape was sustainable. That challenge was ignored.

ESTABLISHMENT MAINTENANCE

The most critical time for any tree is immediately after planting. Depending on the size and type of tree and the quality of the soil, between one and five years of careful monitoring is required to help the tree recover from transplant. A good rule of thumb for time of establishment is one year for every inch of caliper in the northern parts of the United States and six months for every inch of caliper in the southern parts.

The primary maintenance during establishment is water management. Maintaining adequate water to the root package and the soil immediately around the tree solves most establishment problems. Water bags and hand spot-watering are much more effective than an irrigation system. Most irrigation systems tend to apply a small amount of water on a regular basis over a wide area. Newly planted trees need a good soaking at less frequent intervals. Over- and under-watering can both be fatal.

Additional establishment maintenance includes monitoring for disease and insects and removing any staking or other objects that may have been placed around the trunk after the first growing season. Fertilizers and pruning are not critical. Once the tree has rooted out of the root package, watering should be tapered off to force the tree to establish deeper and wider-spreading roots. Weed control within the mulch ring around the tree helps reduce competition, and an occasional application of mulch once the initial layer breaks down will keep soil organisms supplied with a source of carbon.

Establishment maintenance is often included in the initial construction contract, and the designer prepares the documentation for this work in the specifications. Some cities have removed maintenance from the planting contract and issue a separate bid just for maintenance. This eliminates the temptation for the installing contractor to rely on the warranty provision as a fallback for not adequately watering the tree. Poor maintenance may not kill the tree during the warranty period, but it will reduce the tree's chances of reaching maturity.

LONG-TERM MAINTENANCE

It is beyond the scope of this book to discuss the broad range of maintenance needed by urban trees over their life span. There are many texts on this subject, and maintenance of trees is a specialty of the arborist profession. After establishment, the tree, if provided with adequate soil volume and access to natural water cycles, should grow well with minimum maintenance. Providing those critical soil and water resources is the job of the designer.

Over the majority of the United States, trees in adequate soil volumes should grow well with no additional irrigation. Irrigation can make up for some deficiencies in soil volume, but should not be used as a crutch to support inadequate soil design. Irrigation systems rarely survive long enough to be there as the tree matures. It is unreasonable to expect continuous maintenance to keep the tree irrigated.

Designers may not see themselves as needing to know much about maintenance practices. They are designers of the built landscape, and maintenance is someone else's job. This perspective has caused many of the problems currently found with trees.

Designers must become active participants in the maintenance process. The design phase is the first step in the maintenance plan.

Designers need not be able to identify specific diseases or insects, know how to interpret fertilizer recommendations, or write a prescription for compost tea applications. Yet they must be versed in the basic art and craft of maintaining trees, from knowing when a pruning cut was done correctly to informing a client that a crew is over-watering the plants. They must know when they do not know and where to go for assistance.

SUMMARY

- Understand the maintenance capacity of the person or institution that will take over the landscape once constructed.
- Read and follow the requirements of Principles 1 through 9 in this book in order to achieve Principle 10.
- Make maintenance recommendations that are based on scientific research as well as industry practice.
- Listen to maintenance staff recommendations during the design process.
- Know what you do not know. Ask for advice from professionals with expertise in the particular field of knowledge.

REFERENCES

Key References

Gilman, Edward F. 2002. *An Illustrated Guide to Pruning.* 2nd ed. Delmar, Albany, NY. 330 pp.

Harris, Richard W., James R. Clark, and Nelda P. Matheny. 2004. *Arboriculture: Integrated Management of Landscape Trees, Shrubs, and Vines.* 4th ed. Pearson Education, Upper Saddle River, NJ. 578 pp.

Ingham, Elaine R. 2003. *The Compost Tea Brewing Manual.* 4th ed. Soil Food Web Incorporated, Corvallis, OR. 88 pp.

Johnson, Warren T., and Howard H. Lyon. 1991. *Insects That Feed on Trees and Shrubs.* 2nd ed. Cornell University Press, Ithaca, NY. 560 pp.

Lilly, Sharon J. 2001. *Arborists' Certification Study Guide.* International Society of Arboriculture, Champaign, IL. 222 pp.

Sinclair, Wayne A., Howard H. Lyon, and Warren T. Johnson. 1989. *Diseases of Trees and Shrubs.* Cornell University Press, Ithaca, NY. 575 pp.

Other Resources

Derr, Jeffery F., and Bonnie Lee Appleton. 1988. *Herbicide Injury to Trees and Shrubs: A Pictorial Guide to Symptom Diagnosis.* Blue Crab Press, Virginia Beach, VA. 72 pp.

Dirr, Michael A. 1998. *Manual of Woody Landscape Plants.* Stipes Publishing, Champaign, IL. 1,187 pp.

Gilman, Edward F. 1997. *Trees for Urban and Suburban Landscapes.* Delmar, Albany, NY. 662 pp.

Gilman, Edward F., and Sharon J. Lilly. 2002. *Best Management Practices—Tree Pruning.* International Society of Arboriculture, Champaign, IL. 35 pp.

International Society of Arboriculture. 2006. *American National Standard for Arboricultural Operations—Safety Requirements (Z133.1).* International Society of Arboriculture, Champaign, IL.

International Society of Arboriculture. 2005. *Introduction to Arboriculture: Pruning.* DVD-ROM. International Society of Arboriculture, Champaign, IL.

International Society of Arboriculture. 2003. *Introduction to Arboriculture: Tree Biology.* DVD-ROM. International Society of Arboriculture, Champaign, IL.

Lloyd, John, ed. 1997. *Plant Health Care for Woody Ornamentals.* International Society of Arboriculture, Champaign, IL. 223 pp.

Matheny, Nelda P., and James R. Clark. 1991. *A Photographic Guide to the Evaluation of Hazard Trees in Urban Areas.* International Society of Arboriculture, Champaign, IL. 72 pp.

Matheny, Nelda, and James R. Clark. 1998. *Trees and Development: A Technical Guide to Preservation of Trees During Land Development.* International Society of Arboriculture, Champaign, IL. 183 pp.

Mattheck, Claus, and Helge Breloer. 1997. *The Body Language of Trees: A Handbook for Failure Analysis.* Robert Strouts, trans. 3rd ed. Crown Copyright, The Stationary Office, Norwich, England. 240 pp.

Shigo, Alex L. 1991. *Modern Arboriculture.* Shigo and Trees, Associates, Durham, NH. 424 pp.

Tree Care Industry Association. 1998. *American National Standard for Tree Care Operations—Tree, Shrub, and Other Woody Plant Maintenance—Standard Practices (Fertilization)* (A300, Part 2). Tree Care Industry Association, Manchester, NH. 9 pp.

Tree Care Industry Association. 2000. *American National Standard for Tree Care Operations—Tree, Shrub, and Other Woody Plant Maintenance—Standard Practices (Support Systems a. Cabling, Bracing, and Guying)* (A300, Part 3). Tree Care Industry Association, Manchester, NH. 29 pp.

Tree Care Industry Association. 2001. *American National Standard for Tree Care Operations—Tree, Shrub, and Other Woody Plant Maintenance—Standard Practices (Pruning)* (A300, Part 1). Tree Care Industry Association, Manchester, NH. 9 pp.

Watson, Gary W., and E. B. Himelick. 1997. *Principles and Practice of Planting Trees and Shrubs.* International Society of Arboriculture, Champaign, IL. 200 pp.

Whitcomb, Carl E. 1987. *Establishment and Maintenance of Landscape Plants.* Lacebark Publications, Stillwater, OK. 618 pp.

Information Resources

Soil Foodweb, Inc. www.soilfoodweb.com

GLOSSARY

abrupt boundary—see *soil interface.*

abscission layer—area at the base of the petiole where the leaf normally separates from the twig.

absorbing roots—fine, fibrous roots that take up water and minerals.

aerobic—a biochemical process or condition occurring in the presence of oxygen.

aggregate—cluster or mix of small particles of soil and/or organic matter of varying size that are bonded together; sand, gravel, or small rocks in soil; and/or sand, gravel, or small rocks used under paved surfaces.

aggregation—process of binding particles together.

air knife—device that directs a jet of highly compressed air to excavate and loosen soil. Used within the root zone of trees or near underground structures such as pipes and wires to avoid or minimize damage to the roots or structure.

air pruning—method of plant production where the dominant root tips are killed off with dry air to encourage secondary root growth.

anaerobic—biological process that occurs in the absence of oxygen.

anthropogenic material—any objects or materials resulting from or caused by humans.

apical meristem—bud at the tip of a dominant twig or shoot.

arboriculture—practice and study of the care of trees and other woody plants in the landscape.

auger—tool that bores holes in soil or other materials while carrying soil samples away from the bored hole. Fitted with a cross handle for hand use.

available water—water remaining in the soil after gravitational water has drained and before the permanent wilting point has been reached.

balled and burlapped (B&B)—tree or other plant dug and removed from the ground for re-planting, with the roots and soil wrapped in burlap or a burlap-like fabric.

bare root—tree or other plant removed from the ground for re-planting without soil around the roots.

bark—protective outer covering of branches and stems that arises from the cork cambium or cambium.

barrier zone wall—chemically defended tissue formed by the still-living cambium, after a tree is wounded or invaded by pathogens, to inhibit the spread of decay into new annual growth rings. Wall 4 in the CODIT model.

bonsai—art of pruning and managing tree growth through root and vegetative pruning to maintain a miniature size.

branch collar—area where a branch joins another branch or trunk that is created by the overlapping vascular tissues from both the branch and the trunk. Typically enlarged at the base of the branch.

brownfield—abandoned or underused commercial or industrial properties where the site has become contaminated by environmental pollutants.

bud—small lateral or terminal protuberance on the stem of a plant that may develop into a flower or shoot. Undeveloped flower or shoot containing a meristematic growing point.

buffer pH—unit of measurement that describes the alkalinity or acidity of a soil based on the inactive or reserve hydrogen in soil. Used to calculate lime additions to soil.

bulk density—mass of soil per unit volume. Often used as a measure of compaction.

buttress root—roots at the trunk base that help support the tree and equalize mechanical stress.

caliche—layer that was formed by soil particles becoming cemented together by calcium or magnesium, often in the western United States.

cambium—thin layer(s) of meristematic cells that give rise (outward) to the phloem and (inward) to the xylem, increasing stem and root diameter.

carbohydrate—compound, combining carbon, hydrogen, and oxygen that is produced by plants as a result of photosynthesis. Sugars and starches.

carbon cycle—circulation of carbon from the atmosphere into living organisms and then returning to the atmosphere.

carbon/nitrogen ratio—proportion of carbon to nitrogen found in organic matter.

carbon sequestration—removal of carbon from the air by living trees and plants to be stored in their cells.

cation—positively charged ion. In soils, the most abundant cations are calcium (Ca), magnesium (Mg), potassium (K), sodium (Na), and aluminum (Al).

cation exchange capacity—ability of a soil to adsorb and hold cations. Affected by soil pH. Measures soil fertility, and influenced by particle size, clay type and organic composition.

cellulose—complex carbohydrate found in the cellular walls of the majority of plants, algae, and certain fungi.

chlorosis (chlorotic)—whitish or yellowish leaf discoloration caused by lack of chlorophyll. Often caused by nutrient deficiency.

circling root—root that encircles all or part of the trunk of a tree or other roots and could potentially lead to girdling the tree. Frequently caused by plant stock grown in root restrictive containers. Similar to girdling root.

clay—(1) soil particles with a typical grain size less than 0.002 millimeter (USDA classification) and less than 0.005 AASHTO Classification. (2) A soil predominantly composed of such particles.

claypan—layer that was formed by the accumulation of clay particles.

climax species—tree species growing and thriving in a forest having reached maturity (the latest stage of forest succession). Often the most shade-tolerant species in forest succession.

co-dominant leaders—forked dominant branches nearly the same size in diameter, arising from a common junction.

coarse-grained soil—soil with a majority of sand and gravel particles.

cohesion—combination of the friction between soil particles, the strength of the particle bonds, and clay and organic residue that holds together soil aggregates and peds.

compaction—compression of the soil that breaks down soil aggregates and reduces soil volume and total pore space, especially macropore space.

compartmentalization—natural defense process in trees by which chemical and physical boundaries are created that act to limit the spread of disease and decay organisms.

compost—(1) *(noun)* organic matter that has been intentionally subjected to decay processes and is more or less decomposed. (2) *(verb)* To subject organic matter to decay and decomposition processes.

compression—action of forces to squeeze, crush, or push together any material(s) or substance(s). Contrast with *tension.*

consistence—a soil ped's ability to resist crushing when pressure is applied at various moisture levels.

container grown—tree or other plant that has been grown in a container.

containerized—field-grown plant placed into a container for a time and then sold as a container plant. Term does not include a plant initially grown in a container.

contractors—people who perform services, such as construction or installation, for a fee.

cork cambium—meristematic tissue from which the corky, protective outer layer of bark is formed.

CU Structural Soil—developed by Cornell University (Ithaca, New York), this patented soil formula consists chiefly of small uniformly sized and angular stones (80 percent) and soil (20 percent) that, once compacted, can support root growth as well as stability for pavement. The heavy clay loam used within the voids of the stone remains relatively uncompacted.

decision-makers—various types of professionals, such as legislators or property owners, who directly influence the direction of legal policy and land development related to trees.

densiometer—device that measures the density and compaction of a soil.

designers—professionals, such as architects, landscape architects, or urban planners, who conceive and help realize the form of the built environment.

dioecious—species of plants in which male and female flowers are on separate plants. Contrast with *monoecious.*

discontinuity—expression of differences in soil textures and/or compaction levels across adjacent soil types within the landscape.

dry well—below-grade chamber, with stones or gravel inside, used to collect rainwater runoff from nearby buildings and landscape as a means of retaining rainwater and avoiding soil erosion. Water from a dry well is normally expected to percolate into the adjacent soil to improve drainage.

epicormic branches—shoot arising from a latent or adventitious bud (growth point).

evapo-transpiration—loss of water by evaporation from the soil surface and transpiration through plants.

expanding clay—clay that tends to expand when wet and then, when drying, contracts more than other particles in the soil.

expanded shale/ESCS/calcine clays—lightweight rock or clay aggregates that are heated up to high temperatures to increase porosity.

exudates—carbohydrates secreted from roots into the rhizosphere.

fertility—ability of a soil to hold chemicals required by plants.

field capacity—maximum soil moisture content following the drainage of water due to the force of gravity.

fine-grained soil—soil with a majority of clay, silt, and fine sand particles.

fragipan—layers that were formed by compaction of the soil particles.

friable—term used to describe a soil that is at the water content range such that it crumbles easily when moved.

gap-graded—soil with some particles coarse and some fine but without any significant amount of intermediate-sized fine and very fine sand particles.

geotextile—synthetic fabric used to separate two soils or aggregates to filter fine particles to improve bearing capacity. Serves as a partial root barrier. Often acts as a soil interface that impedes water.

girdling root—root that encircles all or part of the trunk of a tree or other roots and constricts the vascular tissue and inhibits secondary growth and the movement of water.

glucose—monosaccharide (sugar) found in nature and used as a physiological source of energy by living organisms.

grafting—to join together tissues from the same or different plants in order to combine desirable characteristics or to affect a repair (bridge graft).

greenfield—undeveloped land.

hardpan—compacted soil layer nearly impervious to water, air, and roots.

heart root—roots that originate near the base of the tree and grow down at a steep angle into the soil.

heart rot—any of several types of fungal decay of tree heartwood, often beginning with infected wounds in the living portions of wood tissue.

heartwood—wood that is altered (inward) from sapwood and provides chemical defense against decay-causing organisms and continues to provide structural strength to the trunk. Trees may or may not have heartwood.

heat island effect—rise in atmospheric temperatures in urban and suburban areas due to isolating air pollutants as well as reflected heat off of buildings, asphalt, and concrete surfaces.

horizon (soil horizon)—layer or zone of the soil profile with physical, chemical, and biological characteristics that differ from adjacent layers.

hormonal regulator (plant growth regulator)—compound that affects the growth and/or development of plants.

humus—dark-colored, stable form of organic matter that remains after most of plant or animal residues decompose.

hyphae—long, root-like, filamentous cells of a fungus.

infiltration—movement of water penetrating the soil surface and into the soil. Contrast with *percolation*.

infiltrometer—device used to measure the rate at which water moves through the soil.

internodal distance (internode length)—length on the stem between two successive nodes.

lateral roots—roots that branch from larger primary roots.

leaf area/root area balance—relative proportion of the photosynthesizing surface area of the leaves to the absorbing root surface area.

LEED certification—nationally recognized certification program by the U.S. Green Building Council for practitioners working on environmentally sustainable projects that follow the principles of Leadership in Energy and Environmental Design (LEED).

lenticel—small opening in the bark that permits the exchange of gases.

lifts—horizontal layer of constructed soil fill. Soil is installed in lifts to achieve proper compaction.

lignin—organic substance that impregnates certain cell walls to thicken and strengthen the cell to reduce susceptibility to decay and pest damage.

loam—soil texture classification containing some proportion of each of the three major soil particle types (sand, silt, and clay). Has good qualities for plant growth.

macronutrient—essential element that is required by plants in relatively large quantities. Contrast with *micronutrient*.

macropore—relatively large space between soil particles that is usually air filled and allows for gravity water movement and root. Contrast with micropore.

maintenance providers—professionals who manage, care for, and maintain installed landscapes.

massive soil—soil that is heavily compacted and forms oversized and extremely dense clumps of soil. Usually human influenced.

meristem—undifferentiated tissue in which active cell division takes place. Found in the root tips, buds, cambium, cork cambium, and latent buds.

micronutrient—essential element that is required by plants in relatively small quantities. Contrast with *macronutrient*.

micropore—space between soil particles that is relatively small and holds soil water by capillary action. Contrast with *macropore*.

monoecious—species with male and female flowers borne on the same plant. Contrast with *dioecious*.

monoculture—continuous stands of the same plant species. A large number of the same plants in a city or region.

Munsell soil chart—nomenclature system used by soil scientists to record soil and communicate soil color.

mycorrhizae—symbiotic association between certain fungi and the roots of a plant.

mycorrhizal—pertaining to a root or fungus that is part of or capable of becoming part of a mycorrhiza relationship.

native (plant)—plants indigenous to a region. Naturally occurring and not introduced by humans.

nitrogen cycle—circulation of nitrogen from the atmosphere into living organisms and then returning to the atmosphere.

nitrogen fixers—certain plants and soil bacteria that, working together, have the ability to convert atmospheric nitrogen into compounds usable by plants.

nutrient-holding capacity—ability of a soil to hold elements essential to plant growth.

organic matter—material decomposed from dead organisms.The organic components of soil. The portion of the organic material in a soil that can be measured by the loss-on-ignition organic matter test.

osmosis—diffusion of water through a semi-permeable membrane from a region of lower chemical concentration to a region of higher chemical concentration.

parent material—soil bedrock or base material such as sediments from which a soil profile develops.

particle flow—movement or migration of soil particles through the soil due to hydrologic, gravitational, or compressive forces.

paver—generic term used to describe a manufactured modular paving unit made up of various materials such as concrete, brick, or plastic.

peds—soil held into small groups by various bonds primarily resulting from weathering, organic content, and biological activity. The strength of the bonds determines the strength of the soil.

penetrometer—device that measures the amount of resistance in a soil to determine relative soil compaction and soil moisture.

penetration resistance—ability of a soil to resist physical penetration by an object or root. Penetration resistance is a function of soil texture, compaction, and moisture.

perched water table—accumulation of water in an upper soil layer above the actual water table, resulting when drainage in an area is impeded by soil interface between two types of soil.

percolation—movement of water through the soil. Contrast with *infiltration*.

petiole—stalk of a leaf.

pH—unit of measure that describes the alkalinity or acidity of a solution. Negative log of the hydrogen ion concentration. Measured on a scale from 0 to 14. Greater than 7 is alkaline, less than 7 is acid, and 7 is neutral (pure water).

phloem—plant vascular tissue that transports sugar and growth regulators. Situated on the inside of the bark, just outside the cambium. Is bidirectional (transports up and down). Contrast with *xylem*.

photoperiod—length of daylight and/or darkness required for certain developmental processes and growth in plants.

photosynthesis—process in green plants (and in algae and some bacteria) by which light energy is used to form carbohydrates (chemical energy) from water and carbon dioxide and expels excess oxygen. Contrast with *respiration*.

plasticity—property of soil whereby it is able to be molded, acting like plastic, after the addition of a specific quantity of liquid.

plastic soil—fine-grained soils that can be molded into different shapes with moderate amounts of pressure.

pleaching—specialty technique of pruning and training branches or vines in which they are interwoven, often to form an arbor, wall, or arching tunnel, or shearing onto a hedge-like structure.

plow layer—layer that was formed by repeated compaction by the bottom of a plow being pushed down by the weight of the soil above.

pollarding—specialty pruning technique in which a tree with a large-maturing form is kept relatively short. Starting on a young tree, pruning cuts are made at the same point in the tree, resulting in the development of callus knobs at the cut height. Requires regular (usually annual) removal of the sprouts arising from the cuts.

pore space—voids left between soil particles filled with a combination of air and water with the proportion dependent on soil water content.

Proctor density—density of a soil, measured as a percentage of maximum density when compacted at optimum moisture.

Proctor test—test that measures the Proctor density in soils.

pumping—soil movement when compacting pressure is applied to soil that is above its optimum moisture content for compaction. At this state, the soil particles move horizontally and eventually upward along the edges of the compacting device, raising the ground on the edges as the soil under the compacting device moves lower. Under these conditions, optimum compaction is not achieved.

ray—specialty tissue in wood that extends radially across the xylem and phloem of a tree and functions in transport, storage, structural strength, and defense.

reaction wood—wood formed in leaning or crooked trunks and stems as a means of counteracting the effects of gravity.

remnant soil—soil in urban areas that has not been highly disturbed and may still support roots and drainage. Remnant soil may be buried under fill soil.

Resistograph—brand name of a device consisting of a specialized micro-drill bit that drills into trees and graphs density differences that are used to detect decay.

respiration—in plants, process by which carbohydrates are converted into energy by using oxygen and expel excess carbon dioxide. Contrast with *photosynthesis*.

rhizosphere—thin layer of soil surrounding the root; soil area immediately adjacent to, and affected by, plant roots. Typically has a high level of microbial activity.

root ball/root package—soil containing all (e.g., containerized) or a portion (e.g., B&B) of the roots that are moved with a plant when it is planted or transplanted.

root cap—group of cells protecting the apical meristem at the root tip.

root collar or root crown—area where the main roots join the plant stem, above and below the ground level. See *trunk flare*.

root plate—area under the ground around the base of the tree where the roots taper away from the trunk (see *zone of rapid taper*). The area of the primary roots that structurally support the forces on the tree.

sand fractions—USDA classification to identify the various sand sizes from fine to coarse.

sapwood—outer wood (xylem) that is active in longitudinal transport of water and minerals.

saturation—point at which a soil will no longer absorb any amount of water without losing an equal amount.

seep—exposed cut in the soil that acts as an outlet for groundwater suspended above a perched water table.

sheeting and shoring—temporary vertical supports constructed during excavation work to reduce the amount of grading required on a site or to support a structure adjacent to the excavation.

soil—surface layers of sand, silt, clay, and organic material on the surface of the earth that support plants. More generally, the material between the rocky parts of the planet and the atmosphere composed of fine- to coarse-grained mineral material.

soil amendment—item added to the soil to improve certain aspects of the soil's condition.

soil food web—complex community of living organisms within soil that depend upon each other and carbohydrates from plants above the soil as food sources. The soil food web is responsible for assisting many plant functions.

soil interface—sharp or distinct line between two different soils and is the result of a dramatic change during the soil-building process.

soil mix—soil medium consisting of soil, sand, compost, leaf mold, or other ingredients produced to construct soils in the urban landscape.

soil profile—vertical section through the soil and all of the soil horizons.

soil series—basic unit of soil classification and mapping used in soil surveys.

soil strength—resistance of peds and structure to rupture. See *cohesion*.

soil structure—arrangement of soil particles into aggregates and larger structures in natural soil.

soil survey—document that maps the predominant soil types in a specific area.

soil texture—relative fineness or coarseness of a soil due to the proportion of different particle size (sand, silt, and clay).

soluble salt—salt compounds in soil.

specifications—precise written documents created to establish detailed construction methods to be carried out by contractors.

staking—supporting a tree with stakes and ties. Usually used in reference to newly planted trees.

starch—chain of sugar molecules linked together that serves as a form of energy storage in plants.

stomata—small pores, between two guard cells on the underside of a leaf and other green plant parts, through which gases are exchanged and water loss is regulated.

strip drain—lightweight, plastic drainage core configured to flow water along the length of the core, wrapped on all sides with geotextile.

subgrade—soil underneath a constructed surface or areas where soils for planting are to be installed.

subsoiling—using heavy machinery to drag ripping tools through the soil to break up subsoil compaction.

suckers—shoot arising from the roots.

sucrose (sugar)—commonly known as table sugar, sucrose is made up of two simple sugar units: glucose and fructose. Sucrose occurs naturally in many green plants as a product of photosynthesis.

sustainability—"meeting the needs of the present without compromising the ability of future generations to meet their own needs." (World Commission on Environment and Development, 1987).

tap root—central, vertical root growing directly below the main stem or trunk that may or may not persist into plant maturity; rarely exists in nursery-produced plants.

tension—in mechanics, the action of forces to stretch or pull apart any material or substance.

terminal bud—bud at the tip of a twig or shoot. Apical bud.

terminal bud dominance—condition in which the terminal bud inhibits the growth and development of the lateral buds on the same stem formed during the same season.

terminal bud scar—scar that encircles a stem after the release of a bud and which marks the position of the bud on the stem.

texture—see *soil texture*.

topsoil—surface layer of soil that may be rich in nutrients from decaying plants and bacterial material, often removed during construction. The O, A, and sometimes portions of the B horizon in natural soils.

tree—woody plant usually having a dominant trunk or trunks and a mature height greater than 15 feet (4.5 meters).

tree grate—porous metal, concrete, or plastic grate installed around the base of a tree, flush with adjacent paving to allow a walking surface close to the trunk of the tree.

tree opening—area within a paved surface where a tree is planted.

tree planter—oversized pot or container filled with a soil to support limited tree growth.

trunk flare or root flare—transition zone from trunk to roots, above the ground where the trunk expands begins to expand to the form root structures that support the tree.

understory species—trees and plants that adapt to live below a mature tree canopy.

urban forestry—management, establishment, and protection of trees and forests within cities, suburbs, and towns.

watersprout—upright, epicormic shoot arising from the trunk or branches of a plant above the root graft or soil line. Incorrectly called a sucker.

weep hole—hole constructed in a wall or other structure to allow water to drain.

wilt point—point at which a plant cannot pull any more water from the soil and suffers permanent damage.

xylem—main water- and mineral-conducting (unidirectional, up only) tissue in trees and other plants. Provides structural support. Arises (inward) from the cambium and becomes wood after lignifying. Contrast with *phloem*.

zone of rapid taper—area around the base of the tree under the ground where the roots taper away from the trunk. The taper reflects the stresses within the root generated by wind and gravity.

For additional arboricultural terminology, see the current edition of the *Glossary of Arboricultural Terms* published by the International Society of Arboriculture.

INDEX

All graphs, tables, photographs, and illustrations are indicated by boldface type.

D

E

F

N

O

P

Q - R

S

T

U

V

W - Z